From Cradle to Grave

Fifty years of the NHS

We are a pragmatic race.
We make things work even when they seem, by theory, to be unworkable.
We shall probably do the same with our health services.

Lord Horder 1939[1]

Having been at the centre since the earliest planning day
I am well aware of the many occasions on which mistakes have been made and yet,
not withstanding considerable knowledge of comparable services of other countries,
in a time of need for myself or my family I would now rather take my chance at random
in the British National Health Service than in any other service I know.

Sir George Godber 1972[2]

From Cradle to Grave

Fifty years of the NHS

Geoffrey Rivett

Published by
King's Fund Publishing
11–13 Cavendish Square
London W1M 0AN

© King's Fund 1997

First published 1997
Reprinted 1998

ISBN 1 85717 148 9

A CIP catalogue record for this book is available from the British Library

Distributed by Grantham Book Services Limited
Isaac Newton Way
Alma Park Industrial Estate
Grantham
Lincolnshire
NG31 9SD
Tel: 01476 541 080
Fax: 01476 541 061

Typeset by Linemead Limited, Hertford
Printed and bound in Great Britain by The Cromwell Press, Trowbridge, Wiltshire

Cover photographs: King's Fund archive
        MEHAU KULYK/SCIENCE PHOTO LIBRARY

Contents

Chapter 1

1948–1957
Establishing the National Health Service

Chapter 2

1958–1967
The renaissance of general practice and the hospitals

Chapter 3

1968–1977:
Rethinking the National Health Service

Chapter 4

1978–1987
Clinical advance and financial crisis

Chapter 5
1988–1997
New influences and new pathways

'Things are not what they used to be'; 'They never were,' replied Mr Punch.

10 DOWNING STREET
LONDON SWIA 2AA

THE PRIME MINISTER

The creation of the National Health Service was a key event in the history of our country and one which changed - and will continue to change - the lives of generations of men, women and children.

The NHS touches every one of us and it is particularly appropriate that we should reflect on this in the 50th Anniversary year of our National Health Service, whilst taking time to consider the opportunities for its future.

Major advances in science, technology and information give us access to treatments and therapies today which would be unrecognisable to the architects of the National Health Service in 1948. However, amidst all the advances, the founding principles upon which they built the NHS have stood firm, providing a quality service for all, regardless of ability to pay.

This book documents a significant chapter in this country's development, celebrating our past and providing us with a perspective which will help us plan for our future. It is also a testament to the contribution of millions of people who have invested their skills and talents in the NHS, working together to provide a service available to everyone.

I am sure readers will be fascinated to learn about the dramatic changes achieved through the efforts of so many people working together over the last fifty years and they will be encouraged by the opportunities this presents for the future of our National Health Service.

October 1997

Tony Blair

Preface

The fiftieth anniversary of the National Health Service falls on 5 July 1998. Already the NHS, which Bevan described as a great and novel undertaking, is the stuff of history. Four out of five people now working in it had not been born when it began. Those with clear memories of the early days grow fewer year by year, and this book is in part a tribute to their work. It is the story of the NHS, how it was set up, what happened next, and why. It aims to give the reader, whether professionally involved in the NHS or not, a chronological framework of the main events, clinical and organisational.

The clinical sections describe vast and wide-ranging developments that have imposed demands on the organisation, finance and structure of the NHS. Much of the story of the NHS is about the interaction of the three main parties involved: those needing care, those who deliver skilled care and those whose task it is to raise the money and see it properly spent. The peculiarly difficult triangular relationship between these interested parties has to be satisfactory if the health service is to function to the benefit of society.[3] Knowledge of the evolution of the service, and the changes brought about by the advance of medical science, should help those whose careers in the NHS will extend into the twenty-first century to be realistic.

Advance in clinical medicine is international and it has often been developments in other countries that have led to new forms of treatment, and sometimes new patterns of organisation. Only rarely do advances stem from the work of a single pioneer; usually they are the work of a team, or several teams. Charles Rosenberg says in his history of hospitals in the USA[4]

> The decisions that shaped the modern hospital have been consistently guided by the world of medical ideas and values . . . the attitudes and aspirations that gave the profession its peculiar identity . . . One can hardly understand the evolution of the hospital without some understanding of the power of ideas, of the allure of innovation, of the promised amelioration of painful and incapacitating symptoms through an increasingly effective hospital-based technology.

Management has a tough task to keep up with clinical progress. The implementation of developments has often been slower in the UK than in other countries. Partly this has been due to innate conservatism, but mainly it has been the result of financial restrictions.

There is no ideal way of dividing this story into sections. The introductory chapter describes the health services in 1948. The next five chapters each cover a decade, and begin with a chronology of events both in the NHS and in national life. The structure of the chapters is consistent so that a particular topic can be followed over the years. In each decade medical progress is considered first, then the developments in general practice and primary health care (the patient's first point of contact with the system) and the hospital service. Lastly, changes at an organisational and managerial level are discussed.

The story of clinical and organisational developments in the NHS can be seen within the wider context of the development of the welfare state, about which Nicholas Timmins has written.[5] To keep within reasonable limits boundaries had to be drawn. This book concentrates on England, for organisational changes in Scotland, Wales and Northern Ireland differed, reflecting the different circumstances. It does not duplicate accounts of the creation of the NHS.[6] It tries to avoid looking at the NHS through the eyes of central government and does not explore the political background as deeply as Rudolf Klein.[7] Neither does it deal with the types of care that shade into social services. The temptation to stray into clinical research leading to advances in medicine, or to explore in any depth the relation between income, illness and mortality, had to be resisted. It was not practicable to include the stories of optical, dental and pharmaceutical services; each could be the subject of a book to itself. A recommended-reading list appears on page 488, and the annual *Health Service Year Book* contains a comprehensive, although managerially slanted, one.

The use of English has changed substantially over the last 50 years. It was assumed in 1948 that doctors were men, and could be referred to as masculine. Concepts were expressed with little regard for the possible offence they might cause; terms such as 'mental defectives' and 'the workhouse' were well understood and few objections were made to their use. They have changed over time: a White Paper in the 1970s referred to the mentally handicapped but we now talk of people with learning difficulties; senile dements became elderly severely mentally infirm (ESMI), a phrase also now consigned to limbo. I have tried to use contemporary terminology and not to change the words people used; increased sensitivity to those with problems is, in itself, part of the history of the NHS.

References

1. Lord Horder. Foreword. In: Herbert SM. *Britain's health: based on the PEP report*. Pelican Special S27. Harmondsworth: Penguin Books, 1939.
2. Department of Health and Social Security. *On the state of the public health*. Report of the CMO for 1972. London: HMSO, 1973.
3. Clark-Kennedy AE. Medicine in relation to society. *BMJ* 1955; 1: 619–23.
4. Rosenberg C. *The care of strangers – the rise of America's hospital system*. New York: Basic Books, 1987, 7.
5. Timmins N. *The five giants: a biography of the welfare state*. London: HarperCollins, 1995.
6. Pater JE. *The making of the National Health Service*. London: King's Fund, 1981.
    Webster C. *The health services since the war*. vol 1. *To 1957*. London: HMSO, 1988.
    Webster C. *The health services since the war*. vol 2. London: Stationery Office, 1996.
    Rivett GC. *The development of the London hospital system 1823–1982*. London: King's Fund, 1986.
7. Klein R. *The new politics of the NHS*, 3rd edn. London and New York: Longman, 1995.

Acknowledgements

I owe a great debt to many colleagues who have helped me reconstruct a period which, though near to us, has seen so much change that it is all too easy for one to forget times past. I have not referenced personal communications though there have been many. Sir George Godber, who was at the centre of the developments of the first three decades and played a substantial role in the solution of problems, was of great assistance. He, Professor Walter Holland, Professor John Blandy and Jane Allen provided extensive comments and editorial assistance; the errors are, however, my own. Barbara, my wife, who was a student nurse when the NHS was established, helped me to expunge jargon and understand nursing issues better. The book would not have been possible without her tolerance and the many people who gave me unstinting and often enthusiastic assistance. They include Professor David Allison, Julia Allison, Michael Ashley-Miller, Sir Francis Avery Jones, Ian Ayres, Alan Bacon, John Ballantyne, John and Pamela Ball, Christopher Bartlett, Mark de Belder, Virginia Berridge, Rudolf Blach, Sir Douglas Black, John Bootes, Sir Christopher Booth, Lord Briggs, Michael Brudenell, Margaret Buttigieg, Professor Charles Calnan, Professor Geoffrey Chamberlain, Sir Tim Chessells, Lady Julia Cumberlege, Deidre Cunliffe, Pamela Davies, Brendan Devlin, William Dinning, Sir Richard Doll, Sir Colin Dollery, Johanna Finn, Professor Malcolm Forsythe, Hugh Freeman, Michael Freeman, Dame Phyllis Friend, Dr Edward Glucksman, Professor Sir David Goldberg, Sir Anthony Grabham, Henry Grant, Professor Sir John Grimley Evans, Stephen Hadfield, Valerie Harrison, Julian Tudor Hart, Professor Charles Harvey, Professor David Harvey, Denis Hill, Arthur Hollman, Anthony Hopkins, John Horder, Sir Godfrey Hounsfield, Sir Donald Irvine, Professor Ian Isherwood, Professor Donald Longmore, Annabelle Mark, Robert Maxwell, Professor Alan Maynard, Pauline Munro, Anthony Pinching, Simon Pleydell, Irene Roberts, Professor Jane Robinson, Henry Rollin, Sir Brian Salmon, Professor Karol Sikora, John Smith, Professor Robert Steiner, Barbara Stilwell, Sir Eric Stroud, Professor P K Thomas, James Thomson, Sir Leslie Turnberg, Professor Owen Wade, Diana Walford, Lord Walton, Professor Michael Warren, John Wickham, David Willetts, Susan Williams, Professor Jenifer Wilson-Barnett, Eve Wiltshaw, Antony Wing, John Yates and colleagues at the King's Fund, Nuffield Provincial Hospitals Trust and the Department of Health. My thanks are due, in particular, to staff of St George's and the Royal Postgraduate Medical School, Hammersmith. My thanks are due to the editor, Gillian Clarke, and the indexer, Martyn Yeo. The librarians at the Royal Society of Medicine, the Department of Health and the West Suffolk Hospital were most helpful.

The columns of the *British Medical Journal* provided a vast amount of material, and have helped to prevent the omission of significant developments; readers should be aware that the BMJ has editorial freedom and its views are not necessarily those of the British Medical Association.

I am particularly grateful to the Dunhill Medical Trust for its ready support during the writing of this book and to the King's Fund Grants Committee for a substantial contribution to the costs of publication. The views expressed are, however, mine.

Abbreviations

AHA	area health authority
AHA(T)	area health authority (teaching)
BG	board of governors
BMA	British Medical Association
BMJ	*British Medical Journal*
CDSC	Communicable Disease Surveillance Centre
CHC	community health council
CHSC	Central Health Services Council
CMO	Chief Medical Officer (of Ministry of Health)
COHSE	Confederation of Health Service Employees
CSAG	Clinical Standards Advisory Group
DGH	district general hospital
DoH	Department of Health (from 1988)
DHA	district health authority
DHSS	Department of Health and Social Security (from 1968)
EC	Executive Council
EMS	Emergency Medical Service
ENB	English National Board (of nursing)
EPHLS	Emergency Public Health Laboratory Service
FPC	family practitioner committee
FHSA	family health services authority
GMC	General Medical Council
GMSC	General Medical Services Committee (of BMA)
GNC	General Nursing Council
GP	general practitioner
JCC	Joint Consultants Committee (of BMA)
HMC	hospital management committee
HMO	health maintenance organisation
HVA	Health Visitors Association
LCC	London County Council
LHA	local health authority
LHPC	London Health Planning Consortium
MH	Ministry of Health
MOH	medical officer of health
MPU	Medical Practitioners' Union
MRC	Medical Research Council
NHSE	NHS Executive
NHSME	NHS Management Executive

PEP	Political and Economic Planning
PHLS	Public Health Laboratory Service
RCGP	Royal College of General Practitioners
RCM	Royal College of Midwives
RCN	Royal College of Nursing
RCOG	Royal College of Obstetricians and Gynaecologists
RCP	Royal College of Physicians
RCS	Royal College of Surgeons
RGN	registered general nurse
RGM	regional general manager
RHA	regional health authority
RHB	regional hospital board
RMO	regional medical officer (of RHA)
RNO	regional nursing officer (of RHA)
SAMO	senior administrative medical officer (of RHB)
SMAC	Standing Medical Advisory Committee (of CHSC)
SNMAC	Standing Nursing and Midwifery Advisory Committee
UGC	University Grants Committee
UKCC	United Kingdom Central Council for Nursing, Midwifery and Health Visiting
WHO	World Health Organization

Introduction: the inheritance

Of course the health service in this country did not begin in the year 1948. Many of us have associations with the between-the-wars health service; a great patchwork, a good deal of good intentions, a great deal of inadequacies.

The Rt Hon Jennie Lee MP, Minister of State, Department of Education and Science (Aneurin Bevan's widow)[1]

The designers of the NHS did not start with a clean sheet of paper. The service was a rationalisation of what existed, conditioned by a need to cajole rather than coerce somewhat reactionary interest groups. Some countries, such as New Zealand and Sweden, had forms of health service but they were not used as models; insularity of outlook prevented that. On the basis of wartime experience it was the hospital service that was most in need of reorganisation. Hospitals were in a muddle and financially at the end of their tether. There were prestigious voluntary hospitals, municipal hospitals displaying the entire spectrum of standards and entrepreneurial cottage hospitals in which local doctors could resurrect dormant surgical skills. In 1948 it had been little more than a decade since the first sulphonamide gave doctors a powerful weapon against streptococcal, meningococcal and gonococcal infections. The next ten years saw dramatic improvements in treatment greatly accelerated by research and development carried out by the medical equipment and pharmaceutical industries.

General practice and primary health care

General practice covered workers under Lloyd George's National Insurance Act of 1911, but not their wives and families, whose proper demands were curtailed by the need to pay fees for service.[2] When they were sick, it was the GP to whom people wished to turn. The work of the GP had been described in idealistic terms by Lord Dawson in his report of 1920, which laid out the structure a health service might take.[3] The GP should be accessible, attend patients at home or in the surgery, carry out treatment within his competence and obtain specialist help when it was needed. He would attend in childbirth and advise on how to prevent disease and improve the conditions of life among the patients. He should play a part in antenatal supervision, child welfare, physical culture, venereal disease and industrial medicine. Nursing should be available, based with the doctor in the primary health centres Dawson envisaged.

This picture was in stark contrast to the day-to-day pattern of the GP's life. In inner cities overcrowding led to domestic violence, lice infestation and skin diseases such as impetigo. CAH Watts, a GP writing of his experiences in a mining community before the second world war, recalled the waiting room with rows of seats for about 60 patients who sat facing a high bench like a bank counter.[4] Behind stood the three doctors and behind them the dispenser. The doctor called the next patient to come forward. Having listened to the complaint, he turned to the dispenser to order the appropriate remedy. There was rarely any attempt at examination. Visits usually numbered about

50 and were made on a bicycle. Diphtheria was endemic and every sore throat was viewed with suspicion. Antiserum was one of the few active treatments available to the GP, and if given within 24 hours of onset the results were excellent. Otherwise, the mortality was about 20 per cent. Patients with diphtheria or scarlet fever were taken away in a yellow fever van to the infectious diseases hospital for at least six weeks; no visitors were allowed. Lobar pneumonia was common, and with the more fortunate patients there was a crisis about the seventh day. It struck terror into the patients' and the doctors' hearts, for the mortality was popularly thought to be at least 50 per cent and sulphonamides were not invariably curative. Most dreaded was tuberculosis, blood in the handkerchief after a fit of coughing. Some families were especially vulnerable and it tended to strike young people. The course could be lingering or extremely rapid, with death within weeks. Lung cancer was rare. If it occurred, it would probably not be recognised.

Almost half the babies were delivered at home, mainly a matter for midwives. Pain relief in labour, although available in hospital, might not be provided in the home. When things went wrong the GP would be summoned, because procedures such as breech birth or manual removal of the placenta might be required. Most GPs used chloroform as an anaesthetic though some felt it was quicker and safer without. As they might have neither the skills nor the equipment to handle problems, in many places obstetric flying squads, based on the hospitals, had been established. These could deal with haemorrhage, shock and eclampsia (fits during late pregnancy, labour and the period shortly after), transfuse patients, give anaesthetics, and undertake operative obstetrics in the home.[5] Tales of obstetric disaster, haemorrhage after delivery and problems with forceps were only too common, although remarkably many women survived crises unthinkable today. Serious infections (puerperal sepsis) killed mothers after childbirth, particularly if there were sore throats going round.

Pain and discomfort were accepted as part of life to be endured with stoicism. The family doctor had to be tough to get on with his many interesting and rewarding tasks. If he had access to a hospital, he might set a simple fracture or reduce a dislocation. Working class people did not expect to be comfortable. Most went hungry and their undernourished children showed evidence of rickets until vitamin D supplements, provided by welfare clinics, controlled it. Many were miserably cold in winter unless they were roasting in front of the coal fire in the kitchen. Successful treatment by the family doctor was accepted with gratitude and the many failures were tolerated without rancour or recrimination. Patients' expectations were not high. The death of children from infectious disease was the way of the world. Mothers of feverish children expected, if the child was not to be admitted to the fever hospital, to be told that bed rest was crucial until the fever had fully subsided. One of the author's predecessors in practice was described as 'a right bastard but a bloody fine doctor'; he used to whip the children out of his way as he rode past. GPs' hours were long, as most practices were single-handed and deputising services were non-existent. Local rota systems operated on a 'knock-for-knock' basis to make a half-day practicable. A car and a telephone were desirable – but not essential. If it mattered enough there was always a way of contacting the doctor sooner or later.

People did not trouble GPs without good cause. Early in recovery patients might dispense with their services. Most had to pay for the doctor and the medicines. The professional attitude to working class patients was frequently robust, and sometimes downright rude, but this was accepted with tolerance. In middle-class practices there were greater courtesies. There was the ritual preparation of a napkin, a spoon and a glass of water for the doctor's visit. There might be five shillings (25p) on the mantelpiece for the fee; three and sixpence ($17\frac{1}{2}$p) if the family was not so well off. High up the social scale the doctor might be treated as a rather superior type of servant. Medical diagnosis was often of academic rather than practical importance. Treatment was limited to insulin, thyroid extract, iron, liver extract for pernicious anaemia, digitalis, the new mercurial diuretics, barbiturates, simple analgesics, morphine derivatives and harmless mixtures.[6]

Entry into a practice was generally by purchase of goodwill, the usual price being one and a half times the annual income.[7] GPs started with a substantial debt. On average about 1,000 national insurance patients generated about £400–£500 per year, an income boosted by the care of the families who were not covered by national insurance.

GPs and specialists

Since the middle of the nineteenth century the voluntary hospitals had been expanding their outpatient departments, for these were their shop windows. The British Medical Association (BMA), representing the GPs' point of view, opposed expansion because of the effect it had on GPs' earnings, but they expanded none the less.[8] By 1939, 6 million attended them every year, in spite of complaints about inadequate waiting facilities and perfunctory and inconsiderate treatment.[9] In contrast the hospitals run by local authorities had poor or non-existent outpatient departments and less reason to build up large ones. The London County Council (LCC) rigidly enforced conditions of attendance at outpatient departments to people referred by their GPs, although patients might be seen once without a doctor's letter, then being referred back to their GP.[10]

In 1946, like everyone else, Britain's GPs were tired from six years of war. The younger ones had been called up, and the older ones had stayed behind – including many women doctors who had qualified at the time of the first world war, when medical schools had opened their doors wider to women. Some saw an atmosphere of demoralisation and disillusion, with poorer relationships within the profession than ever before.[11] Those who had stayed behind had done their own work and that of their colleagues as well, and felt that doctors who had been in the services had enjoyed an interesting time. Those who had served were resentful that their practices had disintegrated, and they had returned to a vastly different world.

Local authority services

In 1948 there were over 150 local authorities in England that had wide and major health responsibilities. Each had a Medical Officer of Health (MOH) who was a chief executive, responsible to his council. His department ran midwifery and child welfare services. Then there was the school health service, under the Education Act 1944, which provided 'all forms of medical and dental treatment, other than domiciliary treatment, to children attending maintained schools'. It was not until 1974 that the school health service became part of the NHS. Environmental pollution, food inspection and food and drugs legislation were also within the province of local authorities. Some ran district medical services under the Poor Law.

The Local Government Act 1929 had given authorities the power to appropriate poor law institutions and develop them into modern hospitals. MOsH such as Sir Frederick Menzies and Allen Daley in London, Tate and Macaulay in Middlesex, Campbell in Lincolnshire, Parry in Bristol, Ferguson in Surrey and John Charles in Newcastle had developed and extended the local authorities' general hospitals. The local authorities also ran fever hospitals, sanatoria and mental hospitals under the supervision of the Board of Control. As a result, MOsH had a role not only in the health of the population but also in the cure of the sick. Allen Daley, as Sir Frederick Menzies had been before him, was interested in medical education partly because of the need to staff the LCC's hospitals; they fought for the establishment of the British Postgraduate Medical School at their Hammersmith Hospital. Indeed the LCC would have liked an undergraduate teaching hospital of its own.

Local authorities ran the tuberculosis sanatoria: 32,600 beds in England and Wales. A suggested norm for tuberculosis was 1.5–2 beds for each death annually; there were 23,000 deaths in 1947 and 52,000 new cases.[12] The local authorities had a responsibility for infectious diseases; in the early 1930s 800 children out of every 100,000 died annually from them. Diphtheria, which had affected 50,000 children a year, was coming under control by immunisation at the start of the NHS. In 1947 a major poliomyelitis epidemic led to 7,000 cases and 500 deaths. There were 1,693 cases in 1948, of which two-thirds were paralytic. In the record time of two weeks the Ministry produced a 15-minute film on its early diagnosis. With the co-operation of the BMA an intensive effort was made to screen it; cinemas and halls were booked on Sundays and local doctors were invited. Within six weeks 17,500 doctors and 16,000 nurses had seen the film. By contrast smallpox was rare, although there was an outbreak in 1948 with 78 cases and 15 deaths. Venereal disease increased with the disturbances of war but some control was kept by better systems of contact tracing.

Health promotion

Health promotion was generally regarded as a good thing. It was stressed both by Lord Dawson in 1920 and by the 1937 report on health services produced by Political and Economic Planning (PEP), a pressure group of businessmen, educationalists, architects, economists, social scientists and sympathetic MPs such as Harold Macmillan. PEP believed that the GPs' non-essential tasks should be removed, that standards of training and equipment should be raised to make GPs more effective family *health* advisers, and that efforts should be made to promote healthy living to reduce the number of sick people needing continuous treatment.[13] There was an active public health movement during the years of war that included GPs, public health departments, health visitors and a few health education officers.[14] Health promotion met clear and obvious needs, and was directed at large scale but simple improvements. Much effort went into sex education, venereal disease, infectious diseases, and maternal and child health. Exhortations on growing your own food, eating well on your rations, and getting fresh air and exercise were plentiful. Many leaflets were targeted at women, to teach them how to care for their families and, in the interests of hygiene, to bring death to bugs and flies. Wilson Jameson, the government's Chief Medical Officer, broke new ground when he spoke openly on the radio about the prevention of venereal disease.

Hospital services

War had badly damaged hospitals in urban areas; not one hospital in London had escaped the bombs. The buildings were not a rich heritage. At St George's the flowers in the ward were placed on a glass-topped table so that the reflections could be seen. At Paddington General the legs of the cots in the maternity department stood in tins of oil to discourage the cockroaches from crawling up. Two-thirds of the hospitals had originally been erected before 1891 and 21 per cent before 1861. They were in poor physical state and lacked diagnostic facilities, pathology and radiology, and operating theatres. During the 1920s and 1930s there had been substantial expenditure on hospitals but their infrastructure, catering and heating, required urgent attention. Most steam heating systems had been introduced around 1900, and the life of boilers was about 50 years.

The work of the hospitals

Hospitals in 1948 provided much accommodation for chronic illness in the elderly, both physical and mental. Medical wards were full of patients with pneumococcal pneumonia, lung abscess, acute nephritis (inflammatory disease of the kidneys), rheumatic fever and rheumatic heart disease, tuberculosis, syphilis in all its stages and brucellosis (an infectious fever usually the result of drinking unpasteurised milk). Treatment was often based on good nursing, bed rest, barbiturate sedation at night and attention to pressure areas. Compared with today there were few drugs to offer – salicylates for rheumatic fever, digoxin for heart disease, sulphonamides and penicillin which were controlling the pneumonias, and soon streptomycin.[15] About 16,000 people were dying annually of rheumatic heart disease. Although the incidence was falling, there were still about 5,000 new cases among children and adolescents each year. Surgical wards had many patients with perforated or bleeding peptic ulcers, bone infections (osteomyelitis) and goitre, as well as urine retention from prostatic enlargement. Tuberculosis of the lungs and of the joints formed a major part of operative surgery.

Patients were often admitted at a late stage in their disease. Diagnosis, prognosis and treatment were often a matter of clinical judgement based on bedside observation over a period of time. Anaesthetics was not yet fully distinct as a specialty and a basic knowledge of its techniques was a useful skill for any young doctor, indeed for medical students. Open ether (dropped onto a mask) was still in use, particularly for children ('blow the gas away'). Induction with nitrous oxide or an intravenous barbiturate followed by nitrous oxide and oxygen, plus ether or triethylene, was the common technique. At The London Hospital any house surgeon who happened to be having a rest or a cup of tea was likely to be summoned to give an anaesthetic for an emergency forceps delivery in the labour ward, above the common room.

Admissions to Kidderminster General Hospital: August 1947 to July 1948 (1479 admissions into 60 adult beds)

Medicine

General	97	(diabetes 21, gastro-intestinal bleeding 24, heart attacks 5)
Chests	21	
Cardiac	28	
Infections	54	(8 tubercular glands of the neck)
Major infections	9	(1 actinomycosis)
Dermatology	8	

Surgery

Appendicitis	111	
Hernia	106	
Acute abdomen	67	
Peptic ulcer	55	(18 perforated)
General	116	(piles 21, varicose veins 32, gall-bladder 15)
Genito-urinary	29	
Orthopaedic	75	
Cancer	45	(21 cancer of breast)
Eyes	40	(cataracts 16)
Ear, nose and throat	162	(tonsils 105, mastoids 14)
Maternity	73	
Gynaecology	117	(fibroids 21, pelvic floor repair 18)
Dilatation and curettage	47	
Children	622	admissions (40 beds)

Source : Pamela Ball (hospital archives)

Virtually all hospitals were subdivided in the same way: general medical and general surgical wards. The maternity department, if one existed, would be separate, as would be the gynaecology wards. Children were frequently placed in adult wards, perhaps in a cubicle. In the larger hospitals there might be separate orthopaedic wards, and provision for infectious cases or for sick members of staff. Hospitals had few consultants, specialisation being in its infancy. Generally there would be only two or three on any one ward. The consultants and the ward sisters therefore came to know each other's ways, and to trust and be loyal to each other. It fell to the sister to help and train newly qualified doctors in the ways of the 'chief'. In the traditional medical 'firm' junior doctors of all grades worked predominantly for one or two consultants, ensuring continuity of care for the patients, a clear chain of command, regular contact that helped the education of the juniors and camaraderie under pressure.[16] The junior doctors, virtually always unmarried, lived in a bachelors' mess and were available night and day.

From the patient's point of view some hospitals had a name for making patients welcome and took pride in keeping it. Friendly doctors, an enlightened matron, well-chosen sisters and contented nurses all played a part. Such traditions were inherited, but bad traditions of grudging, unwilling service also existed. A correspondent to the *Lancet* described her contrasting experiences in two London teaching hospitals. Patients might be left in the dark about their condition and their simplest rights disregarded. Outpatient departments could be comfortable, or the consultant might invite three patients into the consulting room at a time and deal with them together. Student teaching at the bedside might be conducted courteously, or the patient might be ignored and treated as 'teaching material'. Questions about diagnosis and treatment might be answered, or the patients left unseen by a doctor. There might be noise in the wards with carelessly served and uninspiring meals, or well cooked and warm food properly presented in the atmosphere of a good hotel.[17]

Voluntary hospitals

The most prestigious hospitals were 'voluntaries', institutions that were largely financed by voluntary contributions and income from their investments, and were responsible only to themselves. They had grown up in a haphazard fashion. Some were institutions founded centuries previously for the benefit of the sick poor, others by citizens proud of their towns or anxious to perpetuate their names. The best-known were the teaching hospitals: 12 in London, most with centuries of tradition, and 10 in the provinces that had usually been founded in the nineteenth century in association with a civic university. There was a gradation from these teaching hospitals, staffed by consultants not engaged in general practice who gave their services free, to smaller ones such as the voluntary hospitals in places such as Bath and Ipswich.

Next came lesser hospitals staffed by visiting consultants who lived at a distance. The smallest had one or more resident medical officers with a visiting staff of local GPs and perhaps special departments under visiting specialists from distant centres. It was a short step from these to the cottage hospital staffed by GPs, often with consultants on call, in some of which major surgery including gynaecology might be undertaken by GPs. These had often been built in the nineteenth century to provide essential care to otherwise inaccessible country populations, and more opened after the first world war as small memorial hospitals. The matron might combine the functions of ward sister, theatre sister, midwife, radiographer, almoner, resident medical officer and even cook. Then there were convalescent homes, to which people might be transferred when their recovery was assured but they were not yet ready for discharge. Often managed by nursing staff with the support of visiting GPs, they prevented the blockage of beds in the larger hospitals.

The voluntary hospitals aimed to provide quality care to a limited number of patients. They were generally well managed and had the ability to choose their staff and maintain firm discipline. There were extensive outpatient services, the presence of which publicised the hospital and attracted donations. Maternity departments were small. Some categories of patients were unlikely to be admitted – elderly people and those with chronic diseases. Taken as a whole the voluntary system had been in financial straits before the war. Over a thousand in number, they barely made ends meet but a hospital never needed to despair as long as it could proclaim itself to be bankrupt; financial problems could be the basis of an emotional appeal to the public –

shroud-waving as it was known. In the unusual event of a surplus, hospitals invariably planned an extension or development. Money came from charity, hospital savings schemes, the fees of those who could pay and, increasingly, from local authority grants. Hospitals were the focus for charitable effort, run by leaders of local society and doctors' wives. Teaching hospitals and their schools encouraged a feeling of *esprit de corps*. Medical students were often the sons of doctors who had trained in the same hospital. Matron, able to select her student nurses, required the 'school certificate' and tended to choose a 'nice type of girl from a good family'. Discipline was strict, going out with a houseman might be frowned upon; pregnancy was certainly a cause for dismissal. In spite of the hazards there were many doctor–nurse marriages.

Municipal hospitals

Public hospitals grew up separately during the nineteenth century. From the 1830s locally elected bodies, the boards of guardians, had created institutions that housed a range of people from tramps to bed-fast chronic sick. Typically they had casual wards for able-bodied vagrants, a large 'house' for destitute elderly who were not sick, and infirmary wards for the chronic sick. By the 1920s some boards of guardians, particularly in the big cities, had growing infirmary sections that were larger than the rest of the institution, with resident medical staff and some facilities for laboratory tests, X-rays and surgery. In smaller country institutions the 'house' and the 'chronic sick' predominated. Under the Local Government Act 1929 counties and county boroughs took over from the boards of guardians. Institutional funding now came from the rates, but with a block grant from central government covering 40 per cent of the cost. Each authority established a public assistance committee to run the institutions. Most remained as they had been, accommodation largely for the elderly and chronic sick, many of whom would remain there until death, together with occasional maternity patients or children suffering from neglect. Counties and county boroughs could, however, 'appropriate' the hospital sections of these huge institutions to their public health committees, and upgrade them to modern acute hospitals under the management of the MOH. Enthusiasm for this varied and it was the larger authorities that were most active; the smaller county institutions were a less attractive proposition. In some places, such as Middlesex, Surrey, Birmingham, Bristol, Newcastle and London, the hospitals appropriated from the old Poor Law Board became the centre of civic pride and substantial investments were made in their improvement. The LCC intended that all those appropriated should become general hospitals, and the equivalent of the voluntaries. 'Only the best is good enough for the patients in our hospitals,' wrote one LCC councillor. Most councils, however, were selective about the institutions they took over; for example, Leicester took over the city hospital of 600 beds but not the wholly chronic Hillcrest public assistance institution with 370 beds, where visiting GPs provided cover. The county of Leicestershire took over nothing. Nottingham city took over the central hospital but the county took little.

The voluntaries had been unable to keep pace with the growing needs of the population and the municipal hospitals were catching up. The latter were developing better laboratories and theatres although outpatient departments were rudimentary. Nationally they provided three times the number of beds, though many were for long-term care. Medical staffing differed materially from the voluntaries. The senior officer of the hospital was the medical superintendent who, in addition to general administrative duties, usually had clinical responsibility as a physician or surgeon. In the smaller hospitals his responsibilities might spread over a wide clinical field, although most of the work was in the hands of resident medical staff, often of considerable experience and standing. The extent to which consultants from the nearby voluntary hospitals were used was variable; sometimes they visited regularly but more often they were called to specific cases and had no continuing responsibility. The municipal hospitals stood alone when they could.

The municipal hospitals were as ill-co-ordinated as the voluntary ones. The towns were the natural centres for the surrounding population, but an arbitrary line on the map might determine whether a patient had access to a relatively well-staffed modern city borough hospital or a distant and unsatisfactory institution managed by a county council. The municipal hospitals were the last resort for patients unlikely to improve with treatment. The voluntaries were accustomed to transferring chronic cases to them (e.g. cancer patients) and to have little other relationship. Similarly, local authority hospitals took cases of infectious disease from the voluntaries. The role of dumping ground was hotly resented by municipal hospitals, especially when they had developed into well-equipped acute units. There was infighting as the demand for acute hospital care increased and the local authority hospitals took a larger share, particularly in obstetrics. In a few places, such as Newcastle and Lincolnshire, the various hospitals worked side by side without hostility. In Oxford, Lord Nuffield had supported a 'Hospital Council' that had been successful in co-ordinating the two camps. But sometimes there was open war. Most thought of first-class medicine in terms of the London teaching hospitals. Increasingly, however, provincial and non-teaching hospitals were becoming recognised as leaders; for example by 1940 the Birmingham Accident Hospital was pre-eminent in trauma and the first Chair of plastic surgery was held by Thomas Kilner in Oxford. Francis Avery Jones, appointed in 1940 to the Central Middlesex Hospital, established one of the first specialist units in a municipal general hospital. A pioneer gastroenterologist, his guiding principles were that diagnosis should be early and accurate and that treatment should be scientifically based.

Mental hospitals

The beds provided for the mentally ill and mentally handicapped exceeded in number the acute beds of the voluntary and municipal hospitals, but there were never enough. Bomb damage and the use of some accommodation by the wartime emergency medical services increased crowding. Before 1946 there had been little expectation of the inclusion of these services in the NHS, and therefore little planning. The mental health sector was subsumed into the NHS with difficulty, as an unwilling and inferior partner. Although isolated and disregarded, its problems were massive, for the hospitals were old, isolated, poorly provided with amenities and mostly too large, some with over 2000 beds. The ethos of the mental hospitals contrasted starkly with acute hospitals, but not always for the worse. They were surrounded by large grounds, immaculately tended by a well-trained squad of patients, usually chronic schizophrenics. The institutions turned inwards upon themselves with inter-hospital sports competitions and social activities. The discipline among patients, doctors and nurses was firm but at least for the staff the food was excellent. For most patients, however, enforced idleness produced inertia, loss of morale and of self-esteem.[18]

Specialisation and specialist hospitals

Generalism had been paramount, the general physicians and surgeons outranking in status doctors who worked in specialist fields such as ophthalmology and dermatology. The large voluntary hospitals were often slow to provide facilities to those working solely in a minor field. However, Geoffrey Jefferson, Professor of Neurosurgery in Manchester and one of the great men of the time, said that the characteristic clinical theme of the first half of the century had been the rise of specialism. As early as 1900 some had seen the writing on the wall. Jonathan Hutchinson, dissatisfied with the results of his treatment of stone in the bladder, handed cases over to a colleague adept at new techniques. The improvement in results after he ceased to operate gave him the utmost satisfaction and pride.[19] The earliest specialties dealt with conditions that were found in considerable numbers in every district. In 1948 some 'minor' specialties were behind the times; for example, British dermatology lagged behind the rest of Europe where large research-based units were commonly found. Occasionally a pioneer sought to rectify this; Geoffrey Dowling, at Guy's and later St Thomas' Hospitals, formed a journal club for young doctors and organised overseas study weeks.[20]

'Special hospitals', which concentrated on one particular disease or organ system and often led their field, developed in large cities during the nineteenth century. In the provinces where there was only one medical school, the special hospitals and the teaching hospital often came to work with each other. They developed a modus operandi by which diseases of women or diseases of the eye were mostly or exclusively handled by the appropriate special hospital that would teach medical students. In London, however, with its 12 teaching hospitals, special hospitals such as Great Ormond Street and the Brompton undertook little if any undergraduate training and remained entirely separate. While specialists might have beds at both a teaching hospital and a special hospital, considerable antipathy often existed between the two groups. Under the NHS Act 1946 the Minister amalgamated similar special hospitals in London, giving the newly formed groups separate boards of governors. The University of London established an institute for each and the specialist postgraduate hospitals remained distinct both from the general teaching hospitals and from the region's hospitals.

By 1939 units in new specialties, for example trauma and orthopaedics, were increasingly developing in general hospitals. The process was accelerated by war, and units were planned for a regional catchment to deal with plastic surgery and burns, neurosurgery, facio-maxillary surgery, orthopaedics, spinal injuries and rehabilitation. These included Archibald McIndoe's unit for burns and plastic surgery at East Grinstead, Ludwig Guttman's spinal injury centre at Stoke Mandeville and Wylie McKissock's neurosurgical unit at Atkinson Morley's hospital in Wimbledon.

Specialisation had advanced considerably in large city hospitals, but less so in rural areas. In all large centres ENT (ear, nose and throat) and ophthalmology were distinct specialties but in smaller hospitals general surgery might encompass traumatic and orthopaedic surgery, ENT and even gynaecology. Neurosurgery and thoracic surgery had emerged before the second world war. Geoffrey Jefferson and Hugh Cairns had neurosurgical units in Manchester and London (later Oxford) but it was not generally available outside the main centres. Thoracic surgery was even scarcer and radiotherapy was just being reorganised after the 1939 Radium Act. A general surgeon in Grimsby owned 80 milligrams of radium with which he would treat cancer of the cervix. General medicine might cover paediatrics, cardiology or even pathology and radiology, but medical specialties such as endocrinology were emerging. Laboratory and radiological support was basic to their development. While an accurate history and examination remained essential for good diagnosis, test results gained in importance and some specialties owed their rapid advances to better systems of measurement; for example, it was not now possible to practise cardiology without a grounding in electrocardiography. Increasingly, physicians and surgeons worked as teams, patient care crossing the medical/surgical divide. 'It is a regrettable fact,' said a physician, 'that when surgeons invade a province hitherto considered to be purely medical, diagnosis almost at once becomes more exact.'[21] Clinical medicine was entering an exciting phase. New techniques such as needle biopsy were introduced, allowing the effect of treatment to be followed histologically, by microscopical examination of small specimens.

Two patterns of meeting specialist needs therefore evolved. First were the special hospitals, characteristic of the nineteenth century, a time when most advances were made by careful observation and description. Secondly, special units developed in general hospitals, in the age of laboratory studies and experimental research when it was becoming increasingly important and difficult for clinicians to span several fields, and multi-disciplinary working was becoming essential.[22] Superb clinicians, often excellent teachers and authors, were rewriting clinical medicine. The Royal Postgraduate Medical School at the Hammersmith Hospital brought together basic scientific research, physiology and biochemistry, and clinical medicine. The facilities and the approach were attractive to research workers; in medicine the assistants to Professor Francis Fraser included Guy Scadding and Paul Wood, chest and heart specialists. John McMichael, succeeding Fraser, led developments in renal physiology and high blood pressure. Ian Aird, heading the surgical department, worked with Melrose on a pump oxygenator, Melrose developing a method of producing 'elective' cardiac arrest. Sheila Sherlock, at the Hammersmith before moving to the Royal Free, made the liver – a somewhat mysterious organ – understandable, bringing together its pathology and clinical diseases.[23] Knowledge of metabolic pathways, of cellular pathology, the nervous system and the workings of the mind, when added to the rapid development of new drugs, encouraged a new vision of medicine in the future. A medical remedy for cancer would surely be found. If not within the next 50 years, at least within an imaginable span of time medicine would replace surgery. Some hazarded a guess that in time medical methods of treatment would be so effective that there would be one only kind of surgery – traumatic surgery.[24]

The Public Health Laboratory Service

Shortly before the second world war the Medical Research Council (MRC) considered proposals for an emergency bacteriological service, because of the possibility of bacteriological warfare, and the risk that the movement of people in large numbers might lead to outbreaks of infective disease. The Emergency Public Health Laboratory Service (EPHLS) was subsequently established and administered by the MRC. The major epidemics that had been feared did not materialise, and the laboratories came to support the MOsH in their public health work and to provide GPs with access to bacteriology. Benefits flowed from a nationally organised network of laboratories, reporting their findings and exchanging information about new scientific and epidemiological methods. Their work grew rapidly. The EPHLS also undertook research into the accurate identification of strains of bacteria and viruses, developing central reference laboratories. The value of the service ensured its post-war future, and it was agreed that the MRC should continue its management. It was formally re-established as the Public Health Laboratory Service (PHLS) in 1946 with the passage of the NHS Act.[25]

A national transfusion service

In 1939 the MRC agreed to administer blood depots in areas close to concentrations of hospitals yet outside the areas likely to be the target of enemy aircraft. The principles of blood grouping, blood banking and transfusion had been established by that time, and the depots proved their worth at the time of Dunkirk. Towards the end of the war it became clear that, although blood depots had been established to meet the needs of air-raid casualties, the bulk of their work had been with civilians. The rational solution seemed to be a nationwide transfusion service, and plans were made for one to be organised on a regional basis, managed by the regional hospital boards (RHBs).[26] Established in 1946, the work of the National Blood Transfusion Service, and its unpaid donors, would underpin many advances in vascular surgery, transplantation, chemotherapy, the treatment of coagulation disorders and shock from massive blood loss.

Pharmaceuticals

Early synthetic drugs

Drug	Used for
Aspirin	Rheumatic fever
Salvarsan	Syphilis
Suramin	Trypanosomiasis
Sulphonamides	Antibacterial chemotherapy
Isoniazid	Tuberculosis

In the years before the NHS there had been three roots to pharmaceutical development.[27] The first involved the slow accumulation of knowledge about folk medicines, many derived from plants such as the poppy and the foxglove, producing opium and digitalis. Production of these had become standardised by the middle of the nineteenth century. The second was related to the increasing importance of pure natural products such as colchicine and emetine (from plants), and heparin, insulin, sex hormones and vitamins (from animals). Penicillin was the first of many antibiotics to be obtained from micro-organisms. Thirdly, starting in the nineteenth century, was the rapid growth of synthetic medicinal chemistry, leading to salvarsan, aspirin and barbitone, the sulphonamides and later the antihistamines and benzodiazepines. In the 1930s Domagk, the research director at Bayer in Germany, saw promise in two approaches to the control of bacterial infections, enhancing the natural defensive powers of the body by vaccines or sera, or damaging the invading bacteria. It was his inspiration to test prontosil (the first sulphonamide used clinically) in mice, even though it was ineffective in the test tube. After its introduction in 1935 many derivatives were synthesised and the idea was born of designing drugs with specific properties, and assessing their benefits and drawbacks. To the great disappointment of clinical pharmacologists, the sulphonamides were totally ineffective against the tubercle bacillus, a disappointment to recur when in 1943 it was found that this was also true of penicillin. Nevertheless, with penicillin, people with chest infections previously admitted to hospital could be managed in general practice. Venereal disease could be treated more effectively and the long-term complications of syphilis became increasingly rare. Streptomycin, isolated in the USA in 1943, was found to be effective in guinea-pigs against the tubercle bacillus and the first trial in humans took place at the Mayo Clinic in 1944. Almost at once bacterial resistance became a problem and, when streptomycin became available in limited quantities in the UK in 1946, the MRC established a rigorously controlled trial in patients between 15 and 25 years of age with acute progressive bilateral tuberculosis. Within six months its effectiveness was proven.

Many of the newly synthesised agents were found to have unanticipated properties, sometimes initially regarded as unwanted side effects. For example, the observation at Johns Hopkins Hospital, Baltimore, that animals treated with sulphonamides might develop goitres led to the development of a number of drugs acting on the thyroid. Chance observations played their part but, with notable exceptions such as penicillin, the great majority of new medicines were discovered and developed by scientists working in the laboratories of an industry devoted to profit, where there was no sharp dividing line between pure and applied research. There was criticism of minimal modification of a patented drug in order to produce a 'new' one, but sometimes this produced substantial improvements on the original compound.[28]

Research and development

The second world war stimulated scientific developments that had crucial effects on the pattern of medical care, altering the work of the NHS. An example was research at the Royal Postgraduate Medical School at Hammersmith Hospital on crush injury that led to kidney failure. As a casualty hospital taking patients from central London, it received many who had been dug out of bombed buildings after many hours. As a result the hospital developed expertise in renal disease.[29] Ian Aird, a great professor of surgery at the Hammersmith, said on appointment in 1948 that he wanted two things out of life: artificial hearts (he recruited Dennis Melrose) and transplanted kidneys (he recruited Jim Demster).

The health service also inherited technologies developed during the war that were put to medical use. As the Russians moved into East Germany, the Zeiss technicians moved west. With them went the designs for a binocular operating microscope that was soon in production and radically altered ear surgery. Mullard Research Laboratories and Philips developed the principle of the linear accelerator during the war, made possible by Randall and Boot's development of the magnetron, a special type of valve for wartime radar. Cobalt for radiotherapy replaced radium and was produced in the Chalk River plant of Atomic Energy of Canada during the war. Radioactive isotopes produced at the Atomic Energy Research Establishment, Harwell, gave Britain an early lead in nuclear medicine.

In pathology, the development of the electron microscope in the AEI Research Laboratory and the evolution of phase contrast microscopy aided the development of histopathology (the microscopical study of pathological changes in tissues). Continuous flow biochemical analysis developed in Birmingham by Whitehead opened up the prospects for automation in biochemistry. Similarly, Wallace Coulter's use of the 'impedance monitoring' of an orifice through which blood flowed led to the automation of blood cell counting. Scientific developments had a substantial effect on diagnosis and treatment. The health service, in turn, came to provide a large market for science and technology.

Shortage of equipment was a problem. In 1948 many hospitals were without any surgical diathermy machines (used to stop bleeding from small blood vessels), because the more powerful had been requisitioned for use in the nose cones of Blenheim bombers in submarine hunting. It was therefore impossible to cut tissue under water, important in bladder surgery. Endoscopes were primitive. It was the task of the registrar to hold the patient still while attempts were made to force barely flexible gastroscopes down the patient's throat. The standard optical design had changed little since the days of Galileo, and was lit by a small bulb that often failed at the crucial moment. Medical appliances were also rudimentary. There were no adhesive stoma bags, a bulky rubber cup being strapped over a colostomy. This worked fairly well as long as the stools were solid, but not for urine or the contents of the upper intestine. It was only in 1960 when his daughter underwent colectomy for ulcerative colitis that Mr Salt, an engineer, devised an appliance that would stick to the skin without causing soreness.

British medicine had a worldwide reputation for good bedside care and clinical excellence; in the research field it was lagging. The tradition of research in the clinic was a nineteenth century German development, stemming from well organised academic and laboratory facilities. Medical schools in the USA had adopted the model of research-orientated clinical departments after the Flexner Report of 1910. In Great Britain the Haldane Commission (1907–1913) had argued that university departments with full-time staff were urgently needed but the development of clinical research within medical schools developed more slowly in Britain than in the USA.[30] There were a number of outstanding individuals but no structure to encourage an academic and research-based approach to medicine. Virtually all specialists made their living from private practice and had little time for teaching and research. Only with the establishment of academic clinical units headed by salaried senior staff, within university hospitals, could research flourish. In 1939 only six of the twelve London medical schools had a clinical professor in any discipline. Even then a professor in Britain was only one among many consultants, while in the USA he was the head of a department that included all sub-specialties of medicine or surgery, and chief of service of the clinical department. When in the 1930s it was suggested that one of the London teaching hospitals should become a centre for postgraduate education, all refused. The

British Postgraduate Medical School was established in 1935 in association with the Hammersmith Hospital, managed by the LCC, and alone among the London hospitals had academic professional leadership. Private beneficence such as that of Lord Nuffield in Oxford and the government-funded MRC were responsible for most of the other developments in the period before the establishment of the NHS.

Medical education

The medical student course consisted of two parts. During the first two years students studied basic clinical sciences such as anatomy, physiology and biochemistry. Then they began their clinical studies, moving in turn through the hospital departments: medicine, surgery and obstetrics. In parallel there were lectures, seldom closely related to the practical work the students were undertaking. London provided over a third of the country's doctors. Here the medical schools operated individually, largely independently of the University of London and as departments of the hospitals. They provided income from student fees to the consultants and a ready source of cheap junior staff. The provincial medical schools were from the outset an intrinsic and valued part of a multi-faculty civic university.

The Goodenough Report

Service and education are interlinked. In 1942 the Ministry of Health, with the Department of Health for Scotland, established a committee to look at medical education, the clinical facilities required and how they should relate to a new health service. It was chaired by William Goodenough, Deputy Chairman of Barclays Bank and Chairman of the Nuffield Provincial Hospitals Trust. The government already held views on medical education and the members were chosen with these in mind. Goodenough himself was committed to regionalisation; there were two members from University College Hospital, which had the most highly developed professorial system of all the London medical schools; and Janet Vaughan, an eminent haematologist and the Principal of Somerville College, Oxford, who had strong views about women in medicine. Sir Wilson Jameson as CMO of the Ministry kept a watching brief.

The report was published in 1944 at the time of the Normandy landings and attracted little immediate attention.[31] It was, however, the most important statement on medical education for many years.[32] Goodenough made four opening comments:

- Properly planned and carefully conducted medical education was the essential foundation of a comprehensive health service. It was not merely incidental to the hospitals; the spirit of education must permeate the whole health service, professionals and public alike.
- A principal aim of national policy should be the encouragement of the promotion of health.
- It would take time to develop an educational system to meet the needs of a comprehensive health service; developing the teaching staff and the facilities could not happen overnight.
- Greatly increased public funding would be needed to provide the research and education that would underpin the NHS.

The pattern outlined was of university medical schools, a radical idea in London. This meant phasing out Scottish extramural schools and the West London Hospital's school, and changing the constitution of most of the many London medical schools that were subsidiaries of the teaching hospitals rather than academic bodies in their own right.

Goodenough dismissed the idea of university-managed teaching hospitals, and sold the idea of 'university teaching centres'. Such centres would comprise the medical school (integral with a university), a group of teaching hospitals and clinics providing teaching facilities. The facilities should form a geographically compact group, one hospital being the 'parent' and providing much of the teaching. The medical schools and teaching hospitals were receptive to the idea of grouped facilities for it would increase the number of beds available. The wartime emergency medical service had made the teaching hospitals familiar with other hospitals nearby. Goodenough thought that every hospital throughout the NHS should be brought, directly or indirectly, into association with a university teaching centre. These should have a zone of influence and take part in the administration and staffing of the health service more generally. Every medical school should have whole-time professors of medicine, surgery, and obstetrics and gynaecology. Teachers must make their educational work their principal or at least one of their main activities.

Goodenough said that, in the management of teaching hospitals, equal emphasis must be placed on the treatment of patients and on research and the training of students – complementary and reinforcing functions. There was wide agreement about the number of beds required, and the BMA's evidence was specific. Professor Henry Cohen, from Liverpool, explained how the numbers had been worked out, and they were accepted by the Committee. A school admitting 100 clinical students should have access to 950–1000 beds, excluding tuberculosis, infectious and mental diseases, and highly specialised functions such as radiotherapy. Few medical schools had anything like this; by the standards set, ten of the London schools were short of medical beds and seven were short of surgical beds as well. Goodenough thought that the geographical distribution of the London schools was untenable, and that Charing Cross and St George's hospitals should move so that they provided better access to local populations. Expansion of the provincial and Welsh medical schools should be encouraged to meet the growing requirements of the NHS. If new schools were needed, London was not the place for them. Unsuitability for a medical career should be the sole barrier to admission to a medical school – not gender. Financial grants to students for both fees and maintenance should be available, but exchequer grants to the schools should be conditional upon their being co-educational; many in London were not.

The body of the report dealt with the individual specialties, the effects of specialisation, the curriculum and issues of postgraduate education and research. Postgraduate education in London would be reconstituted as a Federation within the University, with Institutes for selected special hospitals. The teaching of social and preventive medicine and of psychiatry, was seen as important. General practice was mentioned largely because of the problems GPs had as a result of their professional isolation. Lastly there was the question of the bill to be met by government to ensure a solid educational foundation for the new NHS. The government agreed to a contribution of £1 million a year.

Although the NHS Bill that came before Parliament gave each teaching hospital its own board of governors, no reference was made to any duty with regard to teaching or research. The academics were alarmed but Aneurin Bevan, the Labour Minister of Health, was under fire from so many quarters that he was loath to accept any more amendments to his Bill. An approach was made to Lord Addison, a doctor and an ex-Minister of Health, and to Lord Sankey, who had chaired a review of the voluntary hospital system in the 1930s. As a result an explicit duty was laid upon boards of governors to provide the clinical facilities necessary for teaching and research.[33] Legislation needed for changes to the medical schools was implemented along with the NHS Act in 1946.

Nursing

No woman should take up the profession of nursing unless she is prepared for hard work, constant subordination of her will, and for continual self denial . . . She must be trustworthy, conscientious and faithful in the smallest detail of duty. She must be observant and possess a real power of noting all details about her patient. She must be promptly obedient and respect hospital etiquette . . . A nurse's manner to her patient should be dignified, friendly and gentle, but no terms of endearment should be used. She should surround herself with mystery for her patient and never discuss her own private affairs.

Probationer's notes, St George's Hospital, 1946

'The greatest satisfaction in life is to be gained from making other people happy,' said an LCC brochure on nursing as a career. Nursing was essentially women's work, a woman's finest qualities were brought out in rendering service to others, and nursing called for all that was best and noblest. Training equipped her, as nothing else could, to cope with all the human emergencies that were encountered in life. The nursing profession had been revolutionised; the nurse was no longer merely useful help in the sick-room. There had been a complete change in status, and the nurse was now regarded by doctors and surgeons as a competent trained assistant. From the outset, the LCC maintained, it was a career of dignity and responsibility.[34]

Nurse education and staffing

Medical and nurse training differed significantly. There were many nursing students, the training was shorter and there was little penalty for giving up. Nursing experience, and the experience of handling people, could be useful in other occupations. In medicine the numbers were smaller, students were often highly selected and had a long training that would be useless unless they completed the course. The educational patterns also differed. Medical education was university based. Nursing schools were part of the hospital's organisation, under matron's control, and the student nurse, unlike the medical student, was a crucial part of the hospital labour force.

Although some hospitals could be choosy and had high entry standards for nurses, most could not afford this luxury. The course lasted three years but, after passing the examinations, the new state registered nurse often had to spend a fourth year as a staff nurse before getting the much-prized hospital badge. That helped to retain nurses. The 'block' system of education, in which nurses spent a number of weeks in the school of nursing at particular times in their course, had been introduced in the 1930s. There might be tension between the sister tutors and the ward sisters. The ward sisters expected students to come to them with some knowledge of basic nursing techniques, able to observe and report on patients, and to be well disciplined. The tutorial staff expected the students to return with clinical experience, and be able to associate theory and practice. Expectations were not always fulfilled.

Nurses have never suffered from a lack of advice. In the years before the NHS there had been several reports on nursing, its problems and its needs. The Royal College of Nursing (RCN) had established a Nursing Reconstruction Committee (1942–1950) chaired by Lord Horder. Three fundamentals inspired his committee's approach: 'the patient, the human touch and informed treatment'.[35] The committee's first task was to get statutory recognition of the assistant nurse. That achieved, it proceeded to consider education and training, and finally recruitment. The committee became convinced that, given a liberal outlook and a carefully planned curriculum, nurse training could be developed into something of great importance. Training was, however, too closely linked with the provision of nursing care, a handicap greater than an educational system should have to face. Entering nursing to receive a professional education, and spending three months in the preliminary training school, the nurse then went on the wards and became an indispensable member of the hospital staff. There was a gap between the theory of the classroom and the practice of the ward, where staff were stretched and supervision by experienced staff might be inadequate.[36] There was the difficulty in recruitment and the wastage caused by marriage. Marriage ended the career of a student nurse. Indeed nursing was seen as an *alternative* to marriage.[37] Many working-class 18-year-olds were interested in boys and an engagement, not education and the classroom. Nursing on the wards interfered with social activities, for many did not know when they would be off duty until sister finished the duty roster; in any case they stayed on duty until work was finished. Student nurses were angered by their pay and, with support from the Confederation of Health Service Employees (COHSE), demonstrated in the streets. They won their battle for a training allowance in 1948 although the RCN felt their conduct had been undignified.[38]

There was always a shortage of nurses. Two categories of nurse had existed from the nineteenth century. Alongside the trained nurses, who were 'state registered', were nursing assistants. In 1943 the Nurses Act granted legal status to assistant nurses, establishing a 'roll' (trained nurses were on a 'register'), and a system of examination, admission and removal of names. In 1948 there were some 20,000 of these state enrolled nurses (SENs). Their presence not only added to the workforce but also made it possible to improve the training of students for the register. Nurses and their professional organisations were always ambivalent about auxiliaries, holding divergent views of their teaching and the length of their training, needing them, sometimes nurturing them – but sometimes rejecting them as 'dilution'.[39] The prime concerns of the RCN were the position and salaries of qualified nurses, and the social conditions they had to endure.

The Wood Report

Nurse training intake and wastage

	Intake	Wastage
General	13,100	4,900 (37%)
Total*	23,100	12,400 (54%)

*Including mental illness and other nursing disciplines

Source: Wood Report 1947[40]

The success of a national health service was going to depend as much on sufficient numbers of adequately trained nurses as doctors. In 1945 the Ministry of Health established a small working party that included two senior nurses, a social scientist and a doctor, chaired by Sir Robert Wood. It was to look at recruitment, the proper task of a nurse, the training required, the annual intake needed and how it was to be obtained, from where nurses were to be recruited, and how wastage could be minimised. The Wood working party had to work fast and it reported in 1947.[40] Little advantage was seen in synthesising existing 'literature' and adding yet another expression of opinion to the large number already available. Wood's aim was to discover the facts and let the facts speak for themselves. Once they were established, it would be easier to gain acceptance of an unpalatable remedy. The starting point was the cost of sickness to the community, the value of working time lost, the cost of treating the sick and the cost of immunisation and clinics for mothers and babies. An estimate of the need for *health* nursing was needed, and then the requirement for *sick* nursing. The working party looked at the size of the nursing profession, and its structure in terms of age, educational background, professional qualifications and socio-economic status. It examined recruitment, wastage and the pattern of training. It looked at 'the mental calibre of the nursing profession' and found a striking range of ability. Wood found it 'inconceivable that persons differing so very widely in their mental capacity should respond to the same training or be fitted to the same functions'. The average was 'probably somewhat above the population as a whole'. Mental hospitals had more than their share of those at the lower end of the scale of intelligence.

The Wood Report (1947): main conclusions

- A twofold division of labour
- All nurses of equivalent status, one common register plus a grade 'ancillary to nursing'
- Stress on social and preventive medicine and the community. Health and sick nursing considered side by side
- Better student selection
- Students relieved of domestic duties
- Two-year training:
    18 months fundamentals
    6 months in a chosen field
- Student status:
    students to receive training grants
    students under control of the training authority, not the hospital
- Three-shift system

The central message of Wood was carefully wrapped. Wood believed that wastage was unacceptably high, being the result of discontent among the students and frustration with harsh and cramping discipline. Senior staff and matrons were to blame for this. Responsible as they were for patient care without an adequate supply of trained staff, as well as training students who were carrying much of the workload, it was inevitable that the needs of patients should be placed before the interests of students. It was no use merely *appealing* to hospital authorities to modify discipline or to adopt more understanding attitudes. The organisation and staffing of training schools needed *structural* changes. There should be a broader training for all nurses, a single General Nursing Council (GNC) with a more substantial educational role, and regional training bodies independent of the NHS, the costs of training coming from outside the health service. This conclusion was threatening to hospital administration and the matrons who ran the schools.

The Wood Report was years ahead of its time.[41] Nursing was a high recruitment but high wastage profession, massively dependent on new student intakes. Fifty-four per cent failed to complete training and the Report was critical of the conditions of training and the training itself. More careful selection was needed, using intelligence tests as well as other selection techniques. The service was dependent on assistant nurses. Although some held that all duties concerned with the patient should be carried out by a trained nurse, supported by ward maids, Wood believed that there would always be scope for a subsidiary nursing grade, taking over some of the repetitive domestic work carried out by student nurses particularly in their first year. Those below the level of ability required for training should be recruited, if otherwise suitable, to jobs ancillary to nursing. Better food and accommodation, and three-shift working, were desirable. Students should no longer be regarded as junior employees subject to an outworn system of discipline. They must be accorded full student status as far as the intrinsic requirements of nurse training permitted. There should be a two-year course, with registration after a third year spent in clinical practice. Training should emphasise social and preventive medicine, considering health and sickness nursing side by side.[42]

The Ministry of Health invited comments. Rosemary White, in later years, said there was a difference in approach between the Ministry and hospital management, which saw advantages in a large and low-paid student work force, and nursing's professional organisations, which placed greater accent on the pay and conditions of trained staff.[43] The RCN commented that Wood had not defined the work of the nurse satisfactorily nor the relationship of nursing to domestic staff, also in short supply. It disagreed with Wood's accent on 'health' nursing, and with the shorter two-year course. The RCN agreed that nurses in training should be students and not primarily employees. It saw no reason why those student nurses who could afford it should not pay for their training as did physiotherapists – provided that the salaries of the qualified nurses were similar to those of other professional workers. It strongly opposed the idea that the Ministry of Health should be involved in nursing education. The RCN recommended that studies be carried out of the varying nursing loads created by patients with particular problems, and the hours of care required by patients in different stages of illness.[44] Nor was the Wood Report received well by the Association of Hospital Matrons. The GNC opposed the separation of training schools from hospitals, and the idea that the training schools should be controlled or inspected by anyone other than itself.[45] The King's Fund said that the role of the nurse was to care for the sick and helpless under medical direction, and that ward sisters should be on an incremental scale so that they would not need to transfer to administration for a better salary. The Nuffield Provincial Hospitals Trust pointed to the failure to answer the first question – 'What is the proper task of the nurse on the ward?' The Trust recommended a job analysis and proceeded to mount one, studying nursing work in hospital wards.[46]

Ministry of Health proposals followed the Wood Report. They were sweeping, ambitious and showed much goodwill towards nurses. Each region would have an educational organisation independent of the hospitals. There would be freedom for nurses to design their own training, build their own centres and create nursing colleges. In many ways the proposals paralleled university education, giving professional independence. The RCN council, on which matrons had a powerful voice, and the GNC discussed the proposals, failed to understand what they offered, drew back in alarm and defeated them.[47] The recommendations carried forward were those concerned with the creation of the NHS, nurse training budgets for regions and reform of the membership of the GNC. The staffing needs of the health service became dominant.

Nursing practice

Common to nursing in all hospitals was the need to provide a 24-hour service, near to the patient and without fail. Ward sisters once appointed might manage their ward for life, taking its name. In some hospitals they had accommodation on the ward, where they slept. Staff nurses were also people of authority. Nurses generally lived in the nurses' home in a protected environment, although in 1948 the Ministry recommended that those trained should readily be permitted to live out. Providing accommodation was expensive, and the Ministry thought it was to the advantage of both the community and the nurse to expect her, like other workers, to find her own accommodation.[48] Hospitals differed in their nursing organisation and tended to suspect innovations developed elsewhere. Nurses from teaching hospitals tended to be the élite of the profession although there was generally fierce pride in one's hospital, wherever it was. Matron's office was keenly aware of what was happening in the hospital, for matron toured the wards each day and the night sister each night, talking to staff and patients. Little escaped their eyes. Wards were run with economy in mind; bandages were washed and matron's office inspected the ward orders to ensure that they were appropriate. The medical staff knew where to turn if there were problems, and the misdeeds of a junior doctor were soon passed on to his chief. Discipline was strict; the uniform was spotless, shoes shone, dress hems had to be level with the apron and hems the same height (14 inches, 35 cm). The dress colour, stripes on the hat and the belt colour identified the seniority of the nurse. Hair was neat, caps were worn and make-up forbidden. The result was stunning. Top hospitals had distinctive outdoor uniforms, recognised by the local population. Those at St George's were made by Harrods; Westminster nurses were recognised by their long capes and bonnets.

ST GEORGE'S HOSPITAL
London, SW1
Duties of the Staff Nurses

1. Staff nurses should manage their work methodically and keep their Wards neat, clean and in good order. They should pay constant attention to the warmth, freshness and ventilation and study the welfare and comfort of their patients in every respect. Every effort should be made to keep the Wards as quiet as possible.
2. The senior Staff Nurse on duty shall deputise for the Ward Sister in her absence, and at such times shall report to the Sister who is 'on call' for her Ward (or in their absence to the Assistant Matron's Office) the admission of any patient who is seriously ill and on any occasion when there is cause for anxiety.
3. Staff Nurses should give a kindly welcome to new patients immediately on their arrival in the Ward, treating them with gentleness and consideration and making them and their friends feel assured from the first that they will be tenderly cared for.
4. The admission of new patients should be carefully supervised, particular attention being given to observing the condition of the pressure areas. Any abrasion of the skin, however slight, must be reported immediately to the Sister in charge. Staff Nurses shall also see that proper care is taken of the clothing and valuables of patients admitted to their Wards.
5. Staff Nurses shall be responsible for looking after relatives and friends visiting the Wards, and shall see that those waiting for long periods in the Hospital receive food and refreshment.
6. An important part of their duties is to assist the Ward Sisters in the training of Student Nurses, teaching them to be accurate, careful and observant, and thorough in every detail.
7. They shall see that all new Student Nurses coming to the Ward understand the clinical work allocated to them and are carefully instructed in all procedures practised in the Ward.
8. They shall study the rules laid down for the care and checking of Dangerous Drugs, and see that these are properly observed.
9. They shall be responsible to the Sister in charge of the Ward or Department for the care of the following: Linen, Instruments, Surgical equipment including surgical stock, Crockery and cutlery. A weekly inventory should be taken and any losses reported immediately to the Sister in Charge. It is recommended that instruments and cutlery in regular use be checked every day.
10. It is a strict rule of the Hospital that nothing may be borrowed from one Ward or Department for another without a written request signed by the Sister or Staff Nurse in charge. At night the request should be made to the Night Sister. This rules also applies to Dangerous Drugs.
11. Staff Nurses should supervise the work of the Ward Maids and Orderlies, instructing new members of the staff in their duties and helping them to feel that they are essential members of the Ward team. They shall see that the Domestic Staff are punctual in arriving and leaving the Ward, and shall teach them to be quiet and thorough in their work and to avoid waste.
12. Constant attention should be paid to every method by which economy may be effected, particularly with regard to food, surgical dressings, lotions, stationery and cleaning materials. Good management in this respect can save the Hospital considerable expense.
13. Any accident affecting either a patient or a member of the Nursing or Domestic Staff on duty in a Ward or Department shall be reported immediately to the Sister in Charge and a written statement made by the member of the Staff involved or witnessing the accident.
14. Staff Nurses should be thoroughly conversant with all the rules made for the prevention of infection in the Hospital and should see that these are conscientiously and carefully carried out.
15. Nursing Procedures practised in the Hospital shall be those laid down in the Nursing Procedure Book, a copy of which shall be available in every Ward and Department.

Muriel B. Powell
Matron
13 December 1951

The NHS brigaded nurses into a single workforce. Henceforth there would be a national pay structure, the Ministry would be concerned with staffing a huge service and professional organisations had a negotiating role. Nurses in the mental institutions had never been accepted by the RCN as on a par with state registered nurses. Other unions had been established by them to fight for better conditions and, simultaneously, better services. Strike action, though not common, was part of their tradition. COHSE was formed in 1946 when two unions merged, and after that it represented many of the nurses in mental hospitals and the auxiliary state enrolled nurses.[49] The RCN found itself having to act simultaneously as a trades union alongside others and as a professional organisation. Doctors had the BMA to deal with their terms of service, and the Royal Colleges to consider educational and professional issues. The RCN had to combine the two functions and was not always successful. Senior officers were frequently more political than professional. With optimism, Dame Louisa Wilkinson, President of the RCN, said things were going to be quite different.[50]

> *Nursing has allowed itself in the past to be taken far too much for granted. We have allowed ourselves to be handmaidens of the medical profession. Nurses have not got the slightest intention of accepting a lower plane than that of an active, loyal and wide-awake partnership with the medical team.*

Nursing in the community

Nursing in the community had a long and honourable history. The first recorded venture was in Liverpool in 1863. In 1889 the Queen's Jubilee Fund endowed the Queen Victoria's Jubilee Institute for Nurses, later the Queen's Nursing Institute. The Institute designed a specific training programme, ran local services, and was the main voluntary organisation doing so. Voluntary associations had to raise funds to pay their nurses' annual salaries. There were village fêtes with stalls and rides on the lake for tuppence and gardens open to the public. Some local authorities looked to voluntary agencies like the Queen's Nursing Institute; others provided their own nursing services.[51] On a national basis, the training of district nurses was not well codified and local authorities could employ those without qualifications in district nursing.[52]

Midwifery, a profession separate from nursing, was regulated under the Midwives Act of 1936. More than half of the babies born were delivered at home, mainly by midwives provided by local authorities or nursing associations. County councils and county boroughs had to provide a domiciliary service directly or through contracts; how they did so was largely for them. Domiciliary midwifery was an entirely female profession, giving a door-to-door service, mostly on bicycle, 24 hours a day, 365 days a year, to an entirely female clientele. Often working in partnerships of two or three, each midwife cared for women in her geographic patch, delivering 50–100 women annually. It was an industrious and insular life. Midwives had a sense of their own worth, with a duty to the public and an accountability to their supervisor. Few mothers saw more than three or four professionals during their pregnancy, and there was a guarantee of continuity of care.[53]

Health visitors had generally undertaken further education after state nurse registration and had midwifery experience. The roots of health visiting were different from the other two nursing professions: it emerged from community work and the radical tradition. It had grown, not out of nursing, but from 'sanitary' visiting in the nineteenth century, particularly in areas with poverty and poor living conditions. Formal training developed early, and led to an examination by the Royal Sanitary Institute. The ethos of health visiting was that of public health and its interests lay in the social conditions affecting the health and welfare of communities, and therefore families. The predecessors of the Health Visitors' Association were involved in most public and social issues – poverty, ill-health, infant mortality, slums and working conditions for women and children. They were early to register as trades unions and were involved in radical politics as the way to bring about change in society. Most of the health visitors' work was with pregnant women, nursing mothers and children under school age.[54] As the idea of maternal education as a weapon in the fight against infant mortality gained ground, there was an increasing demand for their services. The task of the health visitor began with a notification of birth – it was unsolicited.[55] When the NHS began, health visiting was already part of the local authority services, under the control of the medical officer of health. With the advent of the NHS the work of health visitors was expanded to the health of the household as a whole, advice on the care of people who were ill and measures to prevent the spread of infection.[56] Maternity and child welfare remained the centre of their work, which was usually based in a local authority clinic.

Because there was no formal demarcation of duties, there was considerable friction between district nurses, health visitors and midwives. In rural areas where mobility was a problem, one nurse might be a qualified midwife, health visitor and district nurse. She would be well known and well respected by the community.

Nursing administration

There had been nurses in government employ, in the Ministry of Health, since the 1920s. In 1948 Elizabeth Cockayne was appointed Chief Nursing Officer following Catherine Watt, the first CNO. Her career had been varied, involving clinical and educational posts in both the north and south of the country. She was one of the two nurse members of the Wood working party, which did not add to her popularity with the nursing profession. Her staff included public health and hospital nursing officers with regional responsibilities. They were in close contact with professional organisations and advised the Minister, working with medical and administrative colleagues and concerned with matters of nursing policy.[57]

Nursing administration within the hospitals was much the same in the voluntary and the municipal hospitals, not the case on the medical side. The matrons had an informal network and when one was to retire a successor might be agreed on the grapevine. Senior nurses would be moved among the hospitals in preparation for a key position that was becoming vacant; the teaching hospitals often supplied the matrons for municipal hospitals and smaller voluntary hospitals. In large hospitals a matron, with deputy and assistant matrons, managed the ward sisters, and they the more junior nursing staff. Where there was a nursing school, matron controlled it and selected the students. She managed catering, linen supplies and domestic services, and might be responsible for physiotherapists and other disciplines ancillary to medicine. Matron's role was similarly wide ranging in the smaller hospitals. However, the matrons' accountability might differ. In municipal hospitals matron reported to the medical superintendent. In the voluntary hospitals she had more autonomy and was usually appointed by, and was responsible to, the board of governors.

Towards a health system

Districts and regions

The idea of a 'district' general hospital (DGH), providing all the most common hospital services, can be traced back to the nineteenth century.[58] It was adopted after the first world war in Labour Party policies. In his Cavendish lecture of 1918, Bertrand Dawson, a physician at The London Hospital and a military doctor during the war, described how a health service could be co-ordinated. In 1920 he was invited to chair a Consultative Council on the future provision of health services, and he proposed a hierarchical system of primary care centres linked with district hospitals, and regional centres with university teaching hospitals.[59]

The idea of a 'region', an organisational unit larger than the district, emerged in the 1930s. The voluntary hospitals felt a need to combine to defend themselves against the expanding municipal hospitals. The British Hospitals Association, their representative body, asked Lord Sankey to chair a committee, which recommended the formation of regional councils to co-ordinate the planning and organisation over a wide area.[60] Following the Sankey Report the Association began to delineate regional boundaries. Regional organisation, but taking in the municipal hospitals as well, was commended by Political and Economic Planning, and it became the *raison d'être* of the Nuffield Provincial Hospitals Trust, founded in 1939. A regional scheme in London was also supported by the King's Fund, founded in 1897 in celebration of Queen Victoria's diamond jubilee by Edward VII when Prince of Wales.

Professional and geographic factors were dominant in proposals to organise on a regional basis. Rarer and more complex medical problems required larger catchment populations. The local authorities, whose boundaries were historic rather than functional, opposed the idea.[61] With the advent of war an emergency medical service (EMS) organised on regional lines was established under the control of the Ministry. Outside London the EMS regions were similar to those of the British Hospitals Association. In the southeast there was one region, but within it there were radial sectors spreading into the countryside, each with one or more teaching hospitals at its apex.

The Hospital Surveys

Survey areas

1 London and the surrounding area
2 Berkshire, Buckinghamshire and Oxfordshire
3 Eastern area
4 Southwestern area
5 South Wales and Monmouthshire
6 Sheffield and East Midlands
7 West Midlands
8 Yorkshire
9 Northwestern area
10 Northeastern area

There had been a national survey of hospitals in 1938 to consider provision for casualties in the event of war. A year after Dunkirk, on 9 October 1941, the government announced its post-war hospital policy and the decision to survey hospitals in London to provide a firm basis for planning. Shortly after, a second survey was mounted in the northwest and it was rapidly apparent that the whole country needed review. In 1943 further surveys began and there were ultimately ten, co-sponsored by Nuffield Provincial Hospitals Trust and the Ministry. For each region there were two, or later three, surveyors who visited every institution that might be called a hospital. The reports were published in 1945: Sheffield and London first, then the rest. George Godber was one of the Sheffield surveyors, and the detailed knowledge he gathered was the foundation of much of his subsequent work in the Ministry on the development of hospital and specialist services.[62] All the surveys showed wide variation in quality, and major deficiencies in hospital buildings that could only be overcome by rebuilding, although much inefficiency could be remedied more rapidly. The surveys advocated district hospital centres, uniting individual hospitals into a functional whole, with a common staff, grouped within regions resembling the survey areas. Their main value rested on factual reporting on existing buildings and services, and their confirmation of the need for regional planning. The detailed proposals were often suspect but one point of great importance emerged from all – the idea of a general hospital providing all the ordinary range of specialties for a natural population, linked with regional specialty centres. Once planned, the DGH should *then* be given a suitable base. There were then no accepted indices of need, so estimates of hospital size might be almost fanciful, and the location suggested was sometimes at fault. But for the first time the country got away from designing hospitals of some empirically determined size, and was attempting to look how best to provide services for a community.[63]

Together the surveys were known as the Domesday Book.[64] 'Since hospitals are an essential public service,' said the South Wales surveyors, 'it is curious but characteristic that in Britain this, Topsy-like, "just grow'd".' The surveyors did not mince their words, but their harsh statements were written on the assumption that the surveys would pave the way for better things. The three main problems were shortage of beds as a result of poor buildings and equipment, shortage of consultants, and poor patient accessibility to both beds and consultants.

There was no *system*. Complicated cases often received treatment in hospitals without the necessary facilities while simple cases occupied beds in hospitals with high standards of staff and equipment. Shortages of beds and specialists led to long waiting lists even for simple cases. Acute hospitals frequently had to discharge patients before they were fully recovered and the obligation of municipal hospitals to admit patients from within their areas meant over-crowding and under-staffing. Local authority boundaries led to uneconomic development and acted as barriers to admission. Although voluntary hospitals had often tried to expand, restricted sites meant, as at Charing Cross Hospital in the Strand, that the provision of modern facilities was impossible.

Medical staffing had to change. The distribution of specialists had been haphazard, determined largely by the economics of private practice. In municipal hospitals there had been salaried part-time or whole-time specialist posts but they were relatively few. The consequence was too few specialists who were unevenly spread. There had to be a tremendous redeployment of specialists and at least double the number. Outside large centres, where there was little private practice, there were limits on the choice of staff, and hospitals had to get along with the GPs living in the immediate neighbourhood. The West Midlands surveyors said that there had been a tendency for GPs gradually to drift into surgery or whatever branch of medicine was of most interest, and to do this as an off-shoot from general practice. They might be entirely self-taught. Specialist services were scarce; there was only one gynaecologist in the whole of Lincolnshire. In Rotherham the GPs objected to the appointment of full-time surgeons but examination of their results showed that four prostatectomies had been carried out the previous year, only two of the patients leaving hospital alive. Radiological and pathological services were poor. For example, there was no whole-time radiologist in Lincolnshire and Nottingham specialists visited Boston once a fortnight. In Northampton one of the physicians supervised the radiographers and some physicians took it amiss when it was suggested that a radiologist should be running the X-ray department. Similarly, technicians in isolated departments had no senior staff to whom to turn.

The hospital surveyors reserved their bitterest comments for long-stay provision. Often buildings were antiquated, with bare, over-crowded large wards and cheerless uncomfortable day rooms, and primitive facilities for nursing. In most instances the wards did not provide the physical or the mental amenities to be found in a domestic dwelling. In some institutions the ratio of patients to trained nurses was 60 or more to 1. Young children and people with senile dementia were herded together with elderly patients, many of whom might have been able to return to their homes had there been earlier diagnosis and treatment. The surveyors believed that the first need was for every patient to be thoroughly examined and treated.

Labour and the NHS

The Labour Party had put forward proposals for a national hospital service before the first world war, and between the wars there was increasing interest in resolving problems. Several reports – commissioned by the government, produced by independent groups or the work of professional or hospital organisations – had laid out alternatives.[65] In the 1930s whenever a new public service was envisaged, such as civil defence, it was considered as a potential function for local authorities. In the 1940s it became apparent that a health service run by them could be introduced only in the teeth of opposition from the medical profession.[66] A PEP broadsheet, published in July 1942, anticipated Beveridge and called for a national health service. The Beveridge Report on future social insurance aimed for universal coverage, and named 'five giants' on the road to reconstruction: want, disease, ignorance, squalor and idleness.[67] The depression in the 1920s and 1930s, the lack of systematic provision for health care at that time, the experience of communal action in war and the efficiency of the EMS all pointed to the need for a health service. The draft interim report of the BMA's Medical Planning Commission in 1942, which called for the creation of a comprehensive service covering most people, made it easy for Beveridge to assume that one would be created for the whole nation.[68]

The war had increased the sense of social solidarity, and many saw the advantages of a command structure. Most doctors had military experience and knew that service personnel had, from a health point of view, been looked after better than in peacetime.[69] Many of those involved, or who would be important to the future NHS, had at least a social conscience if not an overt inclination to the left, for example George Godber, Richard Titmuss and Richard Doll. Janet Vaughan found it hard to understand how anyone could be a doctor before the war and not become a socialist. Julian Tudor Hart, a Welsh GP, believed that people who had experienced the effect of the market on the distribution of services meeting basic human needs, and the revelation that in wartime the market could be overridden for great purposes, were resolved never to return to the old system.[70] As early as 1943 the Ministry of Health was considering the transition of the wartime EMS into a comprehensive health service, free and available to all.[71] On these foundations a blueprint for a service was accepted by the Conservative Cabinet in the interval between the wartime coalition government and the election of Attlee's Labour government in 1945.

Labour came to power with one of the largest majorities in British history. It was committed to a programme of public ownership and lost no time in carrying it out. The Bills nationalising the Bank of England, coal, and cable and wireless received Royal Assent in 1946. In the following year it was the turn of transport, railways, canals, road-haulage and electricity. The gas industry was nationalised in 1948, and iron and steel in 1949.[72] The NHS was a different type of nationalisation, aiming for a radically new type of service. The NHS Act was introduced four months after the election and passed during the first session of the new Parliament. In the words of the Minister of Health, Aneurin Bevan, the Act would create an atmosphere of greater security and serenity up and down the country for families faced by anxiety and the distress of illness.[73] The inability of voluntary hospitals to raise charitable moneys made it necessary. Rising costs hastened the inevitability of a state medical service. With the advance of science and specialisation, a patient had not one but many doctors. The cost of illness was beyond the purse of the average person. A single patient with tuberculosis, for whom an operation (thoracoplasty) was required, might pay more than £1000 from the time of admission to discharge some months later. It would be a travesty of justice, said Lionel Whitby, Regius Professor of Physic at Cambridge, were treatment to be available only to the few rich people whom successive Chancellors of the Exchequer had allowed to survive.[74]

Until the Labour victory, local authorities looked likely to play a lead role. Bevan came as a man with a mission to change things. He looked at the draft Bill from the previous administration and insisted that the hospitals should be nationalised and that the service must cover everyone. He had seen how previous proposals had been picked to pieces by special interests, the hospitals, local authorities and the medical profession, and what had been a coherent if complicated plan had become an administrative dog's dinner.[75] The Bevan solution, opting for a regional scheme rather than one based on local authority boundaries, was a work of genius. The key was the realisation that, without executive control of both the voluntary and the municipal hospitals, effective hospital planning was impossible. It was like a breath of fresh air to the officials involved, Sir Wilson Jameson, the CMO, who had an instinct for what was required, George Godber who did the medical drafting and John Horton and John Pater who dealt with administrative issues. The regional concept brought together service considerations (the natural territory within which normal and highly specialised services could best be organised) and the university medical schools (the natural centres of research, development and education). These would 'fertilise' the services in the surrounding areas.[76] Indeed it was difficult to conceive of a region without a medical school, and vice versa. With university and medical concurrence, regions could establish an integrated specialist system and rationalise nurse training. Bevan's regions were sizeable; large regions were less likely to attempt detailed local control, but any high degree of local autonomy might have prevented the region from organising a coherent service. Boards had to have the ability to close, amalgamate and expand hospitals. If the boards were too weak, the anarchy of the old voluntary system would begin all over again.[77] There being ten provincial teaching hospitals, that set the number of regions in England and Wales as ten, plus four for London (Wessex became a region in 1959 and Wales separated in 1974). The main oddity was the division of the southeast into four metropolitan regions that met in the centre of London. In the war a radial pattern of organisation had been adopted to make the evacuation of casualties easier. It worked well as it accommodated the teaching hospitals and medical schools. For Bevan it had another advantage, the pattern was utterly unlike that of the London County Council. A single London health authority would have had massive and undesirable political clout and would have been totally insensitive to the periphery. At local level the unit would be not a group of hospitals but a complex of hospitals, GPs and health centres. A partnership of general and specialist practice would make general practice viable and relate the hospital to the community it served.[78]

Bevan refused to discuss the details of his proposals until, after the first reading, there was a measure of parliamentary approval. In the final round of negotiations Bevan accepted key demands from the doctors. For the specialists this was a part- or whole-time salary plus merit awards, and the right to treat private patients in NHS hospitals. For GPs it was a system as far removed from a salary as possible; capitation was a defence against the perils of state servitude.[79] Like it or not, the state and the medical profession had become mutually dependent. Many doctors had received state funds through the Lloyd George national insurance scheme, but now they were even more dependent on government for their incomes and the resources at their command. The state had become dependent on the medical profession to run the NHS and to cope with the problems of rationing scarce resources in patient care.[80] The restrictions imposed by local authority boundaries were removed. The decision to take hospitals into national ownership in 1948 and the inevitable compromises did not please everyone. Herbert Morrison, in the Cabinet, and the local authorities, some themselves Labour, were upset at the loss of their municipal hospitals. The voluntary hospitals disliked their loss of independence. Despite the bickering of 1946/7 nearly everyone was in tune with the broad principles and was prepared to do his or her best to make Bevan's pattern of NHS work. Nurses were strongly in favour, as were the younger doctors. The objectors were the older men who were the controllers of the BMA and its committees. Behind it all was an attitude epitomised by an elderly Civil Defence worker who told Richard Titmuss, the social scientist, that 'The war made us realise that we were all neighbours'. From the rubble of war it was believed that Labour would create a better society.

When Bevan died, in 1960, a *BMJ* editorial described him as the most brilliant Minister of Health the country had ever had, much less doctrinaire in his approach than many of his Labour colleagues, and conceiving the NHS on more liberal lines than his Conservative predecessor. He towered over a long line of Ministers of Health and attracted in the medical profession profound admiration on one side and the sharpest antagonism on the other. The editorial proceeded to claim that the medical profession, rather than Bevan, was the principal architect of the NHS. But when Bevan had left the Ministry of Health in 1951 the *BMJ* had been less generous:

> his vicious attacks on the profession, his attempts to sow discord, and his rudeness in
> negotiation would never be forgotten. He never rose above being a clever politician and
> at critical moments failed to become the statesman. He had done his best to make
> himself disliked by the medical profession, and, by and large, he succeeded.[81]

The NHS framework

The NHS Act established a 'comprehensive health service to secure the improvement in the physical and mental health of the people . . . and the prevention, diagnosis and treatment of illness'. What it did not do was establish an individual entitlement for treatment of particular illnesses, as an insurance scheme would have done. As the NHS was paid for out of taxation, for the first time the Treasury had a powerful influence on the health care system. The NHS would be:[82]

- A service comprehensive in scope, including medical and allied services of every kind. (Earlier there had been the possibilities of excluding mental illness and dentistry but these were brought within the NHS.)
- A service available to all – the universal coverage Beveridge had proposed – in spite of some professional opposition. Internationally the usual basis of public medical schemes was insurance, so a health service funded largely from central taxation was, outside the Eastern Communist block, distinctive.
- A service free at the time of need.
- A pattern of medical remuneration reflecting doctors' wishes.
- A hospital service administered by centrally appointed, not elected, bodies and the officers those bodies appointed with power freely delegated down the line. (The local authority health services were run by elected members and the executive councils largely by nominees of the local authorities and the professions.)

There should have been another distinctive feature, co-operative general practice from shared purpose-built health centres. This idea, advanced by the BMA's Medical Planning Commission, fell victim to professional disquiet, naive over-enthusiasm, high costs and a shortage of building materials. Six months before the NHS began, the Ministry wrote to local authorities to say that no general programme of construction would be implemented.

The service was tripartite and had to be developed in sections. Otherwise, Sir George Godber has said, it would never have been got to work in time. Nor, in 1948, would a unified system have been able to look after primary and community services in addition to the hospitals. Unification could have been a disaster for general practice, which carried much of the burden of the NHS in the early years. There would be the hospital service within a regional framework, the only way to achieve a properly planned service and a reasonable distribution of specialist staff. There were the local authority services that quietly made progress in developing community nursing, home help and immunisation programmes. Then there was general practice where GPs now would look after whole families, not just the bread-winner. Executive councils (ECs), a new, broadened type of 'insurance committee' in which local health authority representatives replaced the old friendly societies, administered the contracts of GPs, dentists, pharmacists and opticians. In these divisions were the seeds of future problems.

Twenty years later Richard Crossman (Secretary of State for Social Services 1968–1970) said that the Bevan compromise gained the support of the consultants by conceding an entrenched position that could not be broken without jeopardising the whole health service. GPs were given a special place, with elaborate safeguards that kept them isolated from the hospitals and from the community services, which were left in the hands of the local authorities and their medical officers of health. Then in order to preserve 'freedom' from despotism still further, all hospitals were nationalised and RHBs were set up. These, in Crossman's view, were remarkable in their powers. They were strong, semi-autonomous boards whose relations to the Minister were like those of a Persian satrap to a weak emperor. If the emperor tried to enforce his authority too far, he lost his throne or at least his resources or something broke down. Health service freedom lay in the fact that the centre was weak, the regions strong and the GPs in their enclave were separated off safe from attack.[83] Although Bevan might have considered the NHS as pure socialism, it was rather closer to impure liberalism. Doctors had been treated with consideration, local administrations enjoyed considerable freedom and the profile of government itself was low. If many remembered the period as a golden age, that was perhaps because it suited almost everyone very well.[84]

During the war MOsH and medical school deans played leading parts as the Ministry's agents controlling hospital and casualty arrangements, which might have led them to

---

London and provincial medical schools (1948)

London medical schools	Provincial medical schools
Charing Cross	Birmingham
Guy's	Bristol
King's College*	Cambridge
London	Leeds*
Middlesex*	Liverpool*
Royal Free	Manchester*
St Bartholomew's*	Newcastle*
St George's	Oxford
St Mary's*	Sheffield*
St Thomas'	Wales†
University College	
Westminster*	

The table excludes schools in Scotland and Northern Ireland.
*These medical schools made use of RHB hospitals for teaching in core subjects such as medicine and surgery.
†Wessex became a region in 1959, and Wales separated in 1974.

expect a more substantial role in the NHS than they were given. In 1948 MOsH remained with their local authorities, but six in England became the Senior Administrative Medical Officers (SAMOs) of the new regional hospital boards. Having been chief executives in the past, they often became their new employer's leading officer, paired with a non-medical secretary.

Regional hospital boards

Although regional boundaries had been drawn as far as possible to coincide with hospital catchment areas, RHBs were not self-sufficient and their boundaries were not meant to be barriers to the flow of patients. By the early summer of 1947 Bevan had consulted widely and appointed the RHB members. They were to act as individuals, not delegates of interest groups. There were few political appointments. Most members were of the old guard to maintain continuity, although a few were dropped as they were entirely out of sympathy with the new regime. There were doctors, there might be a nurse or a dentist, and there were elected members of local authorities. There was usually at least one trades union member but the rest were people who had shown an interest in running health services. Regions had less than a year to appoint staff, learn their jobs, determine their hospital management committees (HMCs) and secure ministerial approval before appointing HMC members. The emphasis was on sound representation of local people and skill in running the existing services.[85] In 1947 the Ministry sent guidance to the new regions in circular RHB(47)1. The RHBs would act as the Minister's agents, but agents on whom he wished to confer the largest possible measure of discretion. From the outset they were to feel a lively sense of independent responsibility.[86] It was for them to decide their committee structure and working methods although they would want to appoint professional advisory committees. Bevan made it clear that, just as he would try not to interfere with regions, regions should not interfere with their HMCs. Formal schemes and plans for the region's services would not be required, for 'the reviewing and organising the service would be a continuous, fluid and developing process not susceptible of reduction to a final paper plan'. Boards would need to work closely with teaching hospitals, universities, the Ministry and local authorities.

Regional functions included:

- planning, medical staffing and hospital capital works;
- managing financial allocations to HMCs, appointing HMC chairmen and members, and controlling HMC staff establishments;
- running some regional services such as blood transfusion and mass radiography;
- providing general advice and support.

The newly appointed members of the RHBs learnt together. They had to get to know each other, to work in temporary accommodation and to build up their staff. To begin with these were few, and the same was true of the HMCs; some barely knew the institutions under their control. Board members drove from one hospital to another, having delightful hospital lunches and teas, welcomed wherever they went and being shown the best and the scandalous.[87]

Boards of governors

Teaching hospitals were selected by the Minister, with university advice, because of their special importance to medical education. They had fought for their independence and won. Their pre-war burden of debt had been lifted and they retained their own – sometimes substantial – endowment funds. To the teaching hospitals were sometimes added local municipal hospitals if they were essential for medical education, or small special hospitals, perhaps a children's hospital or one for ophthalmology. Most continued to be selective in their admissions policy, serving some, but not all, of the needs of those living in their locality. Occasionally, as in Oxford and Cambridge, the boards of governors dominated the provision of acute hospital services in the city and surrounding districts.[88] Each teaching hospital board of governors was directly accountable to the Minister, not to the regional board. Labour Party policy had long been that teaching hospitals that enjoyed a national and international reputation, drawing cases from all over the country, should be maintained and administered under the general control of the Ministry of Health.[89] Their boards of governors were partly appointed by the Minister but also included members nominated by universities, medical staff and RHBs. The relations between the teaching hospitals and the RHBs varied from close co-operation to none whatsoever.

Hospital management committees

Hospitals were managed by HMCs within overall plans of the RHBs. RHBs were instructed to create HMCs by grouping together functionally related hospitals to form the equivalent of a full-scale hospital covering all normal specialties. A group might consist of ten or a dozen units, perhaps a voluntary general hospital, a municipal general hospital, a maternity home, an isolation hospital and three or four GP hospitals in small neighbouring towns. In the North West Metropolitan Board the SAMO arranged their pattern while at home in bed with 'flu. By uniting their governance, it would be easier to rationalise hospital services within them. The guiding principals were decentralisation, encouragement of local interest and the avoidance of large and unwieldy units of management. HMCs might be developed on a functional rather than a locality basis. Mental hospitals had been administered by local authorities and had not been included in wartime hospital surveys. They fiercely defended their independence and were grouped separately under their own HMCs so that the new organisation perpetuated the separation of mental hospitals from the rest of the NHS. Some wondered if it was right for them to be isolated from other branches of medicine and it took ten years to get them meshed in.

The service was planned so that patients could be treated in the hospitals best suited to their needs. Before the NHS, patients were often restricted to one municipal hospital but could wander freely among the voluntaries. Afterwards they would be referred to the hospital 'thought best to meet their needs'. The *Hospitals year book* said

> There are no boundaries on the map where 'A' management committee finishes and
> 'B' management committee starts. For ordinary needs the inhabitants of a town go to
> an acute general hospital in the town run by 'A' group, for treatment of tuberculosis to
> a hospital run by 'B' group, those in need of mental treatment to a mental hospital in

group 'C' and those requiring the attention of a highly specialised kind might find it necessary to go to a hospital in 'D' group, the other side of the region or in another region altogether. This is commonsense; a large number of geographical barriers have been swept away and some of the happenings which in the past have aroused either public resentment or public ridicule should no longer occur.[90]

Finance

Financial data for the years immediately before and immediately after the introduction of the NHS are hard to obtain. The Ministry obtained hospitals' statements of expenditure in 1946/7 and they were asked to provide the actual expenditure in the first few months of 1948.[91] The service had to be kept running, so finance was based on historic spending that depended on the revenue available from local rates and charitable sources. The south was therefore better off than the north.[92] From the outset there was a grossly uneven distribution of money, largely concealed as the accounts for the first two decades of the NHS were presented functionally over the NHS as a whole, not geographically. Little attempt was made to correct this skewed distribution and less to publicise it.

Consultant services

The 1947 circular RHB(47)1 on the functions of RHBs had promised future guidance on the planning of hospital services and the desirable levels of specialist staff. It appeared as *The development of specialist services* (RHB(48)1).[93] It was the work of a group chaired by John Charles, the deputy CMO at the Ministry, which included specialists mainly from provincial teaching centres – Newcastle (William Hume), Sheffield (Ernest Finch), Oxford (J Chassar Moir), Manchester (Geoffrey Jefferson), Birmingham, Liverpool and Bristol. The secretary, George Godber, wrote the circular using his experience of the Sheffield hospital survey, and the result was the consensus of thought at consultant level. An attempt was made to relate staffing to population, emphasising the importance of providing an area service.[94] Estimates of the beds needed by the various specialties were based largely on the past experience of teaching hospitals and had little factual background. It was a successful essay on general principles but not a reliable guide on details. The Royal College of Physicians (RCP) liked it enough to ask for reprints to send to their membership.

Drawing on proposals in the surveys, the regions were seen as an aggregation of 'hospital centres', serving areas determined by geography, population density and transport facilities. Centres would consist of a group of hospitals (managed by the HMC) providing all normal specialist services, functionally united and with a common medical staff. These would become the basis of the future DGHs. Linkage should be maintained by recognising all specialists throughout the region as members of one team, with the opportunity to move between regional and hospital centres.

The largest hospital centre would be the 'regional centre', providing a wider range of services, including those demanding a larger population base, such as plastic surgery, neurosurgery, thoracic surgery and radiotherapy. This regional centre would include the teaching hospital, even though it was outside the curtilage of the RHB. Because the teaching hospitals would be selective about the patients admitted, for reasons of education and research, contiguous HMC hospitals would take the rest. The teaching hospitals alone would not be able to provide all the necessary clinical material for teaching, particularly in the fields of tuberculosis, infectious disease and mental disease; this work would fall to the regional board. One function of the RHB would be the integration of the specialist services of the regional centre with those of the peripheral hospital areas, and cordial relations between the RHB and the teaching hospital's board of governors would be needed.

Even the smallest hospital centre would need a locally resident physician, surgeon, obstetrician and anaesthetist. Most would require more. Some services should be provided by consultants who practised their specialty exclusively, for example radiology, ophthalmology and ear, nose and throat (ENT). Others would often be undertaken by consultants with a special interest, for example cardiology and urological surgery. The specialty of geriatrics had not then emerged and it was assumed that general physicians would be the providers of better treatment of the so-called chronic sick. A hospital area with a population of 100,000–120,000 would probably require

- Three general surgeons and physicians of senior grade (half-time).
- Three general surgeons and physicians of junior grade (half-time).
- No fewer than three surgical and three medical registrars (whole-time).

The circular RHB(48)1 was all-encompassing, with sections covering the full range of hospital specialties. It was made clear that the first responsibility of RHBs was to keep the service running, but they were to look to the future and see their immediate responsibilities against the background of the long term. The new service could not be built on the 'appointed day', when the Act came into force, and RHBs were not to endanger the future by the appointment of inadequately trained people merely because there were pressing service needs.

There remained the issue of specialist pay. Unlike the GPs, the consultants were content to be employees. It was the income that was significant and the basic principles were settled by the Spens reports.[95] By opting for a salary rather than a fee-for-service approach, financial incentives for unnecessary treatment were removed, to the benefit of patients and the exchequer. By paying the same salary in all parts of the country, and in each of the specialties, medical staff planning was made easier. However some specialists, particularly surgeons, had earned large sums in private practice, the leaders of the profession among them. The equality of NHS earnings that Spens proposed was unusual and Bevan conceded the right to private practice, making it possible for those who were energetic and highly skilled to earn substantially more than their colleagues. He also agreed to additional payments for merit, which was not too closely defined. An attempt was made to balance the merit awards committee, which had a non-medical vice-chairman and representatives of teaching and research. The awards, allocated privately, might double a consultant's NHS income although most were smaller in value. Bevan was reported as saying that he had achieved agreement by stuffing the doctors' mouths with gold.

Doctors and the state

Relationships had long been ambivalent. As far back as the nineteenth century there had been proposals for a state-controlled service that had been regarded by many doctors with a mixture of concern, fear and anger. In 1918 Lauriston Shaw, Dean at Guy's, had written that there

> was no consensus about the relationships which should exist between the two parties. An extreme right party believes that beyond securing the proper education of doctors, and providing a sanitary service to safeguard the drains and control epidemics, the state should leave the medical profession alone to carry out its beneficent work in absolute independence of all government control. These devoted individualists are prepared to die in the last ditch before they will sacrifice the smallest outpost of professional liberty. An extreme left party sees salvation in the Fabian socialist proposal of state employment for all doctors. Illness could then be treated, as Beatrice Webb suggested, as a public nuisance to be suppressed in the interests of the community, by compulsion if necessary. Some believe that the government should take responsibility for seeing that its medical employees carried out instructions faithfully to offer or force upon each member of the community the medical services the state considers necessary to maintain physical health. Between these two factions is a large central party which recognises the impracticability of the ideals of the extremists, and seeks to bring an honourable partnership between the state and the medical profession to bring the benefits of medical science to individuals and society irrespective of wealth or social position.[96]

Sir George Newman, the first CMO of the Ministry of Health, speaking to the BMA in 1920 shortly after the Ministry's creation said

> The state has seen in the profession a body insistent upon the privacy and individuality of its work, the sanctity of its traditions and the freedom of its engagements. The profession has seen in the state an organisation apparently devoted to the infringement of these traditions and incapable of putting anything worthy in their place. It has been suspicious and mistrustful of what it considers to be unnecessary intervention. It has feared the imposition of some cast-iron system which might in practice make the practitioner of medicine servile, dependent and fettered.[97]

Although the medical profession had, individually and corporately, seen that a state health service could be beneficial, the suspicion never disappeared. Charles Hill, first known to the public during the years of war as the Radio Doctor, became the medical profession's organiser and mouth-piece in its opposition to some aspects of Labour's plans for the NHS. 'Let us make sure,' he said, 'that your doctor does not become the state's doctor.' The profession in general maintained that its support for a national health service was not in question, but that particular proposals worried them. However, some eminent doctors, such as Lord Horder, never accepted the idea. Horder, a St Bartholomew's Hospital man and a lifelong opponent of the NHS, which he felt could only lower professional standards in medicine, sought to establish a group of those doctors remaining outside the NHS for their mutual protection.[98]

The passage of the NHS Bill into law in November 1946 did not end the bitter conflicts in the months before 5 July 1948, which left the profession with enmity for Mr Bevan and all his works.[99] At the end of May 1948, the BMA recommended that its members accept the NHS and the will of Parliament, but the ill-will lived on. Many doctors of that generation had been taught to disparage medicine as practised under the NHS, to regard the Ministry of Health as its enemy and to speak of the health service in terms of contempt.

The BMA had not yet cast itself as the defender of the health service, but it had adopted its position of habitual opposition to the government of the day. In years to come both Conservative and Labour ministers experienced the implacable anger of the profession when it felt that it was not getting its way. Enoch Powell, Barbara Castle, Kenneth Robinson, Richard Crossman and Kenneth Clarke faced the profession's bitter attacks. The profession was often led by its right wing, but there were, at the same time, many clinicians who were constructive in shaping the NHS. Sometimes senior doctors used offensive language about politicians, while resenting any implication that their own motives were open to challenge. Often, however, personal relationships at a senior level were close and generous. Almost invariably money was at the centre of the row. All Ministers of Health were in the unenviable position of being regarded as agents of the government by the health professions and as agents of the professions by their ministerial colleagues.[100] Nor would the medical profession be alone in its campaigns. Powell referred to the vested interest in denigrating the NHS common to managers and nurses as well as doctors. Government, as the sole supplier of funds, took the blame for everything. Anyone who professed to be satisfied at what was being spent could not unreasonably be represented as a traitor to his colleagues, the professions and the patients.[101] The different perspectives of the professions and the government, each changing its position subtly over time, were sometimes constructive but often negative. The trust in the tried and traditional path was deep, and it might be far too long before general professional consent to change was secured. Doctors and nurses are, in the main, people who want to help patients, not administer an organisation or trade with clients. Closely focused on their patients, their ward or practice, and their specialty, they did not always take a broad view and at times were clearly wrong. But once shown a path to better, more acceptable outcomes, they would take it, and probably find an even better one in the process.

Expert advice to government

Government required expert advice on health issues long before the NHS began. The MRC reported on many issues in the 1920s and 1930s. The NHS Act opened with a resounding statement:

> It shall be the duty of the Minister of Health to promote the establishment of a comprehensive health service designed to secure . . . the prevention, diagnosis and treatment of illness and for that purpose to provide or secure the effective provision of services . . . as set out in the Act.

The responsibility of the Minister was subtly limited. He was not responsible for the prevention, diagnosis and treatment of illness; only for the establishment of a service to secure those desirable results. At first sight there was a clear-cut division between the Minister who provided the framework and the doctor who followed his profession within that framework. But there was a fuzzy border. In the treatment of a single patient it was easy enough to keep the Minister at arm's length. However, if the question concerned the treatment of many similar patients, the Minister might not know the answers but he had to find out. The politician was concerned with the general consequences of individual decisions. He resolved the dilemma by creating a professional advisory system, respectable, august, safe and therefore, in the nature of things, rather elderly. Then if, for example, the General Medical Council (GMC) declined to approve qualifications of doctors trained on astrological principles, the Minister could – very politely – decline to employ them in the NHS.[102]

A major source of expert advice was the MRC, the successor to a committee established under the 1911 National and Insurance Act to administer funds for research into tuberculosis. It had expanded, diversified and been incorporated by Charter, becoming a nearly autonomous body predominantly of scientists, with great liberty in discharging wide terms of reference. Its contributions to health care were many and valuable. Yet there was often a sense of tension between the MRC and the Ministry of Health. This centred around the question of the slant of research, basic and biomedical or operational and immediately applicable to common health problems. Its Secretary, Harold Himsworth, believed that, in the struggle to transform a parochial service into a national one, insufficient attention was paid to how expert knowledge could guide a science-based service.[103] Lord Dawson had maintained that the greatest problem facing modern civilisation was the integration of expert knowledge into the machinery of government. With the advent of the health service a robust system was needed that could handle a wide range of issues and work at all levels of the NHS. The chosen mechanism was a CMO, with an expert supporting staff, and a range of advisory committees of external specialists. Himsworth preferred the solution adopted at the Ministry of Defence, where serving professionals worked side by side with civil servants. When the NHS was established, doctors were to be found in many advisory and managerial capacities throughout the service.

The stage is set

During the run up to the start of the NHS, most of the voices heard had been those of the professional élite, the top doctors, the representatives of the large hospitals and the senior nurses from the voluntaries. The Royal Colleges, then far more the public face of medicine than now, were largely controlled by men from London teaching hospitals. London had a dominant influence on what was now a national service, even though in some clinical fields the provinces were leaders. Less had been heard from the public, from the provinces, from general practice and from the long-stay specialties. The medical and nursing professions were cohorts of different ages, and with different patterns of thought. The older ones, in their 60s in medicine and 50s in nursing, were always over-represented in discussions. As a result true professional views and the importance of new developments did not always emerge. Wisdom sometimes came with age, but sometimes it did not. In medicine the leaders were invariably practising clinicians, although sometimes their working situation was atypical. Nursing, however, was hierarchical. Almost by definition those representing the nurses would long since have ceased to have contact with patients. To find nurses for committees, who were able both to see the broader picture and to bring to a meeting a sense of the world as it was, could be difficult.

On 5 July 1948 some thought they stood on the brink of the abyss, others of the millennium. The problem was to meld a mass of often conflicting institutions, keep them working and then get them to work better. The existing components were to be united into a new system for delivering care to everyone, redistributing staff and facilities. The NHS would also redistribute income and the right wing press saw a socialist attack on the professional classes in many of its features. There was acrimony and anger, hope and enthusiasm, fears and forebodings. There was a wish to make the new system work and a naive belief that all would be well. The lessons of war could be applied to the problems of peace, and a planned solution of many previously insoluble problems was now possible. That was the hope and the inspiration for the future. The urgent need was a planned attack on disease, on the basis of the best available sources of information, on a scale and of an intensity that had not previously been possible. But first, said the *BMJ*, the scarcity of skilled people and the shortage of equipment and institutions must be made good. After that the opportunity for co-operation between the medical profession, the public and the government in building a healthy Britain would be grasped eagerly.[104]

References

1. Department of Health and Social Security. *NHS twentieth anniversary conference*. London: HMSO, 1968.
2. Black D. Medicine and politics. *BMJ* 1988; 296: 53–6.
3. Ministry of Health. *Interim report on the future provision of medical and allied services*. (Chairman: Dawson of Penn.) Consultative Council on medical and allied services, Cmd 693. London: HMSO, 1920.
4. Watts CAH. In my own time: general practice. *BMJ* 1979; 2: 1055–6.
5. Godber GE. The confidential enquiry into maternal deaths. In: McLachlan G, editor. *A question of quality?* London: Nuffield Provincial Hospitals Trust, 1976.
6. Fearnley GR. The changing face of medical practice. *BMJ* 1970; 1: 46.
7. Herbert SM. *Britain's health: based on the PEP report*. Pelican Special S27. Harmondsworth: Penguin, 1939.
8. Rivett GC. *The development of the London hospital system 1823–1982*. London: King's Fund, 1986.
9. Herbert SM. *Britain's health: based on the PEP report*. Pelican Special S27. Harmondsworth: Penguin Books, 1939, 116.
10. Menzies Sir Frederick. Personal memorandum on the LCC hospital services written to the Ministry of Health. 22 August 1941.
11. Elder HHA. Forty years in general practice. *Journal of the College of General Practitioners* 1964; 7: 328–41.
12. Ministry of Health. *Hospital survey – the hospital services of London and the surrounding area*. London: HMSO, 1945, 69.
13. Herbert SM. *Britain's health: based on the PEP report*. Pelican Special S27. Harmondsworth: Penguin Books, 1939.
14. Ewles L. Paddling upstream for 50 years: the role of health education officers. *Health Education Journal* 1993; 52/3: 172–81.
15. Night ward report, St George's Hospital, 1951.
    Richards T. Conversations with consultants. *BMJ* 1988; 297: 51.
16. *The consultant physician: responding to change*. A report of the Royal College of Physicians. London: RCP, 1996.

17. Hospital manners [leading article]. *Lancet* 1948; 2: 775.
A patient. Two hospitals. *Lancet* 1948; 2: 782–5.
18. Rollin HR. *Festina lente: a psychiatric odyssey*. London: BMJ, 1990.
19. Jefferson G. Surgery 1900–1950. *BMJ* 1950; 1: 8–12.
20. Calnan CD. *The life and times of Geoffrey Burrow Dowling*. Oxford: Blackwell, 1993.
21. Curtis Bain CW. Man and the machine. Presidential address to the BMA Annual Meeting. *BMJ* 1949; 2: 1.
22. Ministry of Health. *Postgraduate medical education and the specialties*. Reports on public health and medical subjects, no. 106. (Chairman: Sir George Pickering.) London: HMSO, 1962.
23. Booth CC. Medical science and technology at the Royal Postgraduate Medical School: the first 50 years. *BMJ* 1985; 291: 1771–9.
Sherlock S. Jaundice. *BMJ* 1962; 1: 1359.
24. Fifty years of medicine [leading article]. *BMJ* 1950; 1: 61–2.
25. Williams REO. *Microbiology for the public health. The evolution of the PHLS*. London: PHLS, 1985.
26. Gunson HH, Dodsworth H. Fifty years of blood transfusion. *Transfusion Medicine* 1996; 6, suppl 1: 1–88.
27. Price BJ, Dodds MG. *The quest for new medicines*. Glaxo Research Ltd, 1992.
28. Dunlop Sir Derrick. *Medicines in our time*. Rock Carling Fellowship. London: Nuffield Provincial Hospitals Trust, 1973.
29. Booth CC. Medical science and technology at the Royal Postgraduate Medical School. *BMJ* 1985; 291: 1771–9.
30. Booth CC. Clinical research. In: Bynum WT, Porter R, editors. *Companion encyclopedia of the history of medicine*. London: Routledge, 1993.
31. Ellis J. Medical education in London. *BMJ* 1980; 1: 923–7.
32. Ministry of Health and Department of Health for Scotland. *Report of the inter-departmental committee on medical education*. London: HMSO, 1944.
33. Booth CC. Friends and influence: the history of the '42 Club'. *Journal of the Royal College of Physicians* 1993; 27: 187–91.
34. *Nursing as a career*. London: London County Council, 1934.
35. Lord Horder. Nursing. Extract from a lecture. *Nursing Times* 1953; Oct 17: 1049–50.
36. Seeking the remedies [editorial]. *Nursing Times*, 1948; Oct 23: 771–2.
37. Widening the selection [leading article]. *Nursing Times* 1984; Oct 9: 733–4.
38. Carpenter M. *Working for health: the history of COHSE*. London: Lawrence & Wishart, 1988.
Student status. [leading article] *Nursing Times* 1948; Aug 21: 605.
39. White R. The Nurses Act 1949: service priorities. Occasional paper. *Nursing Times* 1982; Feb 3: 13–15.
Abel-Smith B. *A history of the nursing profession*. London: Heinemann, 1960.
40. Ministry of Health, Department of Health for Scotland and Ministry of Labour and National Service. *Working party on the recruitment and training of nurses. Majority report*. London: HMSO, 1947.
41. Watkin B. *Documents on health and social services policy. 1834 to the present day*. London: Methuen, 1975, 302–11.
42. Scott EJC. The influence of the staff of the Ministry of Health on policies for nursing: 1919–1968. *Thesis*. London: London School of Economics, 1994.
43. White R. The Nurses Act 1949. *Nursing Times* 1982; Jan 27: 9–12.
44. Speaking for nurses [leading article]. *Nursing Times* 1948; Apr 10: 255.
RCN memorandum on the report of the working party on the recruitment and training of nurses. *Nursing Times* 1948; April 10: 260–2.

45. Abel-Smith B. *A history of the nursing profession.* London: Heinemann, 1960.
46. Nuffield Provincial Hospitals Trust. *The work of nurses in hospital wards, the report of a job analysis.* London: NPHT, 1953.
47. White R. The Nurses Act 1949. *Nursing Times* 1982; Jan 27: 9–12.
    White R. *The effects of the NHS on the nursing profession, 1948–1961.* London: King's Fund, 1985.
48. Free to live out [leading article]. *Nursing Times* 1953; Aug 15: 807.
49. Carpenter V. *Working for health: the history of COHSE.* London: Lawrence & Wishart, 1988.
50. Civic reception. *Nursing Times* 1948; Nov 6: 808.
51. White R. *The effects of the NHS on the nursing profession: 1948–1961.* London: King's Fund, 1985.
52. Baly ME. *A history of the Queen's Nursing Institute.* London: Croom Helm, 1987.
53. Allison J. *Delivered at home.* London: Chapman & Hall, 1996.
54. Health Visitors' Association. *Ready as ever . . . the story of the HVA.* London: HVA, 1990.
    Smith J. The archives of the Health Visitors' Association. *Medical History* 1995; 39: 358–67.
55. Wilkie E. *A singular anomaly.* London: RCN, 1984.
56. Watkin B. *Documents on health and social services. 1834 to the present day.* London: Methuen, 1975, 53–60.
57. Cockayne E. Nursing and midwifery divisions: Ministry of Health. *Nursing Times* 1953; May 30: 530–1.
58. Rivett GC. *The development of the London hospital system 1823–1982.* London: King's Fund, 1986, 228.
59. Dawson Sir Bertrand. The future of the medical profession. (Cavendish Lecture) *Lancet* 1918; 2: 83–5.
    Ministry of Health. Consultative Council on Medical and Allied Services. *Interim report on the future provision of medical and allied services.* (Chairman: Lord Dawson.) Cmd 693. London: HMSO, 1920.
60. Voluntary Hospitals Commission. *Report.* (Chairman: Lord Sankey.) London: British Hospitals Association, 1937.
61. Rivett GC. *The development of the London hospital system, 1823–1982.* London, King's Fund, 1986.
62. Ministry of Health. *Hospital Survey – the hospital services of the Sheffield and East Midlands area.* (Surveyors: Parsons LG, Clayton Fryers S, Godber GE.) London: HMSO, 1945.
63. Godber GE. The physician's part in hospital planning. *BMJ* 1959; 1, suppl: 115–18.
64. Nuffield Provincial Hospitals Trust. *The Hospital Surveys. The Domesday Book of the hospital services.* London: NPHT, 1945.
65. Lawson Dodd. *A national medical service.* London: Fabian Society, 1911.
    The Labour movement and the hospital crisis. London: TUC and the Labour Party, 1922.
    Pater JE. *The making of the NHS.* London: King's Fund, 1981.
    Rivett GC. *The development of the London hospital system, 1823–1982.* London: King's Fund, 1986.
66. Webster C. Local government and health care: the historical perspective. *BMJ* 1995; 310: 1584–7.
67. Parliament. *Report on social and insurance and allied services.* (Chairman: Sir William Beveridge.) Cmd 6040. London: HMSO, 1942.
    Timmins N. *The five giants.* London: HarperCollins, 1995.
68. Medical Planning Commission. *Draft interim report.* London: BMA, 1942.
    Honigsbaum F. The evolution of the NHS. *BMJ* 1990; 301: 694–9.

69. Boland ER. Administration of medicine. *BMJ* 1948; 2: 9–11.
70. Tudor Hart J. The inverse care law. *Lancet* 1971; 1: 405–12.
71. Ministry of Health. *Report of the office committee on the 'demobilisation' of the emergency hospital scheme.* London: MoH, 1943.
72. Childs D. *Britain since 1945: a political history.* London: Routledge, 1986.
73. Owen D. *In sickness and in health.* London: Quartet Books, 1976.
74. Whitby L. The changing face of medicine. *BMJ* 1948; 2: 2–6.
75. Lord Taylor of Harlow. How the NHS was born. *BMJ* 1981; 283: 1446–8.
76. Platt H. The place of orthopaedics in medical education and the regional hospital services. *Lancet* 1945; 2: 643–5.
77. The Minister's regions [special article]. *Lancet* 1946; 2: 842–5.
78. Godber Sir George. *Medical care – the changing needs and patterns.* Ciba Foundation 20th anniversary lecture. London: J & A Churchill, 1970.
79. Pater JE. *The making of the NHS.* London: King's Fund, 1981, 142.
80. Klein R. The state and the profession: the politics of the double bed. *BMJ* 1990; 301: 700–2.
81. Aneurin Bevan. *BMJ* 1960; 2: 203–4.
82. Pater JE. *The making of the NHS.* London: King's Fund, 1981.
83. Crossman RHS. *A politician's view of health service planning.* Maurice Bloch Lecture. Glasgow: Glasgow University Press, 1972.
84. Shock M. Medicine at the centre of the nation's affairs. *BMJ* 1994; 309: 1730–3.
85. Godber G. Forty years of the NHS: origins and early development. *BMJ* 1988; 297: 37–43.
86. National Health Service. *Regional hospital boards. General scope of their work and relationship to the Minister and others.* RHB(47)1. London: Ministry of Health, 1947.
87. Blair-Fish HM. A nurse on a regional hospital board. *Nursing Times* 1948; Jul 3: 476.
88. NHS. *Boards of governors of teaching hospitals.* BG(48)1. London: Ministry of Health, 1948.
89. *The Labour movement and the hospital crisis. A statement of policy.* London: TUC and Labour Party, 1922.
90. Administration of the service – the first year. *Hospitals year book 1949–50.* London: HYB, 1950.
91. National Health Service. *Regional hospital boards. General scope of their work and relationship to the Minister and others.* RHB(47)1. London: Ministry of Health, 1947.
92. The British National Health Service. *Conversations with Sir George Godber.* JE Fogarty International Center. Washington DC: US Department of Health Education and Welfare, 1976, 110.
93. National Health Service. *The development of specialist services.* RHB(48)1. London: Ministry of Health, 1948.
94. Godber GE. The physician's part in hospital planning. *BMJ* 1959; 1, suppl: 115–18.
95. Parliament. *Report of the Interdepartmental Committee on remuneration of consultants and specialists.* (Chairman: Sir Will Spens.) Cmd 7420. London: HMSO, 1948.
96. Shaw Lauriston E. Medicine and the state. *Lancet* 1918; 2: 87–90.
97. Newman Sir George. The state and the future of medical practice. *Medical Officer* 1920; Jul 3: 5–7.
98. Independent doctors [annotation]. *BMJ* 1948; 2: 347.
    Obituary of Lord Horder. *The Times* 1955; Aug 14.
99. Platt Sir Robert. *Doctor and patient, ethics, morale government.* The Rock Carling Fellowship. London: Nuffield Provincial Hospitals Trust, 1963, 53–7.
100. Crossman diaries [leading article]. *BMJ* 1977; 2: 1306.
101. Powell JE. Financing the health service. In: *A new look at medicine and politics.* London: Pitman Medical, 1966, 14–23.
102. Powell JE. The elephant and the whale. *BMJ* 1961; 1: 1479–83.

103. Green FHK. The structure and functions of the Medical Research Council. *BMJ* 1948; 2: 462–6.
Himsworth H. On the integration of expert knowledge into the machinery of government. *BMJ* 1980; 281: 1197–9.
104. Retrospect and prospect [leading article]. *BMJ* 1948; 2: 30–1.

Chapter 1

1948–1957

Establishing the National Health Service

Chapter 1

1948–1957
Establishing the National Health Service

Chronology: the first decade

Background	Year	NHS events
Railways and electricity nationalised State of Israel proclaimed Transistor invented Berlin airlift New town designation starts	1948	5 July 1948 NHS established Development of specialist services: RHB(48)1 MRC Social Medicine Research Unit (Central Middlesex)
Pound devalued to $2.80	1949	Powers to introduce prescription charges Aureomycin, chloromycetin, streptomycin/PAS Antihistamines Cortisone and ACTH Vitamin B$_{12}$ Nurses Act creates regional nurse training committees
Korean war begins Election: Labour victory	1950	Link between smoking and lung cancer Ceiling On NHS expenditure imposed Bradbeer Committee appointed on internal administration of hospitals Collings Report on general practice
Election: Conservative victory Festival of Britain	1951	John Bowlby's *Maternal and child heath care* Charges for dental and optical appliances authorised
Death of King George VI Harrow rail disaster	1952	Danckwerts award for GPs Watson and Crick establish the double helical structure of DNA Chlorpromazine London fog College of General Practitioners formed Confidential Enquiry into Maternal Death

Background	Year	NHS events
Korean armistice Elizabeth II crowned Everest climbed	1953	Nuffield report on the work of nurses in hospital wards Heart–lung machine in heart surgery
Food rationing ends First business computer (IBM)	1954	Cohen Committee on general practice First kidney transplant (identical twin) Daily visiting of children in hospital encouraged Bradbeer Report
Credit squeeze Election: Conservative victory Independent Television launched	1955	Acton Society Trust papers on NHS Ultrasound in obstetrics Group practice loan funds
Suez crisis Hungarian uprising	1956	Polio immunisation Clean Air Act Guillebaud: Cost of the NHS Large-scale trial of birth control pills Working Party on health visiting (Jameson)
Macmillan Prime Minister First satellites, Sputnik I and II Treaty of Rome	1957	Willink on future number of doctors Royal Commission on mental illness reported Royal Commission on doctors' pay announced Hospitals to complete hospital inpatient enquiry (HIPE)

On 5th July we start together, the new National Health Service. It has not had an altogether trouble-free gestation! There have been understandable anxieties, inevitable in so great and novel an undertaking. Nor will there be overnight any miraculous removal of our more serious shortages of nurses and others and of modern replanned buildings and equipment. But the sooner we start, the sooner we can try together to see to these things and to secure the improvements we all want . . . My job is to give you all the facilities, resources and help I can, and then to leave you alone as professional men and women to use your skill and judgement without hindrance. Let us try to develop that partnership from now on.

Message to the medical profession. Aneurin Bevan[1]

Preparing for the new service

For almost a century the government's Chief Medical Officers (CMOs) had often begun their annual reports with an account of the year's weather. It was a tradition going back to the Hippocratic view of its effect upon health. Sir Wilson Jameson described the problems of 1947, the year before the NHS began.[2]

The eighth year of austerity, 1947, was a testing year. Its first three months formed a winter of exceptional severity, which had to be endured by a people who in addition to rationing of food were faced with an unprecedented scarcity of fuel. These three months of snow and bitter cold were followed by the heaviest floods for 53 years, which did great damage, killed thousands of sheep and lambs, delayed spring sowing and threatened the prospect of a good harvest which was so urgently needed. Immediately after these four months of disastrous weather there followed a period of economic crisis with an ever-increasing dollar crisis. So acute was the crisis that restrictions more rigorous than any in the war years became necessary. Bread had to be rationed for the first time late in 1946; in September 1947, the meat ration was reduced; in October the bacon ration was halved; and in November potatoes were rationed. A steep rise in the prices of foodstuffs and cattle food followed disappointing harvests in many European countries, due to the hard winter and hot dry summer, and in certain crops, notably corn for animal food, in America. Affairs abroad were as depressing as conditions at home.

Designation of new towns

Crawley	1947
Hemel Hempstead	1947
Harlow	1947
Newton Aycliffe and Peterlee	1947
Welwyn Garden City and Hatfield	1948
Basildon	1949
Bracknell	1949
Corby	1950

Source: The Times October 11 1996

The second world war had created a housing crisis. Alongside post-war rebuilding of existing cities, and the designation of overspill areas, the New Towns Act 1946 led to major new centres of population. The boundaries were drawn generously, land reclamation figured prominently and the problems of high-rise living were avoided. Most were clustered in the southeast. The planners covered thousands of acres of farmland, but they avoided tower blocks and the devastating results of the simultaneous redevelopment of the centres of older towns.

The ethos and the pattern of the NHS had much in common with the newly nationalised state industries, railways, steel and the utilities. Beveridge, in his report in 1942, had proposed state funding but not how the NHS should work in practice.[3] Bevan had worked out the details and the NHS had a command structure, a 'welfare state' ideology and was heavily dominated by those providing the services. On the appointed day 1,143 voluntary hospitals with some 90,000 beds and 1,545 municipal hospitals with about 390,000 beds were taken over by the NHS in England and Wales. Of the ex-municipal beds, 190,000 were in mental illness and mental deficiency hospitals. In addition 66,000 beds were still administered under Public Assistance, mainly occupied by elderly people who were often not sick in the sense of needing health care. Among the residents were some with irrecoverable mental illness, with a generous addition of 'mental defectives' and many old people who would now be regarded as having geriatric problems.

Additional resources were negligible. The appointed day, 5 July 1948, brought not one extra doctor or nurse. What it did was change the way in which people could obtain and pay for care. They ceased to pay for medical attention when they needed it, and paid instead, as taxpayers, collectively. The NHS improved accessibility and distributed what there was more fairly. It made rational development possible, for the hierarchical system of command and control enabled the examination of issues such as equity.[4] *The Times* pointed out that the masses had joined the middle classes. Doctors had become social servants in a much fuller sense. It was now difficult for them to stand aside from their patients' social difficulties or to work in isolation from the social services.[5] The Ministry, having worked for the establishment of the NHS, now became passive.

In making allocations to the regional hospital boards (RHBs) the Ministry of Health worked from what had been spent in the previous year. The boards took major decisions without fuss. Ahead of them lay the task of 'regionalisation', the development and integration of specialist practice into a coherent whole.[6] Many reports were to hand, including the Hospital Surveys and the Goodenough Report on medical education.[7] Bevan held a small dinner party on the first anniversary of the service to thank those who had been concerned with the preparatory stages. He toasted the NHS, and coupled the NHS with the name of Sir Wilson Jameson.

NHS managing bodies (England & Wales) 1948

- 14 regional hospital boards (RHBs)
- 36 boards of governors (BGs)
- 388 hospital management committees (HMCs)
- 38 executive councils (ECs)
- 147 local health authorities (LHAs)

There was uncertainty about who was in charge at region. In most regions there was a viable partnership with no single boss. The senior administrative medical officer (SAMO) was university educated, but this was not necessarily true of the secretary, who drew a lower salary. Regional organisation varied and could be complex. In April 1956 Sheffield RHB had seven standing committees, six standing subcommittees, some chairman's and many other advisory committees, 23 committees of consultants and a nursing advisory committee. There were also nine special committees, five ad hoc building committees, liaison committees with teaching hospitals and the university, and joint committees with other authorities on matters such as the treatment of rheumatic disease. The East Anglian region was simplicity itself: its last remaining committee (finance) had ceased to meet and the board did everything! The subordinate hospital management committees (HMCs) ran the hospitals and sometimes started to rationalise their facilities, but they had little influence on wider issues. Power increasingly lay at the RHB.

The Central Health Services Council

> **Standing advisory committees**
>
> The standing advisory committees are still in existence. Currently there are four, each statutory and uni-professional: the Standing Medical Advisory Committee (SMAC) and its equivalents for nursing and midwifery (SNMAC), pharmaceutical services (SPAC) and dentistry (SDAC). They advise ministers in England and Wales when requested but also 'as they see fit'. Members are appointed by the Minister from nominations by the professions, and include the presidents of the Royal Colleges. Their precise role has changed over the years; initially they prepared guidelines on general clinical problems, usually through subcommittees.

The Central Health Services Council (CHSC), constituted by the 1946 NHS Act, was the normal advisory mechanism for the Ministry of Health. It had a substantial professional component alongside members representative of local government and hospital management.[8] It was large and after the first few years met only quarterly although several of its subcommittees remained influential. The *Lancet* believed that the Ministry never encouraged the CHSC to be a creative force. In its first 18 months a host of novel and difficult problems faced the service and Bevan remitted 30 questions to it. He received advice from the council on these and 12 other topics. At its first meeting a committee was established to examine hospital administration, chaired for most of its existence by Alderman Bradbeer from Birmingham. Other issues included the pressure on hospitals and emergency admissions, the care of the elderly chronic sick, the mental health service, wasteful prescribing in general practice, and co-operation between the three parts of the NHS. Ten standing committees were established, some exclusively professional, and others to examine specific services such as child health, and cancer and radiotherapy.[9] Over the first 20 years of the NHS they produced a series of major reports that altered clinical practice, for example on cross-infection in hospitals, the welfare of children in hospital and human relations in obstetrics. The main committees were the Standing Medical Advisory Committee (SMAC) and the Standing Nursing and Midwifery Committee. Henry Cohen chaired SMAC for the first 15 years of the NHS. A general physician from Liverpool, his intellectual gifts made it possible for him to remain a generalist at a time when specialisation was becoming the order of the day.[10] To begin with there was anxiety in the Ministry that SMAC would prove an embarrassment in its demands, but soon the members had exhausted the issues about which they felt strongly. George Godber found it best to provide SMAC with background briefing on an emerging problem and only then to ask for its advice. The Ministry could not give doctors clinical advice but SMAC could and did – for example, that when drugs were in the experimental stage, or scarce, they should be restricted to use in clinical trials. Later they should be available solely through designated centres, and only when they were proven and in unlimited supply should control be no more than that necessary in patients' interests.

Professional and charitable organisations

The introduction of the NHS affected many organisations that had taken part in the debates preceding the NHS. The British Hospitals Association, which had represented the voluntary hospitals, ceased to have a role and was rapidly wound up. The British Medical Association (BMA) continued at the centre of serious medical politics. For historic reasons GPs had always been powerful within it; they were many and they provided much of its money. When in 1911 Lloyd George's national insurance gave working men a doctor, GPs had to become increasingly active. The GPs' Insurance Acts Committee was continued after 1948 as the General Medical Services Committee (GMSC), a standing committee of the BMA with full powers to deal with all matters affecting NHS GPs. The local medical committees elected it, as panel committees had done previously. It was not until 1948 that consultants had to enter the medico-political arena, which was new and unfamiliar to them. The consultants formed the Central Consultants' and Specialists' Committee, with powers analogous to the GPs' committee as far as terms of service were concerned. The Joint Consultants Committee (JCC) succeeded the earlier negotiating committee, federating the BMA and the medical Royal Colleges, and represented hospital doctors and dentists in discussions with the health departments on policy matters other than terms of service. This complex system did not make for unity of the medical profession, particularly on financial matters.

The three Royal Colleges maintained powerful positions as a source of expert opinion and also in political matters. Charles Moran, Winston Churchill's personal physician, known familiarly as Corkscrew Charlie, was President of the Royal College of Physicians (RCP) from 1941-1950. Alfred Webb Johnson led the Royal College of Surgeons, and their relationship was a little prickly. William Gilliatt, the Queen's obstetrician, was President of the Royal College of Obstetricians and Gynaecologists. As his college dated only from the twentieth century it was regarded as the junior partner. The colleges were London dominated, and their presidents were usually southern; Robert Platt was the first provincial President of the RCP. The RCS had been damaged in the war and there was a chance of getting a neighbouring site so that all three Royal Colleges could be rebuilt together. Alfred Webb Johnson had a vision of a medical area in Lincoln's Inn Fields, perhaps grandiose but it could have created a broad-ranging academy of medicine and a chance to develop methods of reviewing clinical practice.[11] Moran stopped it, fearing that the RCP would become subsidiary. The RCS continued to encourage its own sub-specialties to develop and form close links with the parent organisation.

The Royal College of Nursing (RCN), founded in 1916 as an association to unite trained nurses, emerged as a powerful body now that virtually all nurses were working for the NHS. A decision was taken to discourage membership of mental illness nurses, who stayed with the Confederation of Health Service Employees (COHSE). COHSE hoped to become the industrial union for the NHS but other unions recruited nurses (the RCN), ancillary workers (the National Union of Public Employees and the Transport and General Workers Union), administrative staff (the National and Local Government Officers Association), and laboratory and professional staff (the Association of Scientific Workers, later ASTMS).[12] National medical charities generally acted as pressure groups and they continued their work, now with the NHS in their sights. For example, there was the National Birthday Foundation that campaigned for the extension and improvement of maternity services, the National Association for Mental Health (MIND) promoting the interests of people with mental health problems, and the Association of Parents of Backward Children (later Mencap).

King Edward VII's Hospital Fund for London (King's Fund) had previously provided about 10 per cent of the income of London voluntary hospitals, but the state now funded these. It began to look at new fields, for example the training of ward sisters and catering.[13] The Nuffield Provincial Hospitals Trust had fought for regionalisation, the pattern of organisation Bevan had adopted. It rapidly developed into a think-tank on health service matters but neither the Fund nor the Trust could maintain their direct influence on policy, although they were valuable sources of expertise.

More informal groups had existed before the establishment of the NHS. Wilson Jameson had his 'gas-bag' committee at the London School of Hygiene and Tropical Medicine where he was Dean. The same institution spawned the Keppel Club, in which young doctors from many disciplines came together from 1953 to 1974.[14] A small society with a tight membership, it was entirely apolitical and met monthly for free-wheeling and uninhibited discussion. There was an opportunity to discuss new methods and systems at an intellectual level. Membership was by invitation, and included Brian Abel-Smith, John Brotherston, John Fry, Walter Holland, Jerry Morris, Michael Shepherd, Stephen Taylor, Richard Titmuss and Michael Warren. Until it ended in 1974, when its members were busier and more senior, the club discussed such issues as child health, the care of the adolescent and the aged, general practice, hospital services, mental illness and the collection of information in the NHS.

Medicine and the media

Newspaper and magazine articles on professional issues were uncommon. Medical authors were suspected of advertising, an offence for which they might be struck off the register. Doctors and nurses had mixed views about the media. Some believed that there would be widespread hypochondriasis if it was no longer possible to keep people in ignorance of hospital care and their treatment. Television was slowly spreading from London throughout the country, but as late as 1957 only half the households had a set, and among the professional classes there were even fewer. Educated people often talked about television without actually having seen it. *Emergency – Ward 10*, one of the earliest popular programmes, was thought to help nurse recruitment but was creating a modern mythology about nurses and hospital treatment.[15] When BBC TV ran a programme on slimming and diet, the *British Medical Journal* (*BMJ*) was alarmed by 'this somewhat curious experiment that approached the public over the heads of the practising doctor'.[16]

Medical progress

Health promotion

Health education had been pursued during the years of war. The approach remained mass publicity on all fronts. Messages were didactic and concentrated on the dangers in the home, infectious disease, accident prevention and, in the 1950s, the diagnosis of cancer of the breast and cervix.[17] There was little evidence that this technique, largely modelled on the advertising world, worked. Many doctors felt that the less patients knew about medicine the better, as Charles Fletcher, a physician at the Hammersmith Hospital, discovered to his cost when he advocated pamphlets for patients, explaining the causes of their illnesses and what to do about them.[18] In 1951 the BMA launched a new popular magazine, *Family Doctor*. Primarily a health magazine, its aim was to present simple articles on how the body worked, the promotion of health and the prevention of disease. The editor believed passionately that education and persuasion to adopt a different life style could improve the health of the nation. He felt that the time was past when medicine could be regarded as a mystery. Some subjects, however, were taboo, contraception being one of these.[19]

Bed rest

One of the most important clinical developments was simplicity itself. Richard Asher was a physician at the Central Middlesex Hospital who combined clarity of thought, deep understanding of the everyday problems of medicine and sparkling wit. It was he who gave Munchausen's syndrome its name, after the famous baron who travelled widely and told tales that were both dramatic and untrue. In 1947 he was among the earliest to identify the dangers of institutionalisation and going to bed.[20]

> It is always assumed that the first thing in any illness is to put the patient to bed. Hospital accommodation is always numbered in beds. Illness is measured by the length of time in bed. Doctors are assessed by their bedside manner. Bed is not ordered like a pill or a purge, but is assumed as the basis for all treatment. Yet we should think twice before ordering our patients to bed and realise that beneath the comfort of the blanket there lurks a host of formidable dangers.

Asher pointed to the risks of chest infection, deep vein thrombosis in the legs, bed sores, stiffening of muscles and joints, osteoporosis and, indeed, mental change and demoralisation. He ended with a parody of a well-known hymn:

> Teach us to live that we may dread
>
> Unnecessary time in bed.
>
> Get people up and we may save
>
> Our patients from an early grave.

The medical profession, although not immediately convinced, recognised that here was an issue to be explored. Francis Avery Jones, a gastroenterologist at Asher's hospital, later said that early ambulation saved the health service tens of thousands of beds, and many people their health and lives. Doctors had previously equated close and careful postoperative supervision with keeping people in bed; once they were out of bed there was a danger of premature discharge, and fatal pulmonary embolus might occur. For example, the *BMJ* said that a surgeon would be in a difficult position if he allowed a patient to be discharged the fourth day after appendicectomy or the seventh day after cholecystectomy (as happened in the USA) and developed a fatal embolus in the second week.[21] The probability that the embolus was the result of the closely supervised bed rest was not appreciated.

Surgeons were concerned that incisions would not heal if patients got up too soon but Farquharson, at Edinburgh Royal Infirmary, wrote that the cause of morbidity and mortality after an operation was usually remote from the actual wound. He believed that there was little evidence that wounds needed bed rest to heal. He proved his point by operating on 485 patients with hernia under local anaesthetic and discharging them home before the anaesthetic had worn off. Only one patient out of 200 needed readmission. The patients liked early discharge, they waited only a few days for operation, and the financial savings were considerable.[22]

The quality and effectiveness of health care

Doctors seldom looked at their clinical practice and its results. When, around 1952, a paper was put to the JCC that included lengths of stay, one physician loftily said 'all that is needed is that a consultant should feel satisfied that he has done his best for the patient. This arithmetic is irrelevant.' Death was the clearest measure of outcome, and infant and maternal mortality were studied – but comparisons of the results of different types of treatment were rare. On occasion clinicians might seek Ministry support for medical review projects, but it had to be covert and not an attempt to impose a central system. The use of randomised controlled trials now provided a way of validating clinical practice and the effectiveness of treatments. Matching cases by human judgement was open to error; randomisation involving large numbers provided an even dispersion of the personal characteristics likely to affect the outcome. The principles were established by D'Arcy Hart and Austin Bradford Hill. Austin Bradford Hill crashed three aircraft without injury while serving in the first world war but subsequently developed tuberculosis, which barred him from clinical medicine. He read economics, got a grant from the Medical Research Council (MRC), moved to the London School of Hygiene and determined to make a life in preventive medicine. An inspiring writer, many of his ideas passed into common usage; he understood the ethical and clinical problems that doctors faced, and could convince senior members of the profession that they should adopt controlled trials. A friend of Hugh Clegg, Editor of the *BMJ* from 1947, Hill chose that journal for his publications because of its wide circulation among doctors of all specialties. Clegg wanted good scientific papers and accepted long summaries because many doctors would not be prepared to read the entire papers.[23] Hill fed Clegg the MRC's report on the randomised trial of streptomycin in the treatment of tuberculosis, the trials of cortisone and aspirin in rheumatoid arthritis and the trial of whooping cough vaccine.

The MRC worked with the Ministry of Health and began to establish clinical research units. The provincial universities developed academic units more rapidly than London; for example, Robert Platt, Professor of Medicine in Manchester, and Henry Cohen, Professor in Liverpool. The medical press and contacts between doctors had always helped the dissemination of new clinical ideas. Now the NHS provided a new mechanism. It was said that those in the Ministry could achieve anything if they did not insist on claiming credit. Many doctors would take up a good idea when it was drawn to their attention, if the approach was tactful. The SMAC could be asked to look at specific clinical problems. Regions could then be given guidance that would be adopted throughout the country if it was seen to accord with professional thinking. Once a new idea was spotted, it could be nurtured. Doors could be opened to let people through. Organisations such as the Nuffield Provincial Hospitals Trust, the King's Fund and the Ministry worked quietly together. Some doctors were natural originators, others born developers, and both could be supported. Those seeing the way ahead would try to get others to follow. Postgraduate education, statistical methods, the use of controlled trials, group general practice and the development of geriatric and mental illness services were all ideas fostered and given a platform.

The drug treatment of disease

Before the second world war many drugs had no effect, for good or ill. Placebo prescribing was commonplace, with a reliance on the patient's faith. The first decade of the NHS saw the discovery of a staggering array of new and potent drugs. The drugs that were being developed were expensive and sometimes difficult to produce. Usually they were not immediately released for general use. The tetracyclines and cortisone were not available on GP prescription until 1954/5 when industrial-scale production facilities had been created. Inevitably costs rose. At the end of the 1949 parliamentary session, power was obtained to levy a prescription charge.[24] It was not used immediately but was invoked by the next government and used almost continuously and increasingly thereafter.

Penicillin and streptomycin were available when the NHS began but it was not known how they worked. Biochemistry and cell biology had not developed sufficiently for the underlying mechanisms to be understood.[25] Syphilis and congenital syphilis were among the diseases conquered. Within the next year aureomycin, the first of the tetracyclines, was discovered and proved to be active against a far wider range of organisms. The response of chest infections to antibiotics rapidly revealed a group of non-bacterial pneumonias, previously unsuspected, caused by viruses and rickettsial bacteria. Chloramphenicol was isolated from soil samples from Venezuela and soon synthesised; it worked in typhus and typhoid. In 1950 teramycin, another tetracycline, was isolated in the USA from cultures of *Streptomyces rimosus*. In 1956 a variant of penicillin, penicillin V, became available that could be given by mouth, avoiding the need for painful injections.[26]

The clinical exploitation of a new antibiotic usually passed through two phases: first, over-enthusiastic and indiscriminate use, followed by a more critical and restrained appraisal. Some strains of an otherwise susceptible organism were, or became, resistant to the drug. An early example was the reduction in efficacy of the sulphonamides in gonorrhoea, pneumonia and streptococcal infections. Penicillin withstood the test of time more successfully, but *Staphylococcus aureus* slowly escaped its influence and became resistant. Resistance of the tubercle bacillus to streptomycin was quickly acquired, and resistance was also a problem with the tetracyclines.[27] Erythromycin was discovered in 1952, resembled penicillin in its action, and by general agreement was reserved for infections with penicillin-resistant bacteria.[28] It became policy to use antibiotics carefully and to try to restrict their use.[29]

Cortisone, demonstrated in 1949 at the Mayo Clinic, did not fulfil all early expectations. It had a dramatic effect on patients with rheumatoid arthritis and acute rheumatic fever, but this was often temporary.[30] Supplies were limited because the drug was extracted from ox bile and 40 head of cattle were required for a single day's treatment. Adrenocorticotrophic hormone (ACTH) was even more difficult to obtain, being concentrated from pig pituitaries. Quantities were therefore minute and costs were high, so more economic methods of production were sought. By 1956 prednisone and prednisolone, analogous and more potent drugs, had been synthesised and were in clinical use. Like cortisone they were found to be life-saving in severe asthma. Few effective forms of treatment had been available to dermatologists. Now there were two potent forms of treatments: antibiotics for skin infection and corticosteroids that had a dramatic effect on several types of dermatitis.

The outcome of patients with high blood pressure was well known because there was no effective treatment. Four grades of severity were recognised, based on the changes in the heart, the kidneys and the blood vessels in the eyes. In severe cases, grades three and four, the five-year mortalities (death within five years of diagnosis) were 40 per cent and 95 per cent. Surgery (lumbar sympathectomy) might prolong survival but in 1949 hexamethonium 'ganglion-blocking' drugs were introduced, and the era of effective treatment had begun. At first, drugs had to be given by injection but preparations that could be taken by mouth were soon available. None of the alternatives approached the ideal; surgery was not particularly successful, dietary advice and salt restriction made life miserable, reserpine made patients depressed, and ganglion-blocking drugs had severe side effects, including constipation, fainting and impotence. Only people with the most severe hypertension were therefore considered for treatment.[31]

Vitamin B12 was synthesised and liver extract was no longer required in the treatment for pernicious anaemia.[32] Insulin had been used in the treatment of diabetes since the 1920s but a new group of drugs suitable for mild and stable cases, the oral hypoglycaemic sulphonamide derivatives, were developed. They simplified treatment, particularly in the elderly, and reduced the need for hospital attendance.[33] The antihistamines were introduced mainly for the treatment of allergic conditions. They were associated with drowsiness which, in drivers, caused traffic accidents. Reports from the USA that they cured colds were examined by the MRC; the drugs were valueless. The common cold had again come unscathed through a therapeutic attack.[34]

Chlorpromazine was introduced in 1952 for the treatment of psychiatric illness. It produced a remarkable state of inactivity or indifference in excited or agitated psychotics and was increasingly used by psychiatrists and GPs.[35] The tranquillisers, for example meprobamate, also represented a substantial advance. Barbiturates had been used for 50 years, but they were proving to be true drugs of addiction and were commonly used by suicides.[36] The new drugs undoubtedly had a substantial impact on illnesses severe enough to need hospital admission but whether they helped in the minor neuroses was less certain.[37] William Sargant, a psychiatrist at St Thomas', referred to the extensive advertising and the shoals of circulars through the doctor's letterbox. Big business was beginning to realise the large profits to be made out of mental health. All that was necessary was to persuade doctors to prescribe for hundreds of thousands of patients each week.[38]

Halothane, a new anaesthetic agent, was carefully tested before its introduction, although repeated administration in a patient was later shown to be associated with jaundice.[39] It was neither inflammable nor explosive. Explosions during ether anaesthesia, often associated with sparks from electrical equipment, occurred and inevitably killed some patients.

For many years there had been concern about adverse reactions to drugs and the best way to recognise them. As the pharmaceutical industry developed an ever-increasing number of new products, anxieties increased.[40] The problem came to a head in the USA in 1951, when a few patients were reported in whom chloramphenicol had produced fatal bone marrow failure (aplasia). The American Medical Association appointed a study group to examine all cases of blood disorders suspected of being caused by drugs or other chemicals. The problem was thought to be rare, because chloramphenicol had been widely used, yet it was found that there had in fact been scores of cases of aplastic anaemia and it had taken three years to appreciate the potential toxicity. There was rapid agreement that its use should be limited to conditions untreatable by other means.[41]

Radiology and diagnostic imaging

Tests and investigations were playing an increasing part in the diagnostic process. Radiology revealed the structural manifestations of disease but the basic technology had not changed greatly since 1895 when the first films were taken. An X-ray beam produced a film for later examination, or the patient was 'screened' and the image was examined directly in a darkened room. The radiation exposure was higher with screening and the radiologist had to become dark-adapted before he could work. From the 1930s radiology developed rapidly, but hospital services were handicapped by a shortage of radiologists.

Three developments gave radiology a new impetus. First, in 1954 Marconi Instruments displayed an image intensifier, which produced a much brighter image although the field was only five inches (12.7 cm) wide. It was visible in subdued light and good enough to photograph. The technique was immediately applied to studies of swallowing. Secondly there were improvements in contrast media, used to visualise blood vessels. They were often unpleasant and sometimes risky. From the 1950s new 'non-ionic' agents were introduced. Cardiac surgery was developing fast and catalysed developments in radiology; for example, angio-cardiography in which contrast medium was injected into the blood vessels leading to the heart before a series of X-rays.[42] The third development, in 1953, was the introduction of the Seldinger technique. This made possible percutaneous catheterisation, the introduction of a fine catheter into a blood vessel through a needle, avoiding the need for an incision. A tracer guide wire could be inserted and imaged, and when in position a catheter slid over it. Contrast medium could be injected selectively into blood vessels, under direct vision using the image intensifier, just where it was required.[43]

The availability of radioactive isotopes (radio-isotopes) led to the development of nuclear medicine and a new method of imaging. Radio-isotopes could be introduced into the body, sometimes tagged to tissues such as blood cells. As they were chemically identical to the normal forms, they were handled by the body in the same way. It was possible to measure the presence and amount of the radio-isotope, its spatial distribution and its chemical transformation. The new techniques provided a way of studying, at least crudely, some of the body's functions, as opposed to its structure. Isotopes were chosen to minimise the radiation dose as far as possible. At first radioactive tracer work was the province of the pathologist, as in studies of blood volume and circulation. The development of gamma cameras and rectilinear scanners, however, meant that images could be produced as well as 'counts', and radiologists came to the fore.[44]

Early in 1955 the MRC, at the request of the Prime Minister, established a committee chaired by Sir Harold Himsworth to report on the medical aspects of nuclear radiation. Its report, a year later, contained the unexpected finding that exposure of the gonads to diagnostic X-rays significantly increased the irradiation received, by some 22 per cent.[45] The fall-out from testing nuclear weapons was less than 1 per cent. Shortly after, Dr Alice Stewart published a report suggesting that childhood leukaemia was associated with irradiation of the fetus (and also with virus infection and threatened abortion.)[46] Her findings were not accepted until a second study from the USA confirmed a connection with irradiation during pregnancy. Although radiologists were already concerned about the dangers of radiation exposure, there was some delay in taking greater precautions during pregnancy.

Infectious disease and immunisation

Deaths in England and Wales from infectious disease

	Tuberculosis	Diphtheria	Whooping cough	Measles	Polio
1943	25,649	1,371	1,114	773	80
1944	24,163	1,054	1,054	243	109
1945	23,955	722	689	729	139
1946	22,847	472	808	204	128
1947	23,550	244	905	644	707
1948	23,175	156	748	327	241
1949	19,797	84	527	307	657
1950	15,969	49	394	221	755
1951	13,806	33	456	317	217
1952	10,585	32	184	141	275
1953	9,002	23	243	245	320
1954	7,897	8	139	45	112
1955	6,492	12	87	174	241
1956	5,375	3	92	28	114
1957	4,784	4	87	94	226
1958	4,480	8	27	49	154

Source: On the state of the public health – annual reports of the Chief Medical Officer

The decade saw the end of smallpox as a regular entry in public health statistics, the decline in diphtheria and enteric fever to around 100 cases per year, the greatest ever epidemic of poliomyelitis, and a substantial rise in food poisoning and dysentery, possibly related to better diagnosis now available through the Public Health Laboratory Service (PHLS). It is hard nowadays to appreciate the misery and deaths caused by infectious diseases, which were common and potentially lethal. In 1948 there were 3,575 cases of diphtheria with 156 deaths. Tuberculosis remained a major problem although notifications to the medical officer of health (MOH) and deaths were steadily getting fewer. There were 400,000 notifications of measles with 327 deaths, and 148,410 of whooping cough with 748 deaths. The USA had introduced diphtheria immunisation in the 1930s but it was not until 1940/1 that local authorities, spurred by Wilson Jameson, launched a major campaign in the UK. A long-forgotten clause in a Public Health Act gave local authorities the power to do so. Whooping cough, tetanus and polio immunisation followed. As new vaccines were introduced, each was usually given three times; the schedule for infants became increasingly complex until 'triple' vaccines improved matters.

There had been small sporadic outbreaks of poliomyelitis for many years but the disease assumed epidemic proportions in 1947. Thereafter the numbers fluctuated, but remained at a historically high level for several years with 250–750 deaths annually. It was the custom for cases to be admitted to isolation hospitals, and then transferred to orthopaedic hospitals for the convalescent and chronic stages. Oxford established a team including specialists in infectious disease, neurology and orthopaedics so that patients with severe paralysis could be assessed jointly from the start. Respiratory support with 'iron lungs' was available and passive movement of the limbs reduced the risks of later deformity. The tide turned when Jonas Salk developed an inactivated vaccine in the USA and reported the success of field trials in 1955.[47] Manufacture began in Great Britain under the supervision of the MRC and immunisation of children started in 1956.

Bacterial food poisoning was an increasing problem. Imported egg products from North and South America and, after the war, from China, sometimes contained *Salmonella*. Synthetic cream was associated with many outbreaks of paratyphoid fever, and spray-dried skim-milk was responsible for outbreaks of toxin-type food poisoning.

Cases of smallpox occurred intermittently. In 1950 there was an outbreak in Brighton, introduced by a fully vaccinated RAF officer recently returned from India. There were 26 cases, 13 of which were among nursing and medical staff, domestics and laundry workers at the hospital to which the earliest cases were admitted, and ten deaths[48] In 1952 an outbreak in Rochdale led to 135 cases with one death, and there were further importations in succeeding years.

The death rate from tuberculosis had begun to decline after the first world war, but the incidence was still high and primary infection occurred in nearly half the children before they were 14. When the NHS began there were 50,000 notifications a year and 23,000 deaths. Before streptomycin, doctors relied on the natural resistance of the patient, aided by bed rest and the indirect effect of 'collapse' therapy. To reduce the movement of diseased lung tissue, in the hope that this would assist healing, sections of the rib cage were removed (thoracoplasty), air was introduced to collapse the lung (artificial pneumothorax) or the phrenic nerve would be divided to paralyse the diaphragm. Antibiotics attacked the tubercle bacillus directly. There was insufficient streptomycin to treat everyone who might benefit, and supplies went to those in whom the best results could be expected, young adults with early disease. A rigorously controlled investigation run by D'Arcy Hart and the MRC confirmed the effectiveness of streptomycin. In a second trial the newly discovered para-aminosalicylic acid (PAS) was proved to delay the development of bacterial resistance and a third trial examined the level of dose required.[49] In 1952 isoniazid was introduced. Given alone it was no better than streptomycin and PAS, but triple-drug therapy greatly reduced the problem of the emergence of resistant strains of tubercle bacilli. The results were so good that collapse therapy and surgical methods of treatment were used far less frequently.[50] An MRC trial in India showed that even under the worst social conditions patients rapidly ceased to be infectious if they took their treatment. There was no need to admit patients for long periods to reduce the risk of infection to families and the community. For the first time, early treatment of tuberculosis had major benefits, yet there was an average delay of four months between the first consultation and a diagnostic X-ray; GPs were urged to refer patients more rapidly.[51] In the drive for early treatment, disused infectious disease wards were used, a good example of the new opportunities open to the NHS. In 1948 the waiting list figures had convinced the Manchester RHB that a new sanatorium was urgently required. By 1953 it had not been built but it was now no longer needed as the waiting time for admission had fallen from nine months to a few weeks.[52] Within a few years beds for tuberculosis and the fevers were being turned over to newly developing specialist units, for example neurosurgery. After a successful trial of the tuberculosis vaccine BCG (bacillus Calmette–Guérin) by the MRC, immunisation at the age of 13 was introduced, reducing further the number of new infections. Mass mobile radiography (MMR) units were important tools in 'case-finding'. The vans would visit centres such as colleges and hospitals where there were many young people, and 35mm pictures were taken of images produced by fluorescent screening.

There was a major influenza outbreak in 1951/2. From 5 to 8 December 1952 'smog' (fog filled with smoke) of unusual density and persistence covered the Greater London area. To most, smog was no more than an inconvenience. Those with chronic heart and lung disease were less lucky. Their illnesses got worse and many died. For some years an 'emergency bed service' had operated in London, finding beds for emergency admissions by phoning round the hospitals. It came under pressure and immediately restricted non-urgent admissions, but the media were first to spot the severity of the problem. Florists ran out of flowers for funerals. Newspaper articles drew attention to the death of prize cattle at the Smithfield show. Not until the death certificates had been assembled was the full severity of the episode apparent; there were 3,500–4,000 excess deaths.[53] St George's (Hyde Park Corner), like all London hospitals, admitted many victims of bronchitis and heart failure; as it was not possible to see from one end of a ward to the other, they were divided in two so that patients could be properly observed. A committee under the chairmanship of Sir Hugh Beaver was set up, which rapidly identified the importance of pollution from solid fuels. Its recommendations formed the basis of the Clean Air Act 1956. Emission control was required; industry had to change and methods of manufacturing had to alter. It became an offence to emit dark smoke from a chimney, and local authorities could establish smoke control areas. Following the legislation the age-specific death rates of men in Greater London fell by almost half. The opposition to the control of atmospheric pollution, for example from industry, was slight. This was not the case with smoking, for, although its hazards were far greater, there were issues of individual choice and liberty, and much more antagonism from industry.

Rheumatic fever, associated with streptococcal throat infection, was another common disease of childhood normally requiring admission to hospital. More frequent among the poor, there would be fever, pain and stiffness in the larger joints. Although some children might die of the acute illness (700 in 1949, falling to 174 in 1957), the main problem was that about half developed rheumatic disease of heart valves, which became incompetent (they leaked) or stenosed (they obstructed blood flow). The result was progressive heart failure in adolescence or later in adult life.

Milder infections were not ignored. At Salisbury the Common Cold Research Unit had been established before the war to examine this difficult problem. Volunteers turned up every fortnight to help the scientific work. By 1950 they numbered more than 2,000, including 253 married couples, several being on their honeymoon.[54]

The incidence of venereal disease had increased in both world wars. After 1945 the level began to fall and many venereologists thought seriously of leaving what seemed to be a dying specialty. Venereal disease responded to antibiotics: syphilis was rapidly cured, and cases of congenital syphilis fell steadily as antenatal testing became routine, followed by treatment where necessary. The reduction in gonorrhoea, however, levelled off and drug-resistant strains became apparent. By 1955 the levels were rising again, and they continued to do so. Dr Charles, the CMO, said that sexual promiscuity was as rife as it had ever been in times of peace, and while this was the case the venereal peril would be ever with us.[55]

The PHLS expanded as 'associated laboratories' were incorporated into the main network. Increasingly the laboratories were located on the site of acute hospitals and came to provide bacteriological services to the hospital as well as to the local authorities responsible for the control of infectious disease. The PHLS was becoming involved both in the care of individuals and in the health of 'the herd'. From the early days the PHLS wanted to recruit epidemiologists, but this was opposed by the Ministry and the MOsH. From 1954 its weekly summary of laboratory reports contained hospital as well as community data, and became a comprehensive account of the prevalence of infection. The PHLS was also deeply involved in the study of hospital-acquired staphylococcal infection, for patients in surgical wards were increasingly infected by resistant strains. First detected in 1954, the problem spread rapidly and led to the appointment, in most hospitals, of infection-control nurses. The management of the PHLS was reviewed in 1951 and the MRC was asked to continue to run it.

Orthopaedics and trauma

The war had given orthopaedic surgery impetus. During the latter part of the war, orthopaedic surgeons began to encounter, among prisoners of war repatriated from Germany, fractures treated by inserting a nail throughout the length of the marrow cavity. The method, originally described by Küntscher, was soon seen to be a success, making possible a shorter hospital stay.[56] British surgeons, for example Sir Reginald Watson-Jones, were also developing and using internal fixation for fractures of the femoral neck. In 1949 Robert Danis, of Brussels, described a system of rigid internal fixation that allowed anatomically accurate reduction, compressing the fracture surfaces. This made it easier to get patients up and moving. Because of early rehabilitation, complications of treatment were reduced and there were far fewer bed sores and deaths from thrombosis and pulmonary embolism.[57] At first the plates and screws used were copied from those familiar in joinery; later they were redesigned for the specific needs of fracture surgery. As understanding of fracture healing improved, there was growing recognition that stable fixation of a fracture had immense benefits in terms of restoring the soft tissues for which the bone serves as a scaffold. In addition to the techniques of internal fixation, putting strong inert screws into the fragments of bone and holding them with a light but rigid external fixation system made it possible to correct major damage to soft tissue, vessels and nerves.

The other major pressure on orthopaedic departments was osteoarthritis. Osteoarthritis of the hip was a common and painful condition. Several operations had been devised that relieved pain at the cost of mobility, for example arthrodesis that fused the femur to the pelvis. Among the more successful was Smith-Petersen's procedure, involving the reshaping of the joint surfaces and the insertion of a smooth-surfaced cup of inert metal between the moving parts. Re-operation was sometimes required. Arthroplasty, the total replacement of the joint by an artificial socket and femoral head made to fit each other, gave patients a new and mechanical joint. The procedure was first carried out by Kenneth McKee in Norwich around 1950, using cobalt-chrome components.[58] No great attention was paid to the surface finish or fit, and the method of fixation proved inadequate. Friction in the joint was high and there were both failures and successes. Some of his patients were seen by John Charnley at a meeting of the British Orthopaedic Association, who considered that the procedure might be improved. The Manchester RHB funded him to develop a new unit near Wigan to refine it. The engineering problems were substantial and the results to begin with were not always predictable.

In 1952 112 passengers were killed and 200 were seriously injured in a three-train collision at Harrow. There was chaos. By modern standards the fire and ambulance services were hopelessly inadequately equipped, and were untrained to keep trapped people alive. All that could be done was a little bandaging and to take people to hospital as fast as possible. Edgware General Hospital learned of the crash when a commandeered furniture van arrived with walking wounded. Among those responding to the disaster were US teams from nearby bases, who were trained in battlefield medicine. They were disciplined, brought plasma and undertook triage – sorting casualties into those needing urgent attention, those who could wait and those who were beyond help. It was a new experience for the rescue services; they were amazed and full of admiration.[59] Yet the lessons were not learned for many years. In December 1957 another train crash occurred in thick fog near Lewisham. The ambulances moved 223 people, and 88 died in the accident. The Senior Administrative Medical Officer, James Fairley, called for reports. As at Harrow, there were failures in communication, difficulty in identifying senior staff at the site, inadequate supplies of dressings and morphine, a shortage of ambulance transport and difficulties in creating records and documenting the injured.[60]

Major trauma was also increasing on the roads as traffic was becoming denser. By 1954 there were more than one million motorcycles on the road, and over 1,000 deaths among their riders. Crash helmets were seldom worn and the neurosurgical units picked up the problems.[61] Roughly 50,000 people required admission for head injury annually, and three-quarters of road fatalities were the result of this. The few neurosurgical units whose primary concern had been with tumours were increasingly asked to care for patients with head injury. More units were opened, improving accessibility.

Walpole Lewin, in Oxford, argued for regional planning in close association with a major accident service.[62] Research work at the Birmingham Accident Hospital improved the treatment of injury immeasurably. It was widely recognised that severe collapse after major injury was associated with a vast fall in blood volume, far greater than could be accounted for by external loss. Where had the blood gone, and what should the treatment be? Blood volume studies after accidents made it clear that huge amounts of blood were lost from the circulation into the swelling around fractures. Major burns led to a similar depletion of circulating blood volume. Rapid and large blood transfusion saved lives. Lecturing to the St John's Ambulance Brigade, Ruscoe Clarke appealed for the re-writing of first-aid textbooks. The hot cup of tea and a delay while patients got over the shock of injury had to go; time was not on the patient's side and recovery would only begin after transfusion and surgery.[63] He provided the Association with new text for its handbooks.

Cardiology and cardiac surgery

In the 1940s the only methods available for the diagnosis of heart disease, other than bedside examination, were simple chest X-rays and the three-lead electrocardiograph. The effective drugs were morphia, digitalis and quinidine.[64] The management of heart disease was about to change out of all recognition. It was a subject that attracted the cream of the profession; Paul Wood at the National Heart Hospital was only one among a number of clinicians who educated a new generation of doctors about valvular, ischaemic and congenital heart disease, taught new ways of listening to the heart and interpreting what was heard, and opened new pathways in treatment.[65] Were he to have a heart attack, Wood did not wish to be resuscitated. When he did, some years later, he was not.

Infective disease of the heart had been a major problem but the effectiveness of antibiotics in streptococcal infections, which might otherwise have been followed by acute rheumatism, began to change its incidence. Syphilitic heart disease with aortic incompetence (valve leakage) was yielding to arsenicals and penicillin, heart damage as a result of diphtheria to immunisation and infection of heart valves following rheumatic fever to antibiotics.[66]

There was little effective treatment for coronary artery disease, an increasing problem. Coronary arteries might slowly become narrowed, and a heart attack (myocardial infarct) would occur if arteries suddenly became blocked. Losing its blood supply, heart muscle would be damaged, abnormal rhythms might develop, the patient might suffer great pain and death often occurred rapidly. In 1954 Richard Doll and Bradford Hill reported that there was a high incidence of coronary disease among doctors who smoked, a finding supported a few months later by the American Cancer Society. Its vice-president said that the problems raised by the effects of smoking on the heart and arteries were even more pressing than the more publicised linkage of smoking and lung cancer.[67] An association with high fat consumption was also suggested, for populations with the highest consumption also seemed to have the highest death rate from coronary heart disease. The greater incidence in the better-off countries could, however, be due to other factors such as a low level of physical exercise and other features of high standards of living.[68]

It being an axiom in medicine to rest damaged structures, prolonged immobility was traditional for people with heart attacks. A few specialists, however, suggested that the abrupt and grave nature of the disease, when coupled with long-continued bed rest, devastated the morale of people who had previously been active and healthy. 'Armchair' treatment was introduced without any apparent problems.[69] Anticoagulation by heparin had been used for deep vein thrombosis since the 1930s, and the value of anticoagulants in treating life-threatening pulmonary embolus was beyond dispute. Heparin could be given only by intravenous injection but a family of coumarin derivatives that could be taken by mouth was developed in the 1940s. Control was difficult, and regular estimates had to be made of the 'clotting time'. In heart attacks the evidence of their value was weaker, largely based on a trial in New York in which patients were treated or not according to the day of the week on which they were admitted. Although there was less evidence of effectiveness, a vogue developed for their use.[70] Cardiac arrest, the ultimate danger in a heart attack, was sometimes treated successfully with a new piece of equipment, the external cardiac defibrillator.[71]

Cardiac surgical development was an example of how progress in clinical medicine is the result of developments by many workers in many fields. These included cardiac catheterisation, new methods of measurement, studies on the coagulation of blood, hypothermia, perfusion techniques (the heart–lung machine), pace-making, the use of plastics, new design of instruments and studies of immune reactions.[72] It was the development by Magill and Macintosh of endotracheal anaesthesia (in which a mask was replaced by a cuffed tube inserted into the trachea) that made surgery inside the chest practicable. Cardiac catheterisation was devised in Germany in the 1930s but was not commonplace until the 1950s when it became the tool used to explore the right side of the heart, to measure atrial, ventricular and pulmonary artery blood pressures and to take blood samples. Combined with arterial blood sampling it was now possible to determine the nature of heart valve damage, for example after rheumatic fever. This permitted good case selection and carefully planned heart surgery. Twenty-four hour electrocardiography was introduced in the USA by Norman Holter, improving the diagnosis of abnormality of heart rhythm.

Progress in England centred on Guy's, the National Heart Hospital, Leeds and the Hammersmith, and was led by people such as Russell Brock at Guy's, Cleland at the Hammersmith and Thomas Holmes Sellors at the Middlesex. The heart operations undertaken before 1948 had included surgery to repair congenital defects that could be undertaken rapidly without stopping the heart or opening it, for example operation for patent ductus arteriosus (in which a connection between the aorta and the pulmonary artery remains open after birth). 'Blue babies' with congenital heart disease would seldom outlive their teens without surgery.[73] Brock operated on some, but several of his earliest cases died. The coroner was alarmed and Brock had to explain the risks of surgery and the way the children selected for operation were already near the point of death. Unless surgeons could develop the necessary operative techniques, all such patients were doomed. Wartime experience with the treatment of bullet wounds of the heart had given surgeons courage to challenge the long-held belief that operating on the heart was dangerous. It was commonly believed that rheumatic heart disease was a disorder of heart muscle and not primarily due to valve damage. Some surgeons, however, believed that valve damage was the crucial lesion; in 1948 three surgeons, Dwight Harken and Charles Bailey in the USA and Brock at Guy's, independently performed successful mitral valvotomy for mitral stenosis, widening the opening of valves that had become partially fused and were restricting blood flow. Brock attempted three operations within a fortnight. The surgeons were entering unknown territory and their work proved that the problem of chronic rheumatic heart disease was primarily mechanical. Brock's work was followed by Thomas Holmes Sellors at the Middlesex in 1951.[74] There was a backlog of seriously sick people in or approaching heart failure. The first operations had a high mortality, seven in the first 20 of Brock's series. This rapidly improved to about 5 per cent for mitral valvotomy, and more difficult lesions such as pulmonary stenosis were tackled.[75] Many of the patients were young men and women doomed to an early death without surgery. Sometimes the type of repair needed was beyond the techniques available. Yet risky though the attempts were, particularly on pulmonary and aortic valves, there was often no alternative.

The introduction of hypothermia in the early 1950s was the next advance. It was found that at a body temperature of 30°C the heart could be stopped for ten minutes. The commonest method was immersion in a bath of cold water. It proved possible to repair some atrial septal defects (openings in the division between the two atria) and make an open direct-vision approach to the pulmonary and aortic valves. Hypothermia could also be used in the resection of aortic aneurysms (bulging and weakening of this major artery).[76] Perfusion came next. The technique of producing temporary cardiac arrest using potassium was worked out by Melrose, a physiologist at the Hammersmith Hospital. Heart–lung machines were developed by the Kirklin unit at the Mayo Clinic and in England by Melrose and Cleland at the Hammersmith. There was much to be learned; Kirklin reported six deaths in his first ten cases, and a further six in the next 27.

But by the time he had reached 200 cases, deaths from the procedure were rare.[77] British cardiac surgeons deliberately held back and waited to see what the outcome of Kirklin's work would be. When he had developed reliable procedures three British units at the Hammersmith, Guy's and Leeds began work. All were well equipped, well staffed and expertly run departments. A pattern was set; cardiac surgery became established in regional centres, usually in association with a university teaching hospital. Only near such surgical facilities could advanced cardiology develop effectively.

Cardiac arrest was not necessary for operations on large blood vessels such as the aorta. Coarctation of the aorta, in which the vessel became narrowed, and aortic aneurysms also became manageable surgically.[78] After the introduction of angiography, in which solutions that were opaque to X-rays were injected into blood vessels, the frequency of atheromatous obstruction of the internal carotid artery was realised. Angiography was an uncomfortable and sometimes hazardous investigation. Urged on by George Pickering, Rob and Eastcott performed the first carotid endarterectomy at St Mary's Hospital in 1954 on a woman with transient episodes of hemiplegia and difficulty with speech. Although an increasing number of patients were treated, it remained a risky operation.[79]

Renal replacement therapy

Life-threatening kidney disease might be either acute or chronic. Acute renal failure, from the crush injuries of the blitz, a mismatched blood transfusion or a prolonged low blood pressure from blood loss, might get better if the patient could be kept alive long enough. If great care was taken with fluid intake and diet, some survived. In 1943 it was shown by Kolff in Holland that patients with terminal renal failure could be kept alive by artificial haemodialysis. Few were thought to be suitable for this, and it was mainly used for those in acute renal failure from which spontaneous recovery was to be expected. It was not offered to patients who had an irreversible condition from nephritis associated with streptococcal infection, diabetes or high blood pressure.[80] Indeed it was thought unethical to offer dialysis to those with chronic disease, as it would only delay an inevitable and unpleasant death. However, in 1954 a successful renal transplant was undertaken in the USA. The patient, who had chronic renal failure and would otherwise have died, received a kidney from an identical twin. While only one in 100 would have the chance of a sibling's kidney that the body's immune system would not reject, asking everyone with chronic renal disease whether he or she was a twin was now important.

Neurology and neurosurgery

The great developments in descriptive neurology and neurosurgery largely preceded the NHS, under the influence of North American surgeons such as Harvey Cushing and Wilder Penfield, and British neurologists such as Francis Walshe. The central nervous system once damaged did not regenerate, neither could it be repaired surgically. The specialty centred on the accuracy of diagnosis. Seldom was there any treatment available; only three out of 100 papers published in *Brain* held out any hope for the patient. Shortly before the NHS started, the RCP committee on neurology, seeing a need to develop the specialty outside London, recommended the development of active neurological centres in all medical teaching centres, in which neurology, neurosurgery and psychiatry should work together.[81] At least one such a centre, in Newcastle, equalled anything in the south. There, Henry Miller was followed by John Walton and David Shaw. Miller, who was interested in immunological disease, pointed out the advantages of the neurologist working in a hospital providing district services, who would see local epidemics, deal with people who were at an early stage of their disease and were often acutely ill, and be in close contact with other physicians.[82] Miller, and Ritchie Russell in Oxford who was interested in poliomyelitis, began to re-orientate neurology and link it more closely to general medicine. Attitudes began to change, with concentration on the prevention of damage in the first place, altering the biochemistry of the nervous system, and on rehabilitation. Developments elsewhere in medicine, in clinical pharmacology, imaging and later genetics, drove neurology and neurosurgery, which advanced steadily as specialties rather than experiencing sudden and major developments.

In the 1950s neurosurgery dealt with head injuries, brain tumours, pre-frontal leucotomy for mental illness, destruction of the pituitary for advanced cancer of the breast and precise surgery deep in the brain for Parkinson's disease (stereotaxic surgery). New diagnostic investigations, in particular cerebral arteriography, helped it. Seeing the circulation of the brain was possible by taking a series of radiographs in rapid succession after the injection of contrast medium. Cerebral tumours and intracranial haemorrhage, cerebral aneurysms and cerebral thrombosis were all revealed, making diagnosis more accurate and operation more successful.[83]

Ear, nose and throat (ENT) surgery

Three main developments – antibiotics, better anaesthesia and the introduction of the operating microscope – underpinned advances. Until the introduction of antibiotics the main function of the ENT surgeon was to save life by treating infection, acute or acute-on-chronic, affecting the middle and inner ear, the mastoids and the sinuses. Untreated infection could spread inside the skull, leading to meningitis and brain abscesses. By 1950 such catastrophic diseases were rare. The work of ENT surgeons altered substantially and those mastoid operations still being carried out were usually for long-standing disease.[84]

Zeiss produced the first operating microscope specifically for otology in 1953, revolutionising ENT surgery. Surgeons began to turn their attention to the preservation of hearing, the loss of which they had previously accepted as inevitable. Chronic infection of the middle ear prevented the movement of three minute bones that transmitted sound. Some operations that were now popularised had been attempted 50 years previously, but without magnified vision and modern instruments and drills they had been abandoned. Though simple in conception, the operations demanded scrupulously careful technique and great patience.[85] Among the first to become widespread was an operation for otosclerosis, to free up bones in the middle ear (mobilisation of the stapes), or to remove them (stapedectomy). Tympanoplasty (repairing damage to the opening of the inner ear) was described in Germany in 1953. Under the influence of surgeons such as Gordon Smyth of Belfast the procedure was rapidly introduced into the UK.

The commonest ENT operation, indeed the commonest operation, was 'tonsils and adenoids' (Ts and As). Surgeons seemed most convinced of the benefits whereas the MRC regarded the procedure as a prophylactic ritual carried out for no particular reason and with no particular result. John Fry, a Beckenham GP, in a careful analysis of his patients, concluded that although nearly 200,000 operations were carried out annually, the number could be reduced by at least two-thirds without serious consequences. Operation was usually carried out for recurrent respiratory infections, problems that tended to natural cure at around the age of seven or eight. The operative rates seemed to depend entirely on local medical opinion. A child in Enfield was 20 times as likely to have an operation as one in nearby Hornsey; the children of the well-to-do were most at risk of operation.[86] From the mid-1940s there was dramatic growth in the incidence, or recognition, of 'glue ear' in children, a condition that made them deaf. Thick gluey mucus remained in the middle ear, usually after upper respiratory tract infections. It was uncertain whether this was related to the widespread use of antibiotics, but an operation for inserting a grommet through the eardrum after removing the mucus by suction succeeded Ts and As as the commonest operation world-wide.

In the non-surgical field, the MRC had designed a hearing aid shortly before the NHS began, the Medresco aid. It was developed by the Post Office Engineering Research Station at Dollis Hill, assembled by a number of radio manufacturers instead of the hearing aid industry, and issued free of charge on the recommendation of a consultant otologist. The market was a large one, but the Medresco aid though cheap was behind the times. It consisted of a body-worn receiver connected to an ear-piece. Transistors, incorporated into commercial aids from 1953, were not used in the aids issued free by the NHS until several years later.

Ophthalmology

The availability of free spectacles under the NHS revealed a huge and pent-up demand from the public, largely satisfied by opticians under the supplementary ophthalmic services. Ophthalmologists seldom saved lives but their ability to maintain function by preserving sight ensured the specialty's place in every district hospital. The specialty was a pioneering one, lending itself to technical innovation, but it had a low priority in many undergraduate courses although postgraduate education at hospitals such as Moorfields was world renowned. Many diseases, for example high blood pressure, diabetes and some genetic conditions, involved the eye. Ophthalmology collaborated effectively with many specialties in sharing diagnostic advances such as ultrasound and, later, scanning. Operating microscopes were becoming available. Transplant surgery was being pioneered by ophthalmologists as corneal grafting. The treatment of cataract involved the removal of the now opaque lens, an early example of microsurgery, and the supply of powerful glasses. Operation was postponed until a late stage of visual loss. In 1949 Harold Ridley, working at St Thomas', treated a Spitfire pilot with a piece of Perspex from the cockpit canopy embedded in his eye. The plastic seemed well tolerated and it was suggested that a plastic lens might also be accepted. A surgeon of great skill, he pioneered the implantation of a lens into the eye, and had many successes, although others were not able to achieve his results. Detachment of the retina, a largely untreatable disease, was managed by prolonged bed rest until the photocoagulator was introduced around 1950.

Cancer

The treatment of cancer involved surgery if a cure was thought possible, and if the disease was past the point at which surgery could help radiotherapy was used as palliation. Although surgery was the foundation of treatment in common cancers such as that of the lung, many patients were inoperable when they first presented, and the five-year survival was low.[87] Surgeons became increasingly radical in an attempt to eliminate tumours. Few people were told their diagnosis; only the relatives were informed. The phrase 'cancer chemotherapy' was largely incomprehensible and the claim that malignant disease could be controlled or even cured by drugs was more appropriate to the charlatan than the physician. The physician's place was to administer the medical equivalent of extreme unction – opiates and comfortable words.

Radium or kilovolt irradiation could in fact produce worthwhile remissions and some long-lasting cures but radiotherapy was seldom seen as curative. Radium was replaced as post-war developments in atomic energy made artificial isotopes available. Gamma-emitting sources such as cobalt-60 provided a vastly more powerful source and were first used to treat patients in 1951. This made it possible to deliver a high dose internally without massive skin damage. By 1955 there were 150 telecobalt machines world wide; six years later there were over 1000. Linear accelerators, a by-product of wartime research on radar, were also introduced. The NHS ordered four to be installed in major units, the Hammersmith getting the first in 1953. 'Super-voltage' machines became an intrinsic part of the equipment of radiotherapy departments, and radiotherapy was progressively organised as an integrated regional service.[88] The introduction of radio-isotopes was the great hope for the future, because of the possibility that they would be concentrated selectively in tumours. Only rarely did they prove an advance.

The modern era of leukaemia therapy began in the 1940s with the work of Sidney Farber, then pathologist at the Children's Hospital, Boston. Farber had the idea of disrupting the growth of malignant cells with antimetabolites. The years of 1940–1950 saw the discovery of several drugs later useful in curing cancer. Nitrogen mustard had been used since 1942 and produced striking although temporary regression of the tumours. The next useful drug to be discovered came from the knowledge that folic acid deficiency was associated with bone marrow inhibition. Metabolic antagonists to folic acid, such as aminopterin, were shown to produce temporary remissions in childhood leukaemia.[89] Corticosteroids were also shown to have anti-tumour properties both in experimental animals and in humans. Mercaptopurine was the result of biochemical reasoning that nucleic acid metabolism might be altered. By the 1950s many drug development programmes were under way in the USA, industry was becoming interested and clinical trials were starting. Although medicine remained largely impotent in the face of disseminated cancer, the BMJ optimistically but correctly said that the foundation of a logical approach to the problem had been laid and an efficient machinery for the selection and testing of remedies devised.[90]

A new diagnostic tool for cancer was emerging: exfoliative cytology, looking for malignant cells on mucous surfaces and in body secretions. Before the war, Professor Dudgeon at St Thomas' routinely used cytology in the diagnosis of cancer of the lung and cervical cancer. King George VI's cancer of the lung was diagnosed there by sputum cytology. Papanicolaou's work in 1943 placed this development on an increasingly firm basis and it was developed progressively during the first ten years of the NHS, placing an extra burden on pathology departments.

Smoking and cancer

As the impact of infectious diseases lessened, the importance of cancer increased. Mass radiography, introduced in the years of war to detect tuberculosis, increasingly revealed carcinoma of the bronchus, although it was ineffective as a screening measure. In the first ten years 10 million examinations were carried out and 2,000 cases of intrathoracic cancer were found, 90 per cent of them in men.

Unlike malignancy as a whole, cancer of the respiratory system had shown a steady rise since the early 1920s. Many thought this was due to better diagnosis, or that a fall in the number of cases of tuberculosis had thrown cancer of the lung into greater prominence, or that sulphonamides had allowed people to survive pneumonia long enough to develop the signs of cancer. Studies, some in Germany during the second world war, had associated heavy smoking with lung cancer.[91] Percy Stocks, at the General Register Office, thought that atmospheric pollution might be involved and wrote to the MRC in 1947 to say that further investigation was warranted. With typical common sense Bradford Hill brushed aside the suggestion of air pollution; husbands and wives experienced similar exposures but smoking men got cancer while their non-smoking wives did not.

An MRC conference concluded that it would be unwise to assume that all the rise was an artefact and Bradford Hill was asked to carry out a study, which he did with the help of Richard Doll. The two research workers asked hospitals to notify the admission of patients with possible cancer of the lung, stomach and large bowel; they took their smoking histories and followed them up after discharge. Practically none of those with cancer of the lung were lifelong non-smokers; the rise was a real one and not merely due to better diagnosis. The findings, the result of interviewing 649 men and 60 women with carcinoma of the lung, were presented to Harold Himsworth at the MRC in 1949. Himsworth thought it crucial to ensure, before publication, that the results were right and asked for further hospitals outside London to be included in the study, which was extended to Leeds, Newcastle, Bristol and Cambridge. Published in 1950, shortly after an American case–control study by Wynder and Graham, Doll and Bradford Hill claimed a causal connection between smoking and lung cancer. At ages 45–74 years the risk was 50 times greater among those smoking 25 cigarettes a day or more than among non-smokers.[92] The *BMJ* said that the practical question which doctors in practice had to answer was whether any patients, for instance those with a smoker's cough, should be advised to give up smoking.[93]

Many doctors, unaccustomed to controlled studies, remained unconvinced so Doll and Bradford Hill launched one of the earliest prospective studies. It involved 40,000 doctors, a group that was studied for the next 40 years.[94] They published an extension to their case–control enquiry in 1952. The *BMJ* said that the probability of a causative connection was now so great that one was bound to take what preventive action one could. The younger generation would have to decide, each for himself or herself, whether the additional risk of smoking was worth taking.[95] The Standing Advisory Committee on Cancer and Radiotherapy was chaired by Sir Ernest Rock Carling, himself a lifelong heavy smoker. Meeting twice in the first half of 1952, it advised the Minister that the statistical evidence strongly suggested that there was an association between smoking and cancer of the lung, but this evidence was insufficient to justify propaganda. The Committee thought, in any case, that it would be undesirable for central government to be involved in cancer education, but that it should be left to local authorities and voluntary bodies.[96] The government got no advice on which to act, even if it had been minded to. Richard Doll published further material in 1953, and the following year Bradford Hill and Doll published the preliminary results of the prospective study that succeeded in changing attitudes.[97] Largely for financial reasons the government was not keen to give publicity to the increasingly certain connection between smoking and cancer.[98] A panel subsequently established advised the Minister that it must be regarded as established that there was a relationship between smoking and cancer of the lung, and that it was desirable that young people should be warned of the risks apparently attendant on excessive smoking. On 12 February 1954 the Minister made a statement in the House.[99]

No urgent action was felt necessary. The death of George VI, a heavy smoker who suffered from arterial disease in the legs, coronary artery disease and cancer of the lung, was not associated in the public mind with tobacco.[100] Its addictive properties were hardly recognised, and it was thought that if the risk was made clear people would respond. The tobacco industry spent enormous sums on promotion and the Ministry sat back, baffled. Sir John Charles, the CMO, was not a man to stick his neck out. He talked of the 'mysterious and inexorable rise in cases'. In his reports he said that the convinced individual could largely avoid exposure to tobacco smoke if he so wished. The Ministry asked the MRC if it would undertake further research into the relationship of smoking and cancer and was told that as the answer was known it would be a waste of money. Asked for a formal opinion on the relationship in 1957, the MRC published its response in the professional journals: the increase in lung cancer was attributable to the increase in cigarette smoking.

Obstetrics and gynaecology

Pre-war, the high maternal mortality rate had been of great concern. The chance of a mother dying from her pregnancy or associated causes in 1928 was 1 in 226. Janet Campbell, a Ministry doctor, had devised a pattern of regular antenatal supervision for the poor in London's East End. However, antenatal care remained patchy, many mothers did not use the services and GPs had played only a minor part. By 1948 the maternal mortality rate was falling, although there was no evidence that this was the result of antenatal supervision.[101] The perinatal mortality rate (stillbirths and the number of infant deaths in the first week of life per 1,000 births) had also fallen, but appeared to have levelled out at 3.85 per cent in 1948.

Since the 1930s there had been a gradual increase in babies being delivered in hospital. Cross-infection in maternity hospitals had been a constant danger, but antibiotics had reduced this risk. The Royal College of Obstetricians and Gynaecologists (RCOG) in 1944 had advocated that 70 per cent of deliveries should be in hospital, and ten years later raised its target to 100 per cent. During the 1950s the percentage of births taking place in hospital remained fairly static at around 65 per cent, but then it started to rise.[102] Public opinion was drifting to the view that hospital was best, and mothers increasingly chose it as safest for themselves and their babies. It was free under the NHS, home-helps were in short supply and the home might be unsuitable or overcrowded. The birth rate was rising and the demand for beds outstripped supply, in spite of which maternity beds were sometimes turned over to acute cases and tuberculosis. The Ministry thought it difficult to justify the provision of beds for normal cases 'simply because the mother prefers to have her baby in hospital'.[103] It was said that to get a bed in hospital you had to book three months before you were pregnant; hospitals had a monthly quota and it was first come, first booked.[104] District midwives delivered many at home who could not be fitted into the hospital, even when hospital delivery was indicated. Lack of pain relief was the main complaint women had of the maternity services. Midwives were not permitted to give pethidine until 1951. Only 20 per cent of women delivered at home received any form of pain relief, usually as gas/air, and only half of those in hospital. Because women had to stay in hospital for 14 days, antenatal patients who needed admission, perhaps because they had high blood pressure and toxaemia that posed a hazard to mother and baby, could not be admitted because the obstetric beds were full of mothers most of whom were fighting fit and desperate to go home. In the mid-1950s Geoffrey Theobald, at St Luke's Hospital in Bradford, realised that they could be discharged home safely after 48 hours provided the district midwives kept an eye on them. The 'Bradford experiment' meant more antenatal beds.[105]

The question of home or hospital delivery became contentious, although there was no sound information on which was safer, nor a clear view on the cases that should be booked for hospital. To begin with the accent was placed on housing and social problems. Later it shifted towards obstetric risks, the mother's age and the number of children she had already had. In 1954 Professor WCW Nixon, of University College Hospital, arranged a meeting of experts to discuss the possibility of obtaining data on the relative risks of hospital and home confinement. Out of this grew the perinatal mortality survey of the National Birthday Trust Fund, a charity working to improve the health of mothers and their babies. Not all GPs were up to date; some were unconvinced about the need for systematic antenatal care. The RCOG had stressed that GPs undertaking midwifery should have special experience, and supported the midwives who undertook regular postgraduate training. GPs saw fewer cases, particularly of operative obstetrics. The average GP had 30–40 deliveries a year, including those that went to hospital or were handled by midwives. Was this enough to maintain skills? Some GPs felt threatened and did not want to co-operate in a consultant-led service. Sometimes midwives respected the GPs with whom they came into contact; often they did not.

The maternal mortality was lowest in areas in which there was unified organisation of maternity services. In pioneer areas midwives, GPs and consultants organised themselves in partnership, in the interests of the GP, the mother and the child.[106] In Hertfordshire a system of shared care was adopted in which, after hospital booking, the GP undertook antenatal care until the 36th week. In Bristol, a similar system operated based on a health centre, GPs working alongside midwives and hospital staff in managing pregnancy.[107] In Oxford good relations were established between the RHB, the obstetric departments and the GPs with their local maternity units. The confidential enquiry into maternal deaths, the first serious British scrutiny of the outcome of care, followed a smaller pre-war study in Britain and a classic study of maternal mortality in New York City in 1933. After the 12th British Congress on Obstetrics in 1949, its president, Sir Eardley Holland, suggested an outcome study to Sir Wilson Jameson, who agreed. Sir William Gilliatt, the PRCOG, and George Godber established the framework and the first report covering 1952–1954 was published in 1957.[108] The enquiry was voluntary and confidential, for only if the reports were treated as privileged, and never disclosed to anyone other than the professional staff handling them, could frankness be expected. The registration of a death related to pregnancy was the starting point. Information was obtained from the GP and local obstetrician, the report then going to a regional assessor, a senior obstetrician appointed after consultation with the President of the RCOG. Consultant advisers to the Ministry of Health in obstetrics, anaesthetics and pathology made a final assessment. Avoidable factors were found too often to allow the opportunity to improve matters to pass. Reduction of deaths due to toxaemia and haemorrhage was important. The survey highlighted a danger appreciated since the 1930s, when the first obstetric flying squad was established in Newcastle. Women with a retained placenta after home delivery were often put into ambulances and sent to hospital without either transfusion or manual removal of the placenta, only to be found moribund on arrival.

Obstetrics was developing increasingly fast. In 1955 Ian Donald, in Glasgow, used ultrasound for the first time to examine an unborn baby. It became the preferred technique for monitoring the progress of pregnancy, replacing radiology, which had been shown by Alice Stewart in Oxford to put babies at risk. Theobald introduced a new method of inducing and increasing the strength of labour, the oxytocin drip, and there were advances in reducing postpartum haemorrhage and the delivery of the placenta (the third stage of labour). In a few units (e.g. University College Hospital, London) there was interest in the mother as a person; husbands were allowed and even encouraged to be with their wives during labour, a policy viewed in most hospitals as eccentric.

Paediatrics

Paediatrics, as a specialty, was weak in 1948 and there was little systematic training. Unlike the situation in North America, GPs provided much paediatric care. The problem of infectious disease seemed likely to be solved by the antibiotics. Specialists in diseases of the heart, the lungs and the joints cared for many children, and few of those in a children's ward were under the care of a paediatrician. If born in hospital the baby was in the care of the obstetrician and relationships with paediatricians might be prickly. Many diseases of children were becoming less common, for example rheumatic fever and tuberculous meningitis.

In the years preceding the second world war, special units for premature babies had been created in some places; for example, Mary Crosse's department in the grounds of the Sorrento Maternity Hospital in Birmingham. Crosse and her nurses would go out in taxis with hot water bottles to bring in small and premature babies. Victoria Smallpeace in Oxford was another pioneer. Retinopathy of prematurity, producing blindness in premature infants in the first few weeks of life, was described in Boston in 1942. In the late 1940s and early 1950s the number of cases in the UK surged. For ten years little more was known about the condition than an association with low birth weight and premature baby units; the cause remained a mystery. Mary Crosse in a flash of intuitional brilliance suggested that it might be due to the use of high concentrations of oxygen in incubators.[109] She found no case in Birmingham before 1946, but, out of the first 14, 12 had been on continuous oxygen for between two and five weeks. It was the additional money that came with the NHS, she said, that enabled centres of expertise to buy incubators and the expensive oxygen required. There had been a well intentioned but misguided change in care, indeed nurses and doctors might object to the suggestion that oxygen for sick babies should be restricted. In 1951 the MRC started sifting the records of maternity units and ophthalmic units. This confirmed the connection and showed that a high concentration over a period of several days was dangerous. Oxygen levels were reduced and the incidence of the disease fell greatly.[110] Retinopathy of prematurity was not the only disease caused by medical treatment; increasing interest in the neonate was accompanied by the rapid use of new drugs such as chloramphenicol and the sulphonamides, and as immature babies did not metabolise these like adults, overdosage might occur.

The emotional problems of sick children in hospital were not understood in 1948. Children's wards might only allow parental visits for an hour on Saturday and Sunday, and would discourage telephone enquiries. Children admitted to hospital were usually placed in adult wards and few staff felt it necessary to explain their treatment to them. Simple things, such as moving them from one bed to another in the ward or the use of red blankets, could create anxiety. Some children would react by withdrawing into themselves, others by seeking friendship and reassurance from everyone. However, paediatricians, such as Sir James Spence in Newcastle and Alan Moncrieff at Great Ormond Street, drew attention to the great distress caused by the 'no visiting' policy.[111] Particularly if in hospital for a considerable period, the infant forgot the mother and clung to the nurse when the time for discharge came, to the distress of all three. Nursing staff sometimes became possessive about children. An experiment in daily visiting was tried; the mothers liked it and the nurses preferred the closer contact with the family. John Bowlby, Director of the child and family department at the Tavistock Clinic, published a book on maternal and child health care in 1951. This drew attention to the devastating effect of separation from the mother and was followed in 1953 by a film, A two year old goes to hospital, that showed the traumatic and long-term effects on the young child suddenly separated from the mother and placed in strange surroundings. Daily visiting, seldom permitted previously, was progressively introduced. A second film in 1958, Going to hospital with mother, made it clear that the presence of the mother should be the norm, not the exception. Nurses should change their role from mother-substitute to adviser and friend, giving the mother understanding and the child skilled nursing.[112]

In 1956 Caffey, a radiologist at the Columbia University and Babies Hospital, New York, speaking to the British Institute of Radiology, described a group of children suffering from trauma. Paediatricians, he said, faced with unexplained pain and swelling in the limbs, usually embarked on an elaborate search for vitamin deficiencies and metabolic diseases. Simple trauma was given short shrift by those bent on solving the mysteries of more exotic diseases. Correct diagnosis of injury might, however, be the only way in which abused youngsters could be removed from their traumatic environment. Once the 'battered baby syndrome' was recognised many cases came to light, usually in children under the age of two who had suffered repeated injuries, often ascribed to 'falling downstairs' but in reality caused by their parents. They might have brain injury, fractures of the limbs and ribs, multiple bruises and injuries. Other children who 'failed to thrive' had been persistently underfed or emotionally neglected. Often the families in which the cases arose already had many other problems. There was widespread media interest, and health visitors, GPs and casualty departments now had something else for which to look.[113]

A major cause of babies dying during labour or in the week after birth (the perinatal mortality) was haemolytic disease of the newborn. The condition had been defined and its cause worked out in the USA by Darrow, Levine and Weiner in the 1940s. Six out of every 1,000 babies suffered from it, as a result of incompatibility between a rhesus-positive baby and a rhesus-negative mother who had developed antibodies during a previous pregnancy. Fifteen per cent of the babies affected were stillborn, and some of the others were rescued only by replacing the baby's blood by an emergency exchange transfusion. By the early 1950s mothers developing antibodies to the rhesus factor were admitted to units with special facilities. Exchange transfusions and early induction of labour produced some improvement in the mortality for rhesus-positive fetuses, but there was no way to reduce the numbers of rhesus-negative mothers who became sensitised during pregnancy and delivery.[114]

Geriatrics

The wartime hospital surveys had shown that the care and accommodation for the 'chronic sick' were often inadequate, but the size of the problem made it hard to solve. Care had largely been custodial, with little more than minimal attention from few staff either in the back wards of hospitals or else in units separated from acute services. During the years of war Marjory Warren, at the West Middlesex County Hospital, found herself looking after the chronic sick wards. She argued that geriatrics should be treated as special branch of medicine, staffed by those particularly interested in the subject. With greater effort, more patients could be discharged. The elderly should be cared for within the curtilage of district hospitals where special investigations and rehabilitation were available. A change in the attitude of the profession was called for, and the care of the chronic sick should be an important part of medical and nursing education.[115] Other pioneers included Lionel Cosin, who established the first day hospital in Oxford, and Tom Wilson, the first consultant geriatrician appointed in Cornwall in 1948. They got excellent results and a more intensive use of their beds by treating acutely ill old people vigorously in short-stay wards, taking medical, social and psychological problems into account. The achievement of independence depended on a high standard of medicine, good teamwork and an atmosphere of optimism and activity, combined with the patient's confidence and co-operation.[116] Marjory Warren, speaking in 1950, said people could be treated in their own homes if there was co-ordination of GPs and consultants, domiciliary consultations with the geriatric team, and home helps and district nurses. 'Keep them in bed and keep them quiet' was replaced by 'get them up and keep them interested'.[117] The Nottingham City Hospital established a geriatric unit in 1949, fully staffed with physiotherapy, occupational therapy, chiropody and links with psychiatry and the local authorities.[118] University College Hospital was the first teaching hospital to establish a unit, under Lord Amulree, at St Pancras Hospital. Nursing faced a major new demand, preventing patients from joining the ranks of the bed-fast, stiff, incontinent and dull of mind.[119] There was also a preventive aspect; in Salford a health visiting service was developed for the elderly. The co-ordination of domiciliary services, physiotherapy, chiropody, laundry and bathing attendants could prevent admission to hospital. Health visitors could remedy gaps in the service and deal with the needs of families as whole.[120]

The Ministry guidance on specialist services had suggested that general physicians would give an increasing amount of time to the chronic sick. They did not. In 1954 the Ministry organised a national survey of the services for the elderly, collated by Boucher, the senior medical officer concerned.[121] Some waiting lists were so long that GPs had stopped referring patients. An administrator might determine the priority of admission, sometimes swayed by the importunity of the family doctor. Waiting lists were seldom reviewed and were grossly inaccurate. Accommodation could be in long rambling drafty buildings far from other hospital services. An outside cast-iron staircase served one ward on the first floor over a boiler-house and a paint store. Bed turnover might be as low as 1.4 per year in some regions. In one group of 447 beds the physician 'did not believe in geriatrics'. A nearby colleague with 417 beds was mainly interested in paediatrics and, unable to raise enthusiasm for the elderly, had not visited them for months. In contrast were units that had adopted a more active approach, assessing patients before admission and campaigning for physiotherapy and occupational therapy services. Cosin at Oxford and Olbrich at Sunderland had annual bed turnovers of 3.6 and 5.6. Active treatment, rehabilitation and discharge were coupled with re-admission if patients were unable to maintain independence even with domiciliary services. Where the consultant's primary interest was in elderly people, the service benefited incomparably. If he had other interests, the elderly always took second place to acute patients.

The Ministry could now press for the development of geriatrics as a specialty. A pool of doctors who had trained in general medicine were looking for posts, and geriatrics provided them with opportunities. The Advisory Committee on Consultant Establishments helped them and more than 60 geriatric units were soon established with the more modern philosophy, although most of the new consultants found themselves working in poor accommodation. A new group of specialists had emerged, physicians interested in treating the elderly and not merely looking after them. Their first task was to deal with the vast number of patients they had inherited, introducing active management, cutting the number of beds they needed and reducing the waiting lists. They introduced domiciliary assessment and outpatient care for people waiting for a bed, many of whom had social rather than health problems. If properly used, there was probably no shortage of beds.

Mental illness

Many developments in psychiatric practice took place in the RHB hospitals, often in the provinces, and were largely divorced from the growing points in acute medicine, the teaching hospitals and universities.[122] The psychiatric departments of the teaching hospitals, where they existed, were not part of the mainstream, saw few psychiatric emergencies and undertook a different type of work. Their interests mostly lay in psychological medicine and psycho-neuroses. They drew a different group of patients, often of higher social status, who hoped for greater courtesy and personal attention than was usual in the general hospitals, and that outpatient care rather than admission would follow expert and thorough assessment.[123] Professorial units existed only in Leeds, at the Maudsley and later in Manchester. Before the second world war most psychiatric patients had been 'certified' although the Mental Treatment Act 1930 had enabled the admission of voluntary patients and the establishment of outpatient clinics. By the early 1950s two-thirds of patients were voluntary and not under a compulsory order. As people became more willing to be admitted to a mental hospital, increasing numbers led to overcrowding. Yet services were far from comprehensive, and were poor or non-existent for the elderly who were mentally infirm, for mentally ill offenders and for adolescents. Drug addiction was hardly recognised as a problem, neither was attempted suicide that was occurring more and more often.

Physical methods of treatment had long been used, virtually always for schizophrenia. Convulsion therapy used chemicals to induce fits, but was abandoned as patients could remember the entire episode in frightening detail. Electroconvulsion treatment (ECT), introduced in 1938, produced amnesia, and was given without anaesthesia. Six strong nurses held the patient down, but the strength of the muscle contractions frequently produced injuries, particularly crush fractures of the vertebrae. The introduction of anaesthesia and muscle relaxants overcame many of its evils and ECT clinics treated a dozen or more patients in a session. Deep insulin therapy, also introduced for schizophrenia, was at times hazardous and occasionally fatal. It was progressively questioned and ceased to be used in the late 1950s. Pre-frontal leucotomy was at first regarded as a major advance in therapy but proved to be damaging to the patient's personality. Its use for schizophrenia ceased, and more limited operations came into vogue. Psychiatrists awoke from a wish-fulfilling dream that they had been unwittingly party to a game of 'Emperor's new clothes'.[124] Only ECT, for depression rather than schizophrenia, proved of lasting use. Just as physical methods were being given up, drugs appeared. In 1952 chlorpromazine (Largactil) was introduced. Psychiatric practice was already undergoing major change. Henry Rollin, a psychiatrist at Horton Hospital, Epsom, and the anonymous author of a number of *BMJ* editorials, wrote that such powerful drugs heralded the onset of a revolution in the treatment of schizophrenia. If admission to a hospital was necessary, the stay could now be measured in weeks rather than months.[125] People with a recent onset of illness had a higher likelihood of early recovery and began to be accommodated separately from long-term patients, difficult in hospitals of traditional design where the buildings were arranged for security rather than comfort and resocialisation.[126]

By 1948 some mental hospitals had opened their doors. Their doctors believed that most if not all patients could be persuaded to co-operate and that locked doors, at any rate in day time, should be as obsolete as chains. An attempt was being made to improve the characteristics of the institutions by the introduction of occupational therapy, music and art classes. The *Lancet* published an account of hospitals where this policy worked well.[127] TP Rees at Warlingham Park, Croydon, had kept all but two of the 23 wards open for 12 years, and Macmillan in Nottingham, with 1,100 patients, had all the wards open day and night. Patients did not abscond and they were unlikely to wander off if they had a congenial task. Depressed patients might be at risk of suicide if not treated with ECT on the day of admission but the system was better for both staff and patients. Nurses preferred not being warders, and tensions in the wards were fewer. Overcrowding led to a need to expand outpatient treatment and to Joshua Carse's 'Worthing experiment', based on Graylingwell Hospital, Chichester.[128] The regional board and the Nuffield Provincial Hospitals Trust sponsored a two-year trial of intensive outpatient and domiciliary treatment that was rapidly seen to work, reducing admissions.[129] Psychotherapy was simpler on an outpatient basis, and as the antidepressants were introduced more people could be treated without admission. With better anaesthesia, outpatient ECT was also possible. The next years saw a rapid emancipation from the restricted and isolated world of the old mental hospitals. Sometimes, new ideas, such as Maxwell Jones' 'therapeutic community', were adopted.

The Ministry of Health saw a comprehensive service, integrating hospital and community resources, as a way of reducing overcrowding. The CMO's report said that

> The most successful form of rehabilitation has been a combination of habit-training and full occupation. A start is usually made in the ward containing the worst type of patient, the noisy, violent and destructive, and those with degraded habits. Such patients are split into groups of about ten, each group having one or more specially selected nurses in charge of it. The group is drilled into an unvarying routine with special emphasis on personal hygiene, cleanliness and neatness in dress, which need not imply any harshness since many of these patients appear to be quite indifferent to what goes on, and come after a time to respond mechanically. Full and suitable occupation is provided for the group under the supervision of its 'permanent' nurse. It is most desirable that patients being trained in this way should live in comfortably furnished rooms and that recreations should be provided. It is essential that they should have and retain their own personal clothing and underclothing. Few are the patients who fail to respond to such a regime. It is found that their wards become quiet and peaceful, the use of sedative drugs almost or entirely ceases, and locked wards can be opened.[130]

A committee in 1956 made recommendations about the rehabilitation of the mentally ill before discharge.[131] However, continued support after discharge was not readily to be found. The *Lancet* said that aftercare probably had a more important place in the treatment of the mentally ill than in that of any other type of problem but psychiatric social workers were scarce and aftercare had almost ceased to exist.[132]

The isolation of the mental hospitals and their staffs from the public and the wider health professions was well known.[133] Pioneering work on local services was undertaken in the northwest, where there were many small towns, such as Burnley, Blackburn and Oldham, of an independent turn of mind. Their town-centre municipal hospitals usually incorporated chronic and mental illness wards. From the outset the Manchester

RHB's first chairman, Sir John Stopford, wanted to improve services and by 1950 the RHB policy when appointing psychiatrists was to base them centrally to avoid the divorce of mental illness from the broad stream of general medicine. A planned and coherent system was developed with outpatient assessment and early treatment in general hospital units. These were 100–200 beds in size, each with its own catchment and admitting all patients. To everyone's surprise they seldom needed to send patients to the few, large and distant asylums. Perhaps this was because the units were small and the patients got individual attention, perhaps because they were in the centre of the community and patients didn't lose contact with friends and went into town to local cinemas and football matches. Most psychiatrists felt that co-operation with an integrated geriatric unit was essential as the work overlapped; and that with 100 beds they could deal with a population of 250,000.[134] Another major development was the requirement, set out in the Goodenough Report, that medical schools should have an active department of psychiatry.[135] Increasingly, such departments were developed, and took on catchment areas and often led the way in developing new treatments for the mentally ill, within general hospitals.

Yet those visiting the old asylums, such as Members of Parliament, might be dismayed at what they found. The chairman of the mental hospitals' committee of the Birmingham RHB agreed with the complaints of MPs. Beds were so close that they had to be moved to enable nurses to deal with troublesome patients. Ward temperatures might fall to 2°C in the winter. The weekly cost of care was £4 6s 7d against £13 10s 10d in a general hospital and £22 9s 3d in a teaching hospital. 'Give us an extra 5 shillings per patient', said the chairman, 'and we will achieve miracles.' Lack of staff meant that the patient/staff ratio nationally was 6.6 to 1 in mental illness and 7.0 to 1 in mental handicap hospitals. In Lancashire some nurses banned overtime above the normal 48 hour week to call attention to the problem. As action spread, voluntary admissions had to be restricted.[136]

The basis for reform was provided by the Royal Commission on the Law relating to Mental Illness and Mental Deficiency. Appointed in 1954 by the Conservatives, its membership included the President of the RCP and Dr TP Rees. Joint evidence from the Ministry of Health and the Board of Control provided a set of clear-cut proposals.[137] The Commission reported in May 1957, recommending the repeal of all existing legislation and a single new law covering all forms of mental disorder.[138] Running through the report were two simple ideas: first, that all distinction – legal, administrative and social – between mental illness and physical illness should as far as possible be eliminated; and, secondly, that patients who did not need inpatient care should, wherever possible and desirable, receive treatment while remaining in the community.[139] Compulsory powers of admission should be used less frequently. The assumption should be that mental patients, like others, were content to enter hospital unless they or their relatives positively objected.

The mental hospitals had shared the medical superintendent system of the municipal hospitals and the superintendent was often autocratic. Even consultants might be 'on parade' in his office. Psychiatry, as a discipline, had problems. Its changing world was unfamiliar. Psychiatrists were few and although there were leaders, the quality as a whole was questionable. The Ministry wanted to introduce state enrolled assistant nurses, but the nursing unions and the Mental Health Standing Advisory Committee argued that fully trained staff or student nurses should exclusively undertake mental health nursing. In the event most nursing fell to untrained personnel. The competition of other employers made poor recruitment worse; conditions in the army were better than in the mental hospitals. The wastage among students, who had a different pattern of training from those in the general hospitals, was high, 80 per cent compared with 40 per cent in general nursing.

General practice and primary health care

The NHS Act 1946 provided a family doctor to the entire population. The Bill emphasised health centres that were to be a main feature.[140] At public cost, premises would be equipped and staffed for medical and dental services, health promotion, local health authority clinics and sometimes for specialist outpatient sessions. The programme was aborted before it even started.

Whereas Bevan had persuaded consultants into the service in part by merit awards, the GPs had been unwilling to join until virtually the last moment. The public, however, were encouraged to sign on with those doctors willing to enter the scheme, leaving others with the choice of joining as well or losing their practices. Within a month 90 per cent of the population had signed up with a GP. Eighteen thousand GPs joined the scheme as they saw private practice disappear before their eyes.[141] The NHS Act made it illegal to sell 'goodwill'; instead a fund was established that compensated GPs when they retired, but it was not inflation-linked. The GPs' contract for a 24-hour service, the nature of the complaints procedures and even the patients' NHS cards were virtually unchanged (and still are). GPs, fearing that they might be no more than officials in a state service, argued successfully for a contract *for* services rather than a contract *of* service. As a result they remained independent practitioners, self-employed and organising their own professional lives. The Spens reports determined pay, which was entirely by capitation.[142] GPs' income depended on the number of their patients; even their expenses were averaged and included in the payment-per-patient. Their independence thus assured, GPs were taxed as though they were self-employed, yet, unlike most people in small businesses, they could not set their fees. With a few exceptions, such as payment for a medical certificate for private purposes, no money could pass between patient and doctor. This system, combined with a shortage of doctors, provided no financial incentive to improve services, but neither was there any incentive to over-treat patients.

Variations in list sizes between 1948 and 1989

Locality	1948 Population	GPs	Average lists	1989 Population	GPs	Average lists
Harrogate	47,311	35	1,351	89,542	52	1,706
Wakefield	63,274	18	3,513	109,967	60	1,833
Leeds	421,193	173	2,438	482,936	262	1,840
Bradford	289,699	111	2,610	319,681	162	1,973
England and Wales	41,500,000	16,864	2,461	52,868,542	26,009	2,033

Source: John Ball[145]

The 18,000 GPs, almost entirely male and half of them single-handed, practised mainly from their own homes. Their distribution was uneven, although not so bad as that of the specialists because there was less dependence on private practice. Before the NHS began a few GPs had made an excellent living but many were poorly paid and some had to employ debt collectors. The NHS gave them security and a higher average income. Because they were paid by a flat capitation fee, those in the industrial areas who had large lists of 4,000 suddenly became affluent but had difficulty serving their patients properly. Proud and wealthy GPs in rural or rich suburban residential areas with many private patients, but with small lists, became far worse off.[143] The Medical Practices Committee established a system that defined areas as over-doctored, under-doctored or intermediate, and barred over-doctored areas to new entrants.[144] Half the population lived in under-doctored areas where the average list size exceeded 2,500, designated as in need of more GPs. Here it was possible for any doctor to set up practice, putting up a plate and waiting for patients to come. Eckstein wrote that places such as Harrogate were gorged with GPs while working-class areas nearby in cities such as Wakefield, Leeds and Bradford were comparatively starved.[145] Swindon had average lists of 4,219 in 1948, while the list sizes in Bournemouth averaged 1,334. In 1989 the figures were 2,079 and 1,831. John Ball, later Chairman of the Medical Practices Committee (and of the GMSC), said that there was always a pressure for distribution to revert to under- and over-provision, and control was needed to ensure equality of access in the long term.[146]

The NHS brought fewer changes than the GPs had feared. Patients, uncertain of their rights, came with questions. Many older people, lacking spectacles for years, rushed to have their eyes tested and for some months the service was over-stretched. Much untreated illness was brought to light, particularly in women who had suffered for years from chronic conditions such as prolapse. There appeared to be a rise in the workload. The consultation rates of women and children, who had previously been uninsured, were higher.[147] No longer would people, to avoid the cost of the doctor and the medicine, say that they would be all right once the worst of an illness was over. Perhaps some work now coming to GPs was trivial; there was a belief born of years of rationing that 'a line from the doctor' would work wonders with the housing department. Paperwork changed; bills were no longer necessary but there were forms for eye tests, sickness, milk and coal. Under the Lloyd George national health insurance scheme, GPs had received medical record envelopes in which they had to keep a note of consultations 'in such a form as the Minister determined'. Wisely, ministers never defined how this should be. Now the entire registered population had an NHS envelope, transferred from one GP to another when they moved. It came to contain not only the GP's notes but also hospital letters, so potentially everyone now had a single medical record from birth to death.

A patients' guide, produced by the Ministry in 1948, said that as everyone could now have a GP it was the GP who would

> arrange for the patient every kind of specialist care he is himself unable to give. Except in emergency, hospitals and specialists would not normally accept a patient for advice or treatment unless he has been sent by his family doctor.[148]

The referral system had previously been an ideal to which doctors aspired, but were not bound if it were against their financial interest. Now the NHS established GP referral as almost invariable practice, imposing at least a partial barrier for patients seeking hospital care. The decision to go to hospital was transferred from patient to GP, reducing patient freedom and increasing the cost-effectiveness of the system. The 'gatekeeper system' institutionalised the separation of primary and secondary care. Family doctors defended it because they had continuing responsibility for individual patients, consultants because it protected them from cases that might be trivial or outside their field of interest, and government because it saved money to have a filter system.[149] Relationships between GP and specialist had been altered. Previously specialists had made their money from private practice and many patients came on referral. Once the NHS was established there was no shortage of NHS patients and few consultants made a substantial income from private practice. All were at least partly salaried and most ceased to have any financial reason to be grateful to GPs.

One of the first quantitative accounts of the work of a GP was presented by a young doctor who had recently entered general practice in Beckenham, John Fry.[150] He analysed attendances in 1951 by age and sex, noting the reasons for the consultation. Respiratory infections, digestive diseases, neuroses, skin disorders and cardiovascular problems headed the list. The GP dealt with minor ill-health and those major diseases that did not require admission to hospital. Three-quarters of his patients came to see him during the year. Philip Hopkins, in 1951–1953, studied the impact of general practice on the hospital service. He presented data for a practice of roughly 1500 patients with a consultation rate of 3.3 per year. In three years the practice had referred 860 patients on a total of 1,225 occasions. Of the referrals, 54 per cent were for treatment, often of a nature already clear to the GP. Because direct access to laboratories and X-rays was denied by the local hospital, many were referred solely for a test. Often referrals were to exclude serious illness before a label of psychoneurosis was attached. Only in 183 cases was it for a consultant's opinion on diagnosis or further management.[151] GPs were increasingly interested in practice organisation. Keith Hodgkin reported on the introduction of a radio-telephone into his practice. It enabled him to obtain an ambulance without delay, to continue his rounds while waiting for a delivery and to get hold of a partner if an anaesthetic was required. The problems were cost and the inadvertent reception of his messages on TV sets, so Hodgkin had to watch what he said.[152]

In 1948 there was little information about general practice; by 1952 more was available. There were 17,204 GPs in England and Wales providing unrestricted services, plus 1,689 permanent assistants and another 309 trainees. The number was increasing only slowly. A little over half were in partnership. In rural or semi-urban areas a third of GPs were single-handed, a third in partnerships of two, and a third in larger partnerships. The main surgery would be in a small town or other convenient focal point. In urban areas most of the doctors were single-handed and there were few large groups. The largest lists were found in the industrial Midlands, the northeast coast, south Yorkshire and Lancashire. Even in partnerships the GPs might see little of each other. The arrangement was largely financial, though it was easier to cover the doctors' time off. More rarely, as in Skipton, effective *group practices* were developing in which the partners aimed to work together from the same premises, supporting each other, using a common medical record system and sharing supporting staff.

New entrants to general practice were supplicants; they would be expected to work long hours, reach equality of pay with their seniors in possibly seven years, accept the hierarchical system of the practice, generally behave themselves and probably do most of the practice obstetrics.[153] The Spens Report on GPs' remuneration suggested that 10 per cent of GPs should be selected, because of their success in practice and suitability, to take on a trainee. The senior GP would be able to manage considerably more patients, make his services more widely available and increase his income. The scheme was later developed to provide vocational training, but that was not its original purpose.[154] In 1950 a committee, chaired by Sir Henry Cohen, reported that the status and prestige of the GP should be the equal of colleagues in any and every specialty, and that no higher ability, industry or zeal was required for the adequate pursuit of any of them. Cohen considered that, as general practice was a special branch of medicine requiring supervised training, there should be three years' preparation, one in practice (any principal having the right to train a new entrant) and two in supervised hospital posts. GPs should continue their education and reading throughout their professional life.[155] In 1957 the General Medical Services Committee of the BMA circulated guidance to achieve greater uniformity in trainer selection and to eliminate abuses.

The cost of prescribing by GPs often exceeded substantially their own pay. The introduction of a free and comprehensive health service had coincided with the discovery and large-scale production of valuable expensive drugs. But why should the number of prescriptions rise when more effective drugs should have returned people to health and work in a shorter time? In 1955 the prescription pricing offices began to send GPs analyses of their prescribing costs compared with the average for the area in which they practised, the beginning of a continuous attempt to constrain the growth in cost of pharmaceuticals. In 1957 the Minister established a committee under Sir Henry Hinchcliffe to investigate the cost of prescriptions. Its interim report said that no evidence of widespread and irresponsible extravagance was found.

Morale

The morale of GPs was low. GPs grumbled and there was little constructive discussion about how matters could be improved.

> *Something has gone wrong in general practice today. We treat the same people and similar complaints, and many of us have been doing the job for many a long year, and it is puzzling to say what has happened to bring about the change, for change there is. The doctor is irritable with the patients and they are noticing it and commenting on it. The patients are more aggravating and the doctor is noticing it. GPs had been promised more help, an easier life and no bad debts. He had got much more work, in some cases less income as private practice slumped, no bad debts, no help at all, a lot of personal frustration, had lost his soul when he lost the right to sell his practice, and felt that he no longer ran his practice – it was run for him. The patients had a hospital service which, save in an emergency, they could only use by appointment after a wait of several weeks; and a free GP service rushed to the point of indecency. His haemorrhoids had*

to bleed for six months before he could be treated; her heavy periods for nine months before she could get a hysterectomy. And having been in hospital the patient could be home two weeks before the GP got a report.[156]

As consultant services improved, GPs were losing access to hospital beds and some felt that this made it difficult to improve standards and status.[157] Teaching hospitals gave little priority either to undergraduate or postgraduate teaching for general practice. Both GPs and consultants saw the hospital as the fount of knowledge and GPs felt isolated. They felt embittered and frustrated, had lost their old enthusiasm and succumbed to the line of least resistance.[158]

Theodore Fox, Editor of the *Lancet* published a leader saying

Admittedly general practice in this country was deteriorating long before the NHS was introduced, and its further deterioration is due rather to a heavier load than to any legislative alterations in the Act. But on balance the effects of the Act on such practice have so far been for the worse and there is little evidence that its problems are being squarely faced. Of the two possible policies, the first is to say general practice is so often unsatisfactory that the correct course is to compensate for its defects – to develop hospital and specialist services in such a way that the short-comings of GPs become relatively unimportant. This, we cannot help thinking, is the policy that is, consciously or unconsciously, being followed. The alternative is to make a big positive effort to raise the level and prestige of general practice. This can still be done.[159]

The Collings Report

In 1944 the Nuffield Provincial Hospital Trust's 'Domesday Books' had examined the hospital service and found it wanting. In 1948 the Trust funded Dr Joseph Collings, who had trained in New Zealand as a GP, to look at general practice.[160] Nuffield records are silent on why he was selected. Collings surveyed 55 English practices, all outside London. His report raised an issue that was to dog general practice over the years – the wide and unacceptable variation in standards.

Collings spent between one and four days with each GP, seeing industrial (16), urban-residential (17) and rural practices (22).[161] He was probably looking for the things he wanted to find. He went on to an academic post in the USA at the Harvard School of Public Health, and his critique was saleable journalism, just what the USA then wanted to hear. The Nuffield trustees invited Theodore Fox, of the *Lancet*, to edit the report and left the question of publication to the discretion of their chairman. The chairman of the trustees decided that it should be published by the *Lancet* and not the Trust. Fox was non-partisan, an instrument neither of government nor of the medical profession, but a detached critic of excess on either side. He did not want to promote Collings' view of general practice, but he was fair and would not suppress it.

Collings had expected variations in quality but not how great they were. In city practices the conditions were so bad that he neither saw effective practice nor believed it was possible. He described surgeries without examination couches, where such records as there were lay loose round the room or in boxes, consulting rooms with a chair for the doctor but not for the patient, and couches where boxes and bottles had rested so long that they had stuck to the surface. Symptoms clearly demanding examination or referral were often passed over. Snap diagnosis and outdated medical knowledge were commonplace. Anything approaching a general or complete examination was out of the question under the prevailing conditions. In rural practice the surgeries were more pleasant, although often lacking basic equipment. The country doctor not only spent more time with his patients but also knew them better. Many GPs were good clinicians, good technicians and fine humanists; certainly not all. Urban-residential practice fell between the two; conditions for the patients were better than the industrial surgeries for 'the patient with more cultivated taste expects attention to the niceties'. Taken as a whole, the detailed 30 page report was a damning indictment. Collings wrote that there were no objective standards for practice and no recognised criteria by which standards might be established. 'We can all make mistakes' was certainly true in general practice, but the individual mistake paled into insignificance beside the predisposing factors which made serious mistakes not only possible, but in some circumstances highly probable. The reputation of general practice, Collings said, had been maintained through identification with an ideal picture that would no longer stand up to examination. General practice was poorest in proximity to large hospital centres and improved in scope and quality as one moved away. The worst practice was found where the need was greatest, in areas of dense population. Some premises required condemnation in the public interest. Yet Collings remained an enthusiast for general practice. Instead of building up hospital services he felt the aim should be to see how they could be dispensed with. That meant teamworking of doctors, nurses, social workers and technicians in good premises, which might be based on group practice units perhaps serving 15,000–25,000 people. The widening schism between hospital and practice, the lack of local authority interest and the failure of administrative co-ordination in his view did nothing to help.

The BMJ, provided with a pre-publication draft, disputed Collings' findings. The journal rightly thought that his 55 practices did not truly reflect the whole of general practice and certainly Collings had been selective. The BMJ thought that the report would at least do one good thing – focus the spotlight on general practice, which should be the most attractive career in medicine. The NHS was weighted heavily in favour of the hospital and the specialist. Most of the letters to the BMJ disputed Collings' findings or excused the shortcomings. A minority saw that the report might be the turning point in the NHS and it was up to GPs to take a lead in establishing an integrated service based on general practice.[162] Collings entered the demonology of general practice, but stirred others into activity. His three further articles in 1953 were largely ignored.[163] In them he argued for group practice, rather than health centres. Group practice was evolutionary and was the only way to breathe life back into the finest, dying, elements of traditional general practice. Collings laid out a detailed and costed plan both at practice and at national level. He discussed the staffing, the architectural design of premises and the management and personality issues that arose in groups. He considered the financial inducements required and the financial advantage to government – the better general practice became, the less the work falling on hospitals where care was expensive.

The BMA survey

Charles Hill, Secretary of the BMA, advised the Council that Collings, having been published, had to be 'answered'. He suggested that a general practice review committee should be set up to obtain an authoritative and statistical report on general practice. Stephen Hadfield, an assistant secretary at the BMA, was given the job mainly because he was the member of staff most recently in general practice. Throughout the next year Hadfield visited four or five practices chosen at random each week.[164] His report was fuller, more balanced and statistically based. Analysing his findings, he made judgements of quality of care: 92 per cent of GPs were adequate or something better; 69 per cent left no doubt that patients received what examination was necessary. Three out of four paid reasonable attention to record keeping. Seven per cent of both young and old GPs needed to revise the methods of diagnosis they used. Hadfield was surprised how often the abdomen was examined with the patient standing and clothed. In 10 per cent of surgeries the accommodation was dismal, bare, inhospitable and dirty. Some GPs were clearly discouraged when they saw the lines round the walls where greasy heads had rested or the marks of nailed boots on the floor. Relations with the hospitals were good and probably better than before the NHS, when voluntary hospitals kept outpatients to maintain high attendance records. With public health medicine the position was worse. GPs saw district nurses as the salt of the earth, but reported little co-operation from health visitors and complained bitterly about them as a waste of nursing manpower. Hadfield believed that GPs, hospital consultants and public health doctors had to get to know each other better. They were treading different paths while the NHS was crying out for unified administration. General practice could follow one of two paths: either adjust to the situation and stimulate new clinical interests or move towards an impersonal health service taking general practice into a glorified hospital outpatient department.

There was a delay of a year before Hadfield's report was published. It was passed round the BMA committees for it contained comments about all branches of medicine. The chairman of the review committee wanted to publish, so that the profession might see the evidence and the public would know that the BMA was making a serious effort to raise the status of the GP and the standard of practice. If nothing else, it would make people think and start things moving. Others in the BMA thought that the report should be edited before publication, or should remain private as it showed that not all GPs were quite angelic. The press would make capital out of shortcomings and some GPs would be angry. Yet published it was. Every profession, said the *BMJ*, has its quota of unsatisfactory practitioners; that a few should be outstandingly bad was only to be expected. The remedy was in better selection of students. Unsatisfactory relations with other parts of the service also impeded the work of the GP and the tripartite structure was a root cause of this. Finally the stresses created by the rapid advance in medical science over the previous three decades were responsible for some difficulties.[165]

Good general practice

The Nuffield Provincial Hospitals Trust, inadvertently responsible for stirring up the hornet's nest, tried to remedy the situation. In 1951, Dr Stephen Taylor, doctor, medical journalist, Labour MP and a figure in the political background of the NHS at its inception, lost his seat in the election and was commissioned to examine the acceptable face of general practice. He was as selective as Collings but visited the best, some of whom had been recommended by Hadfield. They were the 'doctors' doctors' with lessons to teach. He worked under the supervision of a steering committee of the great and the good, chaired by Sir Wilson Jameson, to avoid another cause célèbre. Taylor's report, *Good general practice*, described its structure and organisation.[166] Doctors who organised their practices were less stressed, more effective and happier. Whatever the perfection of the NHS administrative framework, Taylor concluded, 'in the final analysis, the quality of the service depends on the men and women who are actually doing the job . . . good general practice begins with the good GP. So most of the conclusions are suggestions for self help.' The *BMJ* commended the book to all young practitioners.[167] Taylor retained his interest in general practice, was involved in the establishment of a teaching practice at St Thomas' Hospital, and was the moving spirit behind one of the earlier health centres, opened in 1951 in Harlow New Town.

The Cohen Committee

After Collings the Central Health Services Council established a wide-ranging review in December 1950. Chaired by Sir Henry Cohen, Professor of Medicine in Liverpool, the committee included leading figures in the hospital and local authority worlds, several well-known GPs and Stephen Taylor. The conclusions of Taylor's book, *Good general practice*, were submitted to the Cohen Committee. The Medical Practitioners' Union (MPU), a national organisation of GPs dating from 1914 with Labour Party links, believed it had some answers. It suggested the development of group practice, revision of the payment system so that GPs were encouraged to spend money on improving their practice, the attachment of nurses and home helps to group practices, and a salaried service for GPs.[168] The Cohen Committee reported in 1954 and endorsed Stephen Taylor's findings but it was not the brightest of bodies and it produced no new thinking.[169] Its value lay in its authoritative nature, seeing general practice as fundamental to health services. Practice could not be replaced by 'congeries of specialisms, nor was it subordinate to them'. Cohen commended group practice, as it encouraged co-operation, and thought it might develop into the natural focus of the 'various domiciliary arms of the health service', securing the advantages of better staffing, accommodation and equipment more easily than health centres. Students should be given the opportunity to study the scope of general practice. More radical ideas were discouraged – long service or merit awards, assisting retirement of elderly GPs, or undergraduate teaching by GP academics.

One problem that faced GPs was the 24-hour commitment. Their contract was to provide a round-the-clock service. As independent practitioners they had to find a substitute to cover holidays and leisure time. The first deputising service made its appearance in 1956 as a private venture of two South African doctors. Against the initial opposition of the BMA, and with no support from government, Solomons and Bane launched an emergency call service, providing duty doctors in cars with two-way radio contact to a central base. GPs, at least in London, now had a new way of covering their practices to give themselves time off duty.[170]

Improving general practice

Three factors helped the restructuring of general practice. First there was a change in the way family doctors were paid, which provided a financial incentive to improvement in ways both the profession and government desired. Secondly, innovative GPs began to paint a vision of practice as it might be, and sell the vision successfully to their colleagues. Articles began to appear describing better systems of practice organisation, record keeping, appointment systems and the work of nurses.[171] Thirdly, professional organisations began to work behind the scenes to improve facilities, such as GP access to diagnostic services. The BMA was already involved. A quiet partnership between government, the BMA and the Royal College of General Practitioners (RCGP) moulded the most important ideas into a new policy. Donald Irvine, an Ashington GP subsequently Chairman of Council of the RCGP and President of the General Medical Council, later listed its six elements:[172]

- Encourage groups.
- Rehouse GPs in properly equipped, purpose-built premises.
- Help individual GPs develop a viable organisation.
- Give GPs access to hospital-based diagnostic services.
- Introduce nurses and other health professionals to form primary health care teams.
- Provide better postgraduate education.

Money, status and recruitment go hand in hand. GP pay was based on the recommendation of the Spens Committee, appointed in 1945 and reporting the following year.[173] The starting point was a workload survey conducted between July 1938 and June 1939.[174] Austin Bradford Hill, the statistician, said that, out of 6,000 doctors selected, less than 1 per cent refused to co-operate. Those who refused were too busy, or had unprintable views about the BMA, the Ministry of Health, statisticians or all three.[175] According to the way the returns were interpreted, the annual consultation rate was somewhere between 4.81 and 5.39 per year. The baseline for earnings was the average pre-war income as declared to HM Inspector of Taxes. As GPs might not always declare their full earnings this was an underestimate. Spens believed that the GPs' average income was too low, in the light of the length of training, the arduousness of life compared with other professions, the greater danger to health, and the skill and other qualities required. Spens thought that before the war many doctors had been deterred from becoming specialists by the certainty of many lean years. The NHS would remove this deterrent, and if GPs were not well paid, recruitment would suffer and only the less able young doctors would enter this branch of medicine, to the detriment of the profession and the public. Spens recommended a level above the pre-war average, and wished to see a system enabling good and energetic doctors to achieve substantial earnings. It left the adjustment to post-war values to others. GPs therefore entered the service paid on a provisional basis with the promise of a review. They rapidly and reasonably became dissatisfied with their earnings and a grossly inadequate betterment factor to bring GP pay up to 1948 levels.[176] The review that had been promised did not materialise and two years after the NHS began the Local Medical Committee Conference instructed the General Medical Services Committee to make preparations for the ending of contracts.[177] GPs had seen the Minister cut the remuneration of dentists and felt at his mercy. The dispute continued until 1951 when it was agreed to go to arbitration.

The Danckwerts award

The report by Mr Justice Danckwerts in March 1952 was a turning point. Taking account of inflation since 1939 and increases in the incomes of other professions, he recommended that the central pool divided among the country's GPs should be increased to £51 million, a rise of roughly 25 per cent. The government had never expected an award of this size but was unable to avoid paying. The figures were related to the number of GPs rather than the size of the population, so if recruitment improved and list sizes fell, the average GP's pay would not be affected even though the workload might fall. Danckwerts said that 'if the number of doctors in the service became unreasonably large this point would require reconsideration'.[178]

It was clear to the Ministry that the size of the award made it possible to improve general practice. The government accepted it subject to agreement on a system of distribution that would provide incentives, which could be done without obviously penalising the 'back-woodsmen'. Within three months there was agreement on

- Changing the flat capitation rate to give a higher return to doctors with intermediate sized lists (500–1500), so that new partners would be taken on more readily.
- An initial practice allowance to make it easier for new doctors to enter practice.
- Financial encouragement to form partnerships and group practices.

The maximum number of patients a single-handed doctor could have was reduced from 4,000 to 3,500, which also became the maximum average for a partnership.[179] The profession was broadly satisfied with the outcome and the award rapidly had the desired effect. GPs received a considerable sum in back-pay; some spent it on modernising their premises. The following year there was a net increase of 806 doctors and 1,118 new doctors joined partnerships. Long-standing assistants often became partners. The number who were single-handed fell by 312.[180] It was an early demonstration of the effect of financial incentives on general practice. The profession agreed that £100,000 each year should be top-sliced to provide interest-free loans to group practices wishing to provide new or substantially better premises. This loan scheme was so popular that some applications could not be approved. In 1954, 36 applications were accepted totalling £159,000. Later, following the Royal Commission on doctors' pay, the scheme was funded directly by the Exchequer and not from top-sliced money. Because it was impossible to identify precisely to whom money should be reimbursed, it was agreed to hold it in trust as a medical charity, the Cameron Fund.

Appointments systems, tried experimentally in a few places, had been shown to reduce the number of visits requested. A more even distribution of doctors was emerging as a result of the work of the Medical Practices Committee. There was a steady decrease in the number of patients living in under-doctored areas, from 21 million in 1952 to 9 million in 1956. Although the arrangements went some way to encourage group practice, it remained difficult for a small practice to find the funds to pay an additional doctor. There were comparatively few vacancies and two-fifths of them attracted over 40 applicants each. The easiest place to enter practice was the north of England, where list sizes were biggest.[181] Health centre development, which might have provided new posts, was minimal. The concept was unpopular with GPs, rents were high and it took a long time to design and build health centres partly because of the need for many parties to agree.

The College of General Practitioners

Two memoranda that proposed a college of general practitioners were presented at a meeting of the BMA General Practice Review Committee in October 1951. Stephen Hadfield, the Secretary, knew that Fraser Rose of Preston was interested in founding a college. At the same time he discovered that a friend of his in private general practice, John Hunt, had a similar desire. John Hunt was invited to a meeting of the Committee and introduced to Fraser Rose. The two wrote a letter to the *BMJ* and the *Lancet*, published on 27 October 1951, proposing a college. It was like a breath of fresh air to many GPs.[182] The idea was discussed for about a year and the strong opposition of the Royal Colleges of Physicians, of Surgeons and of Obstetricians and Gynaecologists was clear, as was often the case subsequently when new colleges were in prospect. They would have supported a joint faculty of general practice within their own structures, but not a separate institution. Additions to their numbers risked weakening their influence; with few colleges, people listened when a leader such as Lord Moran spoke. In November 1952 the College of General Practitioners was formed in secret when the memorandum of articles of association was signed by the 16 members of the steering committee. The creation of a college, according to George Godber, provided 'the banner with a strange device' that people could follow. The College ethos was, from the start, to lead from the front. It encouraged high standards of service, teaching and research, attracting theorists, for theorists cannot usually work alone. After six months there were 2,000 members.[183] Within four years it had developed 22 regional faculties. Although membership increased steadily, only a minority joined; in 1957 the membership was a little over 4,000. College influence was largely restricted to its membership and no responsibility was taken for the weaker brethren. Unlike the older colleges, membership played little part in professional advancement. The GMSC had wider responsibilities and was in a position to influence all GPs, as it did in 1954 when local medical committees were asked to inspect practice premises.[184]

The crux of the College vision was that family medicine had its own skills and knowledge base that were as important as anything the hospital services might bestow upon it. The work of men such as Keith Hodgkin, a GP, and Michael Balint, a psychoanalyst, was central to this. Balint, at case conferences at the Tavistock Clinic, cast new light on the nature of the consultation and was an important figure in the establishment of general practice as a discipline in its own right.[185] He argued for a different type of education and research, and pointed to the relationship of the GP and the consultant as a perpetuation of the pupil–teacher relationship.[186] One of the College's first initiatives was to see what, if anything, medical students were taught about general practice. A survey published in 1953 showed that, although medical students from a number of schools visited GPs, and many schools were 'planning' some opportunity for the teaching of students by GPs, only Manchester and Edinburgh had such a teaching unit in the medical school.[187] It was the beginning of a struggle to attain recognition of general practice as a subject entitled to a place in the overcrowded student curriculum.[188]

The College epidemic observation unit in Surrey began to plot infectious disease in the community. The Birmingham research unit, led by Crombie and Pinsent, was interested in mathematical modelling of general practice and took the lead in national morbidity surveys. Crombie, in a remarkable research project, ran surveys under the auspices of the College and the General Register Office. Between May 1955 and April 1956 careful records of a year's consultations were kept by 106 practices, involving 400,000 patients and 1.5 million contacts.[189] These practices provided a clear description of their clinical work. The study showed who was consulting GPs for what, and what was being referred to hospital. Consultation rates for cancer, neurosis, circulatory and respiratory disease, and arthritis and rheumatism were provided for the first time and the surveys improved knowledge of the incidence and prevalence of most forms of disease. The CMO at the Ministry, Sir John Charles, thought it an important source of data that should affect decisions on medical student training.[190]

Towards a vision for general practice

Iain Macleod, the Minister, addressed the Executive Councils' Association in October 1952 about the future.[191] The BMJ thought it a refreshing and forthright speech in line with BMA policy. Macleod stressed the desirability of treating patients in the community and sending them to hospital only when medical or social conditions made it essential. This would increase the interest of general practice, be of benefit to patients, cut waiting lists and save money. Reduction of list sizes and the development of group practice would help. Co-operation between hospitals and GPs needed improvement, for example by expanding direct access to X-rays and pathology departments that GPs were increasingly using. Without encroaching on the responsibilities of the local health authorities, Iain Macleod thought that the GP should be the clinical leader of a team within which the midwife, the district nurse and the health visitor should all work. The GP should also work more closely with dentists, pharmacists and opticians. There should be the same spirit of teamwork devoted to the patient in general practice as in hospital.[192] A renaissance of general practice began, on a new model laid out by the profession and the Ministry.[193]

The Danckwerts award opened the path ahead but it did not solve all problems. Variation of practice standards remained a consequence of independent practitioner status, for while the energetic could improve their practices substantially and rapidly, not all GPs did and their patients suffered. Enoch Powell wrote in 1966 that whether the practitioner was good, bad (up to the point of incurring a disciplinary stoppage) or indifferent, he got the same payment for the same list. Inside general practice he could increase his earnings only by increasing the size of his list. The doctor was not primarily dependent on ability or reputation to increase his list, and in such competition as there might be, the doctor's willingness to prescribe a placebo or the drug recommended by the patient, or to complete the desired certificate, might be as effective as skilled and conscientious care. The GP's situation combined private enterprise and state service without the characteristic advantages of either. He could not reap the rewards of building up a practice, and the better he did his work the worse off he was. Money spent on premises, equipment and staff did not increase his income, for the cost came from an income that would be undiminished if he did nothing. If he restricted his list to the number that could be treated properly, he merely ended with a smaller income than less able or less scrupulous fellows. Powell believed that the essence of the private enterprise system, competition for gain, had been gouged out of family doctoring, leaving the empty shell.[194]

Local authority health services

The 1946 Act required local authorities to consult hospital authorities and the executive councils about their health service plans.[195] The transfer of the general, long-stay, tuberculosis, infectious disease, mental illness and mental handicap hospitals to the RHBs substantially reduced their role in the direct provision of care, as did the proposed integration of preventive clinical services with general practice. Environmental sanitation was passing to engineering specialists, sanitary inspectors were becoming more expert and independent, and infectious disease seemed to be diminishing and to require collaboration with the PHLS, national and even international authorities. The role of the MOH changed from the development of services to helping services provided by others, co-ordinating them and reviewing their effectiveness. Those believing that public health should be managerial and deliver services saw the passing of a golden age.

However, local health authorities retained broad and important health functions and a few additions, enabling the MOH to maintain a role as guardian of the community's health. Many, for example George Townsend, the MOH for Buckinghamshire, accepted that there had been gains as well as losses, and quietly took the opportunities offered. Several components of health care had been put together for the first time and there was work to be done. Some services had been in difficulties, the voluntary nursing associations were inadequate and failing, and health visiting required reorientation. The NHS Act contained a provision enabling local health authorities to provide 'care and aftercare' that enabled them to develop facilities for the mentally ill and handicapped. Immunisation needed reorganisation, and the programmes had to involve GPs and be capable of prompt expansion. Maternal and child welfare and health visiting were already established; home midwifery had been under partial local authority control; and ambulance services were derived in part from wartime services.

From 1948 local authorities had full responsibilities for nursing in the community and the development of preventive and social support services, for example the home help services. Some large authorities had appointed superintendent nursing officers before the NHS began and all now began to do so, developing leaders of the public health nursing team just as matrons in hospitals were looked on as leaders of hospital nursing teams. At first many used voluntary nursing organisations, such as the Queen's Institute, as their agent. Rapidly, however, local authorities brought the nursing services in-house. Everyone now had access to care, and hospitals discharged patients increasingly rapidly which meant that more acutely sick patients had to be cared for at home, altering the work of the district nurses substantially and revealing shortages of staff. Health visitors had once dealt with a host of minor problems. Now that everyone had a GP, these were taken to the family doctor. GPs were taking an increasing interest in mothers and babies, and it was possible that health visitors might be squeezed out of a viable role.[196] In 1953 a working party was established, chaired by the then recently retired CMO Sir Wilson Jameson, to advise on the work, recruitment and training of health visitors. The health visitor's role was defined as primarily health education and social advice. She should become a general family visitor, making a contribution in fields such as mental health, hospital aftercare and the care of the aged. The Jameson working party saw a need for co-operation with GPs, but dismissed the idea of attaching health visitors to particular practices, thinking that health visitors would work on an area basis.[197]

In 1954 MacDougall, MOH for Hampshire, provided health visitor support for groups of GPs in Winchester by attachment; a little later Warin developed a similar scheme in Oxford, as did Chalke in Camberwell, an inner city area. Community nurses were coming into contact with a wider range of professionals and were now full professional partners and members of the general practice team.[198]

Health centres, first proposed in the Dawson report of 1920, were a local health authority responsibility.[199] Part of the dream of the founders of the NHS, there was no practical experience of their pros and cons. Six months before the start of the NHS the Ministry stated that, because of building difficulties and uncertainty about the best pattern to adopt, no general development of health centres was appropriate. This and GPs' suspicions of a state service, an idea hopelessly entangled with health centres, slowed development to a virtual standstill. Two opened in 1952, a large and costly one (planned before the NHS began) by the London County Council to serve a new housing estate at Woodberry Down[200] and a smaller one, the William Budd health centre in Bristol.[201] In the first 15 years of the health service only 17 were opened. The health centres provided doctors, patients and ancillary staff with many advantages and few disadvantages were apparent. Often, however, GPs used the centres only as branch surgeries.

Health promotion and disease prevention made a measure of progress in the first decade. One pioneer was John Burn, the Salford MOH, who established the first anti-smoking clinic. He helped the development of mental health services, and the use of nursing staff in immunisation and screening clinics. After the London smog of 1952 he was a member of the committee that engendered the Clean Air Act 1956, a massive advance in creating a healthy environment.[202] But there was failure to grasp the nettle, centrally, of the growing consumption of alcohol, or fluoridation or, most of all, smoking-related disease.

Hospital and specialist services

On the appointed day in England and Wales the NHS took over 1,143 voluntary hospitals with some 90,000 beds, and 1,545 municipal hospitals with about 390,000 beds (including 190,000 in mental illness and mental handicap hospitals). Experienced and influential SAMOs, who, in their local authority days, had experience of hospital management, headed most RHBs. They understood the need to develop good specialist services accessible to the entire population. The demand for hospital care was rising. New surgical procedures for common conditions such as varicose veins increased the demand for beds, making it important to discharge people more rapidly. There was great pressure on both acute and long-stay beds, and continuous attempts to increase turnover and occupancy. As a result of the appointment of young well-trained consultants, the quality of provincial district general hospitals improved. Such was Kenneth McKeown, from Hammersmith and King's, who was appointed to Darlington in 1950 as its first consultant surgeon.[203] No longer did major surgical cases have to go to Newcastle, Leeds or London, and McKeown established the hospital as a centre for oesophageal surgery. For the first time, major developments emerged from district hospital specialists. They included Norman Tanner, who worked on the surgery of peptic ulcers at St James' Balham, Harold Burge, who explored the results of vagotomy at the West Middlesex Hospital, and John Paulley at Ipswich, who showed the mucosal abnormalities in coeliac disease. Supporting them were better investigation and diagnostic services with good pathology and radiology departments. Intervention was prompter, and improved anaesthesia, no longer a part-time activity for some GPs, meant safer operations for older people. The very success of the NHS created a problem. Even patients with emergency problems such as retention of urine or with curable diseases might be difficult to admit. The *BMJ* drew attention to the shortfalls in the service; the dangers of going to bed, described by Asher, could be contrasted with the dangers of not going to bed.[204]

St George's female medical ward, June 1951

Diagnosis	Age	Treatment
Tuberculous meningitis	38	Streptomycin/morphine
Haematemesis	67	Ascorbic acid, aludrox, thyroid, gastric diet
Carcinomatosis	80	Nepenthe, pethidine
Right hemiplegia	77	Ammonium chloride
Subacute rheumatism	27	Aspirin
Pernicious anaemia	71	
Fractured femur	70	
Mitral stenosis	33	For valvulotomy
Investigation of headaches	64	Codeine
Costophrenic pleurisy	40	
Laparotomy	65	Nepenthe, gastric diet
Coronary infarction	55	
Ulcerative colitis	44	Low residue diet, chiniofon infusion
Acute rheumatism	24	Salicylates, benadryl
Thyrotoxicosis	24	Bed rest, methyl thiouracil, phenobarbitone
Polyarteritis	30	Aspirin
Coronary infarction	66	Tromexan, complete rest
Investigation of right kidney	60	
Sonne dysentery	74	Thalistatin, barrier nursing
Macrocytic anaemia	71	Digitalis folia
Tubercular peritonitis		Streptomycin, PAS
Congestive heart failure	56	Digitalis folia, cardophyllin
Duodenal ulcer	34	Pethidine, gastric diet
Subacute bacterial endocarditis	22	Morphia, penicillin/streptomycin
Investigation of lung	49	Pethidine

Almost all had daily blanket baths and night sedation

The Portsmouth hospitals took the bold step of issuing a patient questionnaire. Half were returned and two-thirds of those were wholly laudatory. There were, however, suggestions. Perhaps the food might be warmer, and lavatories more available. The hair mattresses were lumpy and the wireless service could be better. Lack of privacy, of chairs for visitors and adequate visiting times featured among the criticisms. Could not mothers be allowed to handle their newborn babies more often before discharge?[205]

Hospital development

With limited materials and a strained economy the government's post-war priorities were housing and education. However, as money and materials permitted, thoughts turned to hospital building. Hospital surveys, such as the one for Sheffield with which George Godber was associated, had outlined a development policy. Sites should be large enough to allow for expansion and the first new buildings on a site must be placed in a way that did not prevent this. Plans should be examined and approved by a central authority, informed by clinicians, matrons and administrators experienced in hospital work.[206] In 1949 the Nuffield Provincial Hospitals Trust, with the co-operation of the University of Bristol, sponsored an investigation into the design of acute hospitals and established a team, led by Richard Llewelyn Davies, that included architects, statisticians, doctors and nurses. Its report, published in 1955 as *Studies in the functions and design of hospitals*, laid the foundation of future hospital design in the UK.[207] An attempt was made to combine experience and new thinking, and to take advantage of good practice and new designs world-wide. The study examined the requirement for hospital accommodation, using information from surveys in the Northampton and Norwich hospital groups to estimate the demand from the surrounding area. It looked at the physical environment, heating, lighting, ventilation, the control of noise and fire precautions and it also covered the detailed design of individual departments. Throughout the study, architectural proposals were put firmly in the context of clinical policies and how staff worked.

Little new hospital construction was possible until 1955. Even then there was not enough money for whole new hospitals, only for individual departments, for example outpatients, and the replacement of antiquated plant in laundries and boiler rooms. The Ministry issued a bulletin on the most urgent problem, operating theatre suites, of which 700 were built in the first decade. Other building guidance followed. Teaching hospitals were now a national responsibility and perhaps a disproportionate amount of money was spent on them, particularly in London. It was necessary to decide how costs should be divided between the NHS and the universities. Most of the cost inevitably fell on the board of governors, but the areas used for teaching (e.g. seminar rooms) were a university responsibility. As to research, the NHS provided facilities for research on patients being investigated or treated, but other facilities such as animal houses and research laboratories were a matter for the university.

Hospital management

While the teaching hospitals had retained their boards of governors and their traditional organisation, other hospitals had been grouped functionally under HMCs. The smaller voluntary hospitals, and municipal hospitals whose system of management owed little to the voluntary tradition, now had to work together. For example, Salford Royal Hospital, small but proud of its past, was now coupled with Hope, the municipal hospital, three times its size, part Victorian buildings and part pre-war modernisation, and an excellent hospital in its own right. In the voluntary hospitals it had been traditional for there to be a partnership between the governing body, the house governor, the matron and the chairman of the medical committee representing the visiting staff. The municipal hospitals, however, had enjoyed little local autonomy. The medical superintendent was in charge, the matron and lay staff reported to him, and he to the MOH. The two types of hospital had to adjust to the new situation.

Bradbeer

The Bradbeer Committee was appointed to examine the situation for the Central Health Services Council in 1950.[208] Bradbeer reported in 1954 that each hospital was a corporate body with a morale of its own that made for efficiency. The report commended the locally based partnership of medicine, nursing and administration that had characterised the voluntaries. Each hospital should have a medical staff committee with a consultant working part-time on administrative matters. At HMC or 'group' level there should be a single administrative officer to whom the governing body could look for the co-ordination of all activities; he (or she) would not be a doctor and there should be a move away from medical superintendent posts. As chief executive officer most business should be submitted through him to the management committee. After Bradbeer, the group secretary became more powerful and more distant from the clinicians and the matrons.

Hospital information systems

Changes in hospital staffing and activity

	1949	1950	1951	1952	1953
Inpatient cases	2.9 million	3.1 million	3.3 million	3.4 million	3.5 million
Outpatients	6.1 million	6.2 million	6.3 million	6.4 million	6.7 million
Medical and dental staff[a]	8,954	9,650	10,237	10,581	10,741
Nurses and midwives[a]	125,752	132,408	136,210	140,964	144,558
Waiting lists[b]	492,000	524,000	496,000	490,000	514,000
Bed turnover[c]	9.5/year	10.1/year	10.7/year	11.2/year	11.6/year

a Whole-time; part-time excluded.
b Includes mental illness and mental handicap.
c All specialties except mental illness and mental deficiency.

Source: On the state of the public health; annual reports of the CMO

Information about the hospitals' clinical services was hard to find and would clearly be needed. From 1949 an annual return was required of all hospitals, showing the number of staffed beds, the number in use, their daily occupancy, the number of patients treated, and the waiting list for admissions on the last day of each year. However, this return was not available until it was months out of date and was not a tool for effective management. Shortly before the NHS began the Ministry's CMO, Wilson Jameson, asked George Godber to look at the problem and a team was assembled chaired by Sir

Ernest Rock Carling, including Austin Bradford Hill, Alan Moncrieff, Francis Avery Jones and Percy Stocks (a statistician from the General Register Office). A front-sheet was designed, simple enough for even the least organised hospital. It recorded key information: name, diagnosis and length of stay. In 1949 the Ministry invited volunteer hospitals to use this sheet and supply a 10 per cent sample of *patient-based* data for analysis, the Hospital In-patient Enquiry (HIPE). A step in the right direction, HIPE relied on medical record officers choosing a random sample of case notes and not, for their convenience, the shortest ones. The scheme became compulsory in 1957 and was run centrally by the General Register Office.[209] Each year the number of beds available rose slightly and the number of cases treated increased by about 100,000, largely from more effective use of beds and shorter lengths of stay. There was little impact on waiting lists, which remained stuck around half a million and were worst in general surgery, gynaecology and ENT. For tuberculosis new methods of treatment, shorter lengths of stay and the use of isolation beds to clear the backlog of patients all but eliminated waiting lists and made resources available for other types of work. Better use was made of existing facilities but the effect of better planning was absorbed in previously unmet needs. Obstetricians were arguing for hospital delivery and mothers were responding. The performance of hospitals differed. Non-teaching hospitals generally had shorter lengths of stay than teaching hospitals. London teaching hospitals on average kept patients longer than those in the provinces, and in extreme cases there were threefold differences.

London

During the blitz the teaching hospitals had been forced to leave London. Some in the Ministry pensively hoped that not all would return, for post-war housing policy was to rebuild homes on the periphery, often in the new towns, and to move the population outwards. All, however, came back. The Goodenough Report (in 1944) and the Hospital Survey for London (in 1945) had argued that three teaching hospitals should move from central London; St George's, Charing Cross and the Royal Free. Bevan wanted the war-damaged St Thomas' to move to Tooting but he was persuaded to change his mind. In 1949 George Godber took him to St George's to persuade that hospital to move to Tooting where general hospital facilities were needed. To help the selection of building schemes and discussions with London University, a new survey of the hospitals was launched in 1955. Four Ministry officials visited all London's hospitals to see what changes might be needed because of the substantial movement of population outwards that was now taking place.[210] They found that hospital development in the new areas had been slow and irregular, that some central hospitals such as St Mary's still served large local populations, but others such as the Middlesex and St Bartholomew's had falling local catchments. Lacking local facilities, the growing peripheral populations were increasingly dependent on central hospitals, so it became policy to develop a ring of district general hospitals in outer London. Teaching hospitals were at greater risk of losing their patients. Yet the University of London believed that the London medical schools, and therefore their matching hospitals, should be as close to the university precinct as possible and opposed plans for relocation. Charing Cross, which had hoped to move to the new hospital being built at Northwick Park, had to remain more centrally, and the Northwick Park site became available to the MRC.[211]

Hospital farms

An unusual activity for a health service, left over from pre-war days, was hospital farming. It had developed mainly in conjunction with mental illness and mental handicap hospitals. The Ministry found that 190 hospitals in England and Wales were farming 40,000 acres without saying much about it. There were 3,800 acres of market garden and 4,000 acres of woodland. There were 7,000 cows and heifers, 25,000 pigs, 5,000 sheep and about 63,600 poultry.[212] Farming as a whole was losing money and there was a tendency to buy extra land to make the farms more economic. The Ministry felt that farming was being developed for its own sake, and included the maintenance of pedigree herds. In 1954 it was pointed out to the NHS that the Minister had no authority to run farms unless they were an essential part of a hospital; were the activities justified in each case? Regional boards set up small committees, and Sir George Godber told the story of rows about the future of a piggery in Kent. When it had reached a conclusion, the committee adjourned to view the pigs – which had all mysteriously disappeared as part of the hospital diet.

Medical education and staffing

Medical education

Medicine was one of the few degrees with a national control on student intake. From 1945 onwards between 2,500 and 2,700 students were admitted annually and the medical profession was concerned that there might be too many doctors.[213] In 1950 the BMJ said it was reasonable to accept the current size of the profession as satisfactory and not to expand it further. It was foolish to spend six years training someone who would then be given routine work that could be done better by a clerk or an auxiliary after six months' instruction. By 1954 numbers had risen by more than a third since 1939. The BMJ pointed again to the risk of overcrowding the medical profession. It was doubtful if the country ought to be paying for the training of so many students; perhaps medical schools should reduce their intakes.[214] One problem was medical immigration; hospital returns did not show the origin of junior staff, and it was not appreciated how many came from Commonwealth countries. More broadly, ensuring enough bright young people in the other professions, teaching, science and engineering was also important. In February 1955 a committee under the chairmanship of Henry Willink was appointed to estimate the number of doctors likely to be required in the long term.[215] It included the great and the good, people such as Lord Cohen, Professor Sir Geoffrey Jefferson and Sir John Charles. Two points of view were put to the committee: first that an adequately staffed, comprehensive and rapidly expanding service needed more doctors; second that too many doctors were already being trained for the positions likely to be available. Even before the recommendations were published some medical schools cut their entries because they had been swamped with ex-servicemen taking medicine, as well as the normal intake of 18- to 20-year-olds and sometimes substantial numbers of students from overseas. The committee, having reviewed each branch of the profession, concluded that there was indeed a risk of overproduction. Because it took at least five years to train a doctor, the numbers in the pipeline were already determined but from 1961 to 1975 a reduced student intake would put the numbers back in balance. After that, expansion would again be needed. The committee arrived at the wrong answer, largely because of a lack of appreciation of the numbers emigrating and immigrating. Willink's name became a byword for disastrous planning.

Women played only a small part in the medical staffing of the health service but their numbers were rising. Because of the recommendation of the Goodenough Committee that medical school funding should be dependent on a policy of co-education, this became the norm. In 1948/9 there were 2,931 women medical students compared with 10,281 men. In London, at University College Hospital and King's College Hospital the ratio was 1 to 5. The nine other schools remained the stronghold of the male. Three 'lagging behind in gallantry' were Guy's, the London and the Westminster, where less than 5 per cent were women.

The aim of medical education had been to produce 'a safe doctor'. On passing finals a student could in theory practice immediately without further supervision. The RCP, in evidence to the General Medical Council, said that it was no longer possible to give a full training in all branches of medicine before qualification and the attempt to do so should be abandoned.[216] From 1 January 1953 full registration for unsupervised practice was not granted without proof of post-qualification experience. Newly qualified doctors had to work in a resident medical capacity at an approved hospital, institution or health centre, for 12 months. Usually this meant six months as house physician and six as house surgeon. At the end of a year they could in theory do anything, although junior hospital doctors continued under supervision, and if entering general practice it would usually be as an assistant.

The specialists of the future were educated in the environment in which they would be working. That was not so for general practice, because undergraduate and postgraduate education was hospital-based. Marshall Marinker called it a colonial epoch with journals carrying good news from the hospital to the GP.[217] However, the BMA under the chairmanship of Henry Cohen, reviewing medical training in 1948, considered that there might be a GP component of undergraduate training, that GPs might be on the teaching staff and that students might visit practices.[218] In 1950 a second committee recommended that future GPs should have a year of supervised practice, though nothing was said about the quality of the trainer.[219] The Goodenough Report had stressed postgraduate education. Sir Francis Fraser, formerly Professor of Medicine at St Bartholomew's and during the war Director General of the Emergency Medical Service, was appointed to develop postgraduate medical education in London. Failing in his ambition to establish a postgraduate teaching hospital in Bloomsbury, he welded the postgraduate institutes into a single school of the university, the British Postgraduate Medical Federation. His experience of wartime organisation had led him to the idea of regional postgraduate education long before the introduction of the NHS.[220]

Hospital medical staffing

From the outset there was a significant difference in the approach to manpower planning for GPs and for consultants. GPs were independent contractors appointing their own successors and colleagues. There were few controls other than a prohibition on entering over-doctored areas. It was largely up to the GPs to decide whether they wanted, or could afford, to expand their practices by accepting more patients or taking on a partner. Government wanted an adequate number of reasonably trained GPs rationally distributed and was not too concerned about the details.

It was different for consultants, who had chosen to be employees. A career structure based loosely on the pre-war hierarchy of juniors in the teaching hospitals was put in place (consultant, senior registrar, registrar, senior house officer and house officer). Pay of consultants and juniors was based on the reports from the Spens Committee, of which Lord Moran was a member. Key recommendations were that there should be equality of remuneration between different branches of specialty practice, and equality of status between different hospitals.[221] If those in prestigious fields were to earn more than others, and the pay was to be greatest in teaching hospitals, there would be no hope of providing a full service throughout the country. Spens recommended that there should be distinction awards allocated by a predominantly professional body, to provide an adequate reward for those of more than ordinary ability. Specialists who undertook teaching responsibilities should also have a claim to higher pay. The Spens reports established a basic grade, equal in all specialties and places, but it looked more equal than it was. Merit awards were slanted towards general medicine and general surgery, the regional specialties and academia.

Permanent consultant posts were not established immediately; in the first year each region was required to set up a review committee with two outside assessors from the Royal Colleges to grade hospital staff. They had to decide how much time should be spent in each hospital, and which individuals should be regarded as consultants. Some, though able to make a valuable contribution to the NHS, were considered below this standard. Many of these were in the tuberculosis service or psychiatry; 2,000 senior hospital medical officer (SHMO) posts were established for them, and they were offered the chance of a later review. Some GPs who had worked extensively in hospital were graded as consultants. Many who had previously held staff appointments turned wholly to general practice or found that specialists had been brought in to take over from them. Over two years the move towards specialism, which had been taking place slowly throughout the century, was completed. The availability of health service finance for consultant appointments accelerated the process of professional evolution and the profession was now divided clearly into consultants and GPs.[222]

In 1948 there were about 5,000 consultants. Establishments could not be brought immediately to the level set out in the Memorandum on the *Development of consultant services.*[223] It took a long time to train specialists and there were severe shortages in pathology, psychiatry, radiology, anaesthetics and paediatrics. Some regions, for example Newcastle, North West Metropolitan and Oxford, moved ahead of others, getting staff while money was still available.[224] Many senior registrar posts were established, particularly in general medicine and surgery, often when the real need was for more consultants. Early statistics suggested that there were twice as many senior registrars as were likely to find consultant posts. In 1950/1 regions were required to appoint small committees of senior or recently retired specialists to give their views about specialist staffing. Some of their estimates were clearly too high and there were such bizarre differences between regions that making the findings of the review public was quite impossible.[225] The Treasury took fright at staff costs and the teams were quietly stood down. A central Advisory Committee on Consultant Establishments was established, chaired by George Godber, which included the JCC and professional advisers. It worked constructively, examining all applications for consultant posts, channelling them to the regions in greatest need, and trying to reduce senior registrars in overcrowded specialties such as general medicine and general surgery, and increase those in anaesthesia, psychiatry and pathology. Consultant numbers slowly increased by about 200 a year but regions did not always get what they wanted. In the early 1950s the South West Metropolitan RHB wanted to improve psychiatric services in the cluster of hospitals near Epsom. It applied for 20 psychiatrists in a single year, equivalent to the entire UK training programme. Sometimes those in general specialties objected to the appointment of colleagues who might, as in dermatology, relieve them of an interesting facet of their work.

The position of young doctors was given less attention. From 1952 controls were imposed on the senior registrar grade. There were 2,800 senior registrars in post although the career structure required only 1,700, and consultants were being appointed at 38–40 years of age, instead of at 32–35. The Ministry helpfully pointed to the vacancies in His Majesty's Forces and the Colonial Medical Service.[226] When the growth in numbers of senior registrars was stopped the registrar grade grew unchecked. Registrars had not committed themselves to particular specialties, and the grade was often used to help staffing problems. This mistake had far-reaching effects for which the health service is still paying.[227] Some registrars were prepared to pursue a slim chance of ultimate appointment as a consultant rather than enter general practice.[228] The position was only made worse by attempts to restrain growth of the consultant grade as an economy measure.[229]

Doctors' pay and the Royal Commission

Doctors' pay became a major cause of dispute. Spens had suggested a starting point based on 1939 money, leaving to others the problem of adjusting this to 'present day values'. A differential had been established between the consultants and the GPs; the Danckwerts review had increased the GPs' pay substantially, closing the gap. There was also concern about cost-of-living adjustments. In 1955 the BMA put forward a betterment factor of 24 per cent to cover the period 1951–1954; the Ministry of Health did not agree. The BMJ said

> This one-sided tearing up of a treaty is something which neither the profession nor we believe the public will in any circumstances tolerate. The recent replies from Ministry spokesmen are what we might expect from the Artful Dodger but not from men in a responsible position.[230]

The Times was similarly attacked by the BMJ. The professional classes as a whole were being squeezed out of decent existence. It was not only their economic position that was at stake but also a way of life that, with all its faults, was a powerful force for good in the country.[231] The government's repeated refusal to deal with pay claims on the basis of the Spens recommendations was seen as a breach of faith; possibly a breach of contract which should be tested in the Courts. Ministers in succession found reasons for inaction; Spens could not be afforded, it was inflexible or unrealistic. Perhaps something new should be sought.[232] Lord Moran said Spens could not be thrown on the dust heap merely because it subsequently proved inconvenient. The government, shaken by the size of the Danckwerts award to GPs, finally repudiated Spens in 1957. It denied that it formed the basis of a contract, implying that doctors could challenge this in court if they wished.

In March 1957, Harold Macmillan, the Prime Minister, announced a Royal Commission on medical pay. It would look at medical earnings in comparison with the other professions, rather than upgrading pay in line with inflation. Sir Harry Pilkington, Chairman of Pilkington Ltd and a director of the Bank of England, was the Chairman. *Punch* published a David Langdon cartoon showing a Greek physician expostulating with Hippocrates about his new oath – 'This is all very fine, Hippocrates, but there's nothing here about pay.'[233] The doctors thought that comparisons might be misleading and initially the BMA refused to co-operate. GPs were 24 per cent worse off than they had been in 1951 and were threatening resignation. The consultants wished to take whatever action they could; some were considering emigration. By May, however, there were new assurances. An exchange of letters between the Prime Minister and the profession led the RCP (rapidly and somewhat eagerly), the GPs and the doctors more generally to accept the Commission and to submit evidence. The BMA did so in November 1957.[234]

Nursing

Nurse education and staffing

There was no provision in the NHS Act 1946 for the training of nurses, and no organisation within the service charged with the responsibility for it. Bevan was well aware of this and the Ministry made farsighted proposals after the Wood Report (published in 1947). During lengthy discussions preceding the passage of the Nurses Act 1949 the nursing organisations whittled away ideas such as student status for recruits to nursing, and new training bodies separated from hospital management. They turned down the very reforms which they later struggled for many years to achieve. The most significant development was probably the growth of experimental forms of training.[235]

From the outset there was a grave shortage of nurses, and many hospitals were critically dependent on students. For 600 beds, Aberdeen Royal Infirmary had 93 trained staff and 330 students.[236] The NHS was reckoned to have 48,000 too few nurses, so that on the one hand there was a need to expand the labour force and on the other an awareness of the risks of diluting a skilled staff by unskilled and semi-skilled people.[237] Nurses were afraid there would be direction of labour, as in wartime, and that they would be sent to any hospital where there was a severe staff shortage. Bevan told them there was no power of direction; at most they would be asked – not ordered.[238] State registered nurses were supplemented by state enrolled assistant nurses who undertook a shorter training and in theory were restricted to more limited roles. There was also a shortage of midwives as a result of public demand for more hospital confinements.[239] There was grave concern about the staffing of sanatoria, chronic sick hospitals, mental illness and mental deficiency hospitals. Better methods of treating tuberculosis solved the first problem, and only slowly did a new outlook on the care of the elderly chronic sick together with the grouping of hospitals made their care easier. The problems of the mental illness and handicap hospitals were approached by attempts to select students more carefully to reduce wastage, recognition of the nursing assistant as an essential member of the team, and secondment of student nurses from general hospitals to gain experience in mental illness nursing as part of their training.

It was recognised that, although many student nurses enjoyed their training, until conditions improved in the worst of the hospitals, students and trained nurses would continue to leave. On the other hand, until the country secured more nurses it would be impossible to improve the conditions of which the nurses complained.[240] Nursing absorbed a large and increasing proportion of young women entering the job market. The Minister of Labour, Walter Monckton, said that in 1939 there had been 160,000 nurses in the country, but by 1952 this had risen to 245,000. The number of women reaching the age of 18 had, over the same period, fallen by 100,000. Twenty-one thousand entered the nurse training schools annually, a high proportion of those with appropriate educational qualifications. Although the NHS would have more things to do, there would be no more people to do them. Policies would have to conform to that reality.[241] Nationally, the 'wastage' in the student years was 55 per cent. Before the second world war the General Nursing Council (GNC) had insisted on a minimum education level for recruits to nurse training, either school certificate or the GNC's own test. This requirement was dropped on the outbreak of war and not restored afterwards. The educational level of nurses had fallen, save in large voluntary hospitals that had been able to maintain an entry requirement and still be selective. The official policy of both the GNC and the RCN was to re-introduce a minimum educational level but there were internal divisions and neither the Minister nor the hospital authorities wished to take the risk of making matters worse.[242] St George's, Hyde Park Corner, was among many hospitals wishing, as Wood had suggested, to improve selection and reduce wastage. A wide and varied group of performance tests were given to a group of 126 nurses who were also assessed by three independent judges on a rating scale covering 18 traits of personality and ability.[243] Intellectual capacity and personal relationships were found to be the key characteristics of the good nurse, and it was hoped that selection based on these principles would reduce the number of unsatisfactory candidates accepted for training.

Horder recommendations (1950)[244]

- Bedside work essential for training
- Hospitals not to exploit students
- Part-time working to be encouraged
- Adequate pay for all nursing posts; equal pay for equal work
- Nurses should help shape policy

Lord Horder's Nursing Reconstruction Committee (1942–1950) issued its third and final report on economic factors and nurse recruitment.[244] Fifteen thousand new students were needed annually, and, unlike entrants to most professions, nurses gave their services while learning.

Hospitals regarded nurses as cheap labour, and there was no reason now, in a state service, for students to continue to subsidise the NHS at the expense of their own training. Students asked for practical bedside training, and for teaching that related theory to practice.

Something was wrong with nursing; Professor Revans of the Department of Industrial Administration, at Manchester University, was funded by Nuffield to study the profession. His work suggested that nursing was a profession in transition. It had developed at a time when there were more women than jobs. Nursing and domestic service had been seen as God's ways of ensuring that the idle fingers of middle and working class women were not led into wickedness by the Devil. Obedience was paramount and authority was worshipped. As a result hospitals, while attracting a large number of recruits, were careless in their handling and blamed the young women for leaving rather than themselves. Hospitals had widely varying levels of sickness and wastage; both were functions of the hospitals' management. While student nurses had many grouses, the greatest was the fear of not being up to the job. Only the ward sister could give her confidence, and ward sisters had many other problems to cope with. Hospitals must address the problem; the age of authority and abundance of cheap labour was coming to an end.[245]

The GNC revised its own training syllabus to include preventive and social issues as well as curative aspects of nursing. In 1956 the RCN published a statement of nursing policy. It reviewed established principles of the nursing profession in the light of social and economic change and developments in medicine, taking into account the recommendations of Lord Horder's committee. The College looked at both 'horizontal' and 'vertical' issues. Horizontally there was the need to sustain recruitment while maintaining standards of entry by careful selection. Nurses in training should be given the tasks important to learning rather than to the hospital. Nursing teams, under the direction of a state registered nurse, were in the best interests both of the patient and of conserving nursing resources. 'Vertically' the profession should develop its leadership and look to the future, bringing into the profession more trained minds with a broad outlook, perhaps through a university degree course. In future nurses should be involved in health service management, as in the tripartite teams of hospital administrator, physician and matron, and make a nursing contribution to policy, for example on management bodies, the Ministry and the Central Health Services Council. Training for leadership and to develop nursing on a factual and research basis was therefore important.[246] One opportunity was the University of London diploma in nursing, a two-year part-time course for nurses both in hospital and in public health. It covered basic medical sciences, preventive and social medicine, social psychology and modern nursing developments. Many of the profession's high-flyers took the diploma. Was there a place for a higher qualification? If it were to be accorded a place in a university, nursing must demonstrate its own principles and laws; it must be neither lesser medicine nor a phase of social work, but valuable in itself. Academic studies would have to be strictly relevant to the practice of nursing, as medical education was relevant to clinical practice.[247]

The influence of North American nursing

For the next 50 years British nursing was continuously under the influence of developments in North America even though, in the view of Virginia Henderson, an outstanding American professional leader and educator, the relationship of the doctor and the nurse in the USA was not the same as in the UK. American doctors *prescribed* nursing care, but nevertheless might feel threatened by the experienced nurse, there being more friction than in the UK.[248]

Nursing in the USA had a long-standing academic basis, while it was only in 1956 that the first British nursing studies unit was established, in Edinburgh. A course in hospital economics for nurses at Teachers College, Columbia University, New York, had been established in 1899. Under the leadership of Adelade Nutting, a Johns Hopkins graduate and former superintendent of their nursing school, the course grew into a nursing department offering a certificate programme, a bachelor's degree and later a graduate programme. From the beginning the Teachers College programme was under pressure to provide nursing with skilled and well-trained educators and administrators, and by the 1930s it had become a cornerstone of nursing education. Virginia Henderson, later on its staff, pointed out that in the early days of nursing research when doctoral degrees in nursing were not available, nurses obtained degrees in sociology, anthropology or psychology instead and would naturally emphasise these disciplines when they began teaching; hence the dominance of social sciences in the American nurses' curriculum.

Nurses in the USA struggled to achieve autonomy as individual workers and as a profession, against hospital management and the existing culture of nursing itself. The general culture assumed

> that the nurse's enduring authority should come from gender, not science; her place of work was the bedside or hospital, not the laboratory. Hospitals, in turn, demanded that nursing provide them with a workforce, not a research team. Physicians primarily wanted assistants, not colleagues. Working nurses often wanted reasonable hours, not more education, and nursing educators believed in science, but could not agree on its meaning.[249]

American academics tried to redefine and change nursing and nursing education. British nurses often went to work or to attend conferences in the USA to see what was happening. Articles appeared in the *Nursing Times* describing systems in use there, such as team assignment.[250] The Wood Report had proposed a two-year course, and the separation of nursing schools from the hospital administration. The *Nursing Times* reported such an arrangement in Windsor, Ontario, which ran from 1948 to 1952. The school was a university institution and controlled the students' time so that bedside clinical experience could be integrated with the course syllabus. There was no conflict, as there was in hospital schools, between the provision of a service and educational requirements. The students liked the course, liked nursing and continued to nurse. However, in spite of worldwide interest the system was ended, in part because of the opposition of hospital management, the doctors and the nursing profession locally.[251] A similar experiment was funded by Nuffield at the Royal Infirmary, Glasgow. It began in 1956 to test a more educational and less vocational system of training. Students were resident in the school, not the hospital, and took a two-year course to their finals, followed by a year as a member of the hospital staff before registration.[252] St George's ran a similar course.

Nursing practice

Nurses were having to adapt to an ever-changing pattern of patient care. Only a short time previously almost all patients were at some stage in their illness completely helpless. Now the aim was to avoid the need for total care or to diminish its duration as much as possible.[253] Nurses needed to go beyond physical needs and consider the relief of anxiety and pain. Earlier discharge from hospital to the community also altered the pattern of the district nurse's work because continued supervision might be required.[254]

The Nuffield job analysis

After the Wood Report, the Nuffield Provincial Hospitals Trust explored the 'proper task of the nurse' and undertook a job analysis of their work in hospital wards, directed by Mr HA Goddard. Nuffield selected hospitals with nurse training schools, so there were no data on hospitals for the chronic sick, a significant gap because some of nursing's worst problems were in the chronic wards where student nurses were seldom seen.[255] Minute by minute, day and night, the activities of nurses of all grades were tracked. Published in 1953, the report demonstrated that what was happening in the wards was not what people thought. It called for a restatement of nursing theory:[256]

- The special province of the trained nurse was satisfying patients' human needs, not just skilled technical nursing.
- Nursing should be done by trained nurses, not supervised by them.
- Trained nurses should be responsible for the total care of a specific group of patients.
- Undisturbed rest for patients was not possible as the day lasted from 5am to 10pm.
- The time spent by sisters teaching student nurses was negligible.
- The end-result of nurse training seemed to be not nursing but administration.

The trained nurse might still attempt to cover all the tasks concerned with the care of the patient, but in practice she could no longer do everything, and many tasks were undertaken by student nurses and orderlies. Basic nursing took up 60 per cent of the time of a first-year student nurse, but as she became more senior she did less of this and an increasing proportion of 'technical nursing'. The heavy contribution made by student nurses to basic nursing exposed the problem with the recommendation by Wood for 'student status'; if education was to take priority over service demands, who would do the work – more auxiliary help on the wards? Sisters who thought they did much teaching, spent half their time on ward organisation and only five minutes a day with student nurses. There were two possible lines of development: the nurse could become recognised as a technician, or she could insist that the basic and technical aspects of nursing were indivisible. In the USA, the head nurse, graduate nurse, practical nurse and nursing aide were each responsible for a particular aspect of the nursing care of a group of patients. The danger was, however, that both basic and technical functions originated in human need and were hard to divide. An auxiliary making a bed might not notice the worsening condition of a patient that would be immediately apparent to a trained nurse. Ward sisters had a particularly difficult role, responsible at the same time for the care of patients, administration of the ward and training student nurses. The study also showed the inhumanity of a system that gave sick people little time to rest during a 17-hour day. Nuffield established an advisory panel to comment on the results of its enquiry. The panel said that nursing should be done by trained nurses, not merely supervised by them. Basic nursing should not be delegated wholly to an auxiliary grade, although a 'second pair of hands' was desirable. Nursing skills should be conserved by the reallocation of many non-bedside tasks, and wards should be divided into a number of nursing teams, each the direct responsibility of a trained nurse. Goddard, the director of the enquiry, was convinced that staff were not used to best advantage, and that there was, in fact, an adequate number of nurses. When hours were spent moving screens about the wards, or chaperoning doctors or on tasks not requiring their skills, the problem was one of maldistribution.[257] The Nuffield project suggested that nurses themselves owed it to their patients to be more active in research, as were the American nurses.[258]

Job assignment

Sister delegates to the nurses different duties, which each nurse carries out for all patients in the ward.

Team nursing

Nursing personnel are divided into two or three teams, where possible a staff nurse acting as team leader, the teams including an assistant nurse, student or pupil nurses and perhaps a domestic orderly. The staff nurse considers the needs of the patients and delegates duties according to the skills of the individuals.

Case assignment

Each nurse is responsible for the total care of a certain number of patients, conducive to seeing the patient as a whole person and considering all his needs, social, mental, spiritual and physical.

Source: Catherine Hall, RCN General Secretary: *Nursing Times*, May 2, 1958.

An RCN official said that patients were being nursed more and more in bits: student nurses did all the basic and most of the technical nursing, and the qualified nurse forsook the bedside for administration.[259] The House of Lords considered the Nuffield Report and Lord Woolton, speaking for the government, said that what the nurses needed was reorganisation. There could be administrative support and greater use of orderlies.[260] Lord Moran said that while he hoped that administration was not the peak of every nurse's ambition, regrettably it represented promotion and was better paid. Moran argued in favour of 'dilution', although this was controversial. There was already dilution in medicine; nurses did jobs the doctors had done years previously. The Minister, Iain Macleod, asked the Standing Nursing Advisory Committee to study the report and patterns of ward organisation. Experiments, particularly in 'team nursing', were set in hand. There was a five-year trial at St George's, led by the matron, Muriel Powell. Patients were divided into small groups of 9–13 patients, each allotted to a separate team of nurses led by a staff nurse. Team methods were based on the principle that good nursing involved the total care of patients, and student nurses liked it because they could practise total nursing within the team. It was a compromise between job assignment that was cheaper but might be associated with poorer care, and case (patient) assignment that was too expensive.[261] On the whole a team system produced high quality personal and technical nursing, and staff satisfaction. There were, however, problems; team nursing was designed to produce a higher quality but not a greater quantity of nursing care, so it was less adaptable at times of pressure and crisis than job assignment. It was not used at St George's at night. The ward teams sometimes competed with each other, even for equipment they wished to use simultaneously. The American literature suggested that team organisation ensured better supervision of auxiliary nursing staff and was more democratic; British literature stressed the more responsible job for staff nurses, with wider responsibilities. It seemed important to keep teams as small as possible, consistent with adequate trained supervision. Muriel Powell also tried case assignment.[262] Junior student nurses were given two patients and seniors five. Students learned quickly, but the young nurse might identify too much with the patient if he was very ill. Routine duties might be ignored; the ward steriliser might boil dry.

In hospital, trained nurses might provide only 25 per cent of patient care; in the district it was nearer 100 per cent. Local authorities developed training schools for their staff. For example, in Essex the scheme, opened in 1951, provided experience for student nurses, a part II midwifery training school and theoretical training for Queen's (district) nurses. There was a central nurses' home, for many of the district nurses were resident; by 8.30 a.m. a fleet of cars and bicycles were ready to leave the home in all directions, as the district nurses went to work.[263]

Dame Elizabeth Cockayne, Chief Nursing Officer at the Ministry from 1948 to 1958, talked on the eve of her retirement about changes in nursing practice.

> We find more physicians discussing patients' problems with the nursing team and we have seen the nurse–patient relationship change with the progress in medicine. The patient's point of view is given more attention today, indeed the patient is part of the team. We find ourselves doing things with patients, and not just for them as previously, leading them to self-direction and graduated degrees of independence. As a profession we need to become increasingly self-analytical, and to examine what we are doing and why.[264]

The image of the nurse was beginning to matter. The *Nursing Times* was displeased with the BBC for its production of a documentary about student nurse training, *Under her skilled hand*. The script did not reflect the dignity and sincerity of the title. What would have been the impression of parents whose daughters were considering nursing as a career?[265]

Nursing uniform

Nurses' uniforms could always stimulate debate.[266] Some saw them as a proof of the nurses' competence and a reassurance to the patient. They viewed any threat to them as an attack on professional dignity. Others held the nurses' cap to be a relic of religious practice and the long starched apron from the base of her starched collar to her ankles to be a hygienic precaution. Now both had shrunk in size to become more a badge of office than a part of hygiene. Serving no practical purpose, some thought they might be banished. The styling and eminently simple but well-cut dresses of American nurses might be envied. Were not British uniforms old-fashioned, difficult to launder and hide-bound by tradition? asked a student nurse in the *Nursing Times*.[267]

Nursing administration

The Nurses Act 1949 implemented some of the less contentious proposals in the Wood Report. The remit and membership of the GNC was broadened and Area Nurse Training Committees were established. The function of these committees, placed between the GNC and the nursing schools, was vague. At a senior management level, when the RHBs were being established, nursing organisations were asked for nominations as members. The RHBs appointed their own senior staff including nursing advisers, the future regional nursing officers (RNOs).

In the hospitals, the role and the pay of the matrons varied according to the number of beds. Those in the teaching hospitals were secure in their power and their posts, responsible to their boards, and independent of regions. Their main concern was to ensure that the board understood that its wider policies might affect nursing. Matrons ran the schools of nursing as well as being responsible for the running of an efficient nursing service. At The London Hospital the matron looked after not only the nursing school but also the schools for radiographers, physiotherapists, occupational therapists and dieticians. Matrons were responsible for the linen room, laundries, female domestics, catering and other departments, controlling many services affecting the patient's environment. A member of Matron's office staff was often the most senior person resident in the hospital at night and the weekend, taking decisions well outside her purely professional capacity.

In the smaller hospitals, matrons had less authority, for up to a dozen hospitals might be grouped within a hospital management committee. The group secretary could not consult all of them about everything yet each felt herself autonomous and neglected. Far from attending meetings of the HMC, the matrons often did not even see the minutes. How did the HMC get nursing advice? Within the groups, division on functional lines was taking place. Initially the catering officers, supplies officers and domestic supervisors, who were undertaking duties previously carried out by the nurses, remained under matron's authority. Following the Bradbeer Report domestic tasks passed increasingly to lay administrators. Often the matron's precise responsibilities were not laid down in a hospital's standing orders, and they found themselves appointing and dismissing staff on the basis of traditional practice, without any written authority to do so.[268]

Emerging problems

Financial disparities and rising expenditure

The initial allocations to the RHBs were not equitable but the way in which the NHS accounts were presented tended to conceal regional disparities. Expenditure was presented under 'functional' subheads, for example the cost of nursing staff by grade nationally, not by region. Regional allocations, settled each year, were composed of two elements: a static or inherited element to keep the service running at the existing level, and a developmental element to cover new services. From 1951 to 1954 the Acton Society, an organisation concerned with the place of large-scale organisations in society, was funded by Nuffield in 1951 to examine the organisation of hospitals under the NHS. The Acton Society recognised that the Ministry was trying to improve matters, but doubted whether the attempt to 'level' the allocations had gone far enough or had been worked out on a fair basis.[269] The Ministry's policy was to use its discretion over the development element to level up the more needy regions. Over the first decade some slight progress was made. The share of one group of regions (Newcastle, Sheffield, Birmingham, Manchester, Liverpool and Wales) increased from 39.11 per cent to 42.22 per cent. The richest regions, the metropolitan boards, fell from 41.72 per cent to 38.30 per cent, and the remainder were stable (Leeds, East Anglia, Oxford and South Western). The Acton Society thought this reasonable, particularly as little evidence was available on the efficiency and economy of different kinds of hospital, taking adequate account of the nature and the quality of the services provided.

It was a long-standing socialist belief that a state medical service would save money. In 1911 Lawson Dodd wrote[270]

> The economy of organisation, the greatly lessened cost of illness due to the increase in sanitary control, and the immense amount saved in the reduced number of working days lost through illness, would make the health tax seem light, and it would be regarded as a profitable form of insurance.

In the Beveridge Report (1942)[271] the Government Actuary said that the fundamental changes envisaged could result in the costs differing materially from the estimates that had been made. However, the report itself stated that the development of health and rehabilitation services would lead to a reduction in the number of cases requiring them. Beveridge, like Lawson Dodd, looked forward to a service that would diminish disease by prevention and cure, and believed that future developments would reduce the number of cases requiring health service care. Enoch Powell, in 1961, referred to this as a miscalculation of sublime dimensions.[272] He thought that, in theory, it would be possible to put together a package of health services limited to those that would maximise the gross domestic product, concentrating on people who had a substantial period of productive life before them. The weakling, the old and the subnormal would be left to die. Powell considered that such a health service would be scarcely conceivable even in a nightmare dictator state. It would not be a health service at all. It seemed virtually certain that the increasing outlay as medical science progressed would be more and more 'uneconomic'. Progress in medicine consisted not of doing things more cheaply and simply, but in discovering complex and difficult things to do that previously could not be done at all. Medicine was buying life at an ever-increasing marginal cost.

The government had moved into strange territory. A free and universally available service on this scale was highly unusual. The provisional estimates of costs for the first year were based on past hospital accounts, some of which were sketchy in the extreme. They were rapidly exceeded. In 1946 when the NHS Bill went to Parliament the estimate of the total net cost annually was £110 million. At the end of 1947 it was £179 million. At the beginning of 1949 a supplementary estimate of £79 million was added and the figures turned out to be £248 million. The actual cost in 1949/50 was £305 million. The following year it was £384 million. The government became alarmed.

Analysing the difficulties

Dr Ffrangcon Roberts, a radiologist at Addenbrooke's, was an early and perceptive commentator.[273] Early in 1949 he drew attention to the unreliability of the predictions because of three factors:

- They ignored the effect of the ageing population.
- They ignored the intrinsically expansile nature of hospital practice; previous government experience had been of chronic care and general practice, not the activities of the voluntary hospitals where the application of science resulted in expansion with accelerating velocity in every branch of medicine.
- They were based on a false conception of health and disease. 'Positive health' was neither easily nor permanently achieved. The fight against disease was a continual struggle which was ever more difficult, promoting the survival of the unfit. We were cured of simpler and cheaper diseases to fall victim later on to the more complex and expensive.

Roberts saw medicine, like other commodities, as a core of essentials surrounded by inessentials extending to luxury and extravagances. The present rate of expenditure would lead to national ruin.

> The alternative is hardly less comforting. It is that a limit will be set by shortage of personnel and materials. This means that medicine will be rationed and controlled, and there is no reason for supposing that nationalized medicine possesses any moral superiority rendering it immune from the vices which rationing and control invariably bring in their train. Medicine is not above economic law but strictly subject to it.

The NHS accounted for no mean percentage of the national budget, and money was also needed for education, transport, industrial equipment and defence. Efficiency and economy were therefore continuing concerns. Whereas in a service such as education the population was limited to those of school or university age, and the costs of teaching determined by the syllabus, there were no similar constraints on the NHS. Within a year Labour was on the defensive about the rising cost. The Conservatives were 'shocked and alarmed', saying that, although they too had planned a health service, a great bureaucracy was growing up and there was enormous and wasteful extravagance. The Minister had shown himself quite irresponsible in financial matters and heedless of the best interests of patients as well of the medical profession. He should go. Bevan replied that it was hard to know what the Conservatives were complaining about – was it the inaccurate estimates or spending the money at all?[274]

Costs kept rising. The BMJ believed that, ignoring the British capacity for muddling through, the NHS was heading in the direction of bankruptcy.[275] The illusion that they were getting something for nothing led people to seek free supplies of household remedies for which they had previously paid, such as aspirin, laxatives, first-aid dressings and cotton wool. Many were going round with two pairs of spectacles when one would have done. Charges would not offend against the concept of a comprehensive service without financial barriers.

The policy, based upon the decisions of the (wartime) Coalition Government, had been put into execution by a Minister who could not resist the temptation of behaving like a fairy godmother to an impoverished nation. The medical profession had welcomed the service in spite of doubts about the role of the state in the care of the sick . . . Now the honeymoon period was over; the relations between profession and state were strained because of shortage of money; and the NHS would have to undergo successive modifications in the next few years if it was not to fail. Perhaps the public saw the main benefit as not paying for medicine at the time of receiving it – and the public had run riot at the chemist's shop.[276]

In 1950 the Chancellor, Hugh Gaitskell, forced the issue of charges. Labour passed legislation making it possible to charge for drugs, spectacles and dentures, but did not impose them. Bevan resigned in 1951, in part because of his opposition to charges but mainly because he felt that government had failed to distribute the tax burden properly between different social classes, and military expenditure had been spared when social services were not.[277] The BMA argued for hotel charges on admission to hospital in its evidence to the Select Committee of Estimates and, in May 1951, charges for dentures and spectacles were introduced. A ceiling was applied to expenditure on the health service. The Chancellor stated that in 1952 the cost of the service would be kept within the same bounds.[278]

The rising cost of prescribing was soon seen as one of the great problems confronting the NHS.[279] Costs rose about 45 per cent during the first five years of the service. In 1950 the CMO wrote to GPs to say that, while they had the right to prescribe whatever was necessary for an individual, unnecessary expenditure should be avoided, and that there were mechanisms to deal with excessive prescribing.[280] In October 1951 Labour lost the general election and the Conservatives came to power. The following year a prescription charge of one shilling (5p) was introduced. The Ministry began to issue 'Prescribers' notes' to GPs as an educative measure. In 1953 the Joint Committee on Prescribing suggested that preparations that were not in the British Pharmacopoeia, Pharmaceutical Codex or National Formulary, that had not been proved of therapeutic value or that had dangerous side effects should not be prescribable under the NHS. Doctors were asked to check the costs of comparable drugs and review the frequency and quantities prescribed. Medical school deans were asked to teach students and young doctors about the cost of prescribing. The *BMJ* saw this as an attempt to deprive doctors of the responsibility of deciding whether, in a particular case, the benefits outweighed the dangers. These were clinical judgements, which had nothing to do with the economics of prescribing. The dangers of restriction, said the journal, were far greater than the dangers of liberty.[281] By 1956, 228 million prescriptions cost £58 million.

Reviewing the NHS – the Guillebaud Committee

In May 1953, the Conservative government appointed a committee, chaired by Claude Guillebaud, a Cambridge economist, to review the present and prospective cost of the NHS, to suggest whether modifications in organisation might permit effective control and efficiency, and how a rising charge could be avoided.[282] The

Committee's work proceeded at a leisurely pace, which was to the advantage of the NHS because in the meantime it was hard for the Treasury to insist on a major economy programme.

It was a review as fundamental as the Royal Commission on the NHS two decades later.[283] The terms of reference allowed the Committee to go well beyond financial issues and that it proceeded to do. Richard Titmuss, a social scientist who had worked at the MRC Social Medicine unit at the Central Middlesex Hospital before moving to the London School of Economics, and Brian Abel-Smith, his assistant and an economist, provided the Committee with a detailed analysis of the costs.[284] Starting with definition of 'cost' in actual prices and 1948/9 prices, and of 'adequate service' (the best service possible within the limits of resources), Guillebaud collected a wide range of evidence and considered the past, present and future of general practice, hospitals, local authority services and population demographics. The report represented a turning point in political thinking about how much should be spent on health care and how one should measure the expenditure.

Cost of the NHS (England and Wales), net actual and 1948/9 prices (£ millions), and as percentage of gross national product (GNP)

	1948/9	1949/50	1950/1	1951/2	1952/3	1953/4
Actual net cost	327.8	371.6	390.5	402.1	416.9	430.3
GNP	9,349	9,907	10,539	11,560	12,487	13,273
1948/9 prices	327.8	369.8	388.3	374.1	370.6	380.8
Proportion of GNP	3.51%	3.75%	3.71%	3.48%	3.34%	3.24%

Source: Report of the Guillebaud Committee[282]

The increased cost, when adjusted for inflation, was less alarming than had been thought. Indeed, as a proportion of gross national product, costs were actually falling. Analysis showed the effect of higher levels of wages and prices, and the significant increase in staff costs, as establishments had been progressively increased. The figures for 1952/3 had to be adjusted for the Danckwerts award to GPs, which added £24 million to gross costs and included back-pay owing. The cost of the service, per head of the expanding population, had risen from £7.65 to £8.75. The report stated that, contrary to public opinion, the diversion of funds to the NHS had been relatively insignificant. Most of the rise in hospital expenditure had been from inflation although there had been a rise in the volume of goods and services purchased. Most of the rise in local health authority costs was due to inflation. Net expenditure on executive council services fell, partly because of charges made to patients. There had been a rise in the cost of drugs, mainly antibiotics, and more prescriptions were being issued. The ways in which these costs could be controlled was considered but a restricted list was rejected. Hospital boarding charges were rejected.

The Committee was concerned at the low level of capital expenditure, roughly £10 million per year compared with pre-war levels nearer £30 million. There could be no doubt about the inadequacy of hospital structure. The Hospital Surveys had estimated that 45 per cent of hospitals predated 1891 and 21 per cent 1861.[285] A return to the pre-war level of spending was recommended. Guillebaud said that it was difficult to see how more money could usefully be spent on health promotion, and the approach to health centres should continue to be experimental. Noting the division of responsibility for maternity services, the result of history rather than logic, an early review was recommended, which was chaired by the Earl of Cranbrook. The care of the elderly also required more attention.

The report provided no basis for a government attack on NHS expenditure on the ground of financial probity. However, accounting systems were improved and the Ministry maintained a year on year record of the changes in the cost of the NHS. Such figures were published at the end of the Report of the Royal Commission on the NHS (1979) and a more recent table appears in Appendix A, re-worked using the most recent set of figures provided by the Treasury. Guillebaud examined organisational issues such as the integration of the tripartite health service and the relationships of teaching hospitals to regional boards. The transfer of local authority health services to regional boards, or vice versa, was seen not as practical politics and no structural change in the organisation was recommended. The former permanent secretary of the Ministry of Health and a member of the committee, Sir John Maude, entered a note of reservation. He analysed past history and the current concerns that the medical profession had about the tripartite system, and came to the conclusion that

> a serious weakness of the present structure lies in the fact that the NHS is in three parts, is operated by three sets of bodies having no organic connection with each other and is financed by three methods one of which differs radically from the other two . . . some regard it as a major flaw in the scheme, others as no more than a piece of administrative untidiness.

Maude thought it might be expedient at some future date to return to the earlier conception of a unified health service based on local government, but, to enable the transfer of the NHS as a whole, reorganisation of local authority administration and finance would probably be needed.[286]

The first review of the NHS had given it a clean bill of health. The Acton Society Trust agreed that the structure was basically sound.[287] The Minister of Health, Mr Turton, hoped everyone would note with satisfaction, but not with complacency, that the NHS record was one of real achievement, but additional money could not be committed because of the economic situation. So long as there had to be a limit on financial resources available, the Minister would not be able to do at once all the things that needed to be done. The government accepted the committee's conclusion that though there were weaknesses the structure was sound, any fundamental change would be premature, and the need for stability over a period of years was important.[288]

From now on it became impossible for governments to attack the NHS. Disagreements in future would be about means, not ends. However, the medical profession was not unanimous that all was well. The right-wing Fellowship for Freedom in Medicine published proposals for the reform of the NHS, advocating state-subsidised compulsory insurance, covering 90 per cent of the cost for those in a position to pay for it, and a free health service for all others.[289] Free drugs should be limited to life-savers and at least some direct responsibility should be placed on patients for their health. The introduction of token charges would make them aware of the great benefits received.

The health service had many achievements to its credit.[290] The *Lancet* believed that it was one of the biggest improvements in the life of the country since the war. Much had been done to better the conditions of medical care, especially in hospital, thanks to the hard and intelligent work of many people, professional and lay. However, NHS administration might be made more efficient and appropriate.[291] In 1957 the BMA Council established its own Committee of Inquiry into the NHS, a successor to the BMA Medical Planning Commission of 1941/2 that had proposed or supported many concepts subsequently incorporated into the NHS.[292] Doctors had accepted the principle of the service, but not all its features. Increasingly they cast themselves as its defenders, rather than its attackers.

References

1. Bevan Aneurin. A message to the medical profession from the Minister of Health. *Lancet* 1948; 2: 24.
2. Ministry of Health. *On the state of the public health*. Report of the CMO for 1947. London: HMSO, 1949.
3. Parliament. *Social insurance and allied services, para 428*. Report by Sir William Beveridge. London: HMSO, 1942.
4. Godber GE. Medicine and the community. *BMJ* 1965; 2: 666.
5. The masses have joined the middle classes. *The Times* 1948; Jul 5.
6. The Regional Board. *Lancet* 1948; 2: 25–6.
7. Ministry of Health and Department of Health for Scotland. *Report of the interdepartmental committee on medical schools*. London: HMSO, 1944.
8. Parliament. Central Health Services Council. *Report for the period ending December 31 1949*. London: HMSO, 1950.
9. The partnership [leading article]. *Lancet* 1958; 2: 28.
10. Lord Cohen [leading article]. *BMJ* 1963; 2: 1545.
11. Smith T. Thirty-four years at the Elephant: George Godber. *BMJ* 150th anniversary issue, 1982; Jul 5: A30–2.
12. Carpenter M. *Working for health. The history of COHSE*. London: Lawrence & Wishart, 1988.
13. The King's fund [leading article]. *Lancet* 1948; 2: 1023.
14. Fry J. The Keppel Club (1952–74): lessons from the past for the future. *BMJ* 1991; 303: 1596–8.
15. Medicine on television. *Nursing Times* 1958; Dec 19:1487–8.
16. Family doctor [leading article]. *BMJ* 1951; 1: 571–2.
    Slimming by television [leading article]. *BMJ* 1951; 1: 627–8.
17. Amos A. In her own best interests? Women and health education. *Health Education Journal* 1993; 52/3: 140–50.
18. Smith T. Charles Fletcher at 80: happy birthday – and sorry. *BMJ* 1991; 303: 6.
19. Brown E. A good innings! *BMJ* 1983; 287: 1940–2.
20. Asher R. Munchausen's syndrome. *Lancet* 1951; 1: 339–41.
    Asher R. The dangers of going to bed. *BMJ* 1947; 2: 967.
    Asher R. Clinical sense. In: Avery Jones F, editor. *Talking sense. A selection of papers*. London: Pitman Medical, 1972.

21. Early rising after operation [leading article]. *BMJ* 1948; 2: 1026–7.
22. Farquarson EL. Early ambulation. *Lancet* 1955; 2: 517–19.
23. Hill AB. Hugh Clegg: recollections of a great editor. *BMJ* 1990, 301, 752-5.
    Sir Austin Bradford Hill [obituary]. *BMJ* 1991; 302: 1017.
24. Proposed charges for prescriptions [parliamentary notes]. *BMJ* 1949; 2: 1420–2.
25. Gale EF. Perspectives in chemotherapy. *BMJ* 1973; 4: 33–8.
26. Penicillin V [leading article]. *BMJ* 1956; 2: 1355.
27. Bacterial resistance to chemotherapy [leading article]. *BMJ* 1952; 1: 425–6.
28. Garrod LP. The erythromycin group of antibiotics. *BMJ* 1957; 2: 57–63.
29. Staphylococcal infections in hospitals [leading article]. *BMJ* 1959; 1: 218–19.
30. Hench PS, Kendall EC, Slocumb CH, Polley HF. The effect of a hormone of the adrenal cortex and of pituitary adrenocorticotrophic hormone on rheumatoid arthritis. *Proceedings of the staff meetings of the Mayo Clinic* 1949; 24: 181–197.
    Hench PS, Slocumb CH et al. The effects of the adrenal cortical hormone on the acute phase of rheumatic fever. *Proceedings of the staff meetings of the Mayo Clinic* 1949; 24: 277–298.
    A new treatment for rheumatoid arthritis [leading article]. *BMJ* 1949; 1: 812.
31. Medical treatment of hypertension [leading article]. *BMJ* 1952; 1: 587–8.
    Gilchrist AR. Treatment of hypertension. *BMJ* 1956; 2, 1011.
32. Vitamin B12 and pernicious anaemia [leading article]. *BMJ* 1949; 2: 1397.
    Vitamin B12 and pernicious anaemia [leading article]. *Lancet* 1950; 1: 500.
33. Hypoglycaemic sulphonamides [leading article]. *BMJ* 1956; 2: 465.
34. Antihistaminic drugs and the common cold [leading article]. *BMJ* 1950; 2: 448–9.
35. Chlorpromazine [leading article]. *BMJ* 1954; 2: 581–2.
36. West ED, Fernandes da Fonseca A. Controlled trial of meprobamate. *BMJ* 1956; 2: 1206.
    Shadow over the barbiturates [leading article]. *Lancet* 1954; 2: 75–6.
37. Ministry of Health. *On the state of the public health*. Report of the CMO for 1956. London: HMSO, 1957.
38. Sargant W. On chemical tranquillizers. *BMJ* 1956; 1: 939.
39. Bryce-Smith R, O'Brien HD. Fluothane. *BMJ* 1956; 2: 989.
40. Doll R. Recognition of unwanted drug effects. *BMJ* 1969, 2, 69–76.
41. Chloromycetin [leading article]. *BMJ* 1948; 2: 428–9.
    Danger of chloramphenicol [leading article]. *BMJ* 1952; 2: 136–7.
42. X-ray image intensifier. *BMJ* 1954; 2: 1044.
43. Isherwood I. Diagnostic radiology. *International Journal of Radiation Biology* 1987; 51: 855–72.
44. Mould RE. *A century of X-rays and radioactivity in medicine*. Bristol and Philadelphia: Institute of Physics, 1993.
45. Hazards of diagnostic radiology [leading article]. *BMJ* 1957; 2: 632–3.
46. Stewart A, Webb J, Hewitt D. A survey of childhood malignancies. *BMJ* 1958; 1: 1495–1508.
47. Vaccine against poliomyelitis [leading article]. *BMJ* 1955; 1: 1016–17.
48. Smallpox [leading article]. *BMJ* 1951; 1: 288–9.
49. Streptomycin treatment of pulmonary tuberculosis: a Medical Research Council investigation [leading article]. *BMJ* 1948; 2: 769–82.
    The controlled therapeutic trial [leading article]. *BMJ* 1948; 2: 791–2.
    Daniels M, Hill AB. Chemotherapy of pulmonary tuberculosis in young adults. *BMJ* 1952; 1: 1162–8.
50. Treatment of pulmonary tuberculosis [leading article]. *BMJ* 1955; 1: 273–4.
51. Stradling P. The practitioner's part in the anti-tuberculosis scheme. *BMJ* 1948; 2: 832–3.
52. Acton Society Trust. *Hospitals and the state*. No. 4. *Regional hospital boards*. London: Acton Society, 1975.

53. Ministry of Health. *Mortality and morbidity during the London fog of December 1952*. Reports on public health and medical subjects, no. 95. London: HMSO, 1954.

54. Ministry of Health. *On the state of the public health*. Report of the CMO for 1951. London: HMSO, 1952.

55. Ministry of Health. *On the state of the public health*. Report of the CMO for 1952. London: HMSO, 1953.

56. Medullary nailing [leading article]. *Lancet* 1948; 2: 383.

57. Arden G, Walley GJ. Treatment of intertrochanteric fractures of the femur by internal fixation. *BMJ* 1950; 2: 1094–6.

58. Charnley J. Surgery of the hip-joint. Present and future developments. *BMJ* 1960; 1: 821–6.
   Osteoarthritis of the hip [leading article]. *BMJ* 1960; 1: 1260–1.
   Freeman MAR. Current state of total joint replacement. *BMJ* 1976; 2: 1301–4.

59. *Rescue*. The Golden Hour. Channel 4 programme. London: Barraclough Carey Productions, 1996.

60. Lessons from Lewisham. *Nursing Times* 1958; June 6: 649.

61. Lewin W, Kennedy WFC. Motor-cyclists, crash helmets and head injuries. *BMJ* 1956; 1: 1253.

62. Lewin W. Planning for head injuries. *BMJ* 1959; 1: 131–4.

63. Ruscoe Clarke A. Recent advances in haemorrhage and shock. *BMJ* 1957; 2: 721–6.

64. Shillingford J. Cardiology. II. Advances in the control, diagnosis and treatment of cardiovascular disease since 1940. In: Walton J, Beeson PB, Scott RB, editors. *Oxford companion to medicine*. Oxford: Oxford University Press, 1986.

65. Wood P. *Diseases of the heart and circulation*. London: Eyre & Spottiswoode, 1956.

66. Cookson H. Thirty years of cardiology. *BMJ* 1957; 1: 659–62.

67. Smoking and coronary thrombosis [leading article]. *BMJ* 1955; 1: 91–2.

68. Dietary fat and coronary disease [leading article]. *BMJ* 1957; 2: 89.

69. Mobilisation after myocardial infarction [leading article]. *BMJ* 1977; 2: 651.

70. Coronary thrombosis treated with anticoagulant drugs [leading article]. *BMJ* 1949; 1: 579.

71. An external defibrillator [leading article]. *BMJ* 1956; 2: 468.
   A new lease of life [leading article]. *BMJ* 1956; 2: 869.

72. Holmes Sellors Sir Thomas. The genesis of heart surgery. *BMJ* 1967; 1: 385–93.
   Cardiac catheterisation [leading article]. *Lancet* 1950; 1: 863.

73. d'Abreu AL. A decade of cardiac surgery. *BMJ* 1958; 1: 959–62.

74. Treasure T, Hollman A. The surgery of mitral stenosis 1898–1948: why did it take 50 years to establish mitral valvotomy? *Annals of the Royal College of Surgeons of England* 1995; 77: 145–51.
   Treasure T. Surgery for mitral stenosis in Guy's and the Middlesex Hospitals, 1948–1953. *Journal of the Royal Society of Medicine* 1996; 89: 19–22.
   Baker C, Brock RC, Campbell M. Valvulotomy for mitral stenosis. Report of six successful cases. *BMJ* 1950; 1: 1283–93.
   Surgical treatment of mitral stenosis [leading article]. *BMJ* 1950; 1: 1306–7; *BMJ* 1953; 2: 1090–1.

75. Mitral valvotomy [leading article]. *BMJ* 1955; 2: 607–8.
   Baker C, Brock R, Campbell M. Mitral valvotomy. A follow-up of 45 patients for three years. *BMJ* 1955; 2: 989–91.
   Holmes Sellors T. Intracardiac surgery. *BMJ* 1955; 2: 1470–3.

76. Hypothermia [leading article]. *Lancet* 1958; 1: 675–6.

77. The artificial heart [leading article]. *BMJ* 1953; 2: 86.
   Cardiac surgery and the artificial heart [leading article]. *BMJ* 1954; 1: 1310–11.
   Extracorporeal circulation [leading article]. *Lancet* 1958; 1: 1056.

78. Cleland W, Counihan T, Goodwin J, Steiner RE. Coarctation of the aorta. *BMJ* 1956; 2: 379.
79. Carotid insufficiency [leading article]. *BMJ* 1961; 2: 38–40.
80. The artificial kidney [leading article]. *BMJ* 1959; 1: 772–3.
81. Hopkins A, Solomon J. *Review of the minutes of the college committee on neurology.* London: Royal College of Physicians, 1996.
82. Miller H. Neurology in the general hospital. *BMJ* 1959; 1: 477–80.
83. Dimant S, Moxon C, Lewtas N. Cerebral angiography in a neurosurgical service. *BMJ* 1956; 2: 10–16.
84. Boyes Korkis F. Suppurative mastoid surgery; yesterday and today. *Lancet* 1954; 2: 883–4.
85. Plastic surgery of the middle ear [leading article]. *BMJ* 1957; 2: 90–2.
86. Fry J. Are all Ts and As really necessary? *BMJ* 1957; 1:124–9.
87. Detecting lung cancer [leading article]. *BMJ* 1954; 2: 582–3.
88. Supervoltage radiotherapy [leading article]. *BMJ* 1961; 1: 193.
    Mould RF. *A century of X-rays and radiotherapy in medicine.* Bristol and Philadelphia: Institute of Physics, 1993.
89. Farber S, Diamond LK, Mercer RD et al. Temporary remissions in acute leukaemia in children. *New England Journal of Medicine* 1948; 238: 787–93.
    Zubrod CG. Historic milestones in curative chemotherapy. *Seminars in Oncology* 1979; 6: 490–505.
90. Scott RB. Cancer chemotherapy – the first twenty-five years. *BMJ* 1970; 2: 259–65.
    Chemotherapy of malignant disease. *BMJ* 1958; 1, 7.
91. Proctor RN. The anti-tobacco campaign of the Nazis. *BMJ* 1996; 313: 1450–3.
92. Doll R, Hill AB. Smoking and carcinoma of the lung, a preliminary report. *BMJ* 1950; 2: 739–48.
    Wynder EL, Graham EA. Tobacco smoking as a possible etiologic factor in bronchiogenic carcinoma. *Journal of the American Medical Association* 1950; 143: 329–36.
93. Cigarettes and cancer [leading article]. *BMJ* 1950; 2: 767.
94. Doll R, Peto R, Wheatley K et al. Mortality in relation to smoking; 40 years' observations on male British doctors. *BMJ* 1994; 309: 901–11.
95. Smoking and lung cancer [leading article]. *BMJ* 1952; 2: 1299–301.
    Doll R, Hill AB. A study of the aetiology of carcinoma of the lung. *BMJ* 1952; 2: 1270–85.
96. Ministry of Health. *On the state of the public health.* The report of the CMO for 1952. London: HMSO, 1953.
97. Doll R. Bronchial carcinoma, incidence and aetiology. *BMJ* 1953; 2: 521–7 and 585–90.
    Doll R, Hill AB. The mortality of doctors in relation to their smoking habits. *BMJ* 1954; 1: 1451–5.
98. Webster C. *The health services since the war.* London: HMSO, 1988, 233–7.
99. Lung cancer and smoking [leading article]. *BMJ* 1954; 1: 445.
100. King George VI [leading article]. *BMJ* 1952; 1: 366–7.
101. Population Investigation Committee and Royal College of Obstetricians and Gynaecologists. *Maternity in Great Britain.* London: Oxford University Press, 1948.
102. Campbell R, Macfarlane A. *Where to be born?* Oxford: National Perinatal Epidemiology Unit, 1994.
103. Great Britain. *Report of the Ministry of Health for 1 April 1950 to 31 December 1951.* Cmd 8655. London: HMSO, 1952.
104. Allison J. *Delivered at home.* London: Chapman & Hall, 1996.
105. GW Theobald [obituary]. *BMJ* 1977; 1: 1163.
106. Young J. Maternity and the national health service. *BMJ* 1950; 1: 393–6.
    Young J. Maternity and the NHS. *BMJ* 1950; 1: 955.

107. James DW. The general practitioner and the maternity service. *BMJ* 1950; 1: 598–602.
Johnstone RW. Fifty years of midwifery. *BMJ* 1950; 1: 12–16.
Redman TF, Walker SCB. Evolution of hospital and local authority antenatal care under the NHS Act. *BMJ* 1954; 2: 41–2.

108. New York Academy of Medicine. *Maternal mortality in New York City.* New York: Commonwealth Fund, 1933.
Ministry of Health. *Report on confidential enquiries into maternal deaths in England and Wales, 1952—1954.* Ministry of Health reports on public health and medical subjects, no. 97. London: HMSO, 1957.

109. Silverman WA. *Retrolental fibroplasia: a modern parable.* New York: Grune & Stratton, 1980.

110. Retrolental fibroplasia [leading article]. *BMJ* 1952; 1: 698-9; and 1955; 2: 110–11.
MRC. Retrolental fibroplasia in the United Kingdom. *BMJ* 1955; 2: 78–82.

111. Moncrieff A, Walton AM. Visiting children in hospital. *BMJ* 1952; 1: 43–4.

112. Going to hospital with mother. *Nursing Times* 1958; Jun 8: 643.

113. Caffey J. Some traumatic lesions in growing bones other than fractures and dislocations. *British Journal of Radiology* 1957; 30: 225–38.
The battered baby [leading article]. *BMJ* 1966; 1: 601–3.

114. Tovey LAD. Haemolytic disease of the newborn and its prevention. *BMJ* 1990; 300: 313.

115. Warren M. Care of the chronic sick: a case for treating the chronic sick in blocks in a general hospital. *BMJ* 1943; 2: 822–3.
Warren M. Care of the chronic aged sick. *Lancet* 1946; 1: 841–3.

116. No room at the hospital [leading article]. *Lancet* 1948; 2: 977.
Warren M. Activity in advancing years. *BMJ* 1950; 2: 921–4
Cosin LZ. The place of the day hospital in the geriatric unit. *Practitioner* 1954; 172: 552–9.

117. Care of elderly patients [London regional conference]. *BMJ* 1949; 1: 1134–5.
Warren M. Hospital and general practitioner. *BMJ* 1950; 2: 363.

118. Morton W. A geriatric unit in a general hospital. *BMJ* 1952; 2: 715–18.

119. Blair-Fish HM. The best use of the professional nurse. *Nursing Times* 1953; Jun 20: 628–30.

120. The challenge of the elderly [leading article]. *Nursing Times* 1953; Jan 25: 737–8.

121. Boucher CA. *Survey of services available to the chronic sick and elderly, 1954—5.* Ministry of Health Report no. 98. London: HMSO, 1957.

122. Hill Sir Denis. *Psychiatry in medicine: retrospect and prospect.* Rock Carling Fellowship. London: Nuffield Provincial Hospitals Trust, 1969.

123. May AR. Prescribing community care for the mentally ill. *Lancet* 1961; 1: 760–1.

124. Rollin HR. *Festina lente: a psychiatric odyssey.* London: BMJ, 1990.

125. Rollin HR. In my time. Schizophrenia. *BMJ* 1979; 1: 1773–5.

126. Ministry of Health. *On the state of the public health.* Report of the CMO for 1951. London: HMSO, 1953.

127. The unlocked door [leading article]. *Lancet* 1954; 2: 953–4
Freedom in mental hospitals – the end and the means. *Lancet* 1954; 2: 964–7.

128. Carse J, Panton NE, Watt A. A district mental health service. *Lancet* 1958; 1: 39–41.
Kessel N. The district hospital is where the action is. In: Cawley R, McLachlan G, editors. *Policy for action.* London: Nuffield Provincial Hospitals Trust. 1973.

129. Harper J. Out-patient adult psychiatric clinics. *BMJ* 1959; 1: 357–60.
Bennett D. The drive towards the community. In: Berrios GE, Freeman H, editors. *150 years of British psychiatry, 1841–1991.* London: Gaskell, 1991.

130. Ministry of Health. *On the state of the public health.* Report of the CMO for 1953. London: HMSO, 1954.

131. *Report of the committee of inquiry on rehabilitation, training and resettlement of disabled persons.* Cmd 9883. London: HMSO, 1956.

132. The future of community care [leading article]. *Lancet* 1950; 1: 216.

133. Ministry of Health. Nursing and the public health. In: *On the state of the public health*. Annual report of the CMO for 1953. London: HMSO, 1954.

134. Smith S. Review of the psychiatric units associated with general hospitals in the area of the Manchester Regional Hospital Board. *RHB papers*. 1960.

135. Ministry of Health and Department of Health for Scotland. Psychiatry. In: *Report of the inter-departmental committee on medical schools*. (Chairman: Sir William Goodenough.) London: HMSO, 1944, chapter 13.

136. Mental hospitals in the news [leading article]. *BMJ* 1956; 1: 502.

137. Unsworth C. *The politics of mental health legislation*. Oxford: Clarendon Press, 1987.

138. *Royal Commission on the law relating to mental illness and mental deficiency 1954—57*. (Chairman: Rt Hon The Lord Percy of Newcastle.) Cmnd 169. London: HMSO, 1957.

139. Robinson K. The public and mental health. In: Freeman H, Farndale J, editors. *Trends in the mental health services*. Oxford: Pergamon Press, 1963.

140. Ministry of Health. *National Health Service Bill. Summary of the proposed new service*. Cmd 6761. London: HMSO, 1946.

141. The first month [leading article]. *Lancet* 1948; 2: 223–5.
Smaller and better practices [leading article]. *Lancet* 1948; 2: 259–60.

142. Parliament. *Report of the inter-departmental committee on remuneration of general practitioners*. (Chairman: Sir Will Spens.) Cmd 6810. London: HMSO, 1946.

143. The Act in action. 2. The general practitioner. *Lancet* 1948; 2: 823.

144. Ball J. Review of the work of the Medical Practices Committee [internal papers]. 1989.

145. Eckstein H. *The English health service*. Harvard: Harvard University Press, 1958.

146. Ball J. The Medical Practices Committee. Paper reviewing its role and function [internal papers]. 1989.

147. Central Health Services Council. *Report of the committee on general practice within the NHS*. (Chairman: Sir Henry Cohen.) London: HMSO, 1954.

148. Ministry of Health. *The National Health Service: patients' guide*. London: HMSO, 1948.

149. Sweeney B. The referral system. *BMJ* 1994; 309: 1180–1.

150. Fry J. A year of general practice: a study in morbidity. *BMJ* 1952; 2: 249–52.

151. Hopkins P. Referrals in general practice. *BMJ* 1956; 2: 873.

152. Hodgkin K. The radio-telephone in general practice. *Lancet* 1954; 2: 1323.

153. Dickinson KG. Changing face of general practice. *BMJ* 1981; 283: 958–9.

154. Ministry of Health and Department of Health for Scotland. *Report of the inter-departmental committee on the remuneration of general practitioners*. London: HMSO, 1946.
Horder JP, Swift G. The history of vocational training for general practice. *Journal of the Royal College of General Practitioners* 1979; 29: 24–32.

155. *General practice and the training of the general practitioner*. (Chairman Sir Henry Cohen.) The report of a committee of the BMA. London: BMA, 1950.
The training of a GP [leading article]. *BMJ* 1950; 1: 1244–5 and 1251–5.

156. Anthony E. The GP at the crossroads. *BMJ* 1950; 1: 1077–9.

157. The general practitioner in the hospital [leading article]. *BMJ* 1950; 1: 653–4.
MacFeat G. The family doctor in the NHS. *BMJ* 1950; 1: 663–4.

158. Grant ID. Status of the general practitioner, past, present and future. *BMJ* 1961; 2: 1279–82.

159. Mechanism and purpose [leading article]. *Lancet* 1950; 1: 27.

160. McLachlan G. *A history of the Nuffield Provincial Hospitals Trust. 1940—1990*. London: NPHT, 1992.

161. Collings JS. General practice in England today. A reconnaissance. *Lancet* 1950; 1: 555–79 + appendices.

162. The GP at the crossroads [leading article]. *BMJ* 1950; 1: 709–10.
Gilliland IC. The GP at the crossroads. *BMJ* 1950; 1: 955–6.

163. Collings JS. Group practice: existing patterns and future policies. *Lancet* 1953; 2: 31–3.
     Collings JS. Group practice: what needs to be done. *Lancet* 1953; 2: 611–15.
     Collings JS. Basic group practice: how it can be done. *Lancet* 1953; 2: 875–7.
164. Hadfield SJ. A field survey of general practice 1951–2. *BMJ* 1953; 2: 683.
165. General practice today and tomorrow [leading article]. *BMJ* 1953; 2: 717–18.
166. Taylor S. *Good general practice: a report of a survey.* London: Nuffield Provincial Hospitals Trust/Oxford University Press 1954.
167. Good general practice [leading article]. *BMJ* 1954; 1: 746–8.
168. Medical Practitioners' Union. *Evidence to the committee on general practice of the Central Health Services Council.* London: MPU, 1951.
169. Central Health Services Council. *Report of the committee on general practice within the national health service.* (Chairman: Sir Henry Cohen.) London: HMSO, 1954.
     Report on general practice [leading article]. *BMJ* 1954; 2: 34–5.
170. Dopson L. *The changing scene in general practice.* London: Johnson, 1957; and *BMJ* 1956; 1, suppl: 261.
171. Cartwright A, Scott R. The work of a nurse employed in general practice. *BMJ* 1961; 1: 807–13.
172. Irvine D. Quality in general practice. In: McLachlan G, editor. *A question of quality?* London: Nuffield Provincial Hospitals Trust, 1976.
173. Parliament. *Report of the inter-departmental committee on remuneration of general practitioners.* (Chairman: Sir Will Spens.) Cmd 6810. London: HMSO, 1946.
174. Cause for dissatisfaction [leading article]. *BMJ* 1949; 1: 186.
175. Hill BA. The doctor's day and pay. *BMJ* 1950; 2: 1218–19.
176. The British National Health Service. *Conversations with Sir George Godber.* Washington DC: US Department of Health, Education and Welfare, 1976, 10.
177. Demand for early settlement [leading article]. *BMJ* 1950; 2: 93.
178. Ministry of Health. *Report for 1952.* Part I, 37-9. Cmd 8933. London: HMSO, 1953.
179. *The NHS (General Medical and Pharmaceutical) amendment (No 2) Regulations 1953.* SI 1953, No. 505. London: HMSO, 1953.
180. Ministry of Health. *Report for the year 1953.* Cmd 9321, London: HMSO, 1954.
181. Ministry of Health. *Report for the year ended 31 December 1954.* Cmd 9566. London: HMSO, 1955.
182. Hunt J. The foundation of a College. *Journal of the Royal College of General Practitioners* 1973; 23: 5–20.
183. RCGP/Fry J, Hunt J, Pinsent RJFH, editors. *A history of the Royal College of General Practitioners: the first 25 years.* Lancaster: MTP Press, 1983.
     Pereira Gray D, editor. *Forty years on. The story of the first forty years of the Royal College of General Practitioners.* London: Atalink, 1992.
184. Doctors' surgeries [leading article]. *BMJ* 1954; 2: 799–800.
185. Balint M. Training general practitioners in psychotherapy. *BMJ* 1954; 1: 115–20.
186. Balint M. *The doctor, his patient and the illness.* London: Pitman, 1957.
187. RCGP. The teaching of general practice by general practitioners. *BMJ* 1953; 1: 36.
188. RCGP/Fry J, Hunt J, Pinsent RJFH, editors. *A history of the Royal College of General Practitioners: the first 25 years.* Lancaster: MTP Press, 1983.
189. Logan WPD, Cushion AA. *Morbidity statistics from general practice,* vol. 1. Studies on medical and population subjects, no. 14. London: HMSO, 1958.
190. The development of general practice [leading article]. *BMJ* 1962; 2: 463.
191. Ministry of Health. *Report for the year 1952.* Cmd 8933. London: HMSO, 1953.
     Closer contact [leading article]. *BMJ* 1952; 2: 823.
192. Minister of Health on future of general practice. *BMJ* 1954; 1, suppl: 358–9.
193. Hunt JH. The renaissance of general practice. *BMJ* 1957; 1: 1075–82.

194. Powell JE. *Medicine and politics*. London: Pitman Medical, 1966.

195. Godber GE. Medical officers of health and health services. *Community Medicine* 1986; 8(1): 1–14.

196. White R. *The effects of the NHS on the nursing profession: 1948—1961*. London: King's Fund, 1985.

197. An inquiry into health visiting (Jameson Report). In: Watkin B, editor. *Documents on health and social services; 1834 to the present day*. London: Methuen, 1975.

198. EB. Health visiting and general practice. *Nursing Times* 1958; Jan 31: 123–4.
Chalke HD, Fisher M. Health visitor and family doctor, an exercise in liaison. *Lancet* 1957; 2: 685–6.

199. Ministry of Health. *Consultative council on medical and allied services. Interim report on the future provision of medical and allied services*. Cmd 693. (Chairman: Lord Dawson.) London: HMSO, 1920.

200. First LCC health centre. *BMJ* 1949; 1: 191.

201. Parry RH, Sluglett J, Wofinden RC. The William Budd health centre – the first year. *BMJ* 1954; 1: 388–92.

202. JL Burn [obituary]. *BMJ* 1973; 1: 118.

203. McKeown KC. *A tale of two citadels*. Edinburgh: Pentland Press, 1994.

204. Hospital admissions in the new service [leading article]. *Lancet* 1948; 2: 618.
Delayed admission to hospital [leading article]. *BMJ* 1949; 1: 532.

205. Patients' suggestions [annotation]. *Lancet* 1954; 2: 374.

206. Ministry of Health. *Hospital Survey: Sheffield and East Midlands*. (Surveyors: Parsons LG, Clayton Fryers S, Godber GE.) London: HMSO, 1945.

207. Nuffield Provincial Hospitals Trust and the University of Bristol. *Studies in the functions and design of hospitals: report of an investigation*. London: Oxford University Press, 1955.

208. Central Health Services Council. *The internal administration of hospitals* (the Bradbeer Report). London: HMSO, 1954.
Hospital administration [leading article]. *Lancet* 1954; 2: 741.
Internal administration of hospitals. *Lancet* 1954; 2: 747.

209. Rowe RG, Brewer W. *Hospital activity analysis*. London: Butterworths, 1972.

210. Clark GA, Winner AL, Barrett RH, Gregson HR. Hospital survey: a survey of the hospital resources of Greater London: London: Ministry of Health. 1956. Unpublished.

211. Rivett GC. *The development of the London hospital system, 1823—1982*. London: King's Fund, 1986.

212. Ministry of Health. *Report of the Ministry of Health for the year ended 31 December 1954*. Cmd 9566. London: HMSO, 1955.

213. How many doctors? *BMJ* 1950; 2: 506.
The enrolment in medicine. *BMJ* 1953; 2: 490.

214. Too many doctors? [leading article] *BMJ* 1954; 1: 33.

215. Ministry of Health and Department of Health for Scotland. *Report of the committee to consider the future numbers of medical practitioners and the appropriate intake of medical students*. (Chairman: Sir Henry Willink.) London: HMSO, 1957.

216. Women in medicine [leading article]. *BMJ* 1950; 2: 822.

217. Marinker M. Changing patterns in general practice – education. In: Teeling Smith G, editor. *Health, education and general practice*. London: Office of Health Economics, 1985.

218. *Report of the medical curriculum committee of the British Medical Association*. London: Butterworth, 1948.

219. Committee of the British Medical Association. *General practice and the training of the general practitioner*. London: BMA, 1950.

220. Sir Francis Fraser [obituary]. *BMJ* 1964; 2: 950–1.

221. Ministry of Health and Department of Health for Scotland. *Report of the inter-departmental committee on the remuneration of consultants and specialists.* Cmd 7420. (Chairman: W Spens.) London: HMSO, 1948.

222. Godber GE. Medicine and the community. *BMJ* 1965; 2: 666.

223. *The National Health Service. The development of consultant services.* London: HMSO, 1950. (previously issued as RHB(48)1)

224. The British National Health Service. *Conversations with Sir George Godber.* JE Fogarty International Center. Washington DC: US Department of Health, Education and Welfare, 1976, 114.

225. The British National Health Service. *Conversations with Sir George Godber.* JE Fogarty International Center. Washington DC: US Department of Health, Education and Welfare, 1976, 90.

226. Displaced registrars [leading article]. *BMJ* 1950; 2: 1158.

227. Ministry of Health. *On the state of the public health.* Report of the CMO for 1967. London: HMSO, 1968.

228. The registrar's plight [leading article]. *Lancet* 1950; 1: 1157.

229. Godber G. Forty years of the NHS: origins and early development. *BMJ* 1988; 297: 37–43.

230. The artful dodger [leading article]. *BMJ* 1956; 2: 216–17.

231. Keeping up with *The Times* [leading article]. *BMJ* 1956; 2: 406–7.

232. Negotiations continued [leading article]. *BMJ* 1957; 1: 92–3
Meeting the new Minister [leading article]. *BMJ* 1957: 1: 450.

233. Langdon cartoon. Reproduced from *Punch* in *BMJ* 1957; 1: 641.

234. Action and reaction [leading article]. *BMJ* 1957: 1: 508–9.
Royal Commission announced [parliamentary notes]. *BMJ* 1957; 1: 592–3.
What is the case? [leading article] *BMJ* 1957; 1: 690–1.
Withdrawal from the NHS [leading article]. *BMJ* 1957; 1: 692.
The changed picture [leading article]. *BMJ* 1957; 1: 1106–7.
Through the looking glass [leading article]. *BMJ* 1957; 1:507–8.
Evidence to the Royal Commission [leading article]. *BMJ* 1957; 2: 1225–6.

235. White R. The Nurses Act 1949: Draft proposals. *Nursing Times* 1982; Jan 26: 9–11.
The Nurses Act 1949. 2. Service priorities. *Nursing Times* 1982; Feb 3: 13–15.

236. Miss F E Kay. *Nursing Times* 1953; Mar 21: 299.

237. Classifying the 48,000 [leading article]. *Nursing Times* 1948; Nov 20: 843–4.

238. Mr Bevan at the RCN. *Nursing Times* 1948; Jun 18: 426.
Making the service a reality [leading article]. *Nursing Times* 1948; Jun 5: 399–400.

239. Cockayne E. Ten years of nursing in the NHS. *Nursing Times* 1958; Jul 4: 762–3.

240. Lord Crook. Medical notes in parliament. *BMJ* 1948; 2: 962.

241. Nursing in the national economy [leading article]. *Nursing Times* 1953; Mar 28: 309.

242. White R. *The effects of the NHS on the nursing profession: 1948—1961.* London: King's Fund, 1985.

243. Petrie A, Powell M. Personality and nursing – an investigation into selection tests for nurses. *Lancet* 1950; 1: 363–5.

244. *The social and economic conditions of the nurse.* Report of the Nursing Reconstruction Committee of the Royal College of Nursing. (Chairman: Lord Horder.) London: RCN, 1950.

245. Revans RW. Twin myths: abundance and authority. *Nursing Times* 1958; May 16: 562–3.

246. Royal College of Nursing. *Observations and objectives: a statement on nursing policy.* London: RCN, 1956.

247. Carter GB. Collegiate education for nursing. *Nursing Times* 1953; Aug 15: 812–13.

248. Smith JP. *Virginia Henderson – the first ninety years.* Harrow: Scutari Press, 1989.

249. Reverby S. A legitimate relationship: nursing, hospitals and science in the twentieth century. In: Lond DE, Golden J, editors.*The American general hospital.* Ithaca: Cornell University Press, 1989.

250. Ceris Jones C. Conference at Johns Hopkins Hospital, Baltimore. *Nursing Times* 1948; Jan 10: 21–5.

251. Carter GB. Windsor, Ontario, experimental school. *Nursing Times* 1953; Mar 28: 316–18.

252. Morgan WF. Experimental training scheme at the Glasgow Royal Infirmary. *Nursing Times* 1958; Sep 12: 1056–7.

253. Cockayne E. Nursing and the public health. In: Ministry of Health. *The state of the public health.* Report of the CMO for April 1950–December 1951. London: HMSO, 1953, chapter 13.

254. Ministry of Health. *On the state of the public health.* Report of the CMO for 1952. London: HMSO, 1953.

255. Birmingham hospital enquiry. *Nursing Times* 1973; Mar 7: 277.

256. Nuffield Provincial Hospitals Trust. *The work of nurses in hospital wards. The report of a job analysis.* London: NPHT, 1953.

257. Goddard HA. Is manpower used to best advantage? *Nursing Times* 1953; Nov 21: 1184–8.

258. Nursing research [leading article]. *Nursing Times* 1953; Jan 3: 1–2

259. Blair-Fish HM. The best use of the professional nurse. *Nursing Times* 1953; Jan 20: 628–30.

260. In Parliament. The Lords discuss nursing. *Nursing Times* 1953; May 23: 520–1.

261. Jenkinson VM. Group or team nursing. *Nursing Times* 1958; Jan 17: 62–4, and 1958: Jan 24 92.
     Easton S. The staff nurse, her role and achievement. *Nursing Times* 1958; May 16: 571.

262. Powell MB. The nursing team and group or case assignment. *Nursing Times* 1953; Dec 12: 1273.

263. MMW. The task of a district nursing administrator. *Nursing Times* 1953; Jul 11: 697–8

264. Britain's chief nurse [leading article]. *Nursing Times* 1958; May 23: 585.

265. A documentary. *Nursing Times* 1953; Feb 14: 151.

266. Cap and apron. *Nursing Times* 1953; Feb 14: 162.

267. Dickson JL. Uniform and the nurse of today. *Nursing Times* 1958; Jun 27: 741.

268. The matron's position [leading article]. *Nursing Times* 1953; Sep 26: 961.

269. Schuster Sir George. *Hospitals and the state: creative leadership in a state service.* Hospital organisation and administration under the NHS, no. 6. London: Acton Society Trust, 1959.

270. Lawson Dodd F. *A national medical service.* Fabian Tract 160. London: Fabian Society, 1911.

271. Parliament. *Social insurance and allied services.* Report by Sir William Beveridge. Cmd 6404. London: HMSO, 1942, 105 and 162.

272. Powell E. Health and wealth. Lloyd Roberts lecture. *Journal of the Royal Society of Medicine* 1962; 55: 1–6.

273. Roberts F. The cost of the NHS. *BMJ* 1949; 1: 293.

274. Cost of the NHS [parliamentary notes]. *BMJ* 1949; 1: 372–4.

275. A failing policy [leading article]. *BMJ* 1950; 2: 1262–3.

276. Paying for the NHS [leading article]. *BMJ* 1951; 1: 462.
     Health service estimates [leading article]. *BMJ* 1951; 1: 746–7.

277. Foot M. *Aneurin Bevan.* Vol. 2. *1945—1960.* London: Davis-Poynter, 1973.

278. Abel-Smith B, Titmuss RM. *The cost of the national health service in England and Wales.* Cambridge: Cambridge University Press, 1956.

279. Ministry of Health. *Report for 1953.* Cmd 9321. London: HMSO, 1954, 65.

280. Jameson Sir Wilson. Economy in prescribing [letter]. *Lancet* 1950; 1: 188.

281. Economical prescribing [leading article]. *BMJ* 1953; 2: 925–6.

282. Parliament. *Report of the committee of enquiry into the cost of the national health service.* (Chairman: CW Guillebaud.) Cmd 9663. London: HMSO, 1956.

283. Parliament. *Royal Commission on the National Health Service.* (Chairman: Sir Alec Merrison.) Cmnd 7615. London: HMSO, 1979.

284. Abel-Smith B, Titmuss RM. *The cost of the national health service in England and Wales.* Cambridge: Cambridge University Press, 1956.

285. Ministry of Health. *Hospital Surveys* (10 volumes). London: HMSO, 1945.

286. Maude EJ. *Reservation about the structure of the NHS.* Report of the Committee of Enquiry into the cost of the NHS. Cmd 9663. London: HMSO, 1956, 274–86.

287. *Hospitals and the state.* Hospital organisation and administration under the NHS, nos 1–6. London: Acton Society Trust, 1955–59.

288. Ministry of Health. *Report for the year 1955.* Cmd 9857. London: HMSO, 1956.

289. Reform of the NHS [leading article]. *BMJ* 1957; 2: 282–3.

290. Godber GE. Health services, past, present and future. *Lancet* 1958; 2: 1–6.

291. The partnership [leading article]. *Lancet* 1958; 2: 27–30.

292. The first decision. The second decision. [leading articles] *BMJ* 1957; 1: 810–11.

Chapter 2

1958–1967

The renaissance of general practice
and the hospitals

1958–1967

The renaissance of general practice and the hospitals

Chronology: the second decade

Background	Year	NHS events
Boeing 707 in service	1958	Effective treatment of blood pressure Thiazide diuretics 44-hour week introduced for nurses Platt Report on welfare of children in hospital
Election: Conservative majority 100 'You've never had it so good' Morris Mini M1 opened	1959	Nursing Studies Unit (Edinburgh) Cranbrook Report on maternity services Mental Health Act Hinchcliffe on cost of prescribing
Last call-up for National service Noise Abatement Act	1960	Royal Commission on remuneration of NHS doctors and dentists Tranquillisers, Librium RCN admits men for first time
Pay pause First man in space	1961	Ampicillin Oral contraception in family planning clinics SNAC on pattern of the inpatient's day SMAC report on accident services Human Tissue Act Thalidomide disaster Platt – hospital medical staffing
Cuban missile crisis 'Turn on, tune in, drop out'	1962	Hospital Plan RCP *Smoking and health* Committee on Safety of Drugs Smallpox scare Porritt Report Oral polio vaccine
Kennedy assassinated Beatles Profumo/Keeler	1963	First liver transplant SMAC on communication between doctors, nurses and patients

Background	Year	NHS events
Labour government Harold Wilson Prime Minister	1964	RCN report on reform of nursing education
US marines sent into Vietnam	1965	Charter for family doctors Downward trend in birth rate TV advertising ban on tobacco SMAC on standardisation of hospital medical records Royal Commission on medical education and Seebohm Commission appointed
Election: Labour returned Sterling crisis; pay freeze England wins World Cup Aberfan disaster kills 144	1966	Salmon on senior nursing staff structure 70 per cent of babies delivered in hospital Measles vaccine Establishment of cervical cytology service New GP contract Enoch Powell's *New look at medicine and politics*
Torrey Canyon disaster First ATM	1967	Coronary bypass grafts Abortion Act Heart transplantation Health Education Council established Cogwheel on organisation of medical work in hospitals Sans everything General Practice Finance Corporation NHS structure to be examined WHO embarks on eradication of smallpox

Ten years on

The beginning of the second decade of the NHS saw the end of the years of post-war austerity. The NHS was also about to make substantial progress. Public opinion surveys showed that the vast majority wanted the NHS to continue, with or without modification. The *Lancet*, which had initially feared that the NHS would prove inflexible, was pleased this was not so. Having urged government to take tuberculosis more seriously and build to provide more beds, this was not now necessary. In the face of the shocking over-crowding of mental hospitals, more beds seemed to be needed. Now enterprising hospital units were looking at a system in which most patients would go on living at home while under treatment. Within another ten years one might be wondering what to do with the many mental hospitals that were plainly unsuitable for the proper practice of psychiatry. The *Lancet* noted that fresh approaches were affecting the nature of the hospital itself; many more patients would in future visit the hospital instead of living in it. 'Cafeteria medicine' had a real future and it was futile to waste the service of skilled nurses on people who did not in the least require them. GPs should pay close attention to the way in which hospitals were reaching out ever further towards the home. A family doctor should give everyday medical care, but a high level of general practice would not be preserved unless those with faith in it were prepared to translate their faith into works.[1]

Although medical staffing had been improved, hospital laboratories and X-ray departments were lagging behind and were ill-equipped to meet new and complex requirements. There had been neither the money nor the time to deal with the run-down condition of hospitals. The *BMJ* saw much in the NHS that was good, and much that was bad. It was the job of the medical profession, in co-operation with the government, to improve matters. The NHS should not be regarded as something fixed and immutable and the private possession of Mr Bevan.

> The end of the first decade of social revolution finds the profession in no mood for jubilation. The politicians must inwardly regret their enormous errors of calculation. Whatever benefits it has received, the public is beginning uneasily to wonder whether the price has not been too high in this free-for-all scramble for medical attention.[2]

The *BMJ* suggested looking at the systems in other countries and thought that patients might take a more direct financial share in their own welfare, though the Chairman of Council of the British Medical Association (BMA) conceded that from the point of view of the 'consumer' it had been an enormous benefit and success, as anyone taken ill on holiday rapidly discovered.[3]

During the anniversary parliamentary debate Bevan, now Shadow Foreign Secretary, was on his feet. Two concepts underlay the health service. First was the provision of a free comprehensive service, and all the drugs and facilities that would not have been available to the masses under the old system. Second was the redistribution of income by central taxation so that those who had the most paid the most. The Conservatives had opposed this redistribution. He spoke of private practice and pay-beds, concessions that were sometimes seriously abused. For financial reasons, he said, some consultants enabled private patients to jump the waiting list. The Minister, Mr Derek Walker-Smith (the seventh in the first ten years of the NHS), pointed to the successes — health promotion, poliomyelitis vaccination and fluoridation of water; the need to plan health services for the ageing population; the developments in mental health; and the potential for economy in the hospital service by using work study, and organisation and methods studies.[4]

Lord Moran had fought for the consultants' interests. He wrote that the overwhelming majority of them would prefer the current conditions. Bevan's plan had been more liberal than that of Willink, the previous Conservative Minister. Under the Conservatives the doctor would have been a local authority employee. Consultant services had expanded; in the Newcastle region there had been 164 consultants in 1949 and in 1957 there were 409. Hospitals had been upgraded and a third of consultants got merit awards. Moran said that clinical research in the NHS was not starved of money — the problem was shortage of good researchers. Under the NHS academic medicine had grown in prestige and influence. However, someone, sometime, somewhere must call a halt to the soaring expenditure on the NHS. Rebuilding was relatively unimportant, particularly of mental hospitals. The priority was people of first-rate ability to add to knowledge of the mind in health and disease. The Ministry should bid in the open market for the best brains; there must be rewards for a few people at the top comparable with those offered in other callings.[5]

Changes in the hospital service, 1949–1958 (England and Wales)

	1949	1958
Occupied beds (1000s)	398	418
Deaths and discharges (1000s)	2,937	3,983
TB occupied beds (1000s)	26	7
Waiting lists (1000s)	498	443
Outpatients (millions)	6.15	6.97
Mental hospitals:		
Certified patients	119,943	76,665
Voluntary patients	20,160	61,120

Source: Annual Report of the Ministry of Health for 1958

Sir Harry Platt, far more progressive than most of his generation, also supported the service. The unification of hospitals of all types into a single system, the establishment of the region as a planning unit and the more even distribution of specialists were substantial achievements.[6] Problems included the fragmentation of the service into three parts. There was excessive expenditure on drugs when the money could be better spent by upgrading hospitals, building new ones and enabling leading hospitals to keep abreast of medical science, particularly the university hospitals.[7]

The BMA representative meeting in Birmingham established a committee with the Colleges and the medical officers of health (MOsH), to review the NHS in the light of ten years' experience, and to study alternative schemes for a health service.[8] It was called the Porritt Committee after its chairman, a natural choice for such a role. Not since the Medical Planning Commission's interim report of 1942, said the *BMJ*, had a group as representative of all branches of medicine been asked for an opinion on how the nation's health services should be organised. The NHS had come to stay but it must not be allowed to become stale.[9]

On becoming Minister of Health in 1960, Enoch Powell agreed that there were risks of rigidity in a great, but centralised, service. He saw three trends running side by side: the growth of community care and after-care of the sick, relieving the hospital; the development of preventive and remedial measures; and the more intensive and efficient use of hospital accommodation. He wanted fewer beds in newer hospitals. The three separate financial systems for hospitals, local health authorities and general practice were a great weakness. The *BMJ* wished his stay in the Ministry long enough for the provision of effective remedies.[10] When in due course he moved from the Ministry, he was one of the few ministers whose departure was a source of 'deep regret' to the profession.[11]

Changes in society

According to Sir Francis Fraser, a physician, Director of the British Postgraduate Medical Federation and one of the group that produced *The development of specialist services*, changes in society were affecting medical practice.[12] Social barriers were disappearing. There was an increasing number of people seeking help for illnesses in which social or mental conditions were important or dominant. Was this the result of the lack of support from religious beliefs, the mechanisation of industry, the loosening of family and community loyalties, increasing urbanisation and new towns, the boredom of life under the welfare state, and a dependence on newspapers, television and wireless for ethical and moral values and codes of behaviour? Many people seemed unable to adapt to the speed of change in social conditions. The young had been acquiring a new degree of economic and social freedom that affected their personal relations with everyone, including their doctors.

Before the second world war Stephen Taylor had described suburban neurosis, anxiety and depression among people living on estates, which he attributed to boredom, loneliness and a false set of values. The war and the air-raids had done much to build a community spirit and reduce neurotic illness. Now new building, large blocks of flats and relocation in new towns were re-creating suburban neurosis. The incidence of 'nerves' on new estates was double that in more settled areas.[13] A more dramatic problem was the emergence of a drug sub-culture. Flower-power, and 'the iconoclasm of hippiedom and the ill-considered advocacy of people who should know better' were creating an atmosphere not only of drug taking but also of opposition to firm action to control its spread. Designer drugs such as the hallucinogen STP, a powerful and dangerous amphetamine derivative, spread from across the Atlantic.[14]

Medicine and the media

Charles Hill, 'the radio doctor', had been broadcasting on health issues since the early 1940s and the media were telling people more about medicine. Many doctors thought that, although people should know about health promotion, detailed knowledge of disease was not desirable. The BMA's own publication *Family Doctor* trod carefully. It did not carry advertisements for the Family Planning Association. There were 'obviously grave doubts about the wisdom of publishing in a popular health magazine issued by the BMA to the public, and read among others by teenagers and by the immature, an advertisement which might be held to give the green light to contraceptive practices.'[15] There was a row in the BMA when, in 1959, *Family Doctor* ran articles on 'Marrying with a baby on the way' and 'Is chastity outmoded'. The entire stock was ceremonially pulped amid accusations that the BMA was engaging in censorship.[16] The BBC televised a series of five programmes on *The hurt mind*, described by Kenneth Robinson* as perhaps the most significant breakthrough in the mass communication field. Doctors, however, alleged large numbers of patients crowded down to their surgeries to ask for electro-convulsion therapy (ECT). Now a new series was planned, *Your life in their hands*. Charles Fletcher, a physician at the Hammersmith Hospital who presented it, was concerned about the problems of doctor–patient communication. He thought doctors failed to explain adequately the nature of illness and its treatment. The programmes included cardiac surgery, a brain operation and an operation on the liver. This open approach was unpopular with many of his colleagues. The *BMJ* considered that it was demeaning for doctors and nurses to appear as mummers on the stage to entertain the great British public. People's anxiety about their health would be heightened, increasing hypochondria and neurosis. Hopefully the BBC would not televise a death on the table in its presentation of topics that, though familiar to medical men, were full of mystery, fear and foreboding to the ordinary person.[17] A doctor wrote to say that as a result of a programme a patient had correctly guessed that he was suffering from cancer. A ward sister was anxious that patients in her ward receiving deep X-ray therapy would realise what it was for. People had fainted while watching televised operations, sustaining head injuries. Writers to the *Nursing Times* were divided in their views: one said that the programmes had sparked interest in nursing among schoolgirls; a patient wrote how encouraging it was to see the rapid developments in medicine; and a third compared the programmes to bygone Sunday visiting at Bedlam and said the BBC had lost all refinement of feeling and sense of proportion.[18] TV had discovered a new and popular genre.

The lay press relished the attempt by some doctors to keep their own secret garden. William Sargant, medical adviser to *The hurt mind*, said that there were 5,000 suicides each year, many among depressed people for whom help was available. If even a few of them went to the doctor to ask for treatment, was this wrong?[19] The BBC's audience research team found its audiences liked the programmes. The study fell short of the quality the *BMJ* expected. Inference from the population studied, it said, would demand a degree of recklessness that would land most statisticians in *Emergency – Ward 10*. Casting its own scientific standards to the wind, the journal said 'There can be no doubt of the danger to the unstable with a morbid curiosity about blood and bowels, to frail worriers, and to those with serious disease who may receive interpretations different from those given by their own doctors'.[20]

---

*Kenneth Robinson, Minister of Health (1964–1968), son of a GP, protégé of Bevan and a member of a regional hospital board (RHB) with a keen interest in mental illness.

The Ministry received many complaints about the gulf in communication between doctors and their patients. Enoch Powell, then Minister of Health, asked the Standing Medical and Nursing Advisory Committees to advise on what could be done. Lord Cohen reported in 1963 that well-founded criticism was rare, but that poor buildings, crowded facilities and lack of secretarial services did not help.[21] Nevertheless, the doctor, nurse and patient were at the centre of the service and must take responsibility. Outpatients should be treated as individuals and listened to, staff should identify themselves and some might wear badges. Clear information about hospital life should be available. The BMJ thought it a disappointing report, not based on enquiries into the extent of the problem. The difficulties lay in the hurried conditions of hospital practice, and the value of ministerial missives was doubtful. When there were enough hospitals, fully staffed and planned on modern lines, doctors would have the time and space to correct the lapses of behaviour that were inevitable when faulty communications corrupted good manners.

Medical progress

Health promotion and screening

By the 1960s many countries were beginning to realise that they faced new health problems requiring different solutions. Infectious disease was being conquered but demographic trends and the growing proportion of old people were leading to a greater prevalence of chronic disease, and mortality from cancer of the lung and coronary thrombosis was increasing. There was concern about persisting inequalities in health and health care and the emergence of new environmental hazards that urgently required regulation. Smoking was prevalent in all classes but public knowledge about the associated health risks was vague and ill-formed. In 1967 the Health Education Council was established, a successor to the Central Council for Health Education, to co-ordinate planning and organisation of health promotion, paving the way for a more scientific approach, a broader conceptualisation and the first tentative attempts at evaluation.[22]

Screening is the presumptive identification of unrecognised disease or defect by the use of tests or other procedures that can be applied rapidly. Screening tests sort out apparently well people who probably have a disease from those who probably do not. They are not diagnostic; suspicious findings are referred for diagnosis and treatment.[23] Screening may be undertaken for research, to protect the public health as in the investigation of an epidemic, or to attempt to improve the health of individuals. It stands apart from traditional medicine in seeking to detect disease before there are symptoms and medical help is sought. Screening therefore had an ethical dimension, for it could change people's perception of themselves from healthy to sick. Intervening in the lives of those who are at no great risk is unreasonable; one cannot assume that diagnosing a disease earlier will necessarily help without randomised controlled trials to check the effectiveness of earlier diagnosis.[24] Multiple screening programmes evolved in the USA during the 1950s. British medical opinion was divided on whether clinical examination and a battery of laboratory tests and X-rays were worth while. The BMJ came down against them, saying that the lay view of matters medical was usually ill-informed and singularly opinionated.[25] Check-ups carried dangers of missing disease already present, false reassurance or undue alarm about an abnormality best ignored.

The regular examinations in child welfare clinics were one form of screening. Among the ideas being explored were selective examinations and 'at-risk' registers. The discovery that screening babies for an inborn metabolic disease, phenylketonuria, was possible, led the Medical Research Council (MRC) to call a conference in 1960. As a result local health authorities were advised to screen babies between four and six weeks old, a task that fell to health visitors.[26] In many areas screening tests for single diseases were now widely applied, for example accurate hearing tests in school children. By the early 1960s pre-symptomatic identification of a wider range of disease was possible. In Rotherham the local authority health department organised screening for five problems: anaemia, diabetes, chest disease, deafness and cancer of the cervix. For three weeks once a year the department did nothing else. Individuals at the lowest risk flooded in; those at high risk did not come. There were a substantial number of positive findings that were referred to GPs, but the communication between the MOH and the GPs was sometimes poor.[27]

There was a naive belief that if something was diagnosed early one could cure people, and if several tests were combined there was a synergy. Some thought that screening should be carried out by group practices, in health centres or with the agreement of the local GPs in local health authority clinics. Others sensed a premature rush into untried and possibly ineffective procedures. People in the MRC, the Nuffield Provincial Hospitals Trust and the Ministry felt the need for caution. Max Wilson, a senior medical officer at the Ministry of Health, was sent to the USA for several months to study screening there and was the joint author of a key report from the World Health Organization.[28] A subcommittee of the Standing Medical Advisory Committee (SMAC), chaired by Thomas McKeown, Professor of Social Medicine at Birmingham, was established to take a calmer look at the possibilities. Archibald Cochrane, who had been involved in several projects related to screening, was a member.

There were four important requirements before screening should be undertaken

- There should be an effective treatment.
- There should be a recognisable latent or early symptomatic stage.
- There should be a suitable test or examination acceptable to those to whom it was offered.
- The criteria for diagnosing the disease should be agreed.

There was little doubt that the early detection of some diseases such as anaemia, glaucoma and cervical cancer was important. It was necessary to have a way of establishing contact with high-risk groups; antenatal services and infant welfare services enabled contact to be made with some age groups, but for others, for example the elderly and those at risk from cancer in middle life, accessibility was not so easy.

Changes in hospital care

A profound change was taking place in medicine, altering the style and organisation of clinical services. Formerly treatment was often determined on a once-for-all basis, and the consultant could visit daily or even only twice a week.[29] Now treatment was a continuous process that in serious cases might alter from hour to hour, in which laboratory investigations played an important part. Diagnosis had depended on history taking, a precise and carefully taught system of questioning to determine exactly what patients experienced, and the timing and nature of symptoms. Although laboratory tests had been available to confirm and occasionally make a diagnosis, the patient's story was pre-eminent, often more revealing than physical examination. Lord Moran had looked after Winston Churchill throughout the war, during heart attacks and other serious illnesses, with no more complex equipment than a stethoscope. Outpatient care became more common and a smaller proportion of patients needed admission. Gone were the days when the outpatient department was merely the place in which eager doctors found candidates for their beds, or dismissed those who had recently occupied them. Whether the outpatient was given the same thoughtfulness, care, understanding and explanation that inpatients could expect from the nurses was doubtful. The responsibility for the patients' comfort, wrote an outpatient sister who later became an author of renown, lay primarily with the nurse but also with doctors, who should remember that to the patients their time was *not* expendable.[30]

Much depended on an increasing ability to measure bodily structure and functions. The introduction of computers aided the process.[31] Better measurement improved the understanding of the physiological effects of disease and the effect of intervention. Radio-isotope techniques, a byproduct of research at the Atomic Energy Research Establishment at Harwell, led to a wide range of new tests for blood loss and blood formation, and for thyroid disease. A paper dip-stick test for sugar and protein in the urine made a common procedure quicker and more pleasant.[32] Biochemistry laboratories reported workloads increasing by 15 per cent a year. Automation in the laboratory became possible. In histology it aided the preparation of specimens, and in haematology the Coulter counter used changes in conduction as cells passed in single file in a rapidly flowing stream through a narrow orifice. In biochemistry continuous flow analytical methods were incorporated into the AutoAnalyzer.[33] Twenty-five different tests were adapted to run on the AutoAnalyzer and multi-channel equipment was developed. Laboratories began to offer package deals in which several related tests were carried out whenever one of them was requested.[34] Bewildered doctors, having asked for a blood urea, found the report gave the results of eleven other unsolicited tests as well! Doing the lot was cheaper than a single test separately. Sometimes the tests that had *not* been requested were abnormal. That might be a good thing if, for example, a new diabetic patient was identified, but sometimes extra time and effort went into chasing an aberrant result to an unwanted investigation.

The MRC's randomised controlled trials provided a new way of determining the effectiveness of treatment. Archibald Cochrane took up and publicised the idea while working at the Pneumoconiosis Research Unit in Wales, arguing for its immense potential. Cochrane's devotion to this cause, and the later publication of *Effectiveness and efficiency* in 1972, left a lasting mark on health care and the health service.[35]

Specialisation

The establishment of the NHS coincided with growth in highly specialised fields of medicine and surgery. Techniques that during the years of war were being laboriously developed in a very few centres, advanced so far that they were becoming an essential part of a regional hospital service.[36] Specialisation, though of great benefit to patients, was not solely a matter of altruistic doctors seeking an ever-deeper understanding of disease. Christopher Booth has suggested that specialisation had three main roots, the most important being the drive of technology. Modern ENT surgery, diagnostic imaging, interventional radiology and minimal access surgery were based almost entirely on the development of instrumentation, and the division of general pathology into biochemistry, histopathology, haematology and microbiology was partly related to major differences in the supporting technology. Secondly, individual doctors pushed themselves and their expertise out of enlightened self-interest. In the nineteenth century this led to the development of the single specialty hospitals; the same motivation exists to this day. Thirdly, those in minor areas of medicine sometimes mobilised sympathy for themselves and their patients. The higher their profile, the greater was their access to distinction awards.

The need to provide specialised services, and sub-specialisation, drove an increase in the number of consultants from roughly 4,500 in 1948 to 7,000 by 1960. George Godber said that specialisation had probably not yet gone far enough; specialist skills should be more widely distributed than they were. Yet there was a need to avoid the division of the care of patients between a multitude of specialties, and a risk of failed communication between disciplines.[37] The main growth was not in the traditionally glamorous fields, but in anaesthetics, radiology, pathology, psychiatry and, later, geriatrics. There was a shortage of recruits and NHS money was sometimes used to establish university Chairs, improve training and raise status. General medicine and surgery divided into sub-specialties and the officially recognised specialties doubled in number. Cardiology split from general medicine although respiratory medicine remained a part of the work of the general physician. Special investigative techniques in cardiology, respiratory medicine and neurology were far past the experimental stage and were needed in at least one centre in every hospital region. Such techniques were central to the development of intensive treatment units (ITUs), born in the early 1960s. The infectious diseases were diminishing and there were fewer consultants in that specialty; in the future it was likely that there would be infectious disease units attached to district general hospitals. Paediatricians were increasingly concerned with the neonatal period. In 1948 it was considered normal for general physicians to look after the chronic sick and elderly as part of their duties. Now geriatrics was developing and appointments of consultant geriatricians were being made. No longer was a consultant pathologist wise to attempt to handle all four sub-disciplines of haematology, biochemistry, histopathology and bacteriology.

In surgery, operations on the central nervous system, the heart and the lungs were now commonplace and these regional specialties were growing. Rapid advances in cardiac surgery had led to its extension to all the principal thoracic surgical units, previously largely concerned with tuberculosis and bronchiectasis (dilation of the bronchi or bronchioles with accompanying infection). Traumatic and orthopaedic surgery were developing, and urology and paediatric surgery were becoming the province of specialist rather than general surgeons.

Some GPs still hoped for their reintegration into hospital work. Others, such as John Fry of Beckenham, were more realistic.[38] Much health care was outside hospital, and more could be if there were better access to hospital diagnostic facilities and more support were available for the care of patients at home. That was what was needed, and not nationwide schemes to give family doctors beds in hospitals. Hospitals served many more than were within their walls.

The drug treatment of disease

In 1959 Beecham Research Laboratories discovered a method for the large-scale production of the penicillin 'nucleus' and within two years was able to prepare several hundred new synthetic compounds. Three seemed useful. Phenethicillin was acid-resistant and could be given by mouth. Methicillin had to be injected but, being resistant to penicillinase, was effective against penicillin-resistant staphylococcal infections, and helped to control the large hospital outbreaks of infection of the previous decade. Ampicillin had, for a penicillin, the remarkable property of a wide range of effectiveness.[39] Griseofulvin was also discovered in 1959 and was the first antibiotic active against fungi that could be given by mouth. It was discovered by ICI but sold to Glaxo because of apparent side effects. Glaxo found that these were temporary and minimal and that griseofulvin could be used to treat fungus infections whether systemic, of the skin or of finger and toe nails. Griseofulvin seemed to protect new skin and nail cells from infection, so if it was administered long enough new healthy tissue replaced the old areas of infection. The clinical results were so dramatic that, when cases were demonstrated at a dermatologists' conference in the USA, the hotel lines were blocked by doctors phoning their brokers to buy shares. Broad-spectrum antibiotics such as tetracyclines were found to be highly effective in treating acne, a common and sometimes disfiguring disease, although how they worked was uncertain. In 1960 metronidazole (Flagyl) was introduced for the treatment of vaginal discharge caused by *Trichomonas vaginalis*.

In the past the treatment of heart failure had been rest, digitalis and mercury-based diuretics such as mersalyl that was given by injection. This meant hospital treatment or regular visits by the district nurse. The discovery in 1957 of chlorothiazide, the first effective oral diuretic, was probably the most important advance in drug treatment since penicillin.[40] People with heart failure could now live a much more normal life, at home, while under treatment. Other more potent compounds of the same group followed rapidly and in 1965 frusemide was a further improvement.[41] The treatment of high blood pressure improved steadily with the introduction of new drugs. Rauwolfia, acting partly as a tranquilliser, was replaced by the oral diuretics often in combination with ganglion-blocking drugs such as mecamylamine, although these produced constipation, blurred vision and difficulty in urination. Adrenergic-blocking drugs (e.g. guanethidine) had fewer side effects, and early death from severe hypertension was now seldom seen.[42] Angina was shown to be relieved by propranolol, a member of a new family of drugs, the beta-receptor blockers.[43]

Pressurised aerosols were introduced for the treatment of asthma in 1960 and rapidly became popular. If used too often they could be toxic, and patients sometimes over-dosed instead of calling for medical help.[44] A GP who found a young asthmatic dead with an inhaler in her hand did not forget the experience. To the surprise of doctors, deaths from asthma rose. A fivefold increase led to a warning in 1967 about the possible dangers of inhalers. Often those who died had never received corticosteroid treatment that could have been life saving; sometimes, incorrectly, doctors had administered sedatives.

A new drug, indomethacin, for the treatment of arthritis, rheumatism and gout, was released in 1965. Although no panacea it was helpful in the relief of pain, inflammation and stiffness.[45] Immunosuppressive and cytotoxic drugs developed for cancer found uses in dermatology, because their action on rapidly dividing cells could control conditions such as psoriasis, pemphigus and systemic lupus erythematosus.

After small trials of oral contraceptives in 1959, the Family Planning Association undertook two large field trials to assess the use of Conovid and Anovlar. The results were good and the products were approved for clinic use.[46] Lower dose preparations of the oral contraceptives were later introduced. By 1968 roughly a million women were using oral contraception. In the early 1960s an alternative became available, intrauterine contraceptive devices that were shown to be highly effective and comparatively safe.[47]

Drugs for the treatment of diseases of the mind came on the market with increasing frequency. Amphetamines had been available since 1935 and until the late 1950s were considered relatively non-toxic, rarely addictive and without serious ill-effects. It then became clear that many people were taking far more than therapeutic doses and were using subterfuge to obtain them. Side effects including psychosis were observed. Weaning patients off amphetamines and 'purple hearts', an amphetamine–barbiturate mixture, was difficult.[48] An alternative group of drugs, the benzodiazepines, came into use. It included chlordiazepoxide (Librium), diazepam (Valium) and nitrazepam (Mogadon). In the laboratory these drugs calmed aggressive animals; in humans they reduced anxiety though with some tendency to produce addiction. Caution and short-term use were recommended, for they made people sleepy, and the additive effect of alcohol could be dangerous.[49] In 1958–1960 drugs for the treatment of depression became available, first the monoamine oxidase inhibitors and then tricyclic drugs such as amitriptyline and imipramine. The treatment of even fairly severely depressed patients became possible without admission to hospital, but the drugs might cause a flare-up of schizophrenia and could not entirely replace ECT.[50] The difficulty of designing good clinical trials made it hard to determine the best way to use the drugs and some had unexpected side effects. Severe headaches after cheese sandwiches seemed unlikely to be related to monoamine oxidase inhibitors, but this was the case and the chemical interaction responsible was identified. Interaction of drugs was a growing hazard; the thiazide diuretics increased the potency of digitalis if the patient became depleted of potassium, and phenylbutazone increased the response to anticoagulants. There was every reason to reduce the risk by prescribing as few drugs as possible for any single patient.[51]

Better anaesthetic agents made for easier induction of anaesthesia, safer operation and speedier recovery. However, it was now usual to give one drug to produce unconsciousness, another as a pain reliever and a third to relax muscles to make it easier to operate. This cocktail of drugs made the classic signs of the depth of anaesthesia difficult to interpret, if not useless. Cases were reported of patients remaining conscious during surgery if the balance of drugs was wrong. Patients had no way of signalling the fact because muscle relaxants paralysed them, yet they suffered extreme pain and could recall staff conversations during the operation.[52]

Adverse reactions

Old, if cynical, advice to medical students had been to use new drugs while they still worked. That was now a dangerous strategy. Penicillin produced allergic reactions. Tetracyclines, considered to have few side effects other than loosening bowel motions, were found to turn children's teeth yellow. Barbiturates, used as sleeping tablets, proved addictive and many family doctors imposed a voluntary ban on their prescription. Was sufficient advice available from independent clinical pharmacologists to put manufacturers' claims into perspective? The pharmaceutical industry spent a great deal of money, took big risks and occasionally produced products of outstanding value. There were vast improvements and economies in medical care. But within the industry were firms with a high sense of duty and others with a high sense of profit.[53] Were drugs released on the market prematurely?

The thalidomide disaster brought professional anxieties to a head. It was released in Germany in 1956, where it was available over the counter; when it was released in the UK in 1958 it was available only on prescription. It was an excellent drug for inducing sleep and an overdose seldom killed – the patient slept soundly and then woke up. Thalidomide was even promoted as safe around a house where there was an inquisitive infant. Then, with little warning, it was found to produce limb deformities in the unborn child. At a paediatric conference in November 1961 it was reported that there was a possibility that, if taken in pregnancy, thalidomide might have harmful effects on the developing embryo. It was rapidly taken off the market. Defects of the hands, the long bones of the arms and legs, and oesophageal abnormalities were rapidly reported world-wide but the number of cases seen in any one clinic was extremely small. Registers of congenital malformations, kept for research purposes in Birmingham and London, provided clear evidence of an epidemic. Medical records were not always available; some had been destroyed. Sometimes people had taken tablets prescribed for friends and relatives, or tablets left over from a previous illness. The reaction was rapid. Assessment centres were established for the sufferers, voluntary agencies offered help and parents' associations were formed. The total number of cases in Britain who survived long enough to be recorded was about 300, far less than in Germany where the problem had first been reported.[54]

There were issues of principle at stake. Fifty years earlier, Sir William Osler had said that the main distinction between humans and the higher apes was the desire to take medicine. Doctors now had to be wary of their instinct to help by reaching for the prescription pad. No systems existed for the early detection of congenital defects, to ensure that new products were safe and efficacious, or to track adverse drug reactions so that the medical profession could be informed. The call for an independent organisation to examine new drugs, particularly for effects on the fetus, intensified.[55] The SMAC suggested that there was a need to assess new drugs before release, detect adverse effects rapidly and keep doctors informed about the experience of drugs in clinical practice. After consultation the Committee on Safety of Drugs was formed, chaired by Sir Derrick Dunlop.[56] It devised a system of checking new drugs that came into operation from January 1964. Drugs then passed through three stages of assessment: laboratory toxicity trials, clinical trials on humans (such as the MRC trials of the anti-tuberculosis drugs) and 'post-marketing surveillance'.[57]

There was still no system to ensure the identification of a rare effect that might arise after general release of a new drug, perhaps only once in a thousand patients. The Committee decided to rely on voluntary notifications and the 'yellow card' scheme was introduced. An estimate of drug usage was obtained from the central prescription pricing bureau and from trade sources. There were two limitations to the yellow card scheme. First, reporting was incomplete and the degree of incompleteness was unknown and variable. Secondly, it was not possible to determine how many patients had been given a drug, or their age and sex. The incidence of a reported reaction could not be compared with its normal incidence in the sick or those who were healthy. Occasionally adverse reactions in a preparation not of vital importance led to its withdrawal, for example a slow-release form of an influenza vaccine. Sometimes there were 'reactions' which were likely to be coincidental, or which, though probably genuine, were outweighed by the undoubted benefits of the drug. In these cases a warning was issued but the drug was not withdrawn.[58] This group included monoamine oxidase inhibitors, pressurised aerosols for asthma and oral contraceptives.

Radiology and diagnostic imaging

Advances in nuclear medicine, and the tracking of isotopes, depended on technical advance in detectors. Rectilinear scanners were developed in the 1950s and allowed the source of radiation to be located and mapped, line by line. The process was slow; in the mid-1960s a liver scan could take up to an hour and the definition of the pictures was poor. Rectilinear scanners were made obsolete by the development of gamma cameras, the first prototype of which was displayed in Los Angeles in 1958.[59] As the quality of gamma cameras improved, and they were coupled to computer systems, they were used to scan the lung, brain, heart, bones, liver and thyroid, providing new information to improve diagnostic accuracy.

The first alternative to radiation in the production of body images was ultrasound, the off-shoot of wartime sonar. Ultrasonic equipment had been used by industry for some years to detect flaws in metal. Ultrasonic sound waves were propagated as a beam, penetrated body tissues and, because some were reflected, could be used to create images. In the 1950s a number of dubious clinical claims were made for the technique. The development of a clinically workable tool was dominated by a few individuals, such as Ian Donald in Glasgow, and workers in the USA and Sweden. In 1958 Donald published the results of investigating 100 patients, mainly gynaecological and obstetric cases. Ovarian cysts, tumours and fibroids could be seen.[60] Twins were also diagnosed.

Endoscopy

Between 1954 and 1970 three inventions, all introduced by Harold Hopkins from Imperial College, changed the face of endoscopy and paved the way for minimally invasive surgery.[61] For a century endoscopes had been rigid metal tubes and it had only been possible to examine the inside of the oesophagus, rectum and colon, lung or bladder until one came to a bend. In any case it was an uncomfortable procedure and much skill and psychology was needed. That all changed. First came the flexible light guide made up of bundles of glass fibres each coated with glass of a different refractive index along which light of unlimited brightness could be guided into any body cavity. The second advance was Hopkins' revolutionary telescope. Instead of using tiny glasses separated by spaces of air, Hopkins used air lenses separated by rods of glass. Needing no tubular metal to keep the lenses apart, the entire width of the telescope was available for the transmission of light. Furthermore, because the rods could be held steady, it was possible to grind and coat their surfaces to a new order of accuracy and the rod–lens telescopes had the precision of a microscope. The powerfully illuminated images amazed the older generation of endoscopists. The third invention was to wind the glass fibres on a wheel and glue them together at one point, at which they were cut. Except at this point the fibres were enclosed in a loose sheath so they were entirely flexible. Where they were cut the fibres coincided with each other so that an image put in at one end came out at the other in dots, like the image of a newspaper photograph. A new family of flexible fibreoptic endoscopes quickly emerged, making it possible to perform gastroscopy, colonoscopy, bronchoscopy, cystoscopy and laryngoscopy without danger or great discomfort. They were steadily improved, so that comparing newer with older ones was like comparing a jet with a piston engine. Through these instruments it was possible to take biopsies, cut strictures, remove stones, destroy small tumours and stop bleeding with diathermy or laser.

Infectious disease and immunisation

The decade saw the conquest of poliomyelitis and the reduction of cases of diphtheria to a trickle, although small localised outbreaks continued to occur mainly among people who had not been immunised. The burden of the infectious diseases and the need for beds were reduced. The waning of the great killing diseases led to a false sense of security and masked their continuing evolution.[62] Few doctors or nurses were now trained to handle them. There was ignorance and an assumption that most of the problems had been solved. Yet food-borne infection increased. The exotic viral haemorrhagic fevers were recognised for the first time; in 1957 a previously unknown communicable disease was reported from Germany. Twenty-seven workers preparing polio vaccine in Marburg developed headache, fever, rash and haemorrhages after contact with African vervet monkeys. Seven patients died of 'Marburg fever' and no form of treatment seemed effective.

Measles vaccine had been under development for several years and was in use in the USA. After a trial by the MRC, the Joint Committee on Vaccination and Immunisation decided in 1965 not to launch a general vaccination programme but to make the vaccine available to GPs wishing to use it. Measles epidemics were a bane of general practice; every second year there would be dozens of calls to miserable and sick children who needed careful supervision because of chest and ear infections, for which antibiotics were frequently prescribed. Some GPs immediately began to immunise 'their' children, seeing a benefit to patients and a reduction in their work. By 1967 their hunch had been validated by a further MRC trial that also revealed the large number of complications, the cost of the antibiotics prescribed, the 5,000–10,000 hospital admissions annually and the deaths that occurred. Routine vaccination against measles was recommended.

The introduction of the injectable Salk polio vaccine reduced the number of cases and deaths but protection was not complete. In 1959 there were 591 cases of paralytic polio in unvaccinated people, but there were also 40 in people who had received an apparently complete course. The MRC organised a trial of a new live attenuated vaccine developed by Albert Sabin.[63] Theoretically this could be expected to give better protection and it did. In 1962 oral polio vaccine was introduced into the routine immunisation programme. The same year Tom Galloway, MOH of West Sussex, pioneered a new approach to the organisation of immunisation programmes. The local authority computer was programmed to use the information collected by health visitors who called to see newborn infants, to summon them to clinics or to their GP's surgery at the appropriate age.[64] A rapid rise in the immunisation rate was achieved and other local authorities soon adopted the system. West Sussex applied the same technique to cervical cytology and Cheshire to child surveillance.

Smallpox entered the country from time to time; in 1962 there were five small outbreaks of smallpox with 62 indigenous cases introduced by travellers from Pakistan, some of whom had presented false vaccination certificates. There was a rush for vaccination: local authority clinics vaccinated more than 3 million people and there were queues outside GPs' surgeries. It was impossible to reassure people that, outside the areas of infection, the risks were virtually non-existent. The SMAC considered the smallpox vaccination programme and decided that, if there were no basic immunity in the population, control of epidemics might not be easy. It recommended continuation of the routine smallpox vaccination programme.[65]

Deaths in England and Wales from infectious disease

	Tuberculosis	Diphtheria	Whooping cough	Measles	Polio
1948	23,175	156	748	327	241
1957	4,784	4	87	94	226
1958	4,480	8	27	49	154
1959	3,854	0	25	98	87
1960	3,435	5	37	31	46
1961	3,334	10	27	152	79
1962	3,088	2	24	39	45
1963	2,962	2	36	127	38
1964	2,484	0	44	73	29
1965	2,282	0	21	115	19
1966	2,354	5	23	80	22
1967	2,043	0	27	99	15

Source: On the state of the public health – annual reports of the Chief Medical Officer

Tuberculosis remained a major problem although notifications and deaths were steadily getting fewer. Routine Heaf tests at the age of 13 showed the extent to which asymptomatic infection was occurring in the community, and a progressive reduction in the number of positive tests was clear evidence of reduced spread. The effectiveness of treatment, particularly in early cases, was an added reason for identifying patients as rapidly as possible, for treatment quickly reduced their infectivity, breaking the chain of spread. Well-organised domiciliary treatment was practicable, effective and safe for family contacts.[66] As the incidence of tuberculosis fell, mobile miniature radiography units picked up fewer cases of tuberculosis, but cancer of the lung was occasionally diagnosed in this way. Because mobile miniature radiography delivered a large radiation dose, its continued use was questioned. The Public Health Laboratory Service continued to grow, and the introduction of tissue-culture led to an expansion of its work in virology. It studied the development of hospital-acquired infection and of food poisoning, and became increasingly involved in the epidemiology of infectious disease.

Venereal disease

In 1955, coincident with the increase of immigration, figures for gonorrhoea and non-specific urethritis began to rise and by 1962 had passed the 1939 level. Granada Television reported on the growing health hazard, interviewing a man who said he had been infected by a debutante and a prostitute who had placed too much faith in a regular check-up.[67] Three causes were suggested, immigration, homosexuality and to a small extent promiscuity among the young.[68] Syphilis seemed controllable, by penicillin and contact tracing, even though extramarital sexual intercourse was coming to be regarded by many as a normal and permissible activity. However, gonorrhoea was less amenable.[69] In women there were often no symptoms to bring them to the clinic. Just under half the male cases were from the indigenous population, a quarter were men infected abroad and a quarter West Indian men. Most of those from the West Indies were infected in the UK, usually by promiscuous women. Indeed figures from Holloway Prison showed that about a third of the prostitutes in prison were infected. A third of all infections in women were among those between 15 and 20 years of age.[70]

Surgery

Information on the work of the hospital service was now available from the Hospital In-patient Enquiry, a 10 per cent sample of the admissions to all hospitals in England and Wales other than those for mental illness and deficiency. Outpatient attendances and admissions were steadily increasing. The commonest cause of admission up to the age of 5 years was for removal of tonsils and adenoids (Ts and As). From 5 to 14 years appendicitis came second to Ts and As. From 15 to 29 head injury and appendicitis were commonest for men and, excluding midwifery, appendicitis and spontaneous abortion for women. Men between 30 and 70 years of age were admitted mostly for hernia, duodenal ulcer, cancer of the lung and prostate disease. Women suffered from disorders of menstruation and prolapse, and leg fractures in the older age groups.[71]

The length of stay in hospital continued to shorten. The Aberdeen Royal Infirmary, faced in 1960 by lengthy waiting lists, adopted Farquharson's technique and established a special team to treat people with hernia and varicose veins as outpatients. Patients went home a few hours after operation and, although the hospital offered to provide after-care, the GPs were more than willing to take this over. Initial anxieties vanished and, because of the noise, poor facilities and irksome discipline, many patients were pleased to leave hospital rapidly. Waiting lists fell, the cost of treatment was probably lower and the results seemed quite as good.[72] By the end of the decade it was seen that, with proper selection of patients, suitable accommodation and organisation, and good communication with GPs and community services, more patients could be dealt with as outpatients or on a day basis. Some now believed that outpatient surgery and day patient facilities should be part of any modern hospital and that the ratio of operating theatres to beds should be increased. Advice on the design and running of day units was published.

Orthopaedics and trauma

Following the work of Danis and Müller, Swiss orthopaedic surgeons formed a group to study the value of fixation and compression of fractures, and to undertake experimental work. This group, the AO or Arbeitsgemeinschaft für Osteosynthesefragen, began to collaborate with the Swiss precision engineering industry, which produced the components emerging from research. An educational programme was created to teach the techniques, John Charnley being among those attending.

The opening of the M1 motorway in 1959 led to a new style of driving and a new pattern of serious injuries. On urban roads, pedestrians were the main victims. On country roads it was motorcyclists. On the motorways the vast majority were occupants of cars. Injuries, the chief killer between 1 and 35 years of age, were more frequent, more severe, occurred throughout the 24 hours and were widely dispersed geographically. In 1966 Dr Ken Easton, realising that people were dying unnecessarily in serious road accidents because blood loss was not treated and the airway was not secured, started an organisation of GPs who were prepared to offer immediate care. This later became the British Association of Immediate Care Schemes (BASICS). Seat belts were made mandatory in new cars in 1967, and it became an offence for someone to drive with over 80 mg of alcohol per 100 ml of blood.

Surgeons knew how massive blood loss could be and that very large transfusions might be needed. The treatment of serious and multiple injuries required immediate blood replacement, diagnosis, ventilation, suction, blood volume studies, metabolic checks, radiology and surgery. A full team was necessary, available only at special centres. The SMAC set up a group to study accident services, chaired by Sir Harry Platt; the group thought that the accident and emergency units (A & E) should be reduced substantially in number, so that staffing was always adequate.[73] A BMA committee also considered the problem in 1961. It examined experience in Birmingham, Oxford and Sheffield. A three-tier system was proposed, with a central accident unit usually attached to a teaching hospital, other accident units in selected hospitals, and support from peripheral casualty services.[74] There was wide agreement that effective treatment of injuries required experience and good facilities that were well organised. A country-wide accident service organised regionally was now necessary, but such a service never became an agreed NHS policy.[75]

John Charnley, funded by the Manchester RHB, made an unsurpassed contribution by developing the surgical, mechanical and implant techniques of hip replacement. He added two elements to McKee's operation. He concentrated on engineering issues, designing a low-friction arthroplasty using a small metal femoral head articulating with a plastic insert in the acetabulum. His first attempts used stainless steel for the head and Teflon for the pelvic component. The wear rate proved unacceptably high, the joint would fill with fine particles of Teflon debris and the femoral head might wear through the cup. With the engineers at Manchester University, he explored the engineering and lubrication problems and switched to ultra-high molecular weight polyethylene. This low-friction arthroplasty proved successful. His second contribution, in 1962, was the introduction of polymethylmethacrylate cement to distribute the stress from the metal components evenly over the bone. His results steadily improved and he was not a person to seek to make private profit out of his work. An impressive speaker and writer, he had data to back his claims and the best technology then available. As he improved the technique, he set about training others in it. Surgeons turned their attention to the knee. By the early 1960s three different prostheses were in use, all cobalt-chrome hinges attached to stems running into the bone cavities of the tibia and femur, in the lower and upper leg. They were not widely used because the early results were not encouraging and if the operation failed revision was difficult.

Cardiology and cardiac surgery

Disorders of heart rhythm commonly cause death because, when cardiac arrest occurs, oxygen lack rapidly causes brain damage. Prompt restoration of the circulation is necessary: if any attempt was made to restart the heart, the method was to open the chest where the patient lay to massage the heart. Following the development of closed heart defibrillation, external cardiac massage was developed at the Johns Hopkins in Baltimore.[76] Successful resuscitation, though rare, encouraged a more energetic approach to cardiac arrest. With these new techniques of monitoring and resuscitation, coronary care units were developed.[77] In 1963 Toronto General Hospital reported the centralisation of patients in a unit with special provision for early detection and treatment of disorders of heart rhythm and cardiac arrest. The improvement in survival was far from spectacular, but a trend was established.[78] As a result, many of the sickest patients in a hospital were moved to a new facility that required nursing staff with new skills. The knowledge needed by intensive care nurses, and the speed with which they had to take decisions, made frequent staff changes impracticable. The nurses developed the necessary expertise and were often able to guide young doctors in the diagnosis and management of coronary artery disease cardiac arrhythmias. Although deaths from heart attacks occurred soon after the onset of symptoms, the delay before admission was on average nearly 12 hours. In 1966 Pantridge, at the Royal Victoria Hospital Belfast, introduced a mobile intensive-care unit – a specially equipped ambulance – to provide skilled care to people on their way to hospital.[79] Mouth-to-mouth respiration and external cardiac massage began to be taught to the public by the first-aid organisations, with professional approval.[80]

Patients with a slow heart rate from heart-block had a high death rate, a low cardiac output and were unable to meet the demands of exercise or emotion. Electronic developments, and the ability to insert a tube or wire safely into the heart, led to the development of pacemakers. Electrical impulses were used to restore a normal heart rate. The first pacemakers were external and uncomfortable for the patient but in 1960 an implantable unit was developed and from then on pacemakers developed rapidly. Improvements in technique, and the development of 'demand' pacemakers that allowed variable rates of pacing, cut the mortality and enabled increasing numbers of patients to live a near normal life with a greater sense of well-being. Some patients with good heart function could even return to work, and the mortality rate for patients with complete heart-block was greatly reduced.[81]

More effective surgery within the heart became possible with the introduction of heart–lung bypass techniques from the USA. Accurate diagnosis, the surgical skill to correct hidden and undiagnosed abnormalities and good teamwork were the keys to success.[82] Characteristically, a procedure had a high mortality when first introduced, but this fell rapidly as experience was gained. From the patient's point of view there was often a case for delay until techniques improved and risks were lower.[83] It was essential to have a well-trained team that could carry out successful perfusion, not only under ideal conditions but also when things went wrong. The Hammersmith Hospital reported a series of cases in which the heart–lung machine was used in ventricular septal defect. Paul Wood, at the National Heart Hospital, said that 85 per cent of cases of congenital heart disease were now operable. Though the risks of operation on septal defects between the left and right side of the heart were falling, morbidity from complications such as cerebral embolism was substantial. Operations were also developed to replace damaged heart valves that either leaked or were blocked. A ball valve designed in the USA by Starr made possible the replacement of the mitral valve, and later of the aortic valve as well. Initially the mortality rates were up to 20 per cent, and replacing more than one valve increased the mortality.[84] Donald Ross, at the National Heart Hospital, was the doyen of aortic valve grafts, also successfully using the patient's own pulmonary valve to replace the more important aortic valve.

Direct surgical attack on blocked coronary arteries now seemed within reach, but a clear picture of the arteries was required before this was possible. Coronary angiography, injecting contrast medium into each artery, was developed at the Cleveland Clinic and introduced to the UK.[85]

Narrowing of the carotid artery had long been known to be one cause of strokes. Surgical treatment was increasingly used for patients who had transient symptoms suggesting impaired circulation to the brain – difficulty with speech or vision, or transient weakness.[86] In the USA the operation rapidly became popular but a more conservative approach was adopted in the UK and soon proved better.

Renal replacement therapy

The nature of renal disease was changing. Nephritis after streptococcal infection was becoming rare; yet there was no reduction in the numbers developing chronic renal failure. Steroids had completely changed the picture in another kidney disease, nephrosis. There were major advances in the treatment of both acute and chronic renal failure. Intermittent renal dialysis was in use in the USA in the early 1950s, and in Leeds from 1956:[87] the patient's blood was passed through coils immersed in special solutions into which impurities passed, before it was returned to the body. Over the next four years several other units that could treat acute renal failure were established, mainly in teaching hospitals. The chief problem was that clots formed in the veins, which could not be used again. It was technological development that altered the nature of the care available. In 1960 Scribner demonstrated an implantable arterio-venous shunt that could be used repeatedly, and although the shunts were not trouble free there was no longer a temptation to dialyse for a long time to delay the need for the next treatment. The combination of the shunt and better dialysis equipment that required no donor blood to prime it raised the possibility of treating chronic renal failure on a considerable scale. The procedure was on probation in the US from 1960 to 1962, when it was recognised as a considerable advance. Clinical opinion in the UK was divided. Douglas Black, in a *Lancet* editorial in 1965, said that such programmes made exacting demands on skills, time and money, and their claims should be compared with other forms of intensive care. (An outbreak of hepatitis in his unit at the Manchester Royal Infirmary affected eight staff and one died.) Other clinicians and patients were indignant; young people were now being treated and, as a result, were leading an active and productive life; should they be allowed to die?[88] A further technical development largely replaced the Scribner shunt and made repetitive dialysis available to virtually everyone.[89] A surgically created interior arterio-venous fistula between the radial artery and vein was developed by Cimino and Brescia in 1966.

Unfortunately, money and trained staff were limiting factors and it was impossible to offer treatment to all who could benefit from it. Renal medicine was one of the first specialties to face the ethical problems of selection of patients and the economic problems of provision. The Ministry set up an expert group chaired by Professor Sir Max Rosenheim, of University College Hospital, to plan development and arrange the supply of dialysers. Exceptionally, government provided money specifically for renal dialysis, £10 million per annum. Plans were made for 10–20 centres and also for home treatment. Nation-wide only 70 patients were receiving treatment in 1965 but between 1967 and 1971 units opened in each region. Further outbreaks of hepatitis affected those in Leeds and Liverpool, with deaths among patients and staff. Some patients were found to be hepatitis carriers, and cross-infection was all too easy. Antibiotics were no answer. Patient care had to become more hygienic and barriers were needed to prevent the transmission of infection.

Renal transplants were undertaken in the early 1960s in patients who were gravely ill, using unrelated kidneys and attempting to suppress rejection by total body irradiation or drugs that had been effective in animals. There were a few successes. Successful transplantation required good surgical techniques, for example a reliable way to join blood vessels, and growth in knowledge about immunology and tissue rejection. Results improved with the introduction of azathioprine in 1965 and transplantation emerged from the experimental stage.[90] Britain was slow in developing a comprehensive policy for handling renal failure; a transplant service became essential, for without it enormous sums would be spent on dialysis. Yet transplantation was possible only on the basis of a renal dialysis service. Who should be treated and how were decisions to be taken? A serious ethical difficulty faced doctors looking after patients with irreversible renal failure. Some 6,000 died annually, half between the ages of 5 and 55, and both dialysis and renal transplants offered over a 50 per cent chance of surviving a year or more. Was the selection of patients, a life or death decision, best left to the consultant?[91] Most units, faced with the impossibility of treating more than a few of those in need, rejected elderly people and people with diabetes in favour of 'happily married patients with young children, who were reliable, stoic and endowed with common sense'. Some preferred to take patients as they presented if a vacancy on the treatment programme was available.[92]

Experimental transplants of the pancreas, lungs, heart and liver were undertaken in animals. The difficulties were greater than with the kidney, where renal dialysis could maintain the recipient in good health. That was not possible for somebody dying of heart or liver disease. The transplanted organs were also harder to maintain in good condition.[93] Because of the wider use of organ transplantation, the Human Tissues Bill was introduced in 1960 to allow, subject to the consent of relatives, other parts to be removed (e.g. skin, arteries and bone).[94] Bone marrow transplants began on an experimental basis. It was found that after lethal whole-body doses of X-rays that destroyed existing lymphoid and myeloid cells, grafts from donors 'took'. After an accident with a nuclear reactor in Yugoslavia, several physicists were treated in this way. Aplastic anaemia (failure of the bone marrow to produce blood cells) was also treated by bone marrow transplantation. However, immunological problems remained and, when tissue typing and matching was imperfect, the graft might attack the host, even if the danger of the host rejecting the graft was overcome.[95] Liver transplantation was pioneered in Denver in the early 1960s. The path to heart transplantation in humans was opened by workers such as Shumway at Stanford, who developed the surgical technique and showed that immunosuppressive agents would prolong the period of graft survival. In December 1967 Professor Christiaan Barnard, in South Africa, replaced the heart of a 55-year-old man, who subsequently died, with that of a road accident victim. Four further heart transplantations were carried out in the next few weeks, arousing worldwide interest.

Neurology and neurosurgery

With the growth of transplantation, determining the time of death of potential donors became increasingly significant. The absence of respiration or a heart beat was no longer enough, for life could be prolonged by the ventilators and organ support systems that were being developed. Removal of organs for transplantation could not be undertaken until it was clear that the body could no longer function as a unified system. It was found that, when the integrating mechanisms in the brain stem failed, recovery was impossible and body dissolution began to take place. Mollaret, a French worker, identified this condition as 'coma depassé' in 1962, and over the next few years many industrialised countries developed and published criteria of brain stem death.

The only treatment available for Parkinson's disease had been brain surgery, for example pallidectomy. A major breakthrough began when workers in Austria discovered that, at post-mortem, the basal ganglia of patients with Parkinson's disease were depleted of dopamine. Infusions of dopamine helped sufferers, but it did not work by mouth because it could not pass the blood–brain barrier. However, in 1966 Cotzias, working in New York, showed that a chemical precursor, levodopa, when administered in large doses relieved symptoms substantially. For the first time a biochemical mechanism had been discovered for a major neurological condition. More important, it was possible to help patients somewhat, and the drug industry became more interested in neurological disease. The management of epilepsy was also improved with the introduction of sodium valproate.

ENT surgery

Routine hearing tests in childhood were introduced. The hearing aid manufacturers introduced innovative behind-the-ear and spectacle aids that were much less conspicuous than the body-worn models. Such aids became available through the NHS in the late 1960s and remain the commonest type in use.

Much deafness was the result of the inability of the small bones in the middle ear to transmit sound. Operations were developed, often overseas, to improve the ability to conduct sound; for example, surgical reconstruction of the middle ear ossicular chain. In 1963 William House, working with neurosurgeons in Los Angeles, developed a new translabyrynthine approach to the internal auditory canal, for the removal of tumours in and around the auditory nerve (acoustic neuromas). Neurosurgeons had been treating these tumours, but the introduction of the operating microscope made new operative techniques possible. The operating microscope was also used in surgery on the nose and larynx.

Ophthalmology

The application to the eye of drugs such as steroids, antibiotics, and beta-blockers in glaucoma saved sight on an enormous scale. Lasers, developed in the early 1960s, rapidly found an application in the treatment of eye disease, replacing older techniques, improving the success rate and reducing the duration of treatment. Coupled with an ophthalmoscope, they could be directed at any part of the internal eye and used for treating detached retina and vascular abnormalities.[96] After early disappointments, lens implants using purer plastics and lenses with loops to aid attachment led to an improvement in the results achievable, but the operation usually chosen was lens extraction followed by the use of high-powered spectacles or contact lenses.

Cancer

The mortality from cancer exceeded 100,000 for the first time in 1962 and even in children it was becoming a more significant cause of death. Supervoltage radiotherapy was now well established, and as equipment improved it was possible to deliver the dose more accurately to the important area. Computing was applied to treatment planning. Increasingly radiotherapists became aware of what they could cure, and what they could not. Radioactive implants, a long-standing form of treatment for some circumscribed tumours, became more sophisticated.

There was an increasing recognition that cancer was a systemic disease, often with distant spread (metastases) very early on. Consequently, a precise knowledge of where the cancer was mattered less than the availability of chemotherapy. A new group of drugs became available, vegetable extracts that shared the property of arresting the separation of chromosomes during cell division. Derivatives of colchicine were used for a while in the treatment of Hodgkin's disease and chronic myeloid leukaemia. Vinca alkaloids from the West Indian periwinkle (vinblastine and vincristine) were also introduced. The first proof that chemotherapy cured metastatic disease came from the work of Li, Hertz and Spencer at the National Cancer Institute in the USA.[97] In 1956 methotrexate was used on a patient with metastatic choriocarcinoma, a rare but rapidly developing tumour that sometimes followed childbirth or miscarriage. Urine tests could identify the cancer, allowing the effect of treatment to be monitored. Actinomycin D and vinblastine were also active, and it was shown that daily treatment was less effective than the administration of one or more drugs every four or five days. Bagshawe at the Fulham Hospital introduced the treatment for choriocarcinoma to England. He advocated a centralised follow-up and treatment service, and a death rate of 95 per cent was turned into a survival of 75 per cent.[98] In the early 1960s a survey showed that 159 patients who had been treated for acute lymphoblastic leukaemia with a variety of agents had survived five years or longer. No patients survived five years without chemotherapy; this led in the USA to the establishment of an acute leukaemia task force to see if cures could be increased. The cure of acute lymphoblastic leukaemia was an important milestone because a rational basis for curative chemotherapy was being developed, bringing together knowledge of the processes of cell division, pharmacology, toxicology, good nursing and developments in clinical medicine.[99] The objective became the destruction of every last leukaemic cell by every means possible, as just one cell could cause relapse. A given drug killed a fraction of tumour cell populations but resistant cells remained and multiplied. There were then five active drugs and switching from one to another, or a combination, killed further cells. Combinations of drugs were used in leukaemia, Hodgkin's disease and testicular cancer. A marker or index for tumour activity was very important; one treated until the marker disappeared, and then some more. Clinicians were learning the right way to use the drugs. Large-scale trials were now necessary to define the best treatment schedules.[100] Some workers, including Farber, suggested that drugs might control metastatic relapses when combined with surgery and radiation. Adjuvant therapy of this type was shown to increase the survival rate after surgery for Wilms' tumour of the kidney.[101] Cancer centres in the UK were slow to adopt the aggressive forms of treatment being developed in the USA. There were few medical oncologists, and surgeons or radiotherapists treated cancer. Some antibiotics showed activity against cancer and the pharmaceutical industry followed up this line of research. By the end of 1967 more than 88,000 compounds had been screened for effectiveness against cancer.

Cervical and breast cancer

Exfoliative cytology, for some years patchily available in specialist departments, offered another chance for reducing cancer. Cancer of the cervix, the fifth most common cancer in women, might be identified early and at a pre-invasive stage. The feminist movement took up this issue as one of it first causes. Political pressure for a service was substantial; if population screening proved practicable it offered a chance to save life. By 1963 it was clear that trained cytologists were rare, so five national training centres were established. In 1965 it was decided to aim for a service offering five-yearly smears to all women over the age of 35 years. The size of the task was substantial and many women were reluctant to accept screening although it was free and became easily available. Those at greatest risk, often in the lower social classes, were the most reluctant to present themselves for screening.

A breast cancer screening programme was launched in 1963 by a health insurance plan in New York. The screening subcommittee of SMAC believed it would be premature to implement such a programme until there was good evidence of its worth; had one been introduced, the UK's radiologists would have had little time for anything else. This recommendation was one of the earliest occasions on which a professional group prevented the national introduction of a procedure for which there was inadequate evidence. The *BMJ* agreed that it would be prudent to consider the costs, value and practicability of mammographic screening, because such a programme would be beyond the resources of most countries.[102]

Smoking and cancer

The epidemic of lung cancer pursued its predictable course, with a steady increase in men and signs that women would suffer more as time passed, because of their increased use of cigarettes. By the early 1960s the public did not lack information, only conviction or willpower. Local health authorities ran health education campaigns without winning the battle. Only by the end of the decade were there any encouraging signs; there appeared to be a reduction in registrations of lung cancer in men aged 40–59.[103] Charles Fletcher, Secretary of the Royal College of Physicians (RCP), and George Godber at the Department of Health needed a way to bypass political constraints and obtain an outspoken report from an authoritative body. The RCP seemed best to both and Sir Robert Platt, who had just been elected its President, agreed. In 1962 the RCP, having studied the available evidence, published *Smoking and health*, showing the connection and also an association with chronic bronchitis.[104] Enoch Powell, (then Minister), a non-smoker, agreed to push the report but would not accept a ban on advertisements; if a company could trade legally, it could legally advertise its wares. The report sold 50,000 copies and had a worldwide influence. Following its publication, doctors began to give up smoking; the public was slow to follow their example and cigarette consumption continued to rise. Tobacco companies began to be concerned about the tar content of cigarettes and reduced it considerably. The difficulty in giving up something that clearly had the features of an addiction became increasingly obvious. Discussions with tobacco manufacturers were unsatisfactory. In 1965 a ban was placed on TV advertising of tobacco. In 1967, when Kenneth Robinson was Minister, no voluntary agreement could be reached with manufacturers to ban coupon gift schemes. The government announced that it would take powers to ban coupons and control other forms of advertising.[105] The case against smoking could be made on many grounds, but not on economics. The non-smoker on reaching pensionable age lived, on average, seven years longer than his smoking colleague.

The hospice movement

For many, cure from cancer was not possible. Too often professionals were ill at ease with the dying, to whom adequate pain relief was not available. Cicely Saunders, initially a nurse at St Thomas' and later training there as a doctor, pioneered better terminal care at St Joseph's Hospice.[106] Helped by a clinical research fellowship in pharmacology, in 1958 she began to investigate terminal pain and its relief. Many new drugs, which complemented the traditional opiates, had become available during the previous ten years. Service, teaching and research were combined with high quality care. A new hospice, St Christopher's, opened in Sydenham in 1967, supported by the Borough of Bromley, the City Parochial Foundation, the BBC *Week's good cause*, the Drapers Company, the King's Fund and the Nuffield Foundation.[107] The hospice movement inherited the long-standing charitable and voluntary tradition in health care. It treated each patient as an individual, was prepared to look death squarely in the face and to encourage the dying and their families to do the same. Only by facing difficulties honestly could the problems and the fear of death be overcome. Controlling pain by large, regular and fully adequate doses of opiates, relieving unpleasant symptoms and providing strong emotional support allowed death to be natural and dignified. The idea slowly spread. From its inception the hospice movement, though voluntary, worked closely with local NHS services to improve quality of care, and co-operated with primary health care teams to raise standards of care for terminally ill people within the community. Consultant posts in palliative care, and training positions, were progressively established. Specialist nurses were appointed in the community, for example the Marie Curie and Macmillan nurses who gave supportive care to people with cancer and their families. The hospice movement had a lesson to teach the health service about the limitations of technology in medicine and patient care.

Obstetrics and gynaecology

The review of maternity services by the Maternity Services Committee, recommended by Guillebaud and chaired by Lord Cranbrook, reported in 1959.[108] To the dismay of obstetricians, Cranbrook saw a need for co-ordination and co-operation rather than reorganisation and unification of services under consultant control. Local liaison committees were therefore established. Cranbrook recommended the maintenance of a good domiciliary maternity service but considered that the balance of advantage favoured hospital rather than home delivery. A hospital delivery rate of 70 per cent was suggested, a figure without scientific justification, derived from a report by the Royal College of Obstetricians and Gynaecologists (RCOG) in 1944. More careful selection of patients for hospital was needed, with local authorities looking at social circumstances, and professionals booking for hospital those with possible obstetric problems, those who had borne four or more children or who were over the age of 35. A first baby was not, of itself, an indication for hospital delivery. Antenatal beds might be needed for 20–25 per cent of deliveries. The Committee supported the traditional ten-day postnatal stay, while welcoming careful investigation of early discharge. The Central Health Services Council (CHSC), examining maternity services in 1961, argued for more humanity.[109] Hospitals were asked to review their procedures and make arrangements for mothers to have companionship and information in labour. The proportion of hospital deliveries began to rise, reaching the Cranbrook target in 1965 and 80 per cent in 1968.

Mothers were pressing for hospital delivery and, in spite of some opposition from the midwives, planned early discharge became more common, sometimes only a few hours after childbirth as soon as the mother was fit to be moved. Often mothers had been admitted only because their previous deliveries had been complicated. If all was well there was no reason to retain them. Less than 1 per cent needed readmission and there were few problems if there was careful selection and good relations between hospital and community staff[110] The duration of hospital stay began to fall nationally and kept falling. Beds ceased to be in short supply and there was increased pressure for nearly all deliveries to take place in hospital. With a reduction in home deliveries, obstetric flying squads were required less often, and tended to restrict themselves to resuscitation before the mother was transferred to hospital. It became policy to co-locate GP maternity units with the consultant units, allowing GPs to practise safely in the knowledge that unpredictable emergencies could be handled in surroundings with better facilities.[111]

The three-yearly reports from the confidential inquiry into maternal deaths showed that childbirth was increasingly safe. The top four causes of death remained constant: toxaemia, haemorrhage, abortion and pulmonary embolism in which arteries in the lungs were suddenly blocked by a blood clot that had formed in leg veins. The surveys showed that avoidable factors were often involved, such as failure to attend for antenatal care, booking the delivery at home or in a GP unit when specialist facilities were required, or failure to seek specialist advice when necessary. They showed the need for the highest anaesthetic skill when women were in labour.[112] Merely by conscientious and wise application of the knowledge available the number of maternal deaths could have been nearly halved.[113]

In 1958 the National Birthday Trust Fund, with the support of the Ministry and the RCOG, undertook a survey of every birth taking place during the week beginning 3 March.[114] NHS staff, nurses, midwives and doctors recorded detailed demographic information, including social class, complications of pregnancy and delivery, and outcome for mother and baby. Analysis of the 17,000 records took a long while, and ill-managed presentation at a press conference in 1962 led to headlines about 'kitchen table midwifery', giving an impression that the survey was an attack on domiciliary midwifery and GPs.[115] The report did not appear until 1963, and the research, both sociological and clinical, had a major influence on the development of maternity services.[116] It had much to say about social class. The death rate of babies in the professional classes was half that in the unskilled labour class. Scarce maternity beds were not allocated equally; better-off women were more likely to give birth in hospital or GP maternity units. The report showed how poor antenatal care might be; blood tests might not be done and blood pressure was often not checked. It was shown that pregnancies lasting more than 42 weeks were associated with higher perinatal mortality rates than those of average duration. This appeared to support the decision taken by some units to induce labour in mothers who were two weeks overdue, a policy later shown to be open to question. Further analysis of the data showed that mothers who smoked had smaller babies and more of them died.[117] One question could not be answered by the survey – the safety of home delivery compared with hospital. The survey assumed that hospital birth was safer, but it was not clear from the data.[118] The cohort of children was followed up annually for many years to see how they developed.

Gynaecology

Increasing attention was paid to emotional factors in illness. Katharina Dalton, a GP and a clinical assistant at University College Hospital, interviewed a group of women in prison, and found that almost half of them had committed their crime during menstruation or the premenstruum. Premenstrual tension appeared to be a factor.[119]

Oral contraception steadily increased, as did the use of intrauterine devices. However, male sterilisation, though a comparatively simple operation, was regarded as a potentially criminal and maiming act. In the mid-1960s lobbying by family planing groups led to vasectomy not only being accepted but actively encouraged by government.

The Abortion Act

There was widespread agreement that some change in abortion law was required but not about what that change should be. Criminal abortion was a leading cause of death associated with pregnancy, but it was not known how many abortions there were. The RCOG thought they were few but others put the number as high as 100,000 a year. The College thought that termination of pregnancy was not so safe and simple as sometimes maintained and that the law did not seriously hamper current medical practice; 2,800 therapeutic abortions were carried out in 1962 and on the shady side of Harley Street business was brisk. Both the BMA and the Royal Medico-Psychological Association published their views, the latter stressing the significance of social circumstances as well as medical and psychiatric criteria.[120] Jeffcoate, Professor of Obstetrics and Gynaecology in Liverpool, believed that a true medical indication for operation did not arise in more than one in a 1,000 pregnancies and that psychiatric indications were easily abused. Others took a more liberal view about psychiatric problems, reactive depression and anxiety states.[121] In 1965 Lord Silkin introduced a Bill that the *BMJ* thought was hurried and ill-considered. When Harold Wilson called a general election in March 1966 it provided a pause for reflection. David Steel, a young liberal MP, drew a favourable place in a subsequent private member's ballot, and introduced a Bill.[122] Kenneth Robinson, as Minister of Health, and Roy Jenkins, as Home Secretary, ensured enough parliamentary time for it. As a result, under the 1967 Abortion Act termination of pregnancy was no longer illegal if two medical practitioners believed that

- The pregnancy would involve risk to the life of the woman, or of injury to the physical or mental health of the woman or any existing children greater than if the pregnancy were terminated.
- There was a substantial risk that if the child were born it would suffer from such physical or mental abnormalities as to be seriously handicapped.

Because it extended the reasons for termination beyond the mother herself, the BMA was troubled by the ethics of including *existing children* in the definition. Within a couple of years a rapid increase in the number of abortions was apparent, increasing the strain on gynaecological outpatient and inpatient departments.

Paediatrics

Pressure from some professionals, the British Paediatric Association, the BMA and the Association for Welfare of Children in Hospital, led to the establishment of a committee to study the arrangements made in hospital for children. It was appointed by the CHSC and chaired by Sir Harry Platt, reporting in 1959.[123] The committee stressed the need to understand and care for the emotional needs of children, particularly when in hospital. There should be separate children's outpatient departments, admission should be avoided where possible and children should not be nursed in adult wards. Children's welfare should always be the responsibility of paediatricians and nurses trained in the care of children. Unlimited visiting of parents should be introduced.

The progressive appointment of paediatricians led to an intense interest in neonatal medicine, and some technologies that were developed improved the care of older children as well. Neonatology began to emerge internationally as a specialty. Efforts were made to transfer mothers in early labour to hospitals with special units, and to provide transport incubators for those born elsewhere. The main concern in caring for premature babies was respiratory distress, hyaline membrane disease, with obstruction to the small airways of the lung. Research revealed that this was the result of lack of 'surface-active agents', as a result of which some of the air cells of the lung collapsed. The principles of care were laid down by people such as Peter Tizzard, who established the first British research unit in neonatal medicine at the Hammersmith, and developed the measurement of arterial oxygen, carbon dioxide and pH. Treatment included the prevention of aspiration (inhaling feeding fluids), early feeding and attempts at mechanical ventilation (that were not particularly successful).

The breakthrough in haemolytic disease of the newborn came in 1967. Two groups, Cyril Clarke in Liverpool and another in New York, showed that it was possible to destroy any fetal cells found in the maternal circulation after delivery (the cause of rhesus sensitisation), by a suitable antibody. The Kleihauer technique had just been described, which allowed the detection of fetal blood cells in maternal blood. It was possible to prevent mothers developing antibodies by giving them anti-D immunoglobulin shortly after the birth of the babies.

Haemophilia, a genetic disease appearing in the male, led to persistent bleeding after minor injury, and bleeding into joints such as the knee. It was treated by freshly collected whole blood or frozen plasma transfusions. It was known that the anti-haemophilic factor (factor VIII) could be separated from plasma, and in the 1960s there were advances in preparing it, by cryoprecipitation and later by plasma fractionation.[124] Patients' outlook changed dramatically as it became possible to reduce the disabling complications.

The rising number of immigrants increased the incidence of two other genetic diseases of childhood. Beta-thalassaemia major, found in people from the Middle East, Africa and southeast Asia, was characterised by the inability of bone marrow to produce an adequate number of red blood cells. Anaemia, slow growth, cardiac failure and death in the late teens were the result. The development of regular blood transfusion regimens, in 1961–1964, was a major advance, for it allowed patients with thalassaemia to grow and to live longer. The result of monthly blood transfusion, however, was to overload the body with iron, which led to liver fibrosis, endocrine deficiencies and growth retardation. The use of iron chelating agents by intravenous injection, which bound the surplus iron and assisted its excretion, helped somewhat. Sickle-cell disease was found in populations of West African origin and in 1949 it became the first genetic disease in which the molecular basis was determined. As a result of this discovery the scope of human genetics was widened and many other 'haemoglobinopathies' were discovered. Sickle-cell crises, with acute pain caused by the blood cells breaking up and blocking the arteries, sometimes produced acute and chronic organ damage. By the age of 40 years, half those with severe disease were dead. The only treatment, temporary in nature, was exchange transfusion in which the patient's blood was replaced with blood from a donor.

In the late 1950s and early 1960s there was a trend to push operative treatment for babies with congenital defects of the spine and brain, meningomyelocele, beyond reasonable limits. Babies with mild degrees of spina bifida could be operated on with a measure of success but those with severe defects might be helped to live for only a while, usually being left with complex physical and mental handicaps, and producing great emotional strain on the families.[125] Yet some units undertook repeated heroic surgery. A paper was put to SMAC with the suggestion of a national conference attended by all shades of opinion, including parents. From that conference came a paper discouraging surgery in cases in which the long-term outlook was hopeless.

The treatment of children of short stature, when due to failure of the pituitary to produce enough growth hormone, was helped by using human growth hormone prepared from pituitary glands obtained at autopsy. Supplies were scarce and treatment, which began in 1959, was centralised in a few units and supervised by the MRC.[126] The children treated grew well. Not for many years was a hazard to this treatment discovered.

Geriatrics

Nowhere was the contrast between what existed and what was possible more stark than in the care of elderly people. The illnesses and disabilities of ageing loomed increasingly large. Most old people did not to report their difficulties until they were well advanced, and mental deterioration was an increasing problem.[127] GPs knew less than they liked to think about patients' sight and mobility. It was difficult to recruit consultants to the specialty, and a large proportion of those who entered it had qualified overseas and geriatrics was often not their initial specialty of choice.

Guillebaud had recognised the need for better housing and domiciliary services so that elderly people could continue to live, wherever possible, in their own homes. Almost 5 per cent of people aged 65 years or more were accommodated in institutions of one type or another. Many were admitted to acute wards of *district general hospitals* (DGHs), but psychiatric and social problems were quite common among them, emphasising the need for psychiatric and geriatric services in the DGH. *Geriatric wards* tended to be occupied by people over 75, and there was no clear division between the patients in them and those in the acute wards, although many would clearly not be restored to a fully independent life. Half had some form of mental illness or dementia. A third group of elderly patients, those in *mental hospitals*, were often suffering from irreversible senile degeneration, but many had physical illnesses as well. Finally both mental and physical problems were common among those in *residential homes.*[128]

Components of a comprehensive psychogeriatric service

- An organisational structure that encourages integration between the services provided by the three parts of the NHS and the voluntary sector
- Psychogeriatric assessment units for early ascertainment of those at high risk
- Community and domiciliary services, clubs, day centres, outpatient clinics and day hospitals
- Hospital inpatient services for short periods of acute illness, and for non-ambulant patients, with an accent on rehabilitation
- Long-term accommodation and sheltered housing

Source: Kay et al. 1966.[128]

Defining the characteristics of a modern geriatric service was not difficult. It was much harder to develop one. In 1961 the Birmingham RHB published a report on its geriatric services. Some were hospital slums that did no more than provide storage space for patients under conditions of considerable difficulty, and often unpleasantness, for the nursing staff. Many hospitals were fit only for demolition and replacement; some were 100 and some 200 years old. Many had no lift and when patients had been manhandled upstairs they were marooned there for the rest of their days, often at considerable risk from fire.[129] In 1965 *The Times* published a letter from a group including Lord Strabolgi, academics, social workers and clergymen. They had 'been shocked by the treatment of geriatric patients in certain mental hospitals, one of the evils being the practice of stripping them of their personal possessions'. They appealed for confidential information about such malpractice. The response overwhelmed them.[130]

Mental illness

Easy and effective treatment, possible with the new drugs, enabled GPs to manage many patients with mild and moderate degrees of anxiety and depression. Psychiatrists were few, their waiting lists were long, and only severe cases generally reached the hospital services. William Sargant, at St Thomas' Hospital, was a protagonist of physical methods of treatment. A charismatic, immaculately dressed, controversial and not universally popular man, he believed that medicine and psychiatry had drifted steadily further apart and needed to be reunited. He thought that the future would see the replacement of specialised psychiatric and psychotherapeutic treatment by physical methods including drugs, and there would be greater understanding of the physiological basis of psychiatric disease. Some psychiatrists, in his view, preferred to remain a segregated group, advocating general philosophies about the need to treat and heal the 'whole person'. Yet it was only when general medicine stopped bothering about the whole person, the internal humours and external vapours, and insisted on treating the liver, the heart, the blood stream, the brain and the nervous system, that general medicine really got started. Each year 20,000–30,000 distraught people tried to kill themselves, many of whom would be helped by simple methods. During the war the Maudsley Hospital, where Sargant had worked, had been evacuated to emergency hospitals without locked doors; military patients were not officially considered mad and refused to think of themselves as such. Locked provision had not been necessary. Subsequently, as the new drugs appeared, these could be assessed in trials on outpatients, and the best ones for different types of depression could be determined. Improvement was often rapid, although it was as essential in psychiatry as in general medicine for the correct dosage to be used for the proper length of time. It was crucial, Sargant thought, to break away from philosophical and metaphysical concepts of disease and the psychotherapeutic approaches that failed most of the neurotic and the mentally ill.[131] 'From being a backwater, ignored as much by the rest of medicine as by the public at large,' said the *Lancet*, 'psychiatry is becoming one of the major specialties. Its professional standards have risen rapidly; it is already based on an impressive body of organised knowledge; and its results on the whole are probably no worse than medicine or surgery.'[132]

The two major reforming pieces of legislation of this century, the Mental Treatment Act 1930 and the Mental Health Act 1959, followed world wars. The 1959 Act, resulting from the recommendations of the Royal Commission in 1957, created a new basis for the treatment of the mentally ill with no more formality than for other illnesses. It aimed to break down segregation, and the feelings of isolation, neglect and frustration that this engendered.[133] Services would now be planned across hospital and community boundaries, by specialists, family doctors and local authority staff, nurses and social workers. Since the 1940s many psychiatrists had realised that long-term residence might result in institutional neurosis, with apathy, withdrawal, resignation and loss of individuality.[134] It was in the best interests of those able to live in the community to do so. Expansion of domiciliary services, residential homes and hostels, day-hospitals and social clubs would be needed and local authorities began to plan buildings to support the new policy.

Earlier treatment was now possible and its effectiveness increased the demand for psychiatric services, particularly outpatient ones. The Manchester experience began to be discussed. Maurice Silverman, from Blackburn, described a comprehensive district service with no selective criteria for admission, dealing with all cases from a population of 254,000. His unit of 100 beds had 488 admissions and 479 discharges in one year and provided domiciliary visiting and day patient facilities. Four of the eight psychiatrists in the Manchester region, each serving a population of 250,000, said that they did not need facilities of the large mental hospitals.[135] In setting up the units, the one thing the RHB was not generous with was consultant staff. Units were run on a shoe-string; supporting staff were thin on the ground, and with so few staff only the severely ill could be treated. That reduced bed needs. There was a sturdy resignation among Lancastrians; they were prepared to suffer and put up with it. The policy was cheap and resulted in the run-down of some very large mental hospitals. The Ministry took note.

Psychiatrists hotly disputed the future organisation of mental health services. TP Rees at Warlingham Park, Macmillan at Nottingham and Russell Barton at Severalls Hospital emphasised the value of the traditional mental hospital that was likely to diminish in size from an average of 1,000 beds to 500. Such hospitals provided a better basis for staff education and, because many psychiatrists worked together, research was easier. Large hospitals could have a range of specialised units impossible within the restricted space of a DGH. In spite of active treatment and rehabilitation some patients would continue to present long-term social and clinical problems.[136] They needed space in which to be peculiar without upsetting others. Thomas McKeown, Professor of Social Medicine at Birmingham, on the other hand, wanted to unite all services including mental illness in one place. He believed that the chief problems that would confront medicine in the future would be prenatally determined mortality and morbidity, mental subnormality and mental illness, and the disease and disability associated with ageing. These would be the functions of the hospital of the future, and a balanced hospital community would be needed. The association of mental illness with other services would raise staffing to a satisfactory level, make for efficiency as common services could be shared, and reduce the stigma and isolation of mental illness.[137]

Bed requirements

In 1961 Tooth and Brooke, a doctor in the Ministry of Health and a statistician in the General Register Office, published in the *Lancet* a prediction of future bed requirements based on cohorts of patients admitted in 1954, 1955 and 1956. It showed that the tide had turned in 1954 and that, although admissions were increasing, the number of inpatients was decreasing and discharge was faster. The paper predicted that there would be a rapid and continuing reduction in the number of beds required, such that in 16 years' time the bed requirements might have fallen from 150,000 to 80,000.[138] Enoch Powell, Minister of Health, was interested in mental care.[139] Seeing the draft before publication, he surprised his audience at a conference at Church House, Westminster, in March 1961 by speaking in dramatic – almost messianic – terms about future policy on mental hospitals. He said of the old hospitals,

> *There they stand, isolated, majestic, imperious, brooded over by the giant water tower and chimney combined, rising unmistakable and daunting out of the countryside . . .*

Not more than half the present number of places was likely to be needed, a redundancy of 75,000 beds. The beds should be in general hospitals. The change would imply the elimination of the greater part of the existing hospitals, a colossal undertaking. He said he would resist attempts to foist another purpose on them. Many staff had given years of service to the doomed institutions and a new pattern of working would demand no mean moral effort from them, as a whole branch of medicine, nursing and hospital administration was transformed.[140] Richard Titmuss, a social scientist, replied that the British tended to express aspirations in idealistic terms. There was little evidence of attempts to hammer out the practice, as opposed to the theory, of community care although policies assumed that *somebody* knew what it meant. To scatter the mentally ill in the community without adequate provision was not a solution, even financially. Powell's proposed reduction implied a remarkable degree of optimism about readmission rates and the part to be played by GPs and local health authorities. Titmuss thought there was drift into a situation in which the care of the mentally ill was transferred from trained staff to untrained or ill-equipped staff or no staff at all. Experienced physicians in mental hospitals had grown wary of miracles and felt in their bones that the psychiatric millennium was not yet at hand. Russell Barton asked whether education for the new service could make up for the failure of teaching hospitals; they were producing doctors lacking even a barn-door knowledge of psychiatry. The involvement of GPs would be essential, though few were enthusiastic or trained for this.

Powell was a crusader and the Ministry had previously seen the NHS benefit from the closure of sanatoria, freeing money that would otherwise have been difficult to obtain. General hospital psychiatry might be economic and the clinical answer to hospital over-crowding. No new large hospitals would be needed. 'We need more psychiatry in fewer buildings,' said Sir George Godber.[141] Inpatient treatment was seen as only an incident in the management of most mental disorders. The aim was to return patients to ordinary life, with support if necessary, as soon as possible. In 1967 new figures showed a continuing fall in numbers, 20,000 between 1954 and 1963.[142] Morbidity surveys and community registers, such as the Camberwell Register created in 1964, offered hope of a better epidemiological basis for planning mental illness services.[143]

Three mental health objectives were fed into the newly developing policy: improvement of the quality of care, reduction of institutional care and transfer into community care. The proposal that the bulk of acute cases would in future be admitted to district general hospitals was an implicit judgement on the traditional unit. It implied that existing mental hospitals were the product of an age that thought in terms of custody, and they had no permanent or valuable role in society. Their functions could be split between district hospitals and the community. No one was likely to defend the image painted by Enoch Powell. Nevertheless, while units based on district hospitals clearly could work, there was an alternative that many other countries had adopted.[144] Sizeable inpatient psychiatric centres could provide clinical treatment plus sanctuary, be large enough to provide all the facilities needed for socialisation of patients and support a team of psychiatrists who could specialise and learn from each other. The impetus towards community was derived from several sources – the new wave of psychotropic drugs, the possibility of cheaper forms of care, and a group of civil libertarians who maintained that mental hospitals were effectively prisons, depriving their inmates of 'freedom' under an authoritarian regime, from which discharge meant a return to a normal life. The doors were opened to a wave of non-medical mental health workers, social workers, nurses, counsellors, self-help groups and patients.[145] There was no doubt that patients *could* be discharged and the beds reduced to the required numbers, but nobody knew what the cost to the community would be. It was not appreciated that many patients would indulge in antisocial conduct, or need 24-hour supervision, or be incapable of caring for themselves. Patients did not always take their drugs after discharge and deviant behaviour might distress relatives. A full community care system was still in its infancy.[146] Local health authorities did not have enough trained staff, nor family doctors the time and experience. The burden on families might be substantial. There were few hostels available and a lack of enthusiasm for their provision. Was a social isolation being substituted for a geographical one? asked the BMJ. What was the state of discharged patients? How many were among the

9,000 offenders referred by the courts for psychiatric reports, the 28,000 homeless discovered by the National Assistance Board or the thousands sleeping rough?[147]

The policy of general hospital psychiatry created uncertainty about the physical conditions in old, over-crowded hospitals with old-fashioned toilet facilities and in poor decorative order. If parts of them were to be closed, what should be spent on upgrading? Some mental hospitals began to divide into two sections, a small short stay-unit with about 20 per cent of the total beds that treated 80 per cent of new admissions, and a larger long-stay section dealing with the chronic sick, those who might recover more slowly and elderly patients too disturbed to be cared for elsewhere. Sometimes a hospital was divided into units with different geographical responsibilities. Alternatively, each team took a special interest in particular types of care.[148] These hospitals had to interdigitate with an increasing number of district hospital units offering intensive treatment to patients from a local catchment area. There was a danger of a split service and two-tier provision. The patients who increasingly went to the district hospitals were the more acute, the younger and the more hopeful. Those in the large old hospitals were the chronic and the elderly severely mentally infirm. Some consultants might be unwilling to work in large chronic hospitals. Nurses from the older hospitals might be rejected by the district hospitals, and some members of staff themselves seemed in need of sheltered employment.[149]

General practice and primary health care

The task and the status

When young doctors entered general practice, they soon discovered that the spectrum of medical problems they encountered was not that of the hospital. Clinical medicine differed from the medicine taught in the teaching hospital, so they had much to learn; indeed ideally much of the GP's education should take place within general practice itself.[150] Care in general practice had to reflect the way human beings behaved and related to each other, and the society in which they lived. The work of Balint at the Tavistock Clinic suggested dimensions of clinical practice quite unlike anything taught or learned at medical school.[151] Ann Cartwright studied general practice in north London from a sociological perspective.[152] Two GPs, John Fry in Beckenham and Keith Hodgkin, continued their analyses of the work of general practice and of the difference between hospital work and their own. GPs managed 90 per cent of their patients alone and hospital specialists saw only 10 per cent, even in conditions that might be regarded as 'hospital' in nature, such as high blood pressure and peptic ulcer.[153] John Fry analysed his hospital referrals. Roughly 18 per cent of his patients were referred each year, 3.7 per cent for an outpatient consultation and 3.8 per cent for admission; the rest were for a test or X-ray. He tried to determine the outcome of hospital referral, which proved difficult. Excluding maternity cases, a year later just over half seemed better, but almost the same number were little different or worse. Perhaps, Fry said, greater attention should be paid to the long-term results of long-established therapies that had become blind routines.[154] GPs had long known that psychiatric illness was common in general practice. A paper in 1966 by Michael Shepherd from the Maudsley showed that it was one of the most frequent causes for consultation and that GPs dealt unaided with the vast bulk of such cases. The implication was that the main need for improvement of mental health services was not a proliferation of specialist agencies, but a strengthening of the family doctor's therapeutic role.[155]

Comparison of morbidity in general practice and hospital per 1000 incidents

Hospital inpatient	Disease	General practice
300	New growths	4
12	Disseminated sclerosis	12
30	Cerebrovascular disorders	2
5	Malignant hypertension	0.5
15	Benign hypertension	6
15	Coronary heart disease	2
40	Rheumatic heart disease	1
0	Upper respiratory infections	250
45	Pneumonia and acute bronchitis	20
90	Peptic ulcer	30
15	Regional ileitis and ulcerative colitis	0
75	Acute appendicitis	1
65	Hernia	2
25	Acute intestinal obstruction	0.5
55	Gall-bladder	0.5
25	Neuroses	140
2	Psychoses	1

Source: Hodgkin 1963, adapted by Fry 1964[152]

Although the 1952 Danckwerts award had remedied the initial injustice of the GPs' pay, specialists regarded themselves, in George Godber's words, as a superior kind of animal. Before the NHS they had received fees from patients referred to them by GPs. Being hoity-toity with colleagues was hardly profitable. Now that most of the consultant's income came as a salary, matters were different.[156] GPs felt that they were held in little respect. Matters were not improved by the evidence of Lord Moran, President of the RCP, to the Royal Commission on Doctors' and Dentists' Pay in 1958.

> The Chairman: *It has been put to us by a good many people that the two branches of the profession, general practitioners and consultants, are not senior or junior to one another, but they are level. Do you agree with that?*
>
> Lord Moran: *I say emphatically No. Could anything be more absurd? I was Dean at St Mary's Hospital Medical School for 25 years, and all the people of outstanding merit, with few exceptions, aimed to get on the staff. It was a ladder off which they fell. How can you say that the people who fall off the ladder are the same as those who do not? . . . I do not think you will find a single Dean of any medical school who will give contrary evidence.*
>
> The Chairman: *I think you are the first person who has suggested to us that general practitioners are a somewhat inferior branch.*[157]

Lord Moran later attempted to retract, stressing that he only wished to secure material rewards for those who spent long years of training as specialists, waiting in comparative penury.[158] Family doctors did not forgive him. John Horder, later President of the College of General Practitioners (CGP), made the introduction of effective vocational training his long-term objective. In the College journal he wrote

> *Specialists expect to remain under part-time training until they are from 33 to 40 years old. Is it surprising that some of them have feelings of superiority – and some of us feelings of inferiority – when our own training is so much shorter? Unless this differential is altered what right have we to expect much change in the other differential?*[159]

The young doctor could immediately become a principal, even if ill-prepared for general practice. Few became vocational trainees; the scheme had a bad name, the number participating was decreasing and those who did might be used as cheap labour without a systematic programme of education.[160] A national system of vocational training by selected and trained teachers seemed crucial, but only in a few places, for example Inverness and Wessex, had there been attempts to construct a training programme.[161] The Wessex course was planned in 1958 and was sponsored by the University of London, with a grant from the Nuffield Provincial Hospitals Trust. It provided two years in hospital posts and one in a training practice. George Swift, the postgraduate adviser, selected the hospital posts and practices, and provided courses for the trainers and trainees.[162] A working party of the CGP was formed to consider vocational training and John Horder was largely responsible for its evidence to the Royal Commission on Medical Education in 1966. The CGP asked for two years' postgraduate education in supervised general practice and three years in hospital posts.[163] The BMJ thought this idealistic and doubted whether it would be wise to make vocational training compulsory; offering GPs good working conditions was more important and the urgent need was for more pairs of hands.[164]

The CGP also wished to see academic departments of general practice in every medical school to ensure that students were presented with a balanced picture of health and disease. The first Professor of General Practice, Richard Scott, was appointed in Edinburgh in 1963. England only slowly followed suit as in Manchester. Keith Joseph later used his contacts to obtain money for Chairs of general practice at Guy's and St Thomas'. The early appointments were of men who had learned their craft in a practical school. There were no academic routes for them to follow and long-established colleagues in other disciplines did not take them entirely seriously. It was another 20 years before Marinker could say that the absence in a medical school of a department of general practice was no longer the hallmark of the traditionalist or super-technologist but merely of the quaint.[165] Academics, for their part, did not feel that the College was the right organisation to press their interests, composed as it was largely of doctors whose main *raison d'être* was to provide health services and who might lack a feel for academia.

Accommodation

In 1962 John Fry visited 33 'good' practices to examine their organisation and premises. There was an 'extraordinary sameness' in them. Even newly built surgeries were inflexible, with little thought for future development and poor accommodation for ancillary staff. Half the practices used an examination room, a third had appointment schemes and almost all worked an off-duty rota. Fry thought that GPs needed an advisory service and financial incentives to plan and redevelop practices.[166]

The health centre had been considered the solution to poor quality premises, paid for, designed and built by local authorities for their own nursing staff, and for GPs who might rent accommodation. In the first decade barely a dozen had opened. Surveying them, the Medical Practitioners' Union (MPU)* found that only 134 GPs were involved and only 33 worked exclusively at the centre. Why had they been so unpopular?[167] It was a good idea to have local health authority staff working alongside the GPs, but communication was often minimal, and sometimes there were even separate entrances. GPs lacked confidence in local authorities, with whom they were often at cross-purposes. They might not be consulted before a new centre was planned. Often the last thing to be built on a new estate, the new residents were already on the lists of neighbouring GPs. Too much had been expected too soon. Although there was a concealed subsidy, rents might be high. Whilst the arguments for health centres remained valid, some new approach such as group practice was required because the nature of society and modern medicine demanded it. GPs in groups practised together, employing ancillary staff. The MPU asked for financial incentives to encourage the development of better premises and the employment of ancillary staff, and local health authorities' support for the groups.

Group practice and primary health care teams

The Danckwerts settlement provided a first stimulus to practice expansion; there was a slow but steady increase in the number of doctors working in partnerships and in the closer proximity of group practice. Following MacDougall in Hampshire, John Warin in Oxford, a member of the Jameson working party on health visitors, tried several ways of achieving co-operation between health visitors and GPs. Liaison schemes proved largely ineffective. In 1956 he arranged the attachment of health visitors to practices and by the end of 1963 every local practice had its own. GPs did not always have adequate accommodation for the health visitor, who needed a car to cover the wider area. However, the difficulties were overcome, nobody wished to return to the former method of working and several practices had begun their own child welfare and antenatal clinics. In 1963 attachment of district nurses to local practices began. It was an immediate success and in 1964 midwives were involved as well. Almost unnoticed, there had been a major development. In Oxford the evolution of the GP/nursing team was near completion, with the GP the leader of the domiciliary team.[168] Other local health authorities also began to 'attach' health visitors or home nurse/health visitors to group practices and health centres. The pattern of nursing in the community changed. Previously each nurse or health visitor had served a small geographical area; now her population became that of the GP's practice.[169] The Queen's Nursing Institute approved the altered orientation of the district nurses, seeing attachment as a watershed in their history.[170]

---

* The Medical Practitioners' Union was founded in 1914 as a trade union and campaigning organisation. A firm supporter of a free NHS, its central belief has been planned and salaried general practice.

As the decade progressed primary health teams increased in number and size. A typical team might be four or five GPs, two health visitors, two district nurses, one midwife, one bath attendant and two relief nurses. The incorporation of nurses was most rapid in rural areas. Here, for geographical reasons, the territory of community nurses and GPs usually coincided. In the cities progress was slower for there was a criss-cross pattern of practices. Although city streets had been allocated to individual nurses, in each one 30–40 GPs might care for a few patients. Nurse management, public health doctors and GPs with a socialist approach to the NHS thought GPs should zone their practices so that their population was local and defined.[171] Senior nurses often opposed attachment schemes, preferring to care for a population defined by geography rather than by GP registration, and fearing the loss of control of community nurses who developed loyalties to the GPs and their patients. Senior community nurses controlled attached staff tightly, determining their numbers and what they might do, rarely permitting them to work within the surgery. GPs, more concerned with individual patients than groups, were not prepared to be organised in this way. In many practices doctors gave injections, took blood and applied dressings. Increasingly GPs began to employ nurses. They valued nurse colleagues increasingly and found it easy to agree a mutually acceptable pattern of working.[172] The two sides failed to see that some services were best provided on a population basis, and others on a practice one; GPs, with a few exceptions, reacted more to patient demand than to the requirements of a population as a whole.

Group practice and practice organisation went hand in hand. In 1959 Bruce Cardew, Editor of the *Medical World* and a leader in the MPU, wished to offer GPs guidance on the introduction of appointment systems. A small group was assembled and produced a handbook and film, sponsored by a drug firm, Lloyd-Hamol Ltd. The company provided free appointment diaries to GPs wishing to use them. The uptake was slow at first, but by 1967 at least a third of the practices had introduced appointments for their patients, to the satisfaction of all concerned.[173] Waiting rooms became more pleasant and less crowded.

The average duration of a consultation was only five minutes and some doctors began to feel that further advance in general practice would occur only if patients were given more time; where was this time to come from?[174] Perhaps home visits, with all the travelling involved, were clinically unproductive. Increasingly, GPs reduced visiting, cutting out routine calls to elderly patients whose condition seldom changed, and to sick children whose parents could bring them to the surgery for an immediate appointment. There was more delegation to ancillary staff to free time for longer consultations. Geoffrey Marsh, a GP in the northeast of England, found that his new practice nurse could successfully relieve the GPs of part of their workload.[175]

There was rapid growth of deputising services in urban areas where the density of the population made them economic. Doctors without access to a deputising service were generally disparaging, but when a service opened most freed themselves of night work for at least some of the week.[176] In 1965 the BMA formed links with a commercial deputising service, providing ethical oversight of its methods of operation and receiving fees in return. Communication systems improved, surgeries installed more phone lines and practices increasingly used radiotelephones.[177]

The trend to more prescriptions at increased cost continued. In its final report in 1959 the Hinchcliffe Committee found no evidence of widespread and irresponsible extravagance.[178] The Committee believed that expensive elegant preparations should give way to simpler preparations of the same drug, and doctors should be convinced of the superiority of a branded product before prescribing it rather than its generic equivalent. It would be a mistake to develop a limited list of drugs but perhaps the quantity prescribed should be kept to a week's supply, save in chronic cases. The Committee disapproved of prescription charges; they were a tax and like all taxes led people to avoid them when they could, and get as much as they could for their money when they had to pay. The Labour Party had never liked prescription charges although they constrained demand. In February 1965 Labour abolished the charge of two shillings (10p) per prescription. More prescriptions were issued for cheap products that patients had previously bought for themselves, such as pain killers and dressings. The number rose by 19 per cent and the total cost by 22 per cent. The incentive to prescribe large quantities to save the patient's pocket disappeared, and smaller amounts were prescribed more often.

The gathering storm

Improved premises and more staff, in the wake of Danckwerts, inevitably meant higher costs. GPs were paid from a 'pool' of money, a global sum divided among GPs. Nothing was ever more meticulously founded on agreement with the medical profession, both in principle and in detail, than the pool. The GPs' accredited representatives had accepted every provision, and many had been warmly advocated to the Royal Commission on doctors' pay or insisted on during negotiations with the Ministry. Practice expenses were reimbursed, but reimbursed unselectively, so that those who spent less than average got back too much and the rest too little. Doctors paying little attention to their facilities were financially better off than those trying to provide a good service.[179] There was also a problem about additional work undertaken outside the NHS for government or local health authorities, for example work for the prison medical service. Extra activity reduced the amount paid for general medical services. The Royal Commission and the Review Body had done well by the consultants but failed to recognise the changes taking place in general practice. Merit awards for GPs as well as consultants had been suggested and a working party proposed that a committee consisting largely of GPs, and advised by local assessors, should select GPs and recommend them for merit awards of not less than £500.[180] At the GPs' annual conference in 1962 they rejected the proposal along with the £500,000 allotted to them.[181]

In 1961 the SMAC established a sub-group to look at the work family doctors were likely to be doing over the next 10–15 years, the organisation of general practice and the support it would require. Chaired by Annis Gillie, the membership included many GPs of experience and distinction. The report, published in 1963, drew attention to educational needs and backed the emerging pattern of groups with attached staff in better premises and more efficient organisation.[182] Gillie saw the GP of the future as the co-ordinator of the resources of hospital and community care, mobilising all those that the patient needed. It was a vision that surprised the older doctor, on his own but doing a straight-forward job under difficult conditions, and fuelled increasing anger among the GPs.

By 1963 GPs were frustrated and the annual BMA meeting in Oxford threatened to raise a hurricane over money. The BMA wanted doctors to speak with a single voice but the consultants were unhappy that the Danckwerts award in 1952 had left them out, and the GPs believed the gap between their pay and that of the consultants was still too wide. One of the effects of the NHS had been to divide the service into three parts, and the same tendency had appeared in the profession's own organisation.[183] By 1964 the correspondence columns of the *BMJ* fairly burst at the seams with protests from disillusioned GPs about the terms of service.[184] Few understood the complexities of their pay system, even when advantageous, creating difficulties for their leadership. A General Practitioners Association was formed as a 'ginger' group to prod the BMA into action. The MPU saw its membership rocket. The chairman of the General Medical Services Committee (GMSC) resigned when draft evidence to the Review Body was savaged, and James Cameron, a thoughtful and experienced Scot, to his horror was elected to a job nobody wanted. The *BMJ* said that there were two problems: payment for the work done and the reform of general practice. There was no unanimity on solutions. Some such as Ivor Jones, a GMSC negotiator, argued for fee-for-service on an American model; a few sought a salaried service and others would have been quite happy to see the NHS disappear.[185] At a conference in May, Ivor Jones outlined the problems:[186]

- Since the NHS had been established the number of consultants had doubled while the number of GPs had increased by only 20 per cent.
- The temporary reduction in medical school intake was affecting the numbers qualifying and the corrective expansion of medical schools would take six or seven years to work its way through.
- Many doctors were elderly and approaching retirement.
- A rise in the numbers of the young and the old was increasing the number of patients for whom the greatest amount of work was necessary.

The Fraser working party

In 1964 Anthony Barber, the Minister, set up a working party, chaired by Sir Bruce Fraser, the Permanent Secretary, which for the first time brought together the Ministry, the BMA and the new College of General Practitioners. It was to recommend changes in the light of the Gillie Report. Local medical committees were asked for their views. Most GPs wished to remain independent contractors, there was little support for either a salaried service or fee-for-service payments to replace capitation, and there was a wish for help with the provision of premises and access to hospital facilities.[187] By August 1964 the ground work had been done, and there was an outline agreement to refund directly part of the cost of providing practice premises and employing practice staff. The Ministry also accepted the principle of improvement grants for premises of up to a third of agreed costs.[188]

In October 1964 a general election was called, Harold Wilson led Labour to a narrow victory and Kenneth Robinson became Minister. Robinson found GPs in a state of 'absolute turmoil' with extremely low morale and, compared with hospital consultants, poorly paid. He and the Fraser working party, were overtaken by a near rebellion. 1964 saw the first reduction in the number of GPs and the numbers fell for the next two years. The mood of dissatisfaction was fanned in January 1965 by an unsympathetic report from the Review Body. While admitting that the number of GPs was not rising, the Review Body would not increase GPs' pay to aid recruitment, for that would produce problems for the hospitals. Nor was it greatly moved by the increase in workload of a more elderly population or GP emigration. The changes recommended would have given GPs on average £250 more, the lion's share going to reimburse the higher expenses of GPs who had invested in their practices and who had previously been underpaid. It looked very much like a nil-settlement and it detonated the profession who denounced without qualification much they had previously advocated.[189] The profession's leaders said the proposals were an insult and a snub, to the irritation of Kenneth Robinson, who wondered whether the eruption would have been so violent and bitter under a Conservative government. Perhaps, he thought, the crisis was deep-seated and could be traced to the family doctor's feeling of insecurity about his place in the world of medicine, working in isolation and unsupported.[190] Dr James Cameron, the new GMSC Chairman, said that the award must inevitably raise in GPs' minds whether it was in the best interests of the patients and the profession to continue to offer professional services within the NHS.[191] The GMSC demanded talks with the Minister on an entirely new contract of service and called for undated resignations to be sent to BMA House for use if necessary. It received 14,000 within a fortnight.

The GPs' charter

Aims of the 1965 Charter

- Increasing recruitment, reducing maximum list sizes to 2,000
- Undergraduate education orientated towards practice, and good postgraduate education
- Improved premises and equipment, and an independent corporation to provide funds
- Adequate supporting staff
- Direct reimbursement of staff and premises expenditure
- Incentives for skills and experience
- Pay to reflect workload, skills and responsibility
- Reasonable working hours with time for study and leisure; freedom from unending responsibility to provide services personally
- Proper pay for work done outside the normal working day
- A worthwhile, effective and satisfying career with clinical freedom in a personal family doctor service

James Cameron, a remarkable but modest man, had to lead from the front because of pressure from the militants, some of whom were for abandonment of the Review Body and direct confrontation with the Ministry. In Birmingham two dozen GPs resigned from the NHS and set up an alternative service; others watched as their experiment slowly failed. Cameron knew that direct confrontation would bring down the GP service, and the GPs' action was already deeply unpopular with the consultants who saw their differential being squeezed.[192] He submitted a 'Charter for the Family Doctor Service', drawn up by the four negotiators behind closed doors over four days at Hove.[193] The far-reaching changes proposed were mainly derived from Hugh Faulkner of the MPU and had been published as a *Blueprint for the future – a ten point programme*. This programme was astutely adopted by the BMA as its own at the last minute. It sought a reasonable workload with time for leisure and postgraduate study, at a reasonable level of pay, and the money for the space, the equipment and the staff necessary for the work. The Charter aimed for a list of 2,000 patients, a reduction in time-consuming form-filling and a limited working day. Better access to hospital facilities, the ability of practices to choose their method of payment and finance for premises were sought.[194]

Kenneth Robinson thought it disgraceful to be expected to negotiate under the pressure of resignations when he wanted to improve matters anyway. He believed the key to modernising general practice was the encouragement of groups with good supporting facilities. Flanked by George Godber and a new Permanent Secretary, Sir Arnold France, he went into an intensive period of negotiation, covering everything save the level of remuneration, which was for the Review Body. to decide. The negotiations were lengthy and intense, and invariably Kenneth Robinson led for the Ministry. GPs never gave their leaders full negotiating powers; everything had to be taken away for approval. Ultimately Kenneth Robinson dropped his insistence on a salaried service option, the profession its desire for item-of-service payment, and an atmosphere of trust developed.[195] Two joint reports published during 1965 showed that progress was being made. The family doctors held their hand to give negotiations a chance. Better incentives were built into the system. There were proposals for an independent finance corporation to make loans for the purchase, erection and improvement of premises. Much of a GP's income would continue to be the traditional payments per patient, but this capitation fee would be higher for people over 65 who needed more attention. To encourage the provision of better services there would be direct repayment of 70 per cent of the cost of employing a receptionist or a nurse so that practices providing good facilities were less penalised. There would be direct repayment of the costs of providing premises, a notional rent reflecting their quality. The central pool was modified so that it covered only general medical services.[196] A basic practice allowance would be paid, and allowances would be greater for practice in groups, in unattractive areas, after vocational training and for seniority. There would also be a small fee for every immunisation given and cervical smear carried out. There would now be more paper work, because the GP's income became the sum of many fees and allowances, each a reward for work done or an incentive to improve the practice.

GPs were balloted on the proposals and agreed that they should go to the Review Body for pricing. There were two last-minute crises. Labour had only a small majority, a general election was called and the Review Body report was delayed. Labour was returned, and Kenneth Robinson continued as Minister. The wisdom of the GPs in going to the Review Body was shown when, taking account of the falling number of GPs and the workload, the Review Body changed its tune and to Kenneth Robinson's surprise suggested a rise of about a third in net remuneration. By then an economic crisis threatened an award of this size and it was rumoured that Kenneth Robinson had threatened to resign if the government reneged on the deal. The recommendation was accepted, albeit phased in over two years.[197] Ivor Jones, one of the doctors' negotiators, developed a plan for an independent medical service as an alternative to the NHS, which was stillborn.[198]

The Charter turned the tide. In 1967 the number of GPs in England and Wales rose (although only by five), continued to rise and list sizes fell. It was the first time that GPs had publicly resigned from the health service and the last time they could credibly threaten to do so. Neither the profession nor the government appreciated that the new dispensation, and public funding for premises and staff, made GPs so dependent on the NHS that any possibility of quitting *en masse* and practising outside the NHS had vanished.[199] During discussions on the Charter the government returned to the question of extra payments for special experience and service to the NHS. The GMSC looked at the issue; it was certainly true that some doctors had greater abilities and some worked harder than others. There was no career structure in general practice but no agreement about the characteristics of the 'better' GP. A GMSC working party suggested 'advancement awards' that did not imply professional merit in the quality of care given to patients, but preparation for practice, postgraduate study, practice organisation, teaching research, administrative service or work for the community. It got no thanks for its efforts. GPs were balloted on the principle and turned it down again, by four to one. Some felt that awards would suborn their leaders; GPs were not going to be divided into sheep and goats.[200]

There was an upsurge of interest in health centres, for the high rentals were now no longer a charge against personal income.[201] Fourteen were opened in 1967 bringing the total number to 45 and another 94 were being planned or built.[202] In the first decade the NHS had opened only ten; now the number rose to a peak of 100 a year in England in the 1970s.[203] Not only were there more centres, they were built for larger populations, often serving 25,000–30,000 or more. An imaginative one was proposed for Thamesmead, a new town within the Greater London Council boundaries, housing 60,000 people on a large area of waste land, with distinctive architecture and a balanced community. The proposals caught the attention of John Butterfield, Professor of Medicine at Guy's, and with the help of Nuffield a model medical service was planned to link the three parts of the NHS and bring preventive and curative medicine together.[204] Doctors were increasingly building their own premises. As they were spending their own money, the designs were carefully sized and seldom luxurious. The way the services were delivered was changing; secretaries and receptionists, nurses, health visitors and midwives were increasingly part of group practice teams and needed space. Trainee GP assistants might be employed. Postgraduate education required library space, and if a practice replaced the medical record envelope (which dated back to Lloyd George) with A4 records the space needed for files trebled. No sooner were new surgeries opened than they were found to be cramped.

George Godber saw his vision of health care as a complex of district hospital and community services, in which centres of general practice were the focal points, coming to pass.[205] He thought it right for immediate needs and any foreseeable development in medicine. Partnership of primary health care and specialised medicine was needed and this meant physical regrouping of the GPs, alongside nursing and other professional help, and a close relationship with the DGH and its resources.

Hospital and specialist services

The power of the regions

As development money flowed, RHBs became ever more powerful. It was the region that determined the priority of new hospital building. The region was in charge of medical staffing, held most consultants' contracts and (save for the teaching hospitals) made senior appointments. Consultants seeking to influence events had to have regional influence. For example, in the South East Metropolitan RHB specialist services were dominated by large teaching hospitals, Guy's and King's. The senior administrative medical officer (SAMO) decided to raise the standing of the hospitals at Canterbury and Brighton, so that there would be centres of expertise nearer the coast. Money was invested in them. The same process was repeated throughout the country and increasingly every hospital became, to a greater or lesser extent, a 'teaching hospital' training postgraduates, family doctors, nurses, auxiliaries and the specialist staff themselves.[206] Regions varied in their ethos; those in the south were used to working in close co-operation with the Ministry of Health, which might be to their advantage. Those in the north were more independently minded and received less money. The teaching hospitals managed by boards of governors certainly required higher staffing levels than non-teaching hospitals, but the balance of advantage in both quantity and quality seemed too much in favour of the teaching hospitals as opposed to the others.

As the health service developed, new 'professions supplementary to medicine' developed, seeking recognition and status. This meant, as for doctors and nurses before them, registration. In 1959 a Bill was published naming eight bodies to register chiropodists, dieticians, medical laboratory technicians, occupational therapists, physiotherapists, radiographers, remedial gymnasts and speech therapists. Each would maintain a register, approve training courses, supervise training institutions and remove from the register those guilty of misconduct. The medical profession sought dominance on the bodies; they obtained representation but not a majority.[207]

The district hospital system

The concept of the district general hospital had been accepted on the basis of the Hospital Surveys (1942–1945) and a population of at least 150,000 was required for the basic specialties. Some specialties, for example ophthalmology and ENT, required nearer 500,000. Cancer care and thoracic surgery needed a minimum population of 1 million, for centralisation was necessary. The regions had populations of this size but it was possible that some services would be so esoteric that even a region would not be large enough and a supra-regional service would be required. Providing the equipment was uneconomic and the results of treatment might be poor if doctors did not see enough cases.

Hospital development had so far been piecemeal and the London teaching hospitals were active in pushing their case. Some used their endowment money for preliminary design work, so they were ready to take any opportunity that presented itself. St Thomas' bought additional land, moved Lambeth Palace Road, paid £250,000 for a block of flats to rehouse displaced tenants, and in 1958 presented plans for a complete rebuild of an eleven-storey patient block fronting the river.[208] A few new buildings began to rise. In 1959 the foundation stone was laid at the new Welwyn–Hatfield hospital. The first stage of the new teaching hospital at Cambridge was completed at the beginning of 1961. In the same year a fine and accessible site in Harrow was chosen for a new district hospital to be built in association with a Clinical Research Centre (CRC) required by the Medical Research Council. The CRC would be an integral part of a hospital dealing with current medical problems and be able to keep in touch with day-to-day clinical practice. There would be 185 beds for clinical research, the emphasis being on common conditions.[209]

Hospital development and design

In 1958 hospital redevelopment was becoming more of a practical proposition. George Godber forecast that it would involve the replacement of multiple, small, bad, old hospitals by large, well planned, modern ones, fewer in number and with fewer beds in total. The mentally ill would probably be accommodated in psychiatric units at general hospitals.[210] Tom McKeown, Professor of Social Medicine in Birmingham, examined the use of beds in all types of hospital in Birmingham. He challenged the traditional organisation of hospital services as outmoded. He thought that only in acute hospitals was the idea of investigation and treatment established. Otherwise people were separated into different hospitals because the infectious had to be isolated, the mentally ill locked up and the chronic sick housed with the destitute. Instead of separate hospitals for each function he proposed a 'balanced hospital community' serving patients of all sorts, classified according to the intensity of care they needed, not their age or mental state. Patients might need full hospital facilities with frequent medical attention and nursing (54 per cent in Birmingham); only simple forms of nursing (9 per cent); supervision only because of their mental state (31 per cent); or no hospital facilities at all, being resident essentially for social reasons (6 per cent). In the balanced hospital community he proposed, the same medical and nursing staff would treat all patients. A single site might become something of a hospital-city, providing buildings of a variety of types with a range of commercial and leisure facilities, so that it blended into the town. The setting would be domestic rather than institutional. From the service point of view it would be better because doctors and nurses would be willing to spend some of their time on the chronic and the mentally ill if they could reconcile that with their other interests. Showing students a more representative selection of patients would improve their education. Research would be better because bright doctors would see common, difficult and inadequately studied conditions. The hospital would no longer look like a forbidding block of flats, but a well-planned housing estate or university centre.[211] It was an interesting idea, but not one suggesting deep clinical insight.

Nuffield concepts

- More medical activity meant more complex and expensive ancillary rooms
- More demand for privacy meant more single rooms and small bays
- Fewer patients were bed-fast
- Nurses' journeys were less in short thick buildings

The Nuffield studies were beginning to influence planning. The Ministry of Health established a small research unit, and regional boards were studying hospital design.[212] Experimental buildings made it possible to test new ideas – medical wards at Larkfield Hospital in Scotland and surgical wards at Musgrave Park Hospital in Belfast. Nuffield's surveys of the case load in Norwich and Northampton produced surprisingly low estimates of bed requirements, partly because of ever-shorter lengths of stay. They raised at least a doubt about the traditional view of the number of beds a population required. Many patients in hospital could have been treated at home. If GPs had access to diagnostic facilities, they might send fewer people to the outpatients department. Nuffield criticised the provision made for children. Many were accommodated in adult wards, particularly for operations on the eyes and for tonsillectomy. The Platt Report[213] argued for admission only when really required, and for children's units with specially trained nurses.

Hospitals were living, changing entities. The hospital design resembled town planning, where traffic routing was necessary so that different zones of a hospital could expand at different rates. In 1958 the Central Consultants and Specialists Committee of the BMA invited two consultants, Lawrence Abel and Walpole Lewin, to report on the increasing inadequacy of hospital buildings. They thought that the hospital building programme, having patiently taken its place in the queue for ten years, should have much higher priority.[214] Advances in medicine and surgery were straining already inadequate buildings. A glaring example was the problem of cross-infection in wards and operating theatres. There was now a far clearer idea of what was wanted. Urgent action was needed, not another survey. New towns should have priority. The policy of the DGH was logical, and would often lead to the immediate closure of smaller hospitals and financial savings. Designs should be flexible to accommodate change, and, to expedite building, some standard designs should be accepted. Tailor-made hospitals would only delay rebuilding.

Since 1939 neither architects nor hospital staff had experience of major hospital schemes, and in 1960 a group from the regions toured the USA, helped by the American Hospital Association and the US Public Health Service. Walpole Lewin and JOF Davies, the senior administrative medical officer of the Oxford RHB, reported on the introduction of central sterilisation, centralised and air-conditioned operating theatres, recovery rooms, progressive patient care and intensive care units. Davies argued for centralisation of district services onto a single site. With adequate domiciliary services to support GPs, the avoidance of admission on purely social grounds and early discharge, the number of acute beds might be reduced to 3 per 1,000 population.[215]

George Godber asked Davies to produce a chapter on hospital design for his first report as CMO in 1960 and Davies echoed Godber's own thinking. There could be no standard design because sites and needs varied so much. Hospital design should reflect social change, as patients expected a greater degree of privacy. It could not be assumed that medical or nursing practice would remain the same. The trend would be towards fewer hospital centres, large enough to justify several consultants in the main clinical and service departments. To the traditional DGH should be added 70–80 beds for short-stay psychiatry, 100 for maternity, 60 for the rehabilitation of elderly patients, and provision for infectious disease. Selected hospitals would have radiotherapy and neurosurgery which required provision on a regional basis. Hospitals would be highly specialised diagnostic and treatment centres, with a large outpatient service to handle all who could be treated without admission, which meant that diagnostic departments should be positioned to serve outpatients and inpatients equally. A regional plan for accident services would also be needed.[216]

Richard Llewelyn Davies who had run the Nuffield Unit (established to consider the architectural designs required for a modern hospital) was now in private architectural practice. Hospitals grew over time as departments expanded. Ordered growth and change had to be allowed for and the site should be planned with this in mind. Expansion had to be possible without cutting off traffic routes or invading space already used for other purposes. Service departments were changing and expanding rapidly and should be separated from ward areas. Llewelyn Davies thought it unlikely that the need for beds would alter radically for a long time ahead. If beds could be used flexibly by any specialty, wards would be the most static part of a hospital. He thought that low buildings were better than high ones, for they were easier to expand, but pointed to experiments with high rise hospitals where all the wards were placed in a tower block over a central stores, kitchen and laundry. In such hospitals nothing was stocked or prepared in ward kitchens; even a glass of milk was sent up when necessary.[217] The Ministry began to play an active role in hospital design, drawing substantially on work by the Nuffield Provincial Hospitals Trust.[218] It undertook research and development, building departments and whole hospitals to test ideas about planning and design, and issued guidance. An early building note, *The district general hospital*, emphasised the importance of the interrelationships of departments of a hospital – theatres and wards, service departments with the wards and outpatient department.[219] While a nationwide spread of well-trained consultants was steadily raising the standard of clinical care, the hospitals in which they worked did not match their skills. Momentum for greater expenditure on hospital building had been growing since Guillebaud but the costs involved had been so enormous that people recoiled from the idea.[220] Now rising sums of money were becoming available for capital development. In their 1959 election manifestos all political parties committed themselves to rapid hospital development, in line with a new vogue for long-term planning. Hospital building was one way of improving the uneven distribution of health services across the country, because revenue went with a new hospital.

The Hospital Plan

Three people were largely responsible for the Hospital Plan. George Godber had long been interested in the organisation of health services. In 1960 Bruce Fraser became

Permanent Secretary at the Ministry of Health, replacing a man who had been sick; Fraser recognised that hospital development had been a manifesto commitment.[221] In July 1960 Enoch Powell became Minister and proved a godsend; he might not have been philosophically committed to the principle of a national health service, but he made it hum. He was shown the five-year plans of the Oxford and Wessex RHBs and saw that, if all 14 regions had similar plans, they could be brought together and turned into a national scheme that the Treasury might be persuaded to fund. Powell decided the principles that were appropriate for a plan and applied them consistently, systematically and nationally. RHBs were asked to reassess their needs and submit proposals for the next ten years. After negotiation with the Ministry these became the basis of the Hospital Plan published in January 1962.[222] This proposed the development of 90 new hospitals from scratch, and the upgrading of 134. The Minister sent a message to his staff.

> The Hospital Plan will determine for many years to come the broad lines of development of the hospital service, and indeed of the Health Service as a whole. No other nation has had – or taken – the opportunity to refashion its hospitals so comprehensively and on so large a scale.

The morning after it was published Enoch Powell called his team together and asked for a further document on local health authority plans. However, local authorities were not under the control of the Ministry, as were the RHBs, and there was little information about any plans that they might have. Powell asked them about their community services, for there was no point having a hospital plan that presumed the existence of facilities in the community if they were not going to be there. Powell was under no delusion that community care was a cheap option. Putting people into an institution was cheap; community care was by definition staff-intensive, and therefore expensive.

The Hospital Plan aimed at a network of DGHs of 600–800 beds, normally serving a population of 100,000–150,000. District by district it outlined phased redevelopment over the next decades. The goal was usually the unification of separate hospitals that worked together as a DGH. The waste of consultant time travelling between different hospitals, the difficulty of providing complete training for nurses, the need to bring geriatric and psychiatric services within the curtilage of the DGH and the improvement in clinical care possible on a single site made this desirable. It was also essential to bring ophthalmology, chest medicine, paediatrics, obstetrics, accident services and the long-stay specialties alongside general medicine and surgery.[223] The BMJ welcomed this drastic reorganisation. Powell had seen the task not as one of rebuilding, but of changing the pattern and content of the hospital service. Finance, the journal shrewdly observed, might be the main problem.[224] The plan contained only passing references to preventive and community services. It suggested the level of provision of beds per 1,000 population for acute, geriatric, maternity, mental illness and mental subnormality services, bearing in mind the support from local authority and GPs. For acute services 3.3 beds per 1000 population was proposed, the national provision then averaging 3.9 beds per 1000. The studies by Nuffield and the Oxford RHB for Reading suggested even fewer, 2 beds per 1,000.[225] The plan acknowledged the opposing pulls of centralisation and accessibility to patients, but considered that the benefits of grouping outweighed the disadvantages of patients having to travel further. DGHs would provide all ordinary specialties but not those that needed a larger catchment area such as radiotherapy, neurosurgery, plastic surgery and thoracic surgery. Outpatient departments would include theatre facilities and there would be day-wards for those not requiring admission. A maternity unit with full and continuous consultant cover would be a normal part of the DGH and most, but not necessarily all, would have an accident and emergency department. Some forms of care previously provided at separate hospitals would now be brought into the DGH. For example, there should be an active geriatric unit (although some patients might move to separate long-stay annexes), and a unit of 30–60 short-stay beds for people with mental illness. The Hospital Plan saw little future role for the existing mental hospitals; some probably could continue, if reduced in size and improved, but eventually many should be abandoned.

The Hospital Plan was sent to local health authorities with Powell's questions about their own plans. Local authority services needed to be organised in parallel with the hospitals, and councils were asked to draw up ten-year programmes. Health policies were set out where they had an influence on local authority services. For maternity there were the recommendations of the Cranbrook Committee that there should be hospital beds for 70 per cent of confinements and a ten-day length of stay, already out of date. The Mental Health Act 1959 meant there was a need for training centres, residential accommodation and social centres. Policy for elderly people was to help them remain in their own homes as long as possible. There proved to be little correlation between health and local authority planning although the norms of the Hospital Plan depended upon community support. Because of their autonomy, the Ministry could not impose any commonality upon them. However, the local authorities responded by developing substantial plans to build residential homes for elderly people and homes and hostels for people with physical or mental disabilities or who were mentally ill.

New hospitals cost more and took longer to build than predicted, and regions' proposals proved wildly optimistic. If a scheme cost more than estimated, it was tailored, or other projects postponed indefinitely.[226] In 1966 the plan was revised as the Hospital Programme.[227] Running costs also rose, and more staff were needed because services were better and more extensive. However, the bed norms were found to be too high, as better facilities meant more patients could be treated. Sometimes, as with maternity services, an early discharge policy meant that a bed shortage changed rapidly into a bed surplus. As lengths of stay fell progressively, revisions of the plan lowered the norms of provision to 2.0–2.5 per 1000 of the population.

Teaching hospitals and the problems of London

Because the teaching hospitals had a national role in education and research, patients might be specially selected, and those requiring more mundane forms of care were often treated in hospitals run by regions and hospital management committees (HMCs). The case-mix of the teaching hospitals, especially those in London, was therefore atypical. Educationally this was silly, for students most need to see ordinary illnesses and a full range of emergency admissions. Was a ward devoted to the rare diseases of calcium metabolism, as at University College Hospital, appropriate for undergraduate teaching? Teaching hospitals would be short of some types of patients, as for example in the case of midwifery, and the medical schools would rely on RHB hospitals. As the RHB hospitals steadily improved, fewer patients came to the teaching hospitals. The plight of those in London was increased by the fall of the central population that had been taking place since the late nineteenth century, speeded by the post-war housing policy of the London County Council. Some teaching hospitals rethought their position. They tried to develop stronger links with local communities and with good DGHs away from the centre. After much debate the policy of 'designation' was agreed. From the mid-1960s some hospitals previously managed by RHBs were transferred to the teaching hospital boards of governors, increasing the beds at their disposal, and placing district responsibilities upon the teaching hospitals.[228]

In London four RHBs with differing approaches and artificial boundaries operated side by side. The structure of many hospitals required urgent attention and a plethora of small specialist units was developing. London still trained many of the country's doctors, there was a need to balance service and teaching needs, and to agree which hospitals and regional services such as heart surgery should be redeveloped. Yet the teaching hospital boards of governors were loath to face these problems. In 1964 four regional joint consultative committees were formed, to bring the RHBs and the boards of governors into more amicable discussion with each other, and a pan-London group was formed. Albertine Winner, an ex-deputy chief medical officer from the Ministry, took charge. The group produced a series of reports on the main specialties and broke new ground by examining requirements on a London-wide basis. Albertine Winner was well liked but no confrontationalist. Neither the RHBs nor the teaching hospitals felt bound by the reports, which were not implemented.

The London postgraduate hospitals

In London most special hospitals retained their independence in 12 postgraduate groups. Some were small and isolated, perhaps with as few as 40 beds, as in the case of the urological hospitals, St Peter's, St Paul's and St Philip's (the three Ps). The Ministry believed that the small hospitals were not viable as independent units, and in the view of Keith Murray, the Chairman of the University Grants Committee, neither were their Institutes. Others were of substantial size, such as Great Ormond Street and the Hospital for Nervous Diseases. In June 1961 Enoch Powell proposed to relocate almost all in one of two groups, in Holborn and the Fulham Road. The *BMJ* approved, for one group would be near the centre of the University of London in Bloomsbury, and the other near Imperial College in South Kensington. Such a grouping in 'friendly proximity' might in the fullness of time lead to close links.[229] However, the special hospitals had fought like tigers for a century to keep their independence. They were not going to give up without a struggle.

Sir George Pickering, who knew London from his St Mary's days but was now Regius Professor of Medicine in Oxford, was asked for advice. Pickering was an original thinker yet completely acceptable in academic circles and he chaired a group of experienced clinicians to consider the principles involved in the organisation of the special hospitals and their postgraduate institutes.[230] The key question was whether hospitals with world league expertise would maintain pre-eminence if they remained essentially single-specialty. The rewards and penalties of isolation were examined. In favour of the single-specialty hospital was the ability to concentrate on one goal, the *ésprit de corps* and the concentration of expertise. Against was the risk of intellectual isolation when medicine was advancing on a broad front. Inevitably some forms of specialised equipment and library facilities, possessed by the general medical schools, would be missing. Pickering came down firmly on the side of association, if not with a general medical school, at least with each other. The ideal association of the postgraduate hospitals and their institutes would comprise four or six of them grouped round the periphery of a circle, each maintaining its own identity, but with shared facilities. The Ministry held discussions in 1961 with the University of London and the two-site solution was agreed. In Chelsea a 19-acre site was identified, near the Brompton and the Marsden Hospitals. However, it proved difficult to get a clear site for development, and to decant and relocate units while keeping them working. Finding enough accommodation for the nursing staff was impossible, and the costs were high. The hospitals and their institutes fought a spirited rearguard action against relocation or merger, and there were too many unanswered questions – whether the hospitals really needed to be in central London, what the Royal Commission on Medical Education would say about the separation of postgraduate hospitals from undergraduate education, and whether such a scheme could succeed without a guaranteed and rapid succession of phases.[231]

Hospital management and Cogwheel

Many features of hospital management, always a fertile field for research, were examined by the Nuffield Provincial Hospitals Trust. Its Secretary, Gordon McLachlan, was in close contact with Sir George Godber and had a sure touch in the identification of key issues. Operational research was applied to outpatient departments, waiting times being a frequent cause of complaint. The *BMJ* agreed that it might be possible to introduce schemes that were helpful for everyone concerned, but the unexpected was apt to happen. More consultants were needed and it was possible to make too much of the problem; for many the regular visit to the outpatient department was the equivalent of going to a club for a good gossip.[232] An emerging problem was the poor communication among the growing number of consultants in any one hospital. In 1948 it was usually possible to accommodate the entire consultant staff in a moderate sized room. The dining room provided a focus and the house governor or hospital secretary was a familiar figure. The doubling of the number of consultants meant that this was no longer the case. There were two or three consultants in most specialties and more specialties than ever before. Consultant services were ceasing to be coherent. Young surgeons would introduce new methods and shorter stays that the older ones might not accept. Clinical departments should have had agreed policies for their resources but did not. Professor Revans described the cult of individualism among medical staff as one of the most obstinate of all hospital problems. Doctors found it hard to talk to each other, let alone with management. The Advisory Committee for Management Efficiency argued that clinicians needed management training. In 1966 Sir George Godber established a working party nominated jointly by the Ministry and the Joint Consultants Committee of the BMA on the organisation of medical work in hospitals. The first of its reports was published in 1967 and was promptly called 'Cogwheel', after the cover motif.[233] Its aim was to develop the review of clinical work in hospitals, and its outcome. Practising doctors could and should improve their administrative systems without waiting for organisational change. The Report offered a simple, credible and flexible solution that was already in use in some hospitals, the clinical division.

> *Specialties falling into the same broad medical or surgical categories should be grouped to form Divisions. Each division should carry out constant appraisal of the services it provides, deploy clinical resources as effectively as possible and cope with the problems of management that arise in its clinical field. A small medical executive committee composed of representatives from each division should be established.*

Whether or not more money was provided, better management by doctors was necessary if the service was to be fully effective and the doctors were to retain their professional freedom.[234] The tenuous links between individual hospitals in the same group and with general practice and local authority services meant inefficiency. GPs and local authority medical staff should be part of the divisional organisation. Clinical divisions should work closely with management, for the two were closely related. In this way the reasons for the substantial variations in clinical practice could be examined, as in the increasing treatment of varicose veins by day surgery and the declining use of tonsillectomy. The *BMJ* was anxious that clinical divisions did not usurp doctors' proper clinical freedom, the traditional duty to treat patients in the way they believed to be best.[235]

Kenneth Robinson, Minister of Health, contrasted the technological developments in medicine, open heart surgery and brain surgery with the parallel managerial revolution in health planning.[236] As in industry, it was logical to think in terms of bigger administrative units. A change in structure was coming; the initial one was curiously static and a system allowing evolution was needed. The Guillebaud report had avoided altering the NHS organisational structure, but this freeze had thawed. Partnership with the medical profession was needed even though the relationship of the profession with the state, as provider of resources, could never be entirely smooth. Successive governments tried to reduce the area of possible conflict but still there was lack of mutual confidence. Why? Ministers, like doctors, wished to provide the best possible service the nation could afford. Management must be effective, planners were needed who could make a common cause with the staff, and health economists were needed too. Partnership between doctors and the state was needed, as well as partnership between the hospitals of the future and group practices providing curative and preventive services. GPs and nurses, working in a group, would give a new dimension to the concept of an all-round personal physician. The *BMJ* said Mr Robinson was more sincere than most of his predecessors but, however well intentioned, he suffered from the layman's inability to understand the finer professional feelings of the doctors with whom he was dealing. Rather than pondering on the irrational behaviour of a seemingly unappreciative lot of doctors, perhaps the Minster might examine the doctors' discontents dispassionately: why were they emigrating, why did they not find satisfaction in the NHS, why had the men in Whitehall multiplied, making them the masters of the men in the field?[237]

Hospital information systems

Better information about activity was required to underpin the expansion of the service. In most countries hospitals had billing systems, accurate information was necessary, and other systems piggy-backed on financial ones. In the NHS there was no patient-related costing system on which to build. Since 1948 the Hospital In-patient Enquiry (HIPE) had provided a 10 per cent sample of inpatient treatment. Now this random sample was extended to 100 per cent coverage in pilot hospitals, and in 1964/5, throughout the Birmingham, Newcastle and Liverpool regions. Hospital activity analysis (HAA), as the 100 per cent system was known, grew out of a wish for patient-based information to help decisions on the use and allocation of hospital resources. HAA provided doctors and administrators at clinical and management levels with details relating to individual patients, including diagnosis and operations, sex, age and marital status of patients, date of admission, discharge and the length of stay. At low cost, it aimed at giving wide benefits to many users. Details of each admission were collected from a standard front-sheet to the notes. RHBs processed the data to provide management and clinical statistics. The scheme was introduced progressively with an emphasis on rapid feedback and accuracy.[238] For the first time it was possible, in theory, for consultants to relate the use of resources to the characteristics of their patients, their diagnoses and operations. The feedback was slow and there were anecdotes about men having hysterectomies and women prostate operations.

HAA was based on admissions, not individual people, and did not link one admission to another. In 1962 the Oxford Record Linkage System (ORLS) tried to make this link. ORLS was funded by the Nuffield Provincial Hospitals Trust and its first director was Donald Acheson, later to become CMO at the Department of Health.[239] Births and deaths were linked with basic information about all hospital admissions, a time-consuming process as all data had to be extracted manually. Computer cards were punched and the files periodically scanned. Hospitals were sent lists of patients dying in the year after discharge, many of the deaths being unknown to the clinicians. Cervical cytologists were sent lists of patients subsequently developing cancer of the cervix, to allow feedback. As a laboratory scale demonstration it provided a new way of looking at patients over a period of time. National expansion was not practical.

Better data made it possible to explore the relationships underlying bed usage. Comparison of the regions showed that the more beds there were, the longer the average length of stay; Liverpool had many beds and lengthy stays; Oxford, with few beds, had the shortest lengths of stay and the highest bed usage.[240] Efficiency became a watchword. The Advisory Committee for Management Efficiency met regularly and advised the Minister on the use of work-study in the hospital service. It looked at costing systems, the presentation and interpretation of hospital statistics and the building programme. In 1965 the RCP held a meeting on computers in medicine. A speaker from Honeywell said that his prescription for computers in medicine was to increase both the size and the frequency of the dose.[241] The Ministry established a new computer policy and development branch and by 1966 the hospital service had eight computers.

NHS expenditure

The Ministry, concerned about the rising cost of the NHS, looked with increasing interest at hospital costs per patient-week and per inpatient stay. Guillebaud had criticised the existing cost returns as inadequate for management purposes and they were improved. When adjustments were made for the changes in salaries and prices the rise in the cost in real terms over the 1950s (1950/1–1958/9) had been minimal, no more than 10 per cent.[242] A working party, set up in 1960 to review the system for estimating and allocating revenue, reported that the existing procedures were defective. The initial estimates from the RHBs added up to so much more than the sums likely to be available that each year regions had to revise their figures downwards. It suggested that forward-look estimates for a single year should be replaced by five-year projections, and that a change to unit and departmental budgeting – as opposed to functional budgeting across the entire authority – should be considered. Hospital costs continued to rise but increasing economic prosperity meant that more money could be spent on the NHS. Up to 1963/4, hospital costs adjusted for rises in pay and prices rose about 2 per cent per year; the rate of increase then rose to 2.5 per cent and the growth of the service was more rapid because of improvements in efficiency.[243]

Medical education and staffing

Medical education

Once it was appreciated that there would be a shortage of doctors, the University Grants Committee (UGC) faced a dual problem: expanding medical education as rapidly as possible without lowering standards, and adapting it to changes in medicine along the lines proposed by Goodenough. One suggestion, soon abandoned, was the establishment of 24 new schools. Central was the belief that the medical course should give students a university education on broad and liberal lines and the UGC was adamant about the need to maintain quality, which meant schools large enough to justify a wide range of specialties and facilities. The decision was taken to combine modernisation and expansion by rebuilding existing schools to about twice their previous size. The UGC defined the facilities and staffing a medical school would need. Large numbers of new academic staff were appointed and required space for learning, teaching and research. This was easier to accomplish in the provincial schools than in London, where the boards of governors were seldom sympathetic to the demands of their schools.

Doctors tended to settle near their medical school, a high proportion of students went to the London schools and specialists were still unevenly distributed. The Sheffield RHB was in the worst position and there was little point in raising its revenue allocation, for on what could it be spent? The region was already advertising for medical staff and attracting few. The solution had to be an alteration in the places where students trained. That required an agreement between the Ministry and the UGC that new schools were required. The new schools needed new and better clinical facilities, but these were also required for service reasons. The capital building programme was therefore modified. The first wave of expansion began about 1962 with the aim of rebuilding all the provincial teaching hospitals to the new requirements. There remained some fundamental structural problems with medical education. In the early 1960s the UGC proposed that there should be a Royal Commission to address three problems that could not be tackled by the UGC on its own. They included

- The further expansion of medical education.
- The organisation and expansion of postgraduate medical education, for which nobody carried statutory responsibility. A better infrastructure was needed if the university-style education recommended by Goodenough was to come to fruition.
- Problems of medical education in London, then training half the medical students.

John Ellis, of The London Hospital, supported by Janet Vaughan, drafted a proposal that went to the UGC and thence to the government. A general election was close, which meant that it was unlikely that the major parties would oppose the concept of a Royal Commission as a way of dealing with a difficult field. In June 1965, the Prime Minister, Harold Wilson, established one chaired by Lord Todd, Professor of Organic Chemistry at Cambridge and a Nobel prize winner.[244] It undertook a fundamental review of the whole structure of medical education, its organisation, content and claims on resources.

Postgraduate education was of increasing importance. In 1960 three consultants from Exeter went to see George Godber at the Ministry and asked him to make a site available for an education centre, rent-free, in the grounds of the new Royal Devon and Exeter Hospital. A week later a group from Stoke-on-Trent went with a similar request. George Godber discussed the idea with Gordon McLachlan at the Nuffield Provincial Hospitals Trust and later with Sir George Pickering. A private conference was arranged at Christ Church Oxford in February 1961, under Pickering's chairmanship, attended by the presidents of the Royal Colleges, representatives of the CGP, and staff from the RHBs. The conference seemed to catch a tide of interest at the flood. Considerable attention had been paid to undergraduate education; with the advance of medical and scientific knowledge the importance and relevance of postgraduate education throughout the doctor's career was now acknowledged. Pickering stressed the importance of organising and improving it and the conference agreed that the basic unit should be the district hospital, each with a clinical tutor responsible for teaching arrangements. The necessary facilities included a seminar room, library, a clinical tutor's room and a lunch room as a focal point where hospital medical staff and GPs could meet.[245] There should be a postgraduate dean appointed by the university medical school, and a strong regional committee to oversee the provision.[246] A sum of £250,000 was provided by Nuffield to supplement local appeals for centre development and the King's Fund helped hospitals in the metropolitan regions. Centres by the score developed all over the country.[247] Within four years 150 were in existence and the Stoke centre was one of the first, George Pickering laying the foundation stone in 1963.

Doctors' pay and the Royal Commission

The Royal Commission recommendations (1960)[248]

Consultants	£2,500 rising to £3,900
Senior registrars	£1,500 rising to £2,100
Registrars	£1,250 rising to £1,400
House officers	£425 rising to £525
GPs	£2,425 average net income from all official sources

The Royal Commission, chaired by Sir Harry Pilkington, took evidence from the Colleges, the Ministry and other organisations. Interested parties watched its work like hawks. The MPU, representing 4,000 GPs, gave evidence; some of its ideas, for example the reduction in the size of a maximum list to 3,000 patients and direct reimbursement of practice expenses, were adopted by the BMA.[248] The Commission reported in 1960, and recommended the appointment of a permanent impartial Review Body that would advise the Prime Minister on pay, deliberate in private and deal with major matters only. The Commission saw no reason to raise pay to attract young people into medicine or dissuade doctors from emigrating. However, it believed that doctors' pay was too low in comparison with other professions, and it recommended an increase of 22 per cent above the 1955/6 level. The Minister of Health agreed to accept the recommendations if the professions would do the same.[249] The consultants already had the distinction award system with additional sums distributed by senior members of the profession under conditions of secrecy. The awards varied from £750 for the 1,600 'Cs' to £4,000 for 100 'A+' awards. The Commission suggested that an additional £500,000 should be set aside to recognise distinguished general practice. The Review Body was established in 1962 under the chairmanship of Lord Kindersley. It would determine pay by the analysis of data rather than by a power struggle, preventing pay disputes from disrupting the NHS. It would give doctors and dentists a guarantee that their wages would not be arbitrarily depressed for political reasons, and assure the taxpayer that the professionals were not earning too much. It would hear evidence from the professions and the health ministries and take into account changes in the cost of living, earnings in other professions and recruitment. Its proposals, though not binding on the government, should be rejected only for the most compelling reasons.

Medical staffing

Government was virtually a monopoly employer of doctors, educating them largely at national expense and employing them on standard salary scales. There was no reason to train more doctors than required for the NHS, where the employment opportunities were determined primarily by government policies. In 1957 Willink had identified the main determinants of demand – the population size and structure, economic growth, policy decisions on the desirable pattern of health care, and assumptions on recruitment, emigration, retirement and death.[250] Complex though the committee's calculations had been, they did not allow adequately for rapid developments in medical technology, immigration of junior doctors from India and Pakistan or the extent of emigration of younger doctors fuelled by a world-wide demand for well-trained doctors. Willink had suggested a reduction by 10 per cent in medical school entry. A serious shortage was first predicted in 1960, and articles by John Seale, a supporter of private practice and a critic of the NHS, fuelled continuing controversy.[251] Seale was bitterly attacked by the Ministry but shortages began to bite.[252]

Lord Taylor, in the House of Lords, drew attention to the fact that, outside the teaching hospitals, the NHS depended heavily on some 4,000 foreign doctors, mainly from India and Pakistan, who had come for experience and to earn a better living than at home. As they came in, British doctors were leaving for other countries.

> I cannot recommend your Lordships to go into such hospitals as a casualty, for there is in many cases no casualty officer. A house-surgeon will have to leave the theatre when he can, to treat you, and his experience will be far less than that of your own general practitioners. When he comes he will probably not be a British graduate and he could well have difficulty in understanding what you say. This is at a time when speed and efficiency may be literally life saving.[253]

It was, he said, 'a pretty ghastly, awful picture'. John Seale's warnings were vindicated. A study by Brian Abel-Smith, commissioned in an attempt to refute Seale, showed that during 1955–1959 an average of 1,664 doctors born and trained in Britain were registered annually in the *Medical directory*. The estimated annual loss by emigration was about 390, nearly one-quarter.[254] They were emigrating partly because those who had left teaching hospitals had little chance of ever becoming a consultant, and often saw general practice as a low status occupation.[255] The Ministry sent a team to North America to help doctors who, having emigrated, might wish to return.[256] Women were an increasing part of the workforce and by 1966 25 per cent of medical students were female. Surveys showed that about 80 per cent were working, half of them full-time.[257] They might take time off for domestic commitments, but at least they tended to stay in the country. In November 1961 the Minister of Health proposed that the annual student intake should be 10 per cent above that suggested by Willink, and in 1963 the Ministry proposed a further increase of 15 per cent. In July 1964 the Minister of Health, Anthony Barber, informed Parliament that the first new school since 1893 would be at Nottingham and that finance would be available in 1967 for a school at Southampton. The annual intake of medical students was raised from about 1,800 to 2,450 between 1960 and 1967.[258]

The Platt Report

The Platt Report (1961)[258]

- Reorganisation of the consultant service
- Increase the number of consultant posts
- Restrict the number of senior registrar posts in line with expected consultant vacancies
- A medical assistant career staff-grade
- Rotational training for senior registrars

Although there was now some control of the number of senior registrars, this was not the case for the more junior registrar grade. This was often used to solve staffing problems, and training might be seen as incidental to practical experience. The registrar grade was allowed to grow, often filled by doctors from developing countries seeking postgraduate experience. The specialties into which doctors crowded were not the ones where there was the greatest need, the 'service specialties' such as anaesthesia and pathology, and new sub-specialties required an increasing number of consultants, a message to be repeated regularly for the succeeding 35 years. To try to get the numbers right a working party on hospital medical staffing, chaired by Sir Robert Platt, was established by the Ministry and the profession in 1958. It was asked to advise on the principles by which hospital staffing should be organised. One of its first actions was to undertake the first detailed census of junior doctors at registrar level and below. Of the 8,272, no fewer than 3,408 had been born outside Great Britain, mainly occupying posts in the surgical specialties and the northern regions.[259] The imbalance of junior and senior posts meant that only a minority of registrars could expect to achieve consultant rank. Two deficiencies were rapidly identified. In spite of the imbalance of juniors and seniors, from the service viewpoint there was a shortage of doctors below the level of consultant, particularly outside the teaching hospitals. There was a lesser shortage of consultants themselves. Platt recommended an increase in the number of consultants and restriction of the number of juniors; the government accepted these broad principles. More consultant posts were created year by year but never enough. The Ministry wanted 400 extra annually but seldom achieved more than 250. There was a perception that some consultants wanted assistants, not colleagues who might compete for private patients. Junior doctors began to appreciate that they could not rely on their seniors to negotiate for them and to talk about an independent body to represent their interests to the Ministry. The BMA wanted to maintain professional unity but there was a divergence of interests.

Nursing

Nurse education and staffing

Hospital nursing staff* (England and Wales)

	1949	1959
Total numbers	137,636	190,946
Registered nurses	46,300	66,582
Student nurses	46,386	54,960
Enrolled nurses	16,076	16,135
Pupil nurses	1,515	5,889
Other	27,355	47,380

*Excludes hospital midwives

Although their numbers both in hospital and in the community had increased by roughly a third in the first ten years of the NHS, there were never enough nurses. The limiting factor was the ability to recruit staff rather than money. Nursing had to compete with other occupations and depended on the supply of young unmarried students and a smaller number of unmarried qualified staff who continued to work until retirement. If the nurses were rushed, it was hard to give good care and to supervise the clinical training of students.[260] Advances in treatment increased the demand. Crowded wards with 'extra beds', poor rewards and widely reported problems in hospitals did little to encourage recruitment. There was a student wastage of 30–50 per cent, 10,000 a year failing to complete their training. Up to 30 per cent, said one matron, had to be accepted. The Editor of the *Nursing Mirror*, in 1958, recalled 20 reports on nursing problems in the previous 25 years. Job analysis, questionnaires, pilot studies and conferences had all taken place. Statisticians, management consultants, eminent doctors and administrators had given advice. Still the same problems remained, unpredictable off-duty, excessive hours, lectures given in off-duty time, outworn discipline, bad conditions, excessive responsibility on night-duty, insufficient care of the student's health, haphazard practical training, ward sisters untrained in human relations and too-early entry through cadet schemes.[261] Students looked forward to leaving the preliminary training school and starting work on the wards, for practical work was regarded as 'real' nursing. Yet young nurses were expected to take on responsibilities that, even with support, they were often incapable of handling. They got 'second-year blues' and gave up. A study in Oxford showed that a third of the students had qualifications that would have gained a place at a teacher's training college, and 5 per cent could have been considered for a university. More than half of the entrants wanted to work in a hospital abroad, in the services, on a ship or as an air hostess.[262]

Believing that complete reappraisal of nursing education was required, in 1961 the Royal College of Nursing (RCN) established a committee, chaired by Sir Harry Platt, which reported in 1964. A *reform of nursing education* recommended two different courses for registered nurses and enrolled nurses. The student nurse must be a student in *fact* and the service she gave must be governed by her educational needs. An educational entry standard was essential (five 'O' levels). There would be two years' academic study and controlled clinical experience, after which she would sit the final examination. A third year would be spent under supervision in hospital. University degrees for nurses should be established. Enrolled nurses, the second grade, would follow a less elaborate apprenticeship training, and ward assistants would support the nursing team.[263] Writing in the *Lancet*, a Coventry consultant said that modern nursing and medicine required an understanding of the reasons for what was done, and if nurses were to be good observers they must know what to look for. Medicine and nursing were allies, each with responsibilities. The *Nursing Times* agreed; doctors should be allies not just in teaching but also in the selection of recruits and the organisation of the school of nursing.[264] In 1962 a minimum educational standard was reintroduced for state registration.[265] To improve the quality of training the GNC proposed that all nurse training schools should have access to a hospital or group of hospitals of at least 300 beds, and that the training course should include experience in general medicine and surgery, gynaecology, paediatrics, theatre work, ENT, ophthalmology and skin cases. This was implemented in 1964 and led to a reduction of about 100 in the 660 general nurse training schools. It became clear that a radical review of nurse training was required, to fulfil the demands of hospital and community services that were working increasingly closely. Basic training should prepare nurses for work in hospital, health centre, general practice attachment or other forms of community care. Post-basic training for specialised clinical care and management required development, and it would be necessary to use the facilities of the national educational system.[266]

Graduate nurses and research departments, though common in the USA, were virtually non-existent in the UK. Nurses with degrees had generally obtained them in unrelated subjects, before changing their career path to enter nursing. Some British nurses, with support from doctors, began to see university qualifications as a precondition of the improvement of the status of nursing. Charles Newman, Dean of the Postgraduate Medical School at Hammersmith, saw three reasons in favour: first, the more kinds of nursing education the better; second, the feminist argument that other professions pursued by women, such as architecture, science and medicine, were university based; and, third, the prestige and status helped to stimulate individuals to do their best. If nursing were university based, there would be more nursing research and the discipline would be more appropriate to current circumstances. Nurses, however, would have to set the matter in motion themselves, and not wait for others.[267] There were counter arguments. Girdwood, an Edinburgh physician, doubted whether it was wise to have three types of nurses, those with degrees, those who were registered, and the enrolled nurses. Nothing should be done to make the trained nurses feel in any way second-class. Hospital doctors did not want 'another colleague with whom to discuss the niceties of acid–base balance'; ward sisters were already well informed. Most girls wanting to be nurses wanted to be just that – not bachelors of science; most girls who wanted to be bachelors of science did not want to be nurses. There was certainly a place for a few university trained nurses, but only a few; the standard of a university degree must remain very high and the need for such a training in nursing was limited.[268]

To meet the demand for more leisure and shorter hours, the recommendation of the Nurses and Midwives Whitley Council that the hours of work should be reduced from 96 hours a fortnight to 84 was slowly implemented from 1958 onwards. At first the teaching hospitals were immune from the shortage of nurses, but not for long. The London matrons had a dining club; discussion started only after the aperitif and the dinner, and in the relaxed atmosphere they confided in each other. Each thought that only *they* had recruitment difficulties. All of them did. Something needed to be done, but recruiting trips round the schools showed that headmistresses now actively discouraged brighter girls from a career in nursing. The London Hospital built a new education department and better nurses' accommodation, established a degree course in association with London University, and began training enrolled nurses. Like everyone else, nurses married earlier. The local health authority nursing services had long employed married nurses, many of whom preferred the hours and the flexibility of work in the community. The increasing number of young married nurses in hospital also demanded latitude in the hours worked. Increasingly, matrons and public health nursing officers found that they could not manage without married nurses, whether they wanted to or not. Attracting older nurses back into the service became important. Better use had to be made of existing resources. Nurses' time should be spent on nursing; assistant nurses should be used increasingly and the growing number of part-time nurses should be encouraged.[269] 'Straight' rather than 'split' shifts made it possible to bring married nurses back into the profession, although refresher courses might be needed. A drastic elimination of non-nursing duties began. Time was saved by central sterilisation systems, by centralising patients needing close supervision in intensive care units and by the introduction of progressive patient care. Five-day wards staffed mainly by part-time nurses were introduced, and a nursing cadet scheme was increasingly used.[270] Midwifery was also short-staffed. One way to attract and retain staff, particularly in fields that were under strength, was the post-registration course, for example in ophthalmology. Increasingly, certificates were offered, each involving service in a hospital that had recruitment problems.

There was dissatisfaction with pay. The RCN represented most trained nurses and students. But two other unions, NUPE and COHSE, represented the enrolled nurses, nurses working in mental illness and mental handicap, and domestic staff. From 1960 to 1961 they were active in seeking higher pay and sometimes shorter hours. In July 1961 the Chancellor announced a pay pause, and while existing agreements were honoured during the pause, the implementation of new agreements would be postponed. In 1962 the nurses and ancillary workers mounted an all-night demonstration in support of pay claims. Planned as part of the opposition to government pay policy, it was followed by a debate in Parliament. The Minister, Enoch Powell, said there were more nurses than ever before. The opposition led by Kenneth Robinson said there were not enough and they were paid pitifully. The government was teaching the lesson that 'power tells' and imposing the pay pause on small people who could not fight back without injuring patients.[271]

Nursing practice

Nurses struggled to solve nursing problems, while all the time medical advances and wider opportunities for women were overtaking them. Doctors never really considered what their clinical advances did to nursing. Shorter lengths of stay, less restriction to bed, active geriatric policies, and the increasing use of one-day-stay beds all had repercussions on the nursing services.[272] The result, in the absence of unified and effective nursing leadership, was to turn the profession into a treadmill. Little thought was given to the intrinsic differences between the professions. Medicine, technology and the pharmaceutical industry had an in-built research ethos, with continual forward movement. If nursing was also to attempt to become research based, what would be the research focus? Much of the work of nursing, other than simple care and support, was dependent on medicine and technology, for these led change. From the moment it became possible to resuscitate a patient with cardiac arrest, having two nurses always on the ward was essential. Should the nurse tend mechanical devices or give traditional nursing care and stand back while technicians looked after the machines? 'Progressive patient care' was suggested as a way of using the limited number of nurses most efficiently.[273] Patients needing constant nursing attention, and those who were ambulant and physically self-sufficient, were removed from the ordinary ward to be nursed in 'intensive care' and 'self-care' units. Some ways of running a ward, such as job allocation, centred control on the ward sister and made the use of lower grade staff easier. Others, for example team nursing, increased delegation and encouraged individual 'patient-centred' care.

Patient welfare was given greater attention with later waking times, greater privacy, better catering and more frequent visiting, particularly for children. Muriel Powell, Matron of St George's, imaginative and described as 'a new look matron', chaired the Standing Nursing Advisory Committee (SNAC) and made her aim the improvement of the patient's lot. Her committee challenged the early waking of patients, to which the Nuffield Report had drawn attention, and the perpetual noise from staff, hospital procedures and hospital equipment that had been the topic of an investigation by the King's Fund in 1958. Two reports were issued in 1961, *The pattern of the in-patient's day* and *Control of noise in hospitals*.[274] The Standing Maternity Committee also issued a report in 1961 on *Human relationships in obstetrics*, about the need to improve the help, companionship and explanation available in labour.

Nursing administration

From the start of the NHS there had been concern about the training of nurses for senior roles. The King's Fund began courses for ward sisters in 1949 and later for matrons. Nurse tutor courses and diplomas in nursing were sometimes used as a preparation for nursing management. Yet, despite fundamental changes in medicine, the administration of nursing had barely changed. Florence Nightingale, said the BMJ, would probably notice little difference between nursing administration in her day and ours.[275] Her contemporary, the great physician Henry Bence Jones, would not be so at home in the administrative maze surrounding the modern teaching hospital. In 1959 the RCN set up a working party to examine the position. In 1964, following the principles of the Bradbeer Report (1954), the RCN recommended radical change, establishing a framework for nursing resembling that for lay hospital management. There should be a group nursing officer with a sphere of control like that of the group hospital secretary. At hospital level a hospital nursing officer should match the hospital secretary, and there should be a 'clinical nursing officer' to serve specialised units, freeing the ward sister from administrative chores and giving her cover.

The Salmon Report

The Ministry of Health was persuaded, in part by senior nurses, that nursing administration particularly in the HMCs had problems. Matrons found contact with group secretaries, who were working at a more senior level, hard to achieve and unproductive. Nurse administration was said to be in a state of chaos (which it was) and to know little about management. The top of the nursing hierarchy was concerned about its status and there was an apparent shortage of staff above the level of ward sister. Matrons in large hospitals resented being lumped together with matrons at cottage hospitals, and hoped for a pay rise. There was no definition of the management and administrative functions of senior nurses from ward sister to matron, nor a recognised way of selecting or training senior nursing staff. In spite of the Bradbeer Report, which had suggested that a triumvirate of administration, medicine and nursing should manage hospitals, nursing occupied a secondary position behind medical and lay administration and was not represented effectively when policy was discussed.[276] The Ministry did not have a clear idea about what was needed. In 1961 Enoch Powell announced his intention to set up an enquiry into senior nursing staff structure. Tricky negotiations over nurses' pay delayed its establishment until July 1963 when Brian Salmon, Director of J Lyons and Vice-chairman of the Westminster Hospital board of governors, was appointed as Chairman. The Committee consisted in the main of nurses, although it included a regional administrator and a senior physician.[277] Clinical matters and pay were excluded from the terms of reference.

The 1966 report proposed an entirely new pattern of nursing administration and a new grading structure.[278] Nursing would match administration neatly all the way down. The decisions needed for policy *formation*, the *programming* of policies, and their *execution* at ward level were seen as three essentially different types. The concept of top, middle and first-line management was introduced. There would now be six grades of nurse manager, two at each level of the organisation. Based on the theory of line management, the report provided outline job descriptions to grade a wide range of nursing posts. Historically catering, cleaning, linen and laundry, and staff homes were usually placed in the matron's sphere; the trend had been to relieve her of these responsibilities, rightly in the view of the Committee. While those who wished to practice a particular nursing specialty could do so, the promotion path to the highest levels of nursing administration would be open to all. Management training for nurses would be introduced and there would be uniform selection and staff reporting systems.

The Minister accepted the recommendations in general and by 1967 pilot trials were in progress. Salmon had provided many grades in the hope that organisations would mix and match, using only what they needed. The staff side took a different view. Every grade would provide a well-paid post. The path to promotion and high salaries was open. Even senior nurses sometimes saw an over-heavy structure as a symbol of status and created unnecessary posts. The results were painful in many ways. Matrons disappeared and unit officers took on management positions without formal training. Many had to reapply for their own renamed positions and sometimes found themselves rejected after years of doing their duties apparently to everyone's satisfaction.[279]

Towards NHS reorganisation

There was growing concern about the nature, control and financing of the NHS. The early debates concentrated mainly on whether socialised medicine was better or worse than private enterprise medicine.[280] NHS advocates drew attention to the inequities of the American pattern while detractors pointed to the obvious deficiencies of the NHS and the emigration of British doctors to apparently greener fields. The BMA fired early shots when it established the Porritt Review.

The Porritt Report

Sir Arthur Porritt, President of the Royal College of Surgeons and of the BMA, and later Governor General of New Zealand, was an archetypal surgeon of the old school. In 1957/8, when the BMA's Committee of Inquiry into the NHS was established, he took the chair. He began as a sceptic, but came out convinced that the NHS had to continue and be improved. Appearing in November 1962, the Report gave two cheers for the NHS, finding the concept sound even though not all the benefits promised had materialised.[281] A monopoly and state-managed service sometimes used for electioneering purposes was to be deplored, but an independent corporation had no practical advantages. Nevertheless, private practice should be encouraged to safeguard the public from the risk that government might in future lay down uniform standards and encroach on professional freedom. The tripartite services should be brought together under a single area board, with boundaries determined by the health needs of the community, on which the profession was adequately represented and whose chief officer was a doctor. The development of general practice should be supported and the size of list should be limited. Comprehensive area general hospitals were desirable and should be the basis of long-term as well as acute care. Individual specialties, recruitment and medical staffing received detailed attention.

Believing that running district hospitals would become ever more complex, the Institute of Hospital Administrators and the King's Fund made radical proposals in a report published in 1967 on *The shape of hospital management?* To safeguard public interest and public accountability a hospital board was required, but there should be a clear chain of command with a general manager supported by medical and nursing directors, a director of finance and statistical services, and a director of general services. The work of committees would be reduced to the essential minimum.[282]

In June 1965 a deputation to Ministers from the Joint Consultants Committee said that, in the light of 17 years' experience, the structure of the NHS should be re-examined. Kenneth Robinson told Parliament that it was a misconception that the royal road to co-ordination was by way of spectacular changes in administrative structure. Willing co-operation between individuals was the key, although he did not wish to exclude for all time the possibility of introducing a more unified type of administration.[283] In July 1966 the BMA Council called for a Royal Commission to advise on the finance and staffing of the NHS.[284] Twelve days later a pay freeze set in and discontents sharpened and rose to the surface. The BMA thought the NHS under-capitalised, over-worked and dependent on overseas doctors. It saw three options: to find more money, to ration free medical care or to let the service run down. Ministers did not consider major change feasible. In 1966 Enoch Powell wrote about the problems frankly in his classic book on politics and the health service. Articles in the medical press and a radio debate followed, between Powell and Professor Henry Miller of Newcastle.[285]

Powell saw that the combination of an unlimited demand and a supply which, though free, was inevitably limited was difficult to reconcile. Rationing through waiting lists was one way but rationing by the profession was more likely to be right than that by a non-professional. A health service free from parliamentary control was a non-runner. Ministers, if they could find a way of avoiding public accountability, would go for it like a shot. But while a corporation that raised money by sales could be largely free of parliamentary control, because the money for the NHS came from the tax-payer it could not. Faced with an inadequate service a corporation could say 'we would love to provide you with a new hospital here, there and everywhere, but it's the Chancellor of the Exchequer who gives us only this sum'. The thing landed back with the political authority. Powell said the phrase 'adequate money' was meaningless. Immediately any new advance was made in medicine, a new frontier of need was opened up. Unmet needs were discovered. Doctors, thinking how glorious it was in the NHS that patients did not have to pay them because somebody else did, had walked into a trap. That 'somebody else' had a limited purse to treat customers with no limitation on their demands. Worse, Powell believed that the NHS had delayed and prevented a vast amount of hospital building that would have taken place immediately after the war, when local authorities were raring to go. The same applied to the number of doctors and the pay of staff. A government decision on total expenditure ended with a pretty specific decision about expenditure on staff. The state had assigned priority to housing and education, not health care. Nationalisation had prevented people from showing what they wanted – more expenditure on health. If the profession wanted freedom and an ethos nearer to its own, some other source of finance than the state would have to be found.

This prescription was not now to the liking of the doctors. The medical profession that had fought about the pattern of the NHS, rather than its principles, was stung by Powell's pessimism. There could be no going back on the NHS. How should it be moulded to meet the needs for care of an affluent and technocratic western society, to allow the full harvest of medicine's great scientific advances? In March 1967 a conference was held in Newcastle. Delegates thought that there was no doubt that the service, getting only 4 per cent of the gross national product, was starved of money. Bring the share up to 6 per cent and many of its troubles would be over. And why not integrate the teaching hospitals, the regional board hospitals and the other two branches of the NHS?[286] An advisory panel of the BMA, with Dr Ivor Jones in the chair, was established to produce a report on health service financing. The Institute of Economic Affairs considered that private health insurance might usefully supplement taxation, fees and charges in financing health care and would become increasingly popular. If people were prepared to pay more for better food, clothing, cars and holidays, it should be possible to encourage them to pay more for better health care. The administrative costs might be higher, but there were a number of alternative schemes, including the introduction of health care vouchers for hospital cover.[287]

However, George Godber could see that substantial progress had been made during the decade.[288] The hospital development programme was under way, although because money was short much of the improvement had come from extending existing hospitals, rather than the replacement really needed. The GPs' charter was encouraging GPs to group and rehouse themselves. Less capital investment was needed but the speed of progress depended on the independently minded GPs. The greatest achievement was probably the development of professional postgraduate education, a necessary complement to the changes in professional organisation.

In November 1967 Kenneth Robinson changed his opinion and said that a full and careful examination of the administrative structure of the medical and related services was needed, not just for the present but looking 10–12 years ahead. Other changes were in the offing, to the social services a result of the Seebohm Commission, and to local government as a result of the Royal Commission. Kenneth Robinson made it clear that such a review would relate solely to the administrative pattern. He was not considering the possibility of an alternative type of NHS, perhaps through private sector financing, as was sometimes urged. He would put forward his tentative proposals in the form of a Green Paper. The NHS was 20 years old; the question now to be asked was whether the existing structure was adequate to meet future needs.[289] Many had a touching belief that altering an administrative framework, which had nothing to do with care either in the community or in the hospitals, would solve the problem that Powell had outlined of expanding demands, free access and restricted spending.

References

1. Home and hospital [leading article]. *Lancet* 1958; 1: 34–5.
2. Freedom to grow [leading article]. *BMJ* 1959; 2: 746–7.
3. Ten years. *BMJ* 1958; 2: 33.
   Dain HG. The national health service after ten years. *BMJ* 1958; 2, special suppl: 1–2.
4. Medical notes in Parliament. *BMJ* 1958; 2: 395–7.
5. Lord Moran. Lessons from the past. *BMJ* 1958; 2, suppl: 3–4.
6. Platt H. Selected papers. *The way ahead – the cost of medical care.* Address to the annual meeting of the Sheffield United Hospitals, 3 April 1958. London: Livingstone, 1963.
7. Platt H. The way ahead. *BMJ* 1958; 2, special suppl: 5–6.
8. The RB and the NHS [leading article]. *BMJ* 1958; 2: 214.
9. Porritt Report on NHS [leading article]. *BMJ* 1962; 2: 1171–3.

10. Lumbering Leviathan [leading article]. *BMJ* 1960; 2: 1369–70.
11. The Minister of Health [leading article]. *BMJ* 1963; 2: 1012.
12. Fraser FR. The challenge to the medical profession. *BMJ* 1960; 2: 1821–6.
13. Taylor S. The suburban neurosis. *Lancet* 1938, 1: 759–61.
    Suburban neurosis up to date [leading article]. *Lancet* 1958; 1: 146–7.
14. STP [leading article]. *BMJ* 1967; 3: 570–1.
15. Doctors' views on health education [leading article]. *BMJ* 1962; 1: 997–8.
16. Brown E. A good innings! *BMJ* 1983; 287: 1940–1.
    O Tempora! [leading article] *BMJ* 1960; 1: 42–3.
17. Disease education by the BBC [leading articles]. *BMJ* 1958; 1: 388–9 and 510–1.
18. Television – informing or misleading? [leading article] *Nursing Times* 1958; Mar 14: 293.
    'Your life in their hands'. *Nursing Times* 1958; Apr 4: 401.
19. Sargant W. The hurt mind. *BMJ* 1958; 1: 517.
20. Your figures in their hands [leading article]. *BMJ* 1959; 1: 101–2.
21. Ministry of Health. Standing Medical and Nursing Advisory Committees. *Communication between doctors, nurses and patients*. London: HMSO, 1963.
    Hospital manners [leading article]. *BMJ* 1963; 2: 265–6.
22. Amos A. In her own best interests? *Health Education Journal* 1993; 52/3: 140–50.
23. Wilson JMG, Jungner G. *Principles and practice of screening for disease*. WHO Public Health Papers no. 34. Geneva: WHO, 1968.
    McKeown T. Validation of screening procedures. In: *Screening in medical care: reviewing the evidence*. Oxford: Oxford University Press for Nuffield Provincial Hospitals Trust, 1968.
24. Cochrane A. *One man's medicine*. The Memoir Club. London: BMJ, 1989, 194–204.
25. Periodic medical examination [leading article]. *BMJ* 1954; 2: 1095.
26. Ministry of Health. *On the state of the public health*. Report of the CMO for 1960. London: HMSO, 1961.
27. Donaldson RJ, Howell JM. A multiple screening clinic. *BMJ* 1965; 2: 1034.
28. Wilson JMG, Jungner G. *Principles and practice of screening for disease*. WHO Public Health Papers no. 34. Geneva: WHO, 1968.
29. Hospital treatment: a changing scene [leading article]. *Lancet* 1957; 2: 1269.
30. Rayner Claire B. A new approach to the outpatient. *Nursing Times* 1958; Jun 13: 688.
31. Automation in medicine [annotation]. *BMJ* 1956; 1: 1477.
32. Baron DN, Newman F. Assessment of a new simple colorimetric test for proteinuria. *BMJ* 1958; 1: 980.
33. Ministry of Health. *On the state of the public health*. Report of the CMO for 1961. London: HMSO, 1962.
34. Whitby LG. Automation in clinical chemistry, with special reference to the AutoAnalyzer. *BMJ* 1964; 2: 895–8.
35. Cochrane AL. *One man's medicine*. The Memoir Club. London. BMJ, 1989.
    Cochrane AL. *Effectiveness and efficiency*. London: Nuffield Provincial Hospitals Trust, 1972.
36. Godber GE. The physician's part in hospital planning. *BMJ* 1959; 1, suppl: 115–158.
37. Godber G. Trends in specialization and their effect on the practice of medicine. *BMJ* 1961; 2: 841–7.
38. Fry J. A general practitioner's views of hospital planning. *BMJ* 1959; 1, suppl: 123–5.
39. A broad-spectrum penicillin [leading article]. *BMJ* 1961; 2: 223–4.
40. Wynne Davies D, Evans B. Early observations of the diuretic effect of chlorothiazide. *BMJ* 1958; 1: 967.
    Bayliss RLS. Diuretics. *BMJ* 1959; 1: 41–3.
41. Stewart JH. Clinical comparison of frusemide with bendrofluazide, mersalyl and ethacrynic acid. *BMJ* 1965; 2: 1277.

42. Julian DG. Drugs in the treatment of hypertension. *BMJ* 1960; 2: 660–2.

43. Keelan P. Double-blind trial of propranolol in angina pectoris. *BMJ* 1965; 1: 897.

44. Increasing deaths from asthma [leading article]. *BMJ* 1968; 1: 329–30.

45. Indomethacin [leading article]. *BMJ* 1965; 1: 1329.

46. Mears E, Grant ECG. 'Anovlar' as an oral contraceptive. *BMJ* 1962; 2: 75–9.

47. Intrauterine contraceptive devices [leading article]. *BMJ* 1965; 2: 249–50.

48. Kiloh LG, Brandon S. Habituation and addiction to amphetamines. *BMJ* 1962; 1: 39–43.

49. Tranquillisers. [today's drugs]. *BMJ* 1963; 2: 163–4.
    Benzodiazepines. [today's drugs]. *BMJ* 1967; 2: 36–8.

50. New drugs for depression [leading article]. *BMJ* 1960; 1: 178–9.
    Drugs for depression [leading article]. *BMJ* 1964; 2: 522–3.

51. Interaction of drugs [leading article]. *BMJ* 1966; 1: 811–12.

52. Consciousness during surgical operations [leading article]. *BMJ* 1959; 2: 810–11.

53. Impartial information [leading article]. *Lancet* 1961; 1: 379–80.

54. Doll R. Recognition of unwanted drug effects. *BMJ* 1969, 2: 69–76.

55. Safety of drugs [leading article]. *BMJ* 1962; 2: 246–7; and letters from Dent CE, Laurens DR, Nixon WCW, Witts LJ and Sorsby A. *BMJ* 1962; 2: 254–5.

56. Dunlop Sir Derrick. *Medicines in our time*. Rock Carling Fellowship. London: Nuffield Provincial Hospitals Trust, 1973.

57. Dunlop D. Use and abuse of drugs. *BMJ* 1965; 2: 438.

58. Doll R. Recognition of unwanted drug effects. *BMJ* 1969; 2: 69–76.

59. Mould RF. *A century of x-rays and radioactivity in medicine*. Bristol and Philadelphia: Institute of Physics, 1993.

60. Donald I, MacVicar J, Brown TG. Investigation of abdominal masses by pulsed ultrasound. *Lancet* 1958; 1: 1188–95.

61. Flexible endoscopes [leading article]. *BMJ* 1954; 1: 90.

62. Ramsay M, Edmond RTD, Alston JM. Future management of infectious diseases. *BMJ* 1964; 2: 1004–5.

63. Trial of living attenuated poliovirus vaccine. A report of the PHLS to the MRC. *BMJ* 1961; 2: 1037.

64. Medicine and the computer: managing a county health service. *BMJ* 1968; 2: 823–4.

65. Ministry of Health. *Annual report for the year 1962*. London: HMSO, 1963.

66. Segregation of tuberculous patients [leading article]. *BMJ* 1967; 3: 3.

67. VD on TV [leading article]. *BMJ* 1960; 1: 1121–2.

68. Jefferiss FJG. The return of the venereal diseases. *BMJ* 1962; 1: 1751–3.

69. Ministry of Health. *On the state of the public health*. Report of the CMO for 1967. London: HMSO, 1968.

70. Ministry of Health. *On the state of the public health*. Report of the CMO for 1961. London: HMSO, 1962.
    DHSS. *On the state of the public health*. Report of the CMO for 1969. London: HMSO, 1970.

71. Davies JOF, Lewin W. Observations on hospital planning. *BMJ* 1960; 2: 763–8.

72. Farquharson EL. Early ambulation: with special reference to herniorrhaphy as an outpatient procudure. *Lancet* 1955; 2: 517.
    Stephens FO, Dudley HAF. An organisation for outpatient surgery. *Lancet* 1961; 1: 1042–4.

73. Standing Medical Advisory Committee. *Accident and emergency services*. (Chairman: Sir Harry Platt.) London: HMSO, 1962.

74. Comprehensive accident services [leading article]. *BMJ* 1961; 2: 161–2.
    Accident Services Review Committee of Great Britain and Ireland. *Interim report*. (Chairman: H Osmund-Clarke.) London: BMA, 1961.

75. Clarke R. The diagnosis and treatment of major injuries. *BMJ* 1959; 1: 125–30.
An accident service for the nation [leading article]. *BMJ* 1959; 2: 1009–10.

76. Kouwenhoven WB, Jude JR, Knickerbocker GG. Closed-chest cardiac massage. *Journal of the American Medical Association* 1960; 173: 1064–7.

77. Brown KWG. Coronary unit: an intensive care centre for acute myocardial infarction. *Lancet* 1963; 2: 349–52.

78. Brown KWG, MacMillan RL, Forbath N et al. Coronary unit: an intensive-care centre for acute myocardial infarction. *Lancet* 1963; 2: 349–52.

79. Pantridge JF, Geddes JS. A mobile-intensive care unit in the management of myocardial infarction. *Lancet* 1967; 2: 271–3.
Immediate coronary care [leading article]. *BMJ* 1968; 3: 134–5.

80. New methods of resuscitation [leading article]. *BMJ* 1962; 2: 1592–3.

81. Cardiac pacemakers [leading article]. *BMJ* 1965; 1: 77.
Long-term cardiac pacing [leading article]. *BMJ* 1968; 2: 2.

82. Extracorporeal circulation [leading article]. *BMJ* 1959; 1: 35–6.

83. Wood P. The selection of cases for cardiac surgery. *BMJ* 1960; 2: 1302–3.

84. Replacement of heart valves [leading article]. *BMJ* 1965; 1: 741–2.
Replacing three heart valves [leading article]. *BMJ* 1969; 3: 666–7.

85. Coronary angiography [leading article]. *BMJ* 1961; 2: 878–9.

86. Kenyon JR, Thompson AE. Carotid artery stenosis. *BMJ* 1965; 1: 1460.

87. Parsons FM. Origins of haemodialysis in the United Kingdom. *BMJ* 1989; 299: 1557–60.

88. Black DAK. Profit and loss in intermittent haemodialysis. *Lancet* 1965; 2: 1058–9.
Profit and loss in intermittent haemodialysis [correspondence]. *Lancet* 1965; 2: 1245–7.

89. Brescia MJ, Cimino JE, Appel K, Hurwich BJ. Chronic haemodialysis using venipuncture and a surgically created arteriovenous fistula. *New England Journal of Medicine* 1966; 275: 1089–92.

90. Calne RY, Loughridge LW, MacGillivray JB et al. Renal transplantation in man. *BMJ* 1963; 2: 645–51.
Dunea G, Makamotot S, Straffon RA et al. Renal homotransplantation in 24 patients. *BMJ* 1965; 1: 7–13.

91. Shackman R. Dilemma of irreversible renal failure. *BMJ* 1967; 1: 623–4.

92. Ogg C. Maintenance haemodialysis and renal transplantation. *BMJ* 1970; 4: 412.

93. Transplanted organs [leading article]. *BMJ* 1968; 1: 71.

94. Ministry of Health. *Report for the year 1960.* Cmnd 1418. London: HMSO, 1961, 52.

95. Marrow transplantation and radiotherapy of cancer [leading article]. *BMJ* 1959; 1: 562–3.
Bone-marrow grafts [leading article]. *BMJ* 1964; 2: 523–4.

96. An eye for a laser [leading article]. *BMJ* 1965; 1: 808–9.

97. Li MC, Hertz R, Spencer DB. Effect of methotrexate upon choriocarcinoma and chorioadenoma. *Proceedings of the Society for Experimental Biology and Medicine* 1956; 93: 361–6.

98. Trophoblastic malignancy [leading article]. *BMJ* 1962; 2: 971–2.
Bagshawe KD. Trophoblastic tumours. *BMJ* 1963; 2: 1303–7.
Bagshawe KD, Golding PR, Orr AH. Choriocarcinoma after hydatidiform mole. *BMJ* 1969; 3: 733–7.

99. Zubrod CG. Historic milestones in curative chemotherapy. *Seminars in Oncology* 1979; 6: 490–505.
Skipper HE. Historic milestones in cancer biology. *Seminars in Oncology* 1979; 6: 506–14.

100. Bodley Scott R. Cancer chemotherapy – the first twenty-five years. *BMJ* 1970, 2: 259–65.

101. Farber S, D'Angio G, Evans A. Clinical studies of actinomycin D with special reference to Wilms' tumour in children. *Annals of the New York Academy of Sciences* 1960; 89, 421–5.

102. Mammography as a screening test for breast cancer [leading article]. *BMJ* 1966; 2: 484–5.

103. DHSS. *On the state of the public health.* Report of the CMO for 1969. London: HMSO, 1970.
104. Royal College of Physicians. *Smoking and health: a report on smoking in relation to lung cancer and other diseases.* London: Pitman, 1962.
105. Ministry of Health. *Annual report for the year 1967.* Cmnd 3702. London: HMSO, 1968.
106. Saunders C. A personal therapeutic journey. *BMJ* 1996; 313: 1599–601.
107. St Christopher's Hospice. *BMJ* 1967; 3: 169–70.
108. Ministry of Health. *Report of the Maternity Services Committee.* (Chairman: Lord Cranbrook.) London: HMSO, 1959.
109. Ministry of Health, Central Health Services Council. *Human relations in obstetrics.* London: HMSO, 1961.
110. Gordon I, Elias-Jones TF. The place of confinement: home or hospital? *BMJ* 1960; 1: 52–3. Early discharge of maternity patients [leading article]. *BMJ* 1967; 3: 508–9.
111. Place of delivery [leading article]. *BMJ* 1966; 1: 493–4.
112. DHSS. *On the state of the public health.* Report of the CMO for 1968. London: HMSO, 1969.
113. Maternal mortality [leading article]. *BMJ* 1960; 2: 123–5.
114. Williams AS. *Women and childbirth. The history of the National Birthday Trust Fund 1928–1993.* Gloucester: Sutton, 1997.
115. Perinatal Mortality Survey. *BMJ* 1962; 2: 1187; and correspondence: 1253–5.
116. Butler N, Bonham DG, editors. *Perinatal Mortality. The first report of the 1958 British perinatal mortality survey.* Edinburgh: E & S Livingstone, 1963.
117. Butler N, Alberman ED, editors. *Perinatal Problems. The second report of the 1958 British perinatal mortality survey.* Edinburgh: E & S Livingstone, 1969.
118. Williams AS. *Women and childbirth. The history of the National Birthday Trust Fund 1928–1993.* Gloucester: Sutton, 1997.
119. Dalton K. Menstruation and crime. *BMJ* 1961; 2: 1752–3.
120. Legalized abortion: report by the Council of the Royal College of Obstetricians and Gynaecologists. *BMJ* 1966; 1: 850–4.
    Therapeutic abortion: report by BMA Special Committee; and Summary of memorandum by RMPA. *BMJ* 1966; 2: 40–4.
121. Jeffcoate TNA. Indications for therapeutic abortion. *BMJ* 1960; 1: 581–8.
    BMA Committee on therapeutic abortion. Indications for termination of pregnancy. *BMJ* 1968, 1: 171–5.
122. New abortion Bill. *BMJ* 1966; 2: 247.
    Majority of 194 in Abortion Bill vote [parliamentary notes]. *BMJ* 1966; 2: 311–12.
123. CHSC. *The welfare of children in hospital.* Report of a committee of the CHSC. (Chairman: Sir Harry Platt.) London: HMSO, 1959.
    Children in hospital [leading article]. *BMJ* 1959; 1: 425–6.
124. Gunson HH, Dodsworth H. Fifty years of blood transfusion. *Transfusion Medicine* 1996; 6, suppl. 1: 1–88.
125. Castree BJ, Walker JH. The young adult with spina bifida. *BMJ* 1981; 283: 1040–2.
126. Children of short stature [leading article]. *BMJ* 1967; 3: 187–8.
127. Williamson J, Stokoe IH, Gray S et al. Old people at home. Their unreported needs. *Lancet* 1964; 1: 1117–20.
128. Kay DWK, Roth M, Hall MRP. Special problems of the aged and the organisation of hospital services. *BMJ* 1966; 2: 967–72.
129. Human warehouses [leading article]. *BMJ* 1961; 2: 100.
130. Martin JP. *Hospitals in trouble.* Oxford: Basil Blackwell, 1984.
131. Sargant W. Drugs in the treatment of depression. *BMJ* 1961; 1: 225–7.
    Sargant W. Psychiatric treatment in general teaching hospitals: a plea for a mechanistic approach. *BMJ* 1966; 2: 257–62.

132. Psychiatry in general hospitals [leading article]. *Lancet* 1963; 2: 1149.
133. Ministry of Health. *Report for the year 1959*. Cmnd 1086. London: HMSO, 1960.
134. Barton R. *Institutional neurosis*. Bristol: John Wright, 1959.
135. Silverman M. A comprehensive department of psychological medicine – a 12 months review. *BMJ* 1961; 2: 698–701.
    Smith S. Psychiatry in general hospitals. Manchester's integrated scheme. *Lancet* 1961; 1: 1158–9.
136. Barton R. The psychiatric hospital. In: Freeman H, Farndale J, editors. *Trends in the mental health services*. Oxford: Pergamon Press, 1963.
137. Cawley RH, McKeown T. Services for the mentally-ill in a balanced hospital community. In: Freeman H, Farndale J, editors. *Trends in the mental health services*. Oxford: Pergamon Press, 1963.
138. Tooth GC, Brooke EM. Trends in mental hospital population and their effect on future planning. *Lancet* 1961; 1: 710–13.
    Ministry of Health. *Report for 1960*. Cmnd 1418. London: HMSO, 1961.
139. Freeman H. In conversation with Enoch Powell. *Psychiatric Bulletin* 1988; 12: 402–6.
140. Everybody's business. Report of the annual conference of the National Association for Mental Health. *Lancet* 1961; 1: 608–9.
141. Ministry of Health. *On the state of the public health*. Report of the CMO for 1959. London: HMSO, 1960.
142. Brooke EM. *A census of patients in psychiatric beds, 1963*. Ministry of Health Reports on Public Health and Medical Subjects no. 116. London: HMSO, 1967.
143. Hill Sir Denis. *Psychiatry in medicine*. London. Nuffield Provincial Hospitals Trust, 1969, 103–5.
144. Jones K. The role and function of the mental hospital. In: Freeman H, Farndale J, editors. *Trends in mental health services*. Oxford: Pergamon Press, 1963.
145. Shepherd M. Primary care of patients with mental disorder in the community. *BMJ* 1989 299: 666–9.
146. Future of the mental hospital [leading article]. *BMJ* 1962; 2: 904–5.
147. Psychiatry in general hospitals [leading article]. *Lancet* 1963; 2: 1149.
    Does the community care? [leading article] *BMJ* 1966; 2: 655–6.
    Future of mental hospitals [leading article]. *BMJ* 1967; 2: 781–2.
148. Ministry of Health. *On the state of the public health*. Report of the CMO for 1962. London: HMSO, 1963.
149. Smith S. Psychiatry in general hospitals. *Lancet* 1961; 1: 1158–9.
150. Marinker M. Changing patterns in general practice education. In: Teeling Smith G, editor. *Health, education and general practice*. London: Office of Health Economics, 1965.
151. Balint M. *The doctor, his patient and the illness*. London: Tavistock, 1957.
    Balint M. The other part of medicine. *Lancet* 1961; 1: 41–3.
152. Cartwright A. *Patients and their doctors*. London: Routledge & Kegan Paul, 1967.
153. Fry J. General practice tomorrow. *BMJ* 1964; 2: 1064–7.
154. Fry J. Why patients go to hospital. *BMJ* 1959; 2: 1323–7.
155. Professor Michael Shepherd [obituary]. *The Times* 1995: Sep 13.
156. The British National Health Service. *Conversations with Sir George Godber*. JE Fogarty International Center. Washington DC: US Department of Health, Education and Welfare, 1976.
157. Lord Moran. Evidence to the Royal Commission on Doctors' and Dentists' Remuneration. *BMJ* 1958; 1, suppl: 27–30.
158. Moran C. The 'Ladder'. *Lancet* 1959; 1: 216.
159. Horder JP. Training for general practice. *Journal of the College of General Practitioners* 1964; 7: 303–4.

160. Whitfield MJ. Training for general practice: result of a survey. BMJ 1966; 1: 663–7.
161. Horder JP, Swift G. The history of vocational training for general practice. *Journal of the Royal College of General Practitioners* 1979; 29: 24–32.
162. Vocational training for general practice [leading article]. BMJ 1966; 2: 251–2.
    Swift G. The Wessex scheme. Conference on vocational training for GPs. BMJ 1968; 2: 759.
163. College of General Practitioners. *Reports from general practice*, no. 5. *Evidence to the Royal Commission on medical education*. London: CGP, 1966.
164. Good general practice [leading article]. BMJ 1967; 3: 754.
165. Marinker M. Should general practice be represented in the university medical school? *BMJ* 1983; 286: 855–9.
166. Fry J, Dillane JB, Lester A. Towards better general practice. BMJ 1962; 2: 1311–15.
167. Medical Practitioners' Union. *Health centre report*. London: MPU, 1960.
    Health centres or medical centres [leading article]. *Lancet* 1961; 1: 149–50.
168. Warin JF. Evolution of a health team. BMJ 1965; 1: 525.
    Warin JF. GPs and nursing staff: a complete attachment scheme in retrospect and prospect. BMJ 1968; 2: 41–5.
169. Fry J, Dillane JB, Connolly MM. The evolution of a health team: a successful general practitioner health visitor association. BMJ 1965; 1: 181.
170. Baly ME. *A history of the Queen's Nursing Institute*. London: Croom Helm, 1987.
171. Wolfinden RC. Health centres and the general medical practitioner. BMJ 1967; 2: 565–7.
172. Hasler J. *The primary health care team*. London: RSM Press, 1994.
173. Cardew B. An appointment system service for general practitioners. BMJ 1967; 4: 542–3.
    Appointment systems in general practice [leading article]. BMJ 1967; 4: 500–1.
174. Reedy BIEC. Changing face of general practice. BMJ 1967; 1: 54.
175. Marsh GN Group practice nurse: an analysis and comment on six months' work. BMJ 1967; 1: 489–91.
176. Dopson L. *The changing scene in general practice*. London: Johnson, 1971.
177. Rivett GC. Use of radio communication in general practice, BMJ 1965; 2: 530–1.
    Rivett GC Miniature radiotelephones in general practice. *Practitioner* 1966; 196: 838–42.
178. Ministry of Health. *Final report of the committee on cost of prescribing*. (Chairman: Sir Henry Hinchcliffe.) London: HMSO, 1959.
179. Fraser B. The doctor and the administrator. BMJ 1968; 2: 553–4.
180. Ministry of Health. *Report for 1962*. Cmnd 2062. London: HMSO, 1963, 47.
181. Merit awards for GPs [leading article]. BMJ 1962; 1: 1125–6.
    General practitioners in conference [leading article]. BMJ 1962; 1: 1675–6.
182. Standing Medical Advisory Committee. *Subcommittee report on the field of work of the family doctor*. (Chairman: Annis Gillie.) London: HMSO, 1963.
    General practice in the future [leading article]. BMJ 1963; 2: 817–18.
183. Present state of medicine. Diagnosis and treatment [leading article]. BMJ 1963; 2: 453–6.
184. Discontent with the pool [leading article]. BMJ 1963; 2: 1143–4.
    The basis of unity [leading article]. BMJ 1964; 1: 253–4.
185. Crisis in general practice [leading article]. BMJ 1964; 1: 851–2.
    Timmins N. *The five giants*. London: HarperCollins, 1995.
186. Conference on general practice. Planning for the future. BMJ 1964; 1: 1502–4.
187. General practitioners in the NHS [leading article]. BMJ 1965; 1: 264–5.
188. Encouraging general practice [leading article]. BMJ 1964; 2: 463.
    Practice expenses: Minister's proposals. BMJ 1964; 2, suppl: 121.
    Ministry of Health. *Annual report for 1964*. Cmnd 2688. London: HMSO, 1965.
189. Fraser B. The doctor and the administrator. BMJ 1968; 2: 553–4.
    Fifth report of the Review Body on the remuneration of general medical practitioners. Cmnd 2585. London: HMSO, 1965.

190. The current turmoil [parliamentary notes]. *BMJ* 1965; 1: 957–6.

191. The Review Body's award [leading article]. *BMJ* 1965; 1: 397.

192. Macpherson G. Reviving the fortunes of general practice: James Cameron and Kenneth Robinson. *BMJ* 150th anniversary issue, 1982; Jul 5: A26–9.

193. Step by step [leading article]. *BMJ* 1965; 2: 1.

194. Charter for general practice [leading article]. *BMJ* 1965; 1: 669.
     Towards a better family doctor service [leading article]. *BMJ* 1965; 1: 875.

195. Discussions must continue [leading article]. *BMJ* 1965; 2: 181.

196. Towards a new contract [leading article]. *BMJ* 1965; 2: 889.
     The majority say yes [leading article]. *BMJ* 1965; 2: 1075.

197. A fresh start [leading article]. *BMJ* 1966; 1: 1183–5.
     Government's decision on Report [leading article]. *BMJ* 1966; 1: 1225.

198. Independent Medical Services [leading article]. *BMJ* 1966; 2: 4.

199. Timmins N. *The five giants.* London: HarperCollins, 1995.

200. Merit awards in general practice [letter] *BMJ* 1967; 1: 175.
     Special experience and service [leading article]. *BMJ* 1967; 1: 318–19.
     Merit awards ballot. *BMJ* 1967; 2, suppl: 25.

201. The British National Health Service. *Conversations with Sir George Godber*. JE Fogarty International Center. Washington DC: US Department of Health, Education and Welfare, 1976.

202. Ministry of Health. *Annual report for the year 1967*. Cmnd 3702. London: HMSO, 1968.
     Health centre explosion. *BMJ* 1967; 4: 759–60.

203. Godber GE. Medical officers of health and health services. *Community Medicine* 1986; no 1: 12.

204. Higgins PM. Thamesmead: dream to reality. *BMJ* 1982; 285: 1264–6.
     Thamesmead: the first phase of community health service. *BMJ* 1967; 4: 676–8.

205. Ministry of Health. *On the state of the public health*. Report of the CMO for 1965. London: HMSO, 1965.
     Ministry of Health. *On the state of the public health*. Report of the CMO for 1967. London: HMSO, 1968

206. Smith RE. Teaching in a non-teaching hospital. *Lancet* 1958; 1: 311–13.

207. Registering medical auxiliaries [leading article]. *BMJ* 1959; 2: 1164–5.

208. The new St Thomas'. *BMJ* 1958; 1: 115; and *BMJ* 1966; 2: 356.

209. Hospital and research centre [annotation]. *Lancet* 1961; 1: 600.
     DHSS. *On the state of the public health*. Annual report of the CMO for 1969. London: HMSO, 1970.

210. Godber GE. Health services past, present and future. *Lancet* 1958; 2: 1–6.

211. McKeown T. The concept of a balanced hospital community. *Lancet* 1958; 1: 701–4.

212. Farrer-Brown L. Hospitals for today and tomorrow. *BMJ* 1959; 1, suppl: 118–22.

213. Central Health Services Council. *The welfare of children in hospital*. Report of a committee of the CHSC. (Chairman: Sir Harry Platt.) London: HMSO, 1959.

214. Abel AL, Lewin W. Report on hospital building. *BMJ* 1959; 1, suppl: 108–14.

215. Davies JOF. A visit to the USA. *BMJ* 1960; 1: 1879–84.
     Davies JOF, Lewin W. Observations on hospital planning. *BMJ* 1960; 2: 763–8.

216. Ministry of Health. *On the state of the public health*. Report of the CMO for 1960. Cmnd 1550. London: HMSO, 1961.

217. Llewelyn Davies R. Architectural problems of new hospitals. *BMJ* 1960; 2: 768–72.

218. Ministry of Health. *Report for the year 1960*. Cmnd 1418. London: HMSO, 1961, 23.
     Nuffield Provincial Hospitals Trust. *Studies in the function and design of hospitals*. London: Oxford University Press, 1955.

219. Ministry of Health. *The district general hospital*. Building Note no. 3. London: HMSO, 1961.

220. The British National Health Service. *Conversations with Sir George Godber*. JE Fogarty International Center. Washington DC: US Department of Health, Education and Welfare. 1976, 18.

221. Allen D. *Hospital planning*. London: Pitman Medical, 1979.

222. National Health Service. *A hospital plan for England and Wales*. Cmnd 1604. London: HMSO, 1962.

223. Ministry of Health. *On the state of the public health*. Report of the CMO for 1962. London: HMSO, 1963.

224. Ten-year hospital plan [leading article]. *BMJ* 1962; 1: 238–9.

225. Barr A. The population served by a hospital group. *Lancet* 1957; 2: 1105–8.

226. Smith J. Hospital building in the NHS. *BMJ* 1984; 289: 1298–300.

227. Parliament. *The National Health Service. Hospital building programme*. Cmnd 3000. London: HMSO, 1966.

228. Teaching hospitals and the community [leading article]. *Lancet* 1971; 1: 584–5.
    Rivett GC *The development of the London hospital system, 1823–1982*. London: King's Fund, 1986.

229. Postgraduate centres for London [leading article]. *BMJ* 1961; 2: 40.

230. Ministry of Health. *Postgraduate medical education and the specialties*. (Chairman: Sir George Pickering.) Reports on Public Health and Medical Subjects no. 106. London: HMSO, 1962.

231. Chelsea Postgraduate Medical Centre. *BMJ* 1966; 1: 1289–91.

232. Waiting for doctor [leading article]. *BMJ* 1958; 2: 901–2.

233. Ministry of Health. *First report of the joint working party on the organisation of medical work in hospitals*. London: HMSO, 1967.

234. DHSS. *On the state of the public health*. Report of the CMO for 1970. London: HMSO, 1971.

235. Modernizing hospital medicine [leading article]. *BMJ* 1967; 4: 252–3.

236. Robinson K. *Partnership in medical care*. Maurice Bloch lecture. Glasgow: Jackson, 1968.

237. Partnership in medical care [leading article]. *BMJ* 1967; 4: 634–5.
    Medical partnership: Minister's lecture at Glasgow. *BMJ* 1967; 4: 675–6.

238. Ministry of Health. *Report for 1967*. Cmnd 3702. London: HMSO, 1968.
    Rowe RG, Brewer W. *Hospital activity analysis*. London: Butterworths, 1972.

239. Acheson ED. *Medical record linkage*. Oxford: Oxford University Press, 1967.
    Record linkage. *BMJ* 1968; 3: 116–17.

240. Ministry of Health. *Report for the year 1960*. Cmnd 1418. London: HMSO, 1961.

241. Computers in medicine. *BMJ* 1965; 2: 1427–8.

242. Ministry of Health. *Report for the year 1959*. Cmnd 1086. London: HMSO, 1960.

243. Ministry of Health. *Report for the year 1967*. Cmnd 3702. London: HMSO, 1968.

244. Commission on education [leading article]. *BMJ* 1965; 2: 57–8.

245. Nuffield Provincial Hospitals Trust: conference on postgraduate medical education. *BMJ* 1962; 1: 466–7.

246. Pickering Sir George. Postgraduate medical education. *BMJ* 1962; 1: 421–5.

247. Lister J. Reflections on building a postgraduate medical centre. *BMJ* 1966; 1: 228–30.

248. Royal Commission. Evidence from Medical Practitioners' Union [leading article]. *BMJ* 1958; 1, suppl: 30–2.

249. Ministry of Health. *Report for 1960*. Cmnd 1418. London: HMSO, 1961.

250. Klein R. The tale of two committees or the perils of prediction. *BMJ* 1976; 1: 25–6.

251. Seale J. Supply of doctors. *BMJ* 1961; 2: 1554–5.
    Seale J. The health service in an affluent society. *BMJ* 1962; 2: 598–602.
    Seale J. Medical emigration from Great Britain and Ireland. *BMJ* 1964; 1: 1173.

252. *Hospitals year book 1965*. London: IHSA, 1965.

253. 'A pretty ghastly, awful picture' [leading article]. *BMJ* 1961; 2: 1548–9.

254. Emigration of doctors. *BMJ* 1964; 2: 50–1.
Campbell AGM. Dangerous trends in medical care. *BMJ* 1965; 1: 507.

255. Pappworth MH. Emigration of British doctors [letter]. *BMJ* 1962; 1: 1075.

256. Emigration of British doctors to the United States of America and Canada. *BMJ* 1968; 1: 45–8.
Return to Britain? [leading article] *BMJ* 1968; 1: 1–2.

257. Lawrie J, Newhouse M, Elliott P. Working capacity of women doctors. *BMJ* 1966; 1: 409–12.

258. Ministry of Health. *Report for 1967*. Cmnd 3702. London: HMSO, 1968.

259. Ministry of Health. *Medical staffing structure in the hospital service*. Report of the Joint Working Party. (Chairman: Sir Robert Platt.) London: HMSO, 1961.
Ministry of Health. *On the state of the public health*. Report of the CMO for 1960. London: HMSO, 1961.

260. Time for nursing [leading article]. *Nursing Times* 1958; Sep 26: 1111.

261. The overtaxed nurse. Conference organised by the Association of Hospital Matrons. *Nursing Times* 1958; Feb 7: 159–160.

262. From student to nurse [leading article]. *BMJ* 1961; 2: 1008–9.

263. RCN/National Council of Nurses. *A reform of nursing education*. (Chairman: Sir Harry Platt.) London: RCN, 1964.
Nursing in the future [leading article]. *BMJ* 1964; 1: 1585–6.

264. Smith RE. Teaching in non teaching hospitals. *Lancet* 1958; 1: 311–13.

265. Ministry of Health. *On the state of the public health*. Report of the CMO for 1960. London: HMSO, 1961.

266. Ministry of Health. *On the state of the public health*. Report of the CMO for 1967. London: HMSO, 1968.

267. Newman C. University education for nurses. *Nursing Times* 1958; Aug 25: 1002–3.

268. Girdwood RH. Some problems of nursing today. *BMJ* 1966; 1: 1411–13.

269. Davies JOH. Observations on hospital planning. *BMJ* 1960; 2: 767.

270. Ministry of Health. *On the state of the public health*. Report of the CMO for 1961. London: HMSO, 1962.

271. NHS Staffing in the context of a strained economy [parliamentary notes]. *BMJ* 1962; 1: 1018–20.

272. Ministry of Health. *On the state of the public health*. Report of the CMO for 1967. London: HMSO, 1968.

273. Raven RW. Progressive patient care. *BMJ* 1962; 1: 43–4.

274. Standing Nursing Advisory Committee. *The pattern of the in-patient's day*. London: HMSO, 1961.
Standing Nursing Advisory Committee. *Control of noise in hospitals*. London: HMSO, 1961.
Standing Maternity and Midwifery Advisory Committee. *Human relationships in obstetrics*. London: HMSO, 1961.

275. Nursing administration [leading article]. *BMJ* 1964; 2: 892–3.

276. Ministry of Health and Scottish Home and Health Department. *Report of the committee on senior nursing staff structure*. (Chairman: Brian Salmon.) London: HMSO, 1966.

277. *Hospitals year book 1965*. London: IHSA, 1965.

278. Ministry of Health and Scottish Home and Health Department. *Report of the committee on senior nursing staff structure*. (Chairman: Brian Salmon.) London: HMSO, 1966.

279. Hector W. Nursing in the UK. In: Walton J, Barondess JA, Lock S, editors. *The Oxford medical companion*. Oxford: Oxford University Press, 1994.

280. Teeling Smith G, editor. The evolution of the NHS debate. In: *A new NHS act for 1996?* London: Office for Health Economics, 1984.

281. Report of the Medical Services Review Committee. Summary of conclusions and recommendations. *BMJ* 1962; 2: 1178–86.

282. Institute of Hospital Administrators and the King's Fund. *The shape of hospital management in 1980?* London: King's Fund, 1967.

283. Integration of health services [parliamentary notes]. *BMJ* 1966; 2: 477.

284. Royal Commission. *BMJ* 1966; 2, suppl: 75–6.
New look at the NHS [leading article]. *BMJ* 1967; 1: 6.

285. Powell JE. *A new look at medicine and politics.* London: Pitman Medical, 1966.
A new look at medicine and politics. *BMJ* 1966; 2: 1315–19.
Powell E, Miller H. Medicine and politics. *BMJ* 1967; 1: 555–9.

286. The North looks ahead [leading article]. *BMJ* 1967; 1: 647–8.
Future of British medicine. *BMJ* 1967; 1: 693–4.

287. Seldon A. Prospects for private health insurance. *BMJ* 1967; 3: 166–8.

288. DHSS. *On the state of the public health.* Report of the CMO for 1969. London: HMSO, 1970

289. Minister to review structure of NHS [parliamentary notes]. *BMJ* 1967; 4: 367.

Chapter 3

1968–1977
Rethinking the National Health Service

1968–1977

Rethinking the National Health Service

Chronology: the third decade

Background	Year	NHS events
Czechoslovak uprising Moon orbited	1968	Ministry of Health and Ministry of Social Security form DHSS (Richard Crossman, Secretary of State) Royal Commission on Medical Education (Todd) Seebohm Report First Green Paper on NHS Reorganisation Designation of RHB hospitals for medical education Prices and Incomes Board no. 60 on Nurses Heart transplants RCN admits student nurses
Man on the moon Age of majority reduced from 21 to 18 British troops in N Ireland Woodstock Boeing 747 in service	1969	Bonham-Carter 'Functions of the DGH' Ely Hospital report published Hospital advisory service Royal Commission on Local Government
Conservative government (Edward Heath) Simon and Garfunkel 'Bridge over troubled water' Alvin Toffler's *Future shock*	1970	Second Green Paper on NHS Reorganisation RCN pay campaign; admits SENs and pupil nurses Peel Report on domiciliary midwifery and maternity bed needs
Decimalisation of currency Increase in pop music festivals	1971	Consultation on NHS reorganisation Briggs (Nursing) Coronary artery bypass surgery *Better services for the mentally handicapped* Harvard-Davies 'Organisation of Group Practice'
Watergate burglary	1972	NHS Reorganisation White Paper Ancillary staff on strike Hunter on Medical Administrators 'Grey Book' on *Management arrangements for the reorganised NHS*

Background	Year	NHS events
		Computerised tomography (CT) Faculty of Community Medicine formed
Yom Kippur war; OPEC rise in oil price Publication of *Small is beautiful* School leaving age raised to 16 UK joins EEC Miners' strike Ancillary staff in hospital strike	1973	NHS Reorganisation Act Health Service Commissioner *Accounting for health* (King's Fund Report)
Three-day working week February election: minority Labour government October election: Labour government with majority of three Microsoft Corporation established Aerosols reported as depleting ozone layer	1974	NHS reorganisation Control of Pollution Act Consultant industrial action over private practice 'Democracy in the NHS' Halsbury Committee on pay and conditions of nurses and professions supplementary to medicine (30 per cent rise) Lalonde on health promotion Health and Safety at Work etc. Act
First North Sea oil Peak inflation: 26.9 per cent US withdrawal from Vietnam	1975	NHS Planning System Whole body CT scanning Controversy over private medicine Merrison: Regulation of the Medical Profession *Better services for the mentally ill*: White Paper London Co-ordinating Committee
International Monetary Fund loan Concorde in service James Callaghan Prime Minister	1976	Health Services Board (private practice) *Priorities for health and personal social services* Royal Commission on NHS established The NHS Planning System Sharing Resources (RAWP) Legislation for mandatory vocational training (from 1982) Normansfield mental handicap hospital scandal *Prevention and health: everybody's business* *Fit for the future* (Court Report on child health) Cimetidine for ulcers UK Colleges' criteria for brain-stem death Hospital Advisory Service becomes Health Advisory Service
	1977	*The way forward* (Priorities for the NHS) 'Health for All by 2000' declaration London Health Planning Consortium Communicable Disease Surveillance Centre formed

Twenty years on

The 1960s had started with optimism, austerity had ended, economic growth seemed assured, poverty was receding and life was improving. From 1964 the situation deteriorated as the international balance of trade swung against the UK and long-range economic forecasts proved wrong. There was severe deflation in 1966, devaluation of the pound in 1967 and the third decade of the NHS began in financial crisis. The time had come to rethink the pattern of the NHS. Alvin Toffler's book *Future shock* described the shattering stress and disorientation induced in people experiencing too much change in too short a time.[1] Clinical development and activity was certainly increasing inexorably. Central planning being in vogue, solutions were sought in changing the management and structure of organisations, small was not considered beautiful and there was a deep belief in the wisdom of management consultants. The arguments and assumptions about the NHS were changing. No longer was it merely a question of whether the nation could afford a health service, and what form of cost control was required. New questions required a more political solution. Were the resources of the NHS correctly deployed, north and south, and between acute and chronic care? What form of management was appropriate? What were the implications of community care? Should the education of doctors and nurses be matched less to acute disease and more to longer term needs? Was there too great a disparity in the income of the high earners in the NHS and the ancillary staff? What was the place of private practice? How far should union power extend?

The future relationship of health and local authority services became a key issue. The closely related reports of the Royal Commission on Local Government and the Committee on the Provision of Personal Social Services (Seebohm) appeared. Seebohm recommended bringing together all personnel concerned with any aspect of personal social care into new social services departments within major local authorities. It argued for 'generic' social workers, which meant the transfer of highly skilled medical social workers from the hospitals to the local authorities and the destruction of bridges that were being developed between social workers and doctors.[2] At the close of 1967 Kenneth Robinson, the Minister, had announced that the government's views on the structure of the NHS would be set out in a Green Paper. After 20 years, said the *BMJ*, the structure was out of date, but at least modernisation and reform might be in sight. There had been widespread demand for a new service designed to meet the requirements of modern medicine. Delay in making the necessary changes had been a major cause of the emigration of doctors. The whole welfare state, and not just the NHS, needed to be recast for the changing needs of the community. The *BMJ* concluded that the integration of the management and financing of the NHS was necessary.[3]

Challenges for the future

Kenneth Robinson chaired a conference to celebrate the 20th anniversary of the inception of the service in 1948. Jennie Lee, Aneurin Bevan's widow, opened it.[4] Bevan, she said, believed that local government could not have coped with the establishment of a health service in 1948 along with all its other responsibilities. The acceptance by the state of total responsibility for a comprehensive health service for everyone was an essential first step. Nevertheless, Bevan had seen that a time might come when the relationship between health and local government would need re-examination, particularly if the units of local government were to become larger.

At the conference Professor John Butterfield, a physician from Guy's Hospital, traced the way patterns of disease and health care had changed. The population had increased by 10 per cent and was better housed. Technological advance had taken place, with developments in electronics and laboratory automation and an explosion in the number of drugs available. Acute and infectious diseases were on the wane, but disability caused by chronic and degenerative and debilitating diseases was increasing. John Reid, the Medical Officer of Health (MOH) for Buckinghamshire, talked of the growing interest in medical care in the community, and the development of group general practice with the attachment of local authority health visitors, social workers, nurses, midwives and auxiliaries. Artificial barriers between the three parts of the service were being removed. Henry Yellowlees, Deputy Chief Medical Officer at the Department of Health, spoke of planning and information, and the effects of different medical policies on the use of resources. JOF Davies, the Oxford Regional Hospital Board's senior administrative medical officer (SAMO), said that reviewing clinical performance and taking advantage of operational research and statistics was important. Desmond Bonham-Carter, Chairman of the Board at University College Hospital, looked at personnel issues. Some people had suggested that the health service was on the verge of general management on an industrial model. General managers would then have authority over medical and nursing directors. His view was that, even if such a manager were paid more than leading consultants and top posts were open to all, a general manager would be unable to dictate to medical, nursing and other disciplines, because their decisions depended on clinical and professional judgements. Trades union representatives raised the need to value the many skills required in the NHS; the problem of recruiting, training and retaining staff; the problems of a tripartite service; and ensuring involvement of the staff side in proposals for change. The unions saw increasing government involvement in negotiations on pay and conditions of service, incomes policies and the pursuit of productivity. They did not believe that any change of government in the next 20 years would alter this fundamentally, because government was increasingly involved in the national economy.[5]

Much of the agenda for the next decade had been outlined. 'Forward into the 1970s' said Kenneth Robinson, closing the conference. An economic crisis in January 1968 again forced the government to cut public expenditure. Faced with the alternative of reducing hospital building or re-imposing prescription charges, Labour maintained the building programme and introduced a charge of 2s 6d (12½p) per item, with certain categories of patient exempted.

Medical progress

Health promotion

People were living longer and the major causes of death were changing. Public health measures needed a new perspective. In 1974 Lalonde, a minister in the Canadian government, published an outstanding report that focused attention on four main factors: human biology, environment, life style and the organisation of health care. Much premature death and disability was preventable.[6] Some hypotheses might be sufficiently valid to warrant taking positive action. Being slim was better than being fat; it was better not to smoke cigarettes; alcohol was a danger to health, particularly when driving a car; and the less polluted air and water were the healthier we were. The report received international acclaim and led to publications in the USA, Australia and the UK. In November 1975, in response to concern about the disparity of spending on curative as opposed to preventive services, a parliamentary subcommittee began a special enquiry into preventive medicine. David Owen, then Minister of Health, wished that a major effort to bring health promotion to the forefront of NHS through the planning system would mark his time in the Department. In 1976 the government published *Prevention and health: everybody's business.*[7] The main killer diseases, coronary heart disease, lung cancer and bronchitis, were largely caused by people's behaviour. Both individuals and government must accept responsibility for health. Cigarette smoking, lack of exercise, the fats in the diet and obesity were part of the life style of advanced, urban, industrial high-consumption societies. The various government publications sparked debate, for resources were limited and had to be focused on where they would do most good. Some saw the accent on life styles as only half the story, blaming the victim instead of dealing with underlying socio-economic factors affecting health. Government accepted that it had a role to play through fiscal policy, environmental controls, education and housing. But as there was a class gradient in diet, exercise and smoking, had not the trades unions a role as well?[8] Government could not move too far ahead of public opinion, but no single measure would have done more to prevent disease than making tobacco and alcohol progressively more expensive – instead of cheaper – in terms of the labour required to buy them, save perhaps the prohibition of advertising of tobacco. In April 1977, shortly before the 30th anniversary of the NHS, David Ennals, Secretary of State for Social Services in the Callaghan administration, commissioned a review of the available information about differences in health status between the social classes, the possible causes, the implications for policy, and the further research required. Sir Douglas Black, Professor of Medicine in Manchester, chaired the review and was helped by CS Smith, Secretary of the Social Science Research Council, Professor JN Morris, Director of the Medical Research Council (MRC) Social Medicine Unit, and Professor Peter Townsend, from Essex University.

Causes of increased mortality 1968–1978

Cause of death	Percentage increase	Cause of increase
Cancer of the oesophagus	12	Alcohol
Cancer of the lung	48	Cigarettes
Cancer of the pleura	43	Asbestos
Cancer of the breast	11	?
Cancer of the cervix	59	Multiplicity of sexual partners
Skin melanoma	37	Partly UV light
Alcoholism	141	Alcohol
Drug dependence	263	Addictive drugs
Cirrhosis of the liver	54	Alcohol
Motorcycle accidents	58	Motorcycles

Source: R Doll (1983)[9]

Although everyone eventually succumbs to one condition or another, it was commonly argued that redistributing funds in favour of prevention could reduce the burden of disease and the cost of the NHS. A series of reports from the Royal College of Physicians on smoking, atmospheric pollution, fluoridation, dietary fibre and coronary thrombosis had encouraged interest in prevention. Health promotion, Richard Doll argued, was primarily about the identification of measures proven to prevent the onset of disease, implementing them and measuring what was achieved. Many diseases that were increasingly taking their toll were amenable to prevention, in particular cancer of the lung and heart disease. Prevention of trauma had been successful; in spite of the enormously increased number of vehicles and the rise in population, a series of regulations had held deaths on the road to around 6,000 per year for the past 50 years. Sometimes the public would resist a measure that would reduce the toll of disease greatly, while pressing for action that would not only be costly but also produce minimal benefits.[9]

The contribution of acute medicine to health

Thomas McKeown believed there had been undue concentration on acute medicine and the hospital services. He disagreed with the idea that improvement in health must be based on understanding the structure and function of the body and the processes of disease. At a symposium in 1970, and in his Rock Carling monograph of 1976, he examined the causes of death, the reasons for improvement in human health over the past two centuries, and the parallel development of medical science and the hospitals.[10] He thought that past improvement had mainly been due to changes in behaviour and the environment, better food, cleaner water and an improved standard of living. One must look to these for further improvement. He thought that medical science and medical services were misdirected. Society's investment in health was not well used because it rested on a false assumption about the basis of human health. It was assumed that the body was a machine whose protection from disease and its effects depended primarily on intervention. The patient's demand for acute care and the physician's wish to provide it were the result. The requirements for health were simple: to be born healthy, to be adequately fed, to be protected from a wide range of hazards in the environment, and not to depart radically from the pattern of personal behaviour under which people evolved by smoking, over-eating or leading a sedentary life. Environmental change, personal preventive measures and therapeutic intervention had to be brought together.[11] It was a critique echoed by others. McKeown's conclusion, that until the beginning of the twentieth century it was unlikely that immunization or therapy had a significant effect on the mortality of the population, was a foundation of what became known as 'the new public health'.

McKeown played down the contribution of clinical medicine. He hunted for evidence for his theory, ignoring the dubious nature of statistics a century old. Henry Miller, the neurologist, now Vice-Chancellor of Newcastle University, believed that public health doctors in general discounted the clinician's contribution because much of medicine was aimed at the reduction of suffering and the improvement of function, and it was hard to identify a substantial impact on mortality rates.[12] During the previous 30 years clinical medicine had been transformed, the conquest of poliomyelitis and syphilis being examples. An effective accident service would also make a major contribution to public health. Miller had no doubt that the hospital system would survive as the functional and intellectual hub of the NHS. Julian Tudor Hart, a GP at Glyncorrwg in Glamorgan deeply committed to a socialist analysis of society, also thought clinical medicine helped people but he thought that resources were distributed in an inefficient way. In his inverse-care law he said that the availability of good medical care tended to vary inversely with the need of the population served. Those doctors most able to choose went to work in middle-class areas. Places with the highest mortality and morbidity got the rest, often doctors from abroad who had difficulty obtaining the most sought-after jobs. In the areas with the most sickness and death, GPs had more work, larger lists, less hospital support and 'traditional' but ineffective ways of working. The hospital doctors in these areas shouldered heavier case-loads with fewer staff and less equipment, more obsolete buildings and a shortage of beds. Tudor Hart was worried by calls on the right for a return to an insurance-based system and the marketplace. He believed that the NHS had brought a substantial improvement in access to health care for those previously deprived, chiefly as a result of the decision to remove the NHS from market forces.[13]

The quality and effectiveness of health care

Archibald Cochrane's *Effectiveness and efficiency* stimulated much thought. Quality was a major theme underlying many aspects of health care rather than an isolated topic of its own, and was the topic of a Nuffield Provincial Hospitals Trust symposium.[14] The direction of the quality movement in health care was affected by the country's social and economic culture. In the UK, the NHS tended to insulate people from the need to consider costs and quality together.[15] In the USA rising costs led to the introduction of 'utilisation review' and a demand for more information about costs and quality. Professional Standards Review Organisations (PSROs) were introduced in 1972. Money went into research projects. Dr RH Brook and his colleagues, at Baltimore City Hospital, evaluated the quality of care of patients treated for urinary tract infection, uncontrolled hypertension and ulcers, all conditions in which it was relatively easy to define adequate investigation, treatment and follow-up.[16] They found a wide variation in quality. David Rutstein, at Harvard, suggested that the occurrence of an unnecessary disease, disability or untimely death was a sentinel event requiring search for remediable underlying causes. He believed that such an approach could be used more widely than deaths in childbirth or during surgery.[17] Avedis Donabedian, an American academic and perhaps the most influential theorist in the field of quality assurance in health care, provided a framework that clarified thinking.[18] Quality could be looked at from three standpoints:

Structure	The adequacy of facilities and equipment, the qualifications of the medical staff and their organisation, 'proper' settings for health care
Process	Whether what was thought to be 'good' care was given, the appropriateness and completeness of the history and examination, justifiable diagnosis and therapy, co-ordination and continuity of care
Outcome	What the result was in terms of patient satisfaction, quality of life, illness and death (morbidity and mortality)

Two features, said the *BMJ*, must underlie any worthwhile system of medical audit: first it must be effective and secondly it must be totally independent of the state. That said, the profession should not only be concerned about its standards but also be seen to be.[19] The Maternal Mortality enquiry was an example of an outcome study that revealed problems with the structure and processes of care. Disquiet at the conditions in long-stay hospitals had led to reviews. Surgeons took an increasing interest in their results.[20] A call for the widening of audit came from doctors and public alike, and increasingly it was felt that people had the right to reassurance that there was monitoring of clinical standards, as there was in education and child care. Audit systems were developed. A standard of care, perhaps based on published research work, would be established. Professional activity would be compared with the standard, and the results of the evaluation used to modify clinical conduct. The audit might be conducted by the professionals themselves or by an external agency.

Enquiries into the structure, the processes and the outcome of care revealed that resources were not always used to the best purpose. In 1969 the BMA Planning Unit drew attention to the unaccountable variations in the frequency of some routine operations from city to city and hospital to hospital, in the mortality from standard surgical procedures, and the duration of stay in hospital of patients with similar diseases. Did patients with hernias or varicose veins who stayed in hospital a couple of weeks really do better than short-stay or outpatient cases? Did patients with coronary heart disease do better under continuous monitoring in hospital or at home with simple nursing care? At what point did population screening cease to pay dividends and become counter-productive? Such questions required answers that could only come from the professions; a government department could not furnish them.[21] The Planning Unit also considered the complex and expensive forms of treatment being introduced, in particular organ transplantation. Some argued that these should be discouraged, in the dubious expectation that this would in some way lead to improvement in the quantity or quality of existing services. The Planning Unit thought that to slow research activity would be incompatible with professional freedom and with the enterprise expected of NHS staff.

The interests of staff and public might conflict; the medical profession was prepared to consider quality within an educational framework. People who had reason to question the quality of the care they had received looked for something with more bite. In 1976 there were 17,000 complaints about hospital treatment, one for every 300 patients admitted. Hospitals, said the *BMJ*, should have a simple system for handling complaints. But care was needed – the medical profession was beginning to look at ways of improving standards through voluntary medical audit, and an open-ended complaints procedure including matters of clinical judgement might postpone audit for another generation.[22] In any case, financial problems were also a threat to quality. At a BMA Council meeting Dr Appleyard, a paediatrician, said that the profession should tell Mr Ennals (then the Secretary of State) that it was no longer prepared to cover up the inadequacies of the health service. What was the position of a consultant who decided that staffing levels were insufficient and patients were at risk? A small group of the Joint Consultants Committee was appointed to consider a way to identify hospitals that were becoming dangerous to patients.[23]

A parliamentary commissioner on administration (ombudsman) had been appointed in the late 1960s, and the parliamentary select committee reporting in 1971 recommended the inclusion within his remit of complaints about hospitals.[24] The medical profession had no objection to complaints about the failure of an ambulance to arrive or the squalid condition of a casualty department. The difficulty arose, however, if a patient died and relatives thought he might have survived had the treatment been different – a matter that could already be pursued though the courts. The Health Service Commissioner, Sir Alan Marre, opened his doors in October 1973 and there were several no-go areas. Patients who had appealed to a tribunal or had gone to court, or had the right to do so, normally could not take their grievance to the Commissioner. Neither were actions that were the result of clinical judgement included.[25]

Changes in society

Changes in life style were affecting health and the health service. Overseas package holidays became widely available, skiing became more popular and eating patterns altered. Increased car ownership altered leisure activities; exercise became fashionable and aerobics was introduced. The Woodstock festival was held in 1969; the young were urged to 'turn on, tune in and drop out'. The following year a festival in the Isle of Wight attracted 200,000 people over a period of a few days. As nobody knew how many would come, the catering and sanitary facilities were strained. Festivals became a regular occurrence and initially there was much goodwill although the personal conduct of those attending attracted media interest. Local doctors and voluntary organisations gave their time generously and little drug misuse was apparent. Those attending were said to have a natural dignity, grace and happiness that were difficult to credit unless seen.[26] The BMJ was less enthusiastic.[27]

> If the festivals are not the degraded orgies that they are sometimes made out to be, nor are they quite the care-free wandervögel, healthful communing with nature that their admirers have occasionally supposed. They are commercial ventures which can succeed financially or fail, and the people who attend them pay for their entertainment – apart from the considerable number of gate crashers. A fully satisfactory public health service for the occasion should therefore be included in the cost of it.

Advances in technology

Ever-more complex diagnostic techniques, multitudes of drugs and highly complex surgery were changing the face of medical practice. Sub-specialisation increased. Some orthopaedic surgeons tended to deal with fractures, others with joint replacement. Increasingly the treatment of a single patient required the co-operation of different specialties, as in the case of cardiac and pulmonary resuscitation, renal dialysis and transplantation. Medical laboratory work was expanding. Computers, initially linked to analytical equipment, were increasingly built into laboratory systems. The fibreoptic endoscopes, developed in Japan by Olympus and other companies, could now be used to look at the oesophagus, stomach, duodenum and colon, and to take samples for pathological examination (histology and cytology).[28] 'Spare-part' surgery was growing, as metal, plastic or dead tissues were used to replace parts of the body with a relatively inert mechanical function, such as arteries, valves and joints. Transplants were increasingly successful.[29] Most acute hospitals had intensive care units, patients with heart attacks being brought together and continually monitored by nurses watching ECG displays and starting resuscitation when necessary.[30] No wonder, wrote a physician, that sympathy seemed less of a priority, for doctors were human and there was a limit to the capacity to absorb and transmit all this and sympathy too. Reversion to the gentler manner of a bygone age seemed unlikely.[31]

The drug treatment of disease

Genetic engineering slowly began to influence the development of new drugs. Stanley Cohen and Herbert Boyer at Stanford University combined their knowledge of enzymes and DNA, and in 1973 published a method of inserting foreign genetic material into bacterial plasmids.[32] The Cohen–Boyer patent, which earned Stanford an ever-increasing amount ($15 million in 1995), was one of the first steps in developing recombinant techniques.

In spite of the many new antibiotics, ward infections by strains that were difficult to treat became more common.[33] The drugs that remained effective had to be used with caution and in the knowledge of the changing patterns of resistance. During the 1950s staphylococci were increasingly found to produce penicillinase that inactivated the antibiotic. The production of penicillinase-stable penicillins such as methicillin gave clinicians a temporary respite, but then methicillin-resistant strains appeared. It seemed as if the main classes of antibiotics had now been identified, and henceforth discoveries were little more than additional members of an existing group.

The traditional treatment of stomach and duodenal ulcer had been based on diet, alkalis and, if these failed, surgery (partial gastrectomy or vagotomy and drainage). Relapse after medical treatment was almost invariable and recurrence after surgery was common.[34] Now there was a new answer. Histamine had long been known to stimulate gastric acid secretion but antihistamine drugs did not relieve ulcer symptoms. In 1964 James Black examined several hundred chemicals with a slightly different pharmacological action and found some that did reduce gastric acid secretion. The first compounds to be tried were not effective by mouth or had unacceptable side effects. However, in 1976 cimetidine, and later ranitidine which required fewer daily doses, proved a breakthrough, helping duodenal and gastric ulcers to heal. They were so effective, and adverse reactions so few, that some GPs instead of waiting for X-ray examinations made a diagnosis by seeing if the new drugs gave relief. Long-term administration seemed necessary, which helped them to become the first products to generate $1 billion revenue.[35]

Advances also occurred in the treatment of asthma. An entirely new agent was introduced, disodium cromoglycate (Intal), which inhibited a bronchial reaction to inhaled allergens. It was best used as prophylaxis by regular administration of the dry powder in a special inhaler. Better bronchodilators, which made breathing easier, became available. For example, salbutamol partly replaced isoprenaline, which had been used for many years.[36] The treatment of high blood pressure was also improved.

Many people could not tolerate the side effects of the earlier drugs but the introduction of beta-receptor blocking drugs (such as propranolol in 1969) that were effective and easier to take improved compliance.[37] In 1974 Peter Ellwood and collaborators at the MRC Epidemiology Unit in Cardiff published a paper on the possible use of aspirin to prevent myocardial infarction; the result was suggestive but statistically inconclusive.[38]

The 'non-steroidal anti-inflammatory' drugs were a major advance in the management of arthritis. Aspirin, the mainstay of treatment, was a discovery of the nineteenth century chemical industry. In the 1950s alternatives such as phenylbutazone became available, followed in the 1960s by other drugs including indomethacin, and a range of propionic acid derivatives including ibuprofen and naproxen.[39] The way in which they relieved symptoms remained a mystery until 1971 when John Vane offered an explanation of their activity in blocking prostaglandin synthesis and release. Parkinson's disease was also helped by the introduction of levodopa in 1970.

By 1968 a million women were on the contraceptive pill and there was growing concern about its side effects. A strong relationship was reported between the use of the pill and death from pulmonary embolus or cerebral thrombosis (a stroke caused by a clot forming in a major artery to the brain).[40] The Committee on Safety of Drugs recommended the use of low-dose preparations. The thalidomide disaster of 1961 was casting a long shadow. Manufacturers now had an entirely rational fear of adverse publicity and expensive litigation, and might only undertake costly research and testing on drugs with a potentially large market.[41]

Misuse of drugs steadily increased. There were few, if any, valid indications for the use of amphetamines but the Association of the British Pharmaceutical Industry was opposed to a ban. Several groups of doctors, including the Inner London Medical Committee, overrode the industry and recommended a prohibition of their use.[42] Barbiturate abuse was also common. Young addicts found them lying around the home, and sometimes stole prescription pads from surgeries or burgled pharmacies. A campaign to restrict their use was also launched; benzodiazepines were just as effective and their addictive properties still seemed low.[43]

Drug interaction and 'bioavailability', the extent to which a product administered can be used by the body, became important. Digitalis had been one of the few effective cardiovascular drugs although determining the ideal dose for an individual patient had always been difficult. It became possible in 1968 to measure plasma concentrations accurately by tests using radio-isotopes (radio-immune assay). The research workers developing the technique were the first to notice that batches of digoxin manufactured after May 1972 produced twice the previous plasma levels, although the tablets had the same content. What had changed was the formulation, the fillers, buffers and stabilisers used. A warning was immediately issued about this first major example of a bioavailability problem. Drugs might interact with each other. Anticoagulants had been used widely in the treatment of heart attacks. However, careful control was needed. Indomethacin, salicylates and sulphonamides enhanced their effect; sedatives and tranquillisers might inactivate them.[44]

The pattern of suicide changed. Suicide from coal gas and barbiturate poisoning had been common but became less so, because natural gas had a lower carbon monoxide concentration and barbiturates were less commonly prescribed. Potential suicides chose from the ever-widening range of sedatives, tranquillisers and antidepressants; suicide from prescribed drugs increased.[45] Accidental overdosage could also occur, particularly in children, so protective packaging began to be introduced. Even coffee had hazards; too much produced symptoms indistinguishable from those of anxiety neuroses. Sudden withdrawal might also produce severe headaches. To what could one turn for relief?[46]

Radiology and diagnostic imaging

Advances in surgical treatment imposed new diagnostic demands on X-ray departments, for example a series of pictures in rapid succession to give a moving image. More films meant more radiation and greater risks for both patients and staff. However, it became possible to cut radiation exposure by three-quarters when rare earth intensification screens, which produced a brighter image, were introduced. Simultaneously, new contrast media were introduced that were safer and less unpleasant for the patient. Image intensifiers were developed further and produced clearer and more detailed images. Coupled to TV systems and cine equipment they were rapidly applied to studies of the oesophagus, gut and heart. Because images could be recorded in digital form, they could be compared and manipulated using the ever-increasing computer power that was becoming available.

Sometimes new methods of producing pictures did not use X-rays. Another name was therefore found for X-ray departments – diagnostic imaging. Radio-isotope imaging systems were becoming better and gamma cameras were increasing in efficiency. Unlike rectilinear scanners, they could detect radiation all over the area being examined at the same time, so they were quicker in use and could show radio-isotopes moving from one part of an organ to another. Ultrasound was widely available and the quality of sensors and computing improved rapidly. Moving images could now be seen using 'real-time' ultrasound, and the newer scanners were smaller, easier to install and easier to use. Already widely used in obstetrics, cardiology also benefited. Blood flow and valve movement could be measured as new techniques were used, such as the Doppler effect.

The most important advance of the decade was the introduction of X-ray computed tomography. Since the first X-rays in 1895 all radiographs had shared the same constraint, a two-dimensional image. The limit on progress was thought to lie in the systems producing radiation. Now orthodoxy was challenged. Interest shifted from the source of the radiation to the detection of the image. Advances in detection, combined with a finely collimated beam, allowed a 1000-fold increase in the power of systems. Godfrey Hounsfield, an engineer at EMI (Electrical Musical Industries), announced the development of X-ray computed tomography at the British Institute of Radiology Congress in 1972. Hounsfield modestly wrote that the technique of CT scanning might open up a new chapter in X-ray diagnosis. Tissues of near similar density could be separated and a picture of soft-tissue structure within the skull or body could be built up. It was a fundamental advance in diagnostic medicine. Instead of film, X-rays registered on sensitive crystal detectors. The patient was scanned by a narrow beam that was moved across the body and also rotated around it. A huge number of readings were fed into a computer that mathematically worked out the values of density of each 'pixel' of the image. It displayed cross-sectional images in an entirely new way.[47] Ian Isherwood, Professor of Diagnostic Radiology at the Manchester Royal Infirmary, said the new process opened the brain of the patient and the mind of the doctor.[48] One could not only look at an image but could also formulate questions to ask of it.

Hounsfield worked with Dr James Ambrose, at the nearby neurosurgical unit at Atkinson Morley's Hospital where the earliest clinical images were created. It was the improvement of computer processing that made the early scans possible, but 15 minutes of computing was needed to create a single picture. Hounsfield recognised its significance in radiology but was unable to interest his company in its development; EMI was more used to marketing the Beatles' music and did not have the infrastructure to support major medical instrumentation. Visiting radiologists understood the potential and Ian Isherwood encouraged the Department of Health to support the new technology. The Department funded the development of a head scanner and the second prototype was installed in 1971 at the National Hospital for Nervous Diseases, Queen Square.

Scanners revolutionised the diagnosis of stroke and intracranial haemorrhage (bleeding within the skull). At first the new technique was used only by neurologists because the part being scanned had to be surrounded by a water jacket and remain completely still. Normal structures of the brain were beautifully shown, and the position and nature of space-occupying lesions could be seen with great accuracy.[49] The scanner that neurologists required was small and the images were so good that they rapidly displaced older examinations such as cerebral arteriograms and air encephalograms that were painful and risky. With the development of larger whole-body scanners in 1975, first used by Louis Kreel of Northwick Park, the results particularly from scanning the chest and pelvis opened new diagnostic possibilities.[50] International interest in the new technology was keen and firms based outside Great Britain with long experience in radiology (such as Philips and Siemens) developed new generations of equipment. CT scanning, unknown at the beginning of the decade, was an ambition of every district general hospital (DGH) by its end. Initially introduced to regional and neurological centres, many DGHs began to appeal for charitable funds even though each scanner carried with it high running costs. The images from the new techniques were digital and it became possible to record digital images from conventional X-ray equipment. Magnetic disks could now store them, opening the possibility of doing away with a silver-based photographic process.[51]

Interventional radiology

The trend in diagnostic imaging had been towards less invasive procedures, yet imaging and surgery began to converge as a new sub-specialty, 'interventional radiology', developed. Image intensifiers allowed radiologists to work in normal room lighting. The improved ability to pass fine catheters along blood vessels into the smallest branches, and to see precisely where they were, meant that it was possible for radiologists to carry out quasi-surgical procedures under radiographic control. Interventional radiology became the umbrella term covering many therapeutic and diagnostic procedures. Catheters could be manipulated to reach most parts of the body and a wide range of lesions could be treated. The principal techniques were the obliteration of abnormal blood vessels such as angiomas with materials including gel-foam or polyvinyl alcohol foam, increasing blood flow in narrowed vessels, and dissolving blockages formed by thrombosis with clot-dissolving agents.[52]

Infectious disease and immunisation

Communicable diseases could still produce a surprise. What was true of one microbe, said James Howie, Director of the Public Health Laboratory Service (PHLS), was not necessarily any guide to the life style of another. The diseases displayed the versatility of the microbes that caused them.[53] Viruses were generally associated with acute illnesses; now evidence was accumulating that they were also responsible for a variety of subacute or chronic degenerative conditions such as Creutzfeldt–Jakob disease (CJD), and two diseases in animals, scrapie in sheep and mink encephalopathy.[54] Though rare, the extraordinary nature of their agents that were highly resistant to normal methods of sterilisation made them of interest.

Counter-measures could be developed only by slow and often tedious methods. There were three main methods of control: immunisation, hygiene and chemotherapy. Immunisation had substantially reduced the common diseases of childhood. Measles immunisation became public policy in 1968 but the levels of cover were often disappointing. For whooping cough there had usually been more than 100,000 notifications a year before immunisation was introduced in the 1950s. This had fallen to around 2,400 by 1973 when the vaccination rate was over 80 per cent. In 1974/5 public concern followed presentation of data about the problem of neurological complications associated with immunisation. Cover fell from 80 per cent to 30 per cent and major epidemics of whooping cough followed in 1977–1979 and 1981–1983. It took ten years for balance to be restored.

Hygiene remained important. Salmonella food poisoning, often following the consumption of cold or incompletely heated chicken, milk and eggs, could be traced back to poultry-processing plants, to their suppliers, to the breeding stock and to the food mixtures that were often heavily contaminated. Was there an effective system of inspection? asked the BMJ. Animal carcasses, environments, infected raw material fed to animals, processing plants and slaughter-houses were the source of human infections, and it was improbable that salmonellosis was the only example of an animal infection important to humans and animals, and to the economics of farming and food processing.[55] A major achievement of the PHLS was the discovery that many cases of diarrhoea for which no other bacteriological cause could be found were due to *Campylobacter jejuni*, which was difficult to grow in the laboratory. It soon became apparent that such infectious were even more common than those due to *Salmonella*.

Blood transfusion had long been known to be responsible, on occasion, for jaundice. This was especially so when large donor pools were used as the starting material for dried plasma. In the late 1960s a test had become available for hepatitis B antigen, and blood donor screening was introduced. Worldwide elimination of smallpox was now in sight and the WHO intensified its campaign. In the UK the risks from rare but serious complications of immunisation were much greater than from the disease itself.[56] Routine smallpox immunisation in childhood ceased in 1971. In 1973, however, when smallpox was considered no longer to be a risk in the UK, an outbreak originated from a laboratory at the London School of Hygiene and Tropical Medicine.[57] There was a failure to follow up contacts, and secondary cases were initially missed. Following the report on the handling of the outbreak the Communicable Disease Surveillance Centre (CDSC) was established in 1977, as part of the PHLS, to handle outbreaks that crossed organisational boundaries. The value of the CDSC was proved in 1978, when a technician in Birmingham also contracted smallpox from a laboratory.

Marburg fever was the first of several new viral haemorrhagic fevers to be reported. In 1969 another was recognised, Lassa fever, named after the place in Nigeria where it was first seen. It was related to a reservoir of infection in sub-saharan Africa. In 1976 a further epidemic erupted in Zaire and southern Sudan, with appallingly high mortality. Hundreds died, including 40 hospital workers. The causal agent, resembling Marburg virus but serologically distinct, was called Ebola virus. Such untreatable and apparently easily communicable infectious diseases caused great anxiety. The risk that people might travel by air during the incubation period led to plans for high-security infectious disease units. Travellers returning to Britain with a temperature were sometimes suspected of Lassa fever, though the diagnosis was rarely confirmed. A laboratory worker at Porton Down accidentally pricked his thumb while working with Ebola virus and six days later became ill and was transferred to an infectious disease unit at Coppetts Wood Hospital in north London where a plastic isolater, developed by Trexler, was available for use.[58] A permanent high-security unit was planned for Coppetts Wood but was delayed interminably while there were public protests and arguments about the design. The hospital was next to an infants' school and the area medical officer said that the proper place for swamp fevers was swamps – not Haringey.

Malaria had been eradicated from Britain long before the start of the NHS, with the exception each year of a few hundred imported cases, usually in tourists, business people, children visiting parents who were stationed overseas, immigrants returning home for a visit and, to a lesser extent, new immigrants. In the 1960s the number of cases had been low, probably because of worldwide mosquito eradication programmes. The number of cases in Britain reflected the changes taking place in the tropics. There were great hopes that DDT and other insecticides would make possible the control of malaria by eradicating or reducing mosquito populations. It was a bitter disappointment to find that mosquitoes could develop resistance to insecticides and that organophosphate residues from the insecticides were entering human food cycles.

In 1976 an outbreak of 180 cases of severe respiratory disease with 26 deaths occurred in the USA among people who had attended an American Legion convention. The bacterium responsible for Legionnaires' disease was rapidly isolated. The first British outbreak occurred in Nottingham in 1977. The infectious agent was subsequently found in water from cooling towers and air-conditioning systems, and the infection might therefore circulate throughout buildings.[59] Further British outbreaks included one in London, near the BBC in Upper Regent Street. Some episodes of illness many years previously could now be attributed to the same cause, for samples of patients' blood had been kept.

Sexually transmitted disease

Syphilis was under control but gonorrhoea and non-specific urethritis were still increasing. A hundred years previously the Chief Medical Officer (CMO) had argued that venereal disease (VD) was a just retribution for sin. Now it was seen as a penalty of ignorance in the young, for which their elders were responsible.[60] Ambrose King, the venereologist at The London Hospital, warned about the possible failure of the VD services. The public was ill-informed, doctors were poorly educated in the subject, the facilities for treatment were often in the poorest buildings in the hospital, laboratory standards varied and contact tracing was inadequate. King wrote that VD did not appeal to tender hearts and swayed no votes. Most money went into researching the complex problems of a few, little into really big medical problems affecting large numbers of people.[61]

Orthopaedics and trauma

Organisations such as Arbeitsgemeinschaft für Osteosynthesefragen (AO) continued to develop systems of fixation, improving the design of tapped screws to fix bone fragments, and developing the use of implants to span fragments and maintain length and alignment. Road traffic accidents remained a major feature of the work of orthopaedic departments. Because of the high incidence of head injury among motorcyclists, crash helmets were made compulsory in 1974; paradoxically the enforcement of their use meant that more motorcyclists survived their head injuries, and presented orthopaedic units with severe multiple injuries that formerly would have been seen only in the mortuary.

Hip replacement had emerged as one of the most important developments of modern surgery. A wide range of less sophisticated operations (hip fusion, arthroplasty and new femoral heads) were now superseded by total replacement as the treatment of choice. In 1972 John Charnley reported long-term follow-up of 379 operations, carried out between 1962 and 1965, with excellent results.[62] The need for surgery of the knee was at least as great as in the hip, but the mechanics of the joint were much more complex. Caution was needed because, if the operation went wrong, putting matters right was difficult. In the 1950s and early 1960s hinge joints had been used, but they tended to loosen or break. Major effort went into development; Michael Freeman introduced a prosthesis in 1968 in which the joint surfaces alone were replaced, the upper with metal and the lower with polyethylene, the condylar knee replacement.[63] It depended upon the patient's own ligaments for stability and was not suitable in cases of gross destruction of the joint, but the design was progressively improved. In the 1970s a two-piece prosthesis with a mechanical link was introduced. The failure rate remained higher than with the hip and, although the relief from pain was substantial, a walk across uneven ground was seldom possible.[64] Initial experiments were undertaken with other joints, the shoulder and the elbow. All operations had the potential to produce problems – infection, loosening of the components or the wearing out of the prosthesis.

Cardiology and cardiac surgery

With better forms of treatment, the prevalence of heart failure particularly from high blood pressure fell. Heart attacks, most dangerous in the first minutes, presented an increasing problem. A big reduction in the mortality of the disease depended on prevention rather than technology. Evidence incriminated high blood pressure, smoking, obesity, a high intake of saturated fat from dairy products and physical inactivity. Many common foods seemed 'super-saturated', from roast beef to bangers and mash.[65]

In 1971 Brighton followed Belfast in the introduction of mobile coronary care ambulances staffed by specially trained personnel who could recognise abnormalities of heart rhythm from the ECG and correct them by the use of a defibrillator.[66] Because there might be a delay before a call was received, there were doubts about the effectiveness of such services. In hospital the technology of coronary care units steadily improved, with automatic preset alarms warning nurses if the patient's heart beat became too fast or slow, and indwelling cardiac catheters to monitor heart function. From six weeks' bed rest in hospital, the norm in 1948, treatment for a heart attack had moved on. By the 1970s experience showed that rapid mobilisation could be advocated confidently. In an uncomplicated case the patient could be out of bed in a day or two and discharged in a week to ten days. It was now known that within a month the damage to the heart had largely healed and a normal life could be resumed.[67] Archibald Cochrane was responsible for a study from Bristol which revealed that selected patients treated at home did as well as those treated in hospital and raised a question about the effectiveness of hospital care. However, the groups studied differed in their characteristics, and the study did not alter policy on hospital admission.

After a slow start, ultrasound (echocardiography) was increasingly important in cardiology, particularly in the assessment of valve disease. Heart valve damage because of rheumatic fever had been a major problem. By the 1970s the scene had changed, for two reasons. First, there had been an astonishing fall in the incidence of rheumatic fever, probably related to better housing that reduced overcrowding, and possibly a diminished virulence of the alpha-haemolytic streptococcus or better control of infections.[68] Second, the surgical treatment of damaged heart valves had improved and was now a routine procedure. The death rate during operation for valve replacement was about 10 per cent, and athough patients never regained the heart function of a healthy young adult, most were well satisfied with the improvement. The valves might be mechanical, for example the Starr–Edwards caged-ball type that proved highly durable, or tissue, human 'homografts' or pig aortic valves, both of which were widely used but less durable.[69]

Infants and children with congenital heart disease and a poor chance of survival had been among the earliest cardiac surgical patients. Initially, because of the limited techniques available and the complexity of the abnormalities, full restoration of normal anatomy and function was seldom possible. Now major abnormalities were increasingly tackled in units such as Great Ormond Street, the Brompton and Guy's hospitals, where there was great expertise in the care of small and sick infants.

The acceptance that surgery had a place in the treatment of coronary heart disease was largely the result of work at the Cleveland Clinic, Ohio. In 1962 selective coronary angiography was introduced, which showed the position of blocked arteries, and by 1967 a surgical technique was developed to use a graft to bypass obstructed coronary arteries. The ability to stop the circulation and use a heart–lung machine (perfusion) gave the surgeon enough time to perform the operation. Surgery was found to improve angina better than medical treatment. By 1971/2 increasing numbers of operations were performed in Britain and the procedure began to dominate cardiac surgery.[70] By 1974 the mortality was as low as 3 per cent in patients with severe stable angina.

Surgeons had been doing experimental heart transplants in animals for many years. A human heart transplant was carried out by Christiaan Barnard in South Africa in 1967. Norman Shumway then performed two at Stanford, California. Early in 1968 the Board of Medicine of the American National Academy of Sciences issued guidance on the experience, laboratory facilities and ethical safeguards that should be in place in cardiac surgical centres considering transplantation.[71] The first heart transplant in Britain was carried out at the National Heart Hospital by Donald and Keith Ross on 3 May 1968. There was a second, both followed by the patients' death. The surgeons had underestimated the need for careful patient selection and the problems of tissue typing, and they lacked the laboratory and pathology services that Shumway had. They misjudged the media interest, and some senior members of the medical profession were highly critical of the operations and thought them attention seeking. The third transplant took place at Guy's in 1969 and the *Daily Telegraph* published the name and biographical detail of the donor, a nurse killed in a road accident. An unrepentant newspaper rejected the hospital's protests. The *BMJ* thought it breathtaking that the paper thought it knew better what was good for the patient than the doctors or relatives.[72]

World-wide, many hospitals undertook a few heart transplants, but few of the patients survived. Almost all units rapidly stopped heart transplantation and a voluntary moratorium seemed to come into force. The transport of brain-dead donors in ambulances was leading to widespread distaste. Concerned about the ethics of the operation, the adverse publicity and the costs, Sir George Godber convened a group of experts, including those involved with the London patients, to ensure that the medical profession acted on a matter of public concern. Sir George said that clinical decisions about the treatment of individual patients were for the consultants concerned, but the diversion of resources from other hospital work was a matter that involved management. The expert group advised that heart transplantation was still largely experimental and there was no advantage in replicating work being done elsewhere. Regions were told not to make special resources available to support programmes and, as a result, heart transplants ceased for the time being in Britain.[73] Shumway and his team in Stanford quietly continued their clinical work and their long-standing research programme. In 1971 their success rates were improving. Of 26 patients, 13 left the hospital of whom seven were alive a year later. A further report of 150 consecutive patients between 1968 and 1978 showed a one-year survival rate of 70 per cent – comparable with that of renal transplantation. The success was the result of teamwork with full immunological, pathological and microbiological services. In 1977 the UK Transplant Panel defined the conditions required in cardiac surgical units planning heart transplantation and the ban was rescinded in 1979.[74]

Organ transplantation

Organ transplantation began as laboratory research on animals, was used experimentally in humans by a few clinics and became accepted as a form of treatment of general application.[75] Sometimes, as in liver transplantation, the mortality was extremely high at the beginning, but with experience it diminished substantially. The search for new and more specific immunosuppressive agents proved frustrating. Roy Calne, an English surgeon then in Boston, investigated the use of a derivative of 6-MP, azathioprine, used in the treatment of leukaemia, and showed that it prevented the rejection of kidney grafts in dogs. Subsequently, the introduction of cyclosporin in the late 1970s, combined with steroids, changed the whole picture.[76] Getting excellent results in many patients, even with kidneys transplanted from unrelated donors, was now possible. Liver transplantation, first reported in 1963, was more difficult, particularly as the liver was sensitive to interruption of its blood supply, and had to be cooled rapidly and perfused if it was to survive until reimplantation.[77] Nevertheless the procedure was increasingly successful and a joint programme began at King's College Hospital and Addenbrooke's in 1968. By 1979 there had been 83 liver transplants with steadily improving results.[78] Research in basic immunology and tissue typing allowed clinicians to select donors with theoretical expectations of better results. The improvements in immunology also made bone marrow transplantation possible and in the late 1960s a role for it was identified in aplastic anaemia (failure of the bone marrow to produce blood cells) and leukaemia.[79] Although these techniques were effective, they were costly. Clinicians did not always discuss the financial consequences with hospital management before beginning programmes locally.

Renal replacement therapy

It was now well established that active life could be prolonged in renal failure by maintenance dialysis and renal transplantation, but lack of facilities meant that most of those who would benefit still died.[80] Home dialysis did little to relieve the pressure, although two-thirds of patients on dialysis treated themselves in their own homes. This was in part because of slow opening of new dialysis units and partly because of the risk of hepatitis B, although the control measures that were introduced in 1970 were largely effective.[81] After five years' effort, dialysis units were accepting only 500 patients a year out of an estimated potential three times that size. Once patients were on treatment they were there for years, blocking the units for new cases. Expansion of transplant facilities was urgently required, for a successful transplant removed the need for regular dialysis, made a place available for another patient and was probably cheaper in the long run. Kidneys were scarce. A national organ matching and distribution service was established in 1972 and it was found that many first transplants rapidly failed, probably reflecting the low quality of donor kidneys.[82] Increasingly, kidneys from living donors, often relatives, were used. The results were better and the effect of removal of a kidney from an otherwise healthy person was negligible.[83] Antony Wing, a nephrologist at St Thomas' Hospital, produced a graph showing a relationship between the total number of renal patients on programmes in different countries and the gross national product of each. The prospect of survival apparently depended on the economic productivity of the country of residence.[84] Dialysis and transplantation were now both established procedures and were interrelated. Neither could stand alone, for patients might need to move from one treatment to another, if for example a transplant failed.[85]

ENT surgery

A new surgical approach to the internal auditory canal was introduced by Ugo Frisch in Zurich. Hopkins had developed his fibreoptic lens system in 1954, but it was not until the mid-1970s that fibreoptic endoscopy revolutionised the examination of the nose and sinuses, also making possible the development of endoscopic sinus surgery.

Ophthalmology

Developments in operating microscopes, instruments and lasers were applied to the diagnosis and treatment of eye disease, leading to operative procedures that were often time consuming for the surgeon but made earlier discharge possible. Better anaesthesia and less traumatic surgery led to successful surgery on older patients than ever before, and they were operated on at an earlier stage of disablement.[86] Phaecoemulsification, a method of breaking up the opaque lens followed by aspiration to remove the lens fragments, was introduced into cataract surgery by Kelman in 1967.[87] Increasingly, lens implants were the treatment of choice.[88] Once, a cataract operation had been followed by three weeks in bed. Now early mobilisation was the order of the day. Sometimes surgeons extracted both cataracts at once, not generally regarded as good practice. Patients could expect to be up and watching television two days after operation. Some diseases had previously been untreatable, for example the retinal damage found in most diabetics after 10–20 years. The Birmingham Eye Hospital reported a controlled series showing that photo-coagulation by laser that destroyed the growth of abnormal new blood vessels, and could arrest the development of the disease.[89]

Cancer

The late 1960s and early 1970s saw a breakthrough in cancer chemotherapy. Gordon Hamilton-Fairley, at St Bartholomew's, saw what was happening in the USA and had the vision and drive to fight for chemotherapy and oncology in the UK. In the 1950s acute lymphatic leukaemia had proved to be curable. In the 1960s it was the turn of Hodgkin's disease, which had usually been fatal though treated for many years by radiotherapy and the early cytotoxic drugs such as nitrogen mustard. In early cases radiotherapy had cured a few patients. Combination therapy was discovered almost by chance. In 1964 the National Cancer Institute put together four drugs, each of which had some therapeutic effect but different toxic effects. The combination they chose to use was hard to better, and consisted of nitrogen mustard, oncovin (vincristine), prednisolone and procarbazine (MOPP). There were apparent cures, which led to a redoubling of effort. The combination of vinblastine and chlorambucil raised the remission rate to 63 per cent.[90] The radiological technique of lymphography, which made it possible to see affected lymph glands in the abdomen, and biopsy of spleen, bone marrow and liver, showed that the disease spread progressively. The spread could be accurately staged (assessed) and improved irradiation facilities made it possible to treat larger volumes of tissue. With increasing success, it became imperative that patients, often young adults, were handled from the outset at centres of expertise. Between 1972 and 1977 there was also a dramatic improvement in the remission rate of acute lymphoblastic leukaemia.[91] Cisplatin, introduced in 1972, had been discovered accidentally after Rosenberg, studying the effect of electrical currents on bacterial growth, found that bacteria did not multiply properly. It was the platinum electrode that was responsible and the guess that something that stopped bacteria dividing might do nasty things to cancer cells led to further work. It proved useful for several tumours, including testicular cancer.

Openness with patients was now required, for the new patterns of chemotherapy were not compatible with reticence about the diagnosis.[92] On both sides of the Atlantic enthusiasm grew among oncologists. Perhaps all that was necessary was to discover the right combination of drugs and each cancer in turn would be cured. A campaign in the USA to 'conquer cancer' painted a rosy picture of the outlook, with little stress on the poor prognosis of the more common cancers such as breast, lung and stomach. The mortality for cancer of the breast had altered little in 50 years. Since the 1950s it had been known that some breast cancers were hormone dependent. Anti-oestrogens provided a possible line of attack but many had severe side effects making them unacceptable to most doctors and patients. In the early 1970s several compounds, such as tamoxifen, were reported as arresting or reversing tumour growth. They became widely used, first in advanced breast cancer, subsequently at earlier stages, and to stop recurrence in the other breast.[93] Chemotherapy was already well established in advanced and inoperable disease and was used to reduce tumour size and make radiotherapy easier. With the discovery that tamoxifen and cytotoxic treatment improved the results, there was a swing away from radical surgery, partly because of a growing belief that treatment influenced survival less than the intrinsic behaviour of the tumour and the extent of the disease at the time of presentation.[94]

The results of screening for cancer of the cervix began to be analysed and there was debate over its effectiveness. In 1976 the Canadian government published a report of its experience with mass screening. The incidence of the disease had fallen alongside the introduction of the programme, and, although it was not possible to prove that screening was responsible, the report concluded that many cases of carcinoma that were still localised to the cervix would have spread had they not been treated.[95]

A further report on smoking was published in 1971 by the Royal College of Physicians. Some 50,000 deaths a year could conservatively be attributed to it, and the list of associated diseases now extended to chronic bronchitis, coronary artery disease and cancers of the of the mouth, pharynx and larynx.[96] Cigarette consumption continued to rise although the prevalence of smoking was beginning to fall. Three factors were recognised as affecting consumption: health publicity, tax increases and controls on smoking in the workplace.

Obstetrics and gynaecology

The number of maternal deaths had fallen from 67 per 100,000 in 1952 to 19 per 100,000 in 1969. The causes remained the same: abortion (other than termination of pregnancy), pulmonary embolism, haemorrhage and toxaemia.[97] The improved results were not due to any one factor but to higher standards of surveillance, earlier detection of complications and more effective preventive action and treatment.[98] A healthier population played its part as well.

Hospital deliveries were rising; by 1968 the figure was 80 per cent. The average length of stay after delivery, however, continually decreased and a rising number of maternity beds became available. As hospital confinement grew, GPs increasingly restricted their involvement to antenatal and postnatal care.[99] Women were generally delivered by midwives both at home and in hospital, but there was little contact between the two branches of the profession. In 1967 a committee was established, chaired by Sir John Peel, to consider the future of the domiciliary midwifery service and the need for maternity beds. The findings of the Perinatal Mortality Survey undertaken by the National Birthday Trust Fund influenced the Peel Report, published in 1970.[100] Cranbrook had recommended a 70 per cent hospital confinement rate, Peel now advocated 100 per cent and both assumed that hospital delivery was safer without actually establishing this. It became policy to concentrate obstetrics in properly equipped and staffed units, and to discourage isolated GP units. It was the death knell for the domiciliary midwife, who found that the work she had chosen and which she enjoyed was now branded as unsafe and inappropriate.[101] District midwives were retitled community midwives and became part of the primary health care team, working with GPs. Home birth was barely viable. As the numbers fell, neither GPs nor domiciliary midwives had enough experience to give them the confidence and the skills required.

While there was agreement that a unified obstetric service was desirable, relationships between obstetricians and GPs could be touchy. Consultants were sometimes prepared to work in a service with GP obstetricians only if they could lay down strict rules of practice, whereas the GPs might want to work in a unified service only if they could enjoy unfettered clinical responsibility.[102] The presidents of the Royal College of Obstetricians and Gynaecologists (RCOG) and Royal College of General Practitioners (RCGP) agreed to a joint committee to discuss the problems. Both Colleges favoured the closure of small isolated GP obstetric units and the complete integration of consultant and GP facilities. Improving the survival and quality of the fetus was thought to mean hospital delivery and fetal monitoring, a technique developed in the USA in the 1960s that spread rapidly in the UK. Fetal heart rates were measured and the acid–base balance was checked by fetal scalp blood sampling. The techniques were introduced without any substantial clinical trials, the results were not always fully understood and mothers were often worried about the nature of the attention they were receiving. Women, however, wished to take a more active part in their care and there was pressure to make hospitals more personal and less authoritarian. Some obstetricians had long aimed for this; for example, the baby might be placed in the mother's arms immediately after delivery, a simple philosophy but one sometimes difficult to imbue into those involved.[103]

Abortion

The Abortion Act 1967, the result of David Steel's private member's Bill, had changed the ambiguous and unsatisfactory state of the law. Genetic medicine created a further indication for termination; prenatal diagnosis of some congenital and inherited conditions was now possible by sampling amniotic fluid at the 16th week of pregnancy, allowing termination if indicated and acceptable to the mother. Abortions could be carried out only in NHS hospitals or other premises approved by the minister, and each had to be notified confidentially to the CMO. Neither the Ministry nor the gynaecologists had expected such a great change from the more liberal attitude by society and the GPs to abortion, and no extra staff, outpatient or theatre time were funded.[104] The number of abortions rose annually for the first six years to 167,000 in 1973, after which it fell slightly, perhaps because of the introduction of free contraception. Numbers rose again in 1977/8, perhaps owing to adverse publicity about the side effects of oral contraceptives.[105] The whole character of gynaecologists' outpatient work changed and waiting times for routine procedures got longer, particularly as few terminations were treated as day cases in the NHS, as they were in private clinics. Initially about 60 per cent of operations were carried out in NHS hospitals but there were wide regional variations in services. Only 20 per cent of women seeking a termination in the West Midlands region had NHS care in their home health region, compared with 90 per cent in Northern region.[106] In some areas gynaecologists were not prepared to carry out many – or any – terminations and women turned to voluntary organisations. The proportion of terminations performed in these 'approved' places rose because NHS beds were never increased to meet the demand. In 1968 there had been 50 deaths associated with abortion; such deaths fell steadily and in 1978 there were only five.[107] Up to a third of patients came from overseas, mainly France, Germany and the USA, although after 1973 the number of non-residents fell as other countries liberalised their legislation. The number of foreign women coming was said to have made Britain the abortion centre of the world, and private clinics were thought to be making exorbitant profits.

Opposition to the Act did not cease once it had become law. Despite 15 attempts to change it, mainly by reducing the time limit for abortion, the Abortion Act 1967 survived its first two decades unaltered. In February 1971 the government set up a committee of inquiry, not into the principles that underlay the Act but the way in which it was working. Reporting in 1974, the committee supported the Act and its provisions, though it criticised the inequalities of provision and laxity of some parts of the commercial private sector.[108] Abortion was sometimes the result of an inadequate family planning service. It was estimated that there were some 200,000 unwanted pregnancies a year and the country's family planning services were inadequate. Only one local authority out of six had a full service but family doctors and gynaecologists were not entitled to prescribe contraceptives for social reasons within the NHS. The voluntary sector tried to fill the gap, the Brook Advisory Service establishing clinics for teenagers. The *BMJ* argued that the expense of including contraception within the NHS would be small compared with the alternative, the cost of illegitimate births and abortions.[109]

Paediatrics

An appreciation of the unique nature of paediatric disease, and the ability to save children who might previously have died, spurred the appointment of many more paediatricians. Adults' physicians felt less comfortable managing children's care than in the past. The newcomers were interested in neonatal problems; particularly in the lowest social classes, the perinatal and neonatal mortality was high in comparison with other developed countries. The 1960s saw a proliferation of special care baby units

(SCBUs). Most of the babies admitted were not under-weight; almost half were there for observation, needed no treatment and left the unit within three days.[110] It proved difficult to organise an effective neonatal service. District paediatricians might prefer to maintain their own special care unit, even though it was half-empty. Obstetricians were sometimes loath to allow paediatricians to care for babies, and might oppose the transfer of mothers in premature labour to hospitals where there were good facilities for very small babies. In neonatal *intensive* care units the survival rates of small babies continued to improve and by 26–27 weeks the chances of survival had reached 50 per cent.[111] Intensive care cots were, however, in short supply. It was now possible to use machines for long periods to help babies breathe, and provide advanced monitoring.[112] Jonathan Shaw introduced total parenteral nutrition in 1973, allowing babies to be fed with fat, protein and carbohydrates intravenously.

Some major problems were diminishing. From 1970 the perinatal deaths from haemolytic disease of the newborn fell rapidly.[113] Far fewer children had orthopaedic problems. Screening shortly after birth for congenital dislocation of the hip was introduced, leading to early and successful treatment. Tuberculous bone disease became uncommon. Babies born with meningomyelocele were less frequent, as cases were identified by ultrasound at an early stage of pregnancy and termination was offered. The treatment of thalassaemia was improved by the introduction of desferrioxamine in 1975, first intramuscularly and in 1977 by continuous subcutaneous infusion using a battery-operated pump. In 1966 the amino-acid sequence of human growth hormone was determined, and by 1970 synthetic hormone was produced in small amounts, although to begin with this was too impure to be given to humans.[114]

A three-year review of services for children, Fit for the Future, chaired by Donald Court and reporting in 1976, did not have the impact that it might have done.[115] The report was lengthy and made many recommendations, some of which were controversial – for example that some GPs should specialise in providing the paediatric care for their practice and that health visitors should have geographic rather than practice responsibilities. In the furore that followed many sensible proposals were ignored. The report saw health surveillance, and the provision of treatment where necessary, as one of the main functions of child health services. It recommended special arrangements for the care of handicapped children, and the setting up of district handicap teams, the beginning of a structured team approach to the care of long-term disability and mental handicap in children.

Geriatrics

Improved teaching in undergraduate medical schools and better recruitment to geriatrics aided the specialty. Acute medical units might now be hard to distinguish from geriatric ones with active clinical policies. The crucial development of the decade was the recognition that most people admitted to medical wards were elderly, so the key to the care of old people lay in the acute wards. That was where unnecessary long-stay problems had been generated in the past. Many surgical procedures were predominantly required by elderly people, for example cataract operations and hip replacements. Traditionally the patients entering the geriatric service were selected largely by GPs or doctors in accident and emergency departments, rather than by geriatricians. There was dispute about the pattern of geriatric care, particularly as general physicians saw a risk to their resources. Should general physicians accept patients, however old, making geriatricians unnecessary? Should there be a defined age at which everyone was admitted under the care of a geriatrician, allocating patients on the basis of age rather than clinical requirements? Should geriatricians cease to be separated from consultant colleagues? In Newcastle the medical staff decided to integrate geriatrics with other general medical services, pooling beds as part of multi-consultant teams, all taking part in acute medical emergency work.[116] In Oldham the unit was also an intrinsic part of the DGH, and provided total medical care with virtually no waiting list. Turnover more than kept pace with demand.[117] When the new Northwick Park Hospital opened, the geriatrician, Malcolm Hodkinson, decided that from the outset his department would have neither a waiting list nor a system of pre-admission assessment. The emphasis would be on active treatment and early discharge. Those who could not be discharged, roughly half, were transferred to two smaller hospitals so that the department followed a scheme of progressive patient care. The morale of the staff improved and there was less tendency to treat geriatrics as 'the poor relation' of medicine.[118] As geriatric departments became smaller, with short waiting lists, experimental systems of integration were possible. The aim was early discharge. There was never enough welfare accommodation although local authority provision in England and Wales increased by a third between 1961 and 1966.[119] The responsibility for the care of those not needing technological care was passing slowly to the local authorities.

New facilities were becoming available, for example geriatric day hospitals where patients, brought by ambulance, spent four to eight hours a day. Everything the patients did in the day hospitals was planned to overcome their disabilities. Some patients were there for assessment, avoiding hospital admission, or for short periods of physiotherapy and occupational therapy before discharge to community care. Others attended regularly, and, because they were under supervision, admission might be avoided. Patients came in roughly equal proportions from GPs and hospital doctors, and the units acted as a midway point between the acute inpatient unit and the community social day centre.[120] In 1960 there had only been a dozen but ten years later there were 120.

Mental illness and the long-stay hospitals

Inpatient care for mental illness (England and Wales)

	1954	1969
Beds	157,427	133,667
Inpatients	152,197	116,275

The Hospital Plan of 1962 had stated that some of the mental illness services for a district should be at the DGH. Earlier estimates of the need for beds had been based on a custodial approach; newer estimates looked at balanced psychiatric units working alongside other specialties in a district hospital, and in partnership with the local authority social services departments.[121] Although the numbers admitted continued to rise, length of stay fell. Between 1954 and 1969 inpatient numbers fell nationally by 31 per cent, and in the Oxford region by 45 per cent but only by 18 per cent in Liverpool. Eason and Grimes, Department of Health and Social Security (DHSS) statisticians, showed that the number of 'old' long-stay patients, though continuing to decline, was doing so ever more slowly. While 50 beds per 100,000 of the population seemed adequate for acute adult admissions, additional beds were required for long-stay patients and for elderly severely mentally infirm people. The large isolated hospitals still treated most admissions (77 per cent). General hospital units treated only 17 per cent and the teaching hospitals 7 per cent. In the Manchester region 44 per cent of patients went into DGH units. In East Anglia none did.[122] A review of the functions of a DGH in 1969 suggested that *all* the district's psychiatric services should be on site but, for financial and logistic reasons, it would be 25 years or more before such a policy could be fully implemented and all the large mental illness and mental handicap hospitals had closed.[123]

From the Manchester experience it appeared that three 30-bed units, each with its own nursing and medical team, could meet the needs of a district of 180,000. Only a few patients, for example disturbed adolescents, drug addicts and those who were violent, would not be appropriate for a DGH. Critics said that the enterprise and enthusiasm of the staff of these units was not in question, but they had over-rated their achievements. Some units had only one consultant for populations of 200,000, there were few other medical staff and little support from social workers or psychologists. The service was cheap and the bed usage remarkably low, but the standard was satisfactory only for communities who had known nothing better. There had been no systematic descriptions or evaluations of the many DGH units established by 1960.[124]

Community-based psychiatric services required complementary residential and day services provided by the local authority social services department, and it helped if health and social services worked with the same population.[125] 'Sectorisation' was advocated, each psychiatrist having a little patch, convenient to the social service department of the local authority. The development of community links was clearly worthwhile, but should the consultant be chosen by post-code? The ethos of mental hospitals had changed from a medical autocracy to a more diffuse, multi-disciplinary quasi-democratic administration operating through a multiplicity of committees.[126] Until 1948 the medical superintendent reigned supreme, for better or worse; the decisions were his. As medical superintendents disappeared, problems were discussed at length and decisions were hard to come by. Some hospitals, such as Claybury, had also adopted the concept of the therapeutic community, treatment by committee as some called it. The authority of doctors was, at times, reduced to vanishing point. The power structure was changing; nurses were being trained as therapists to work in teams and make possible the treatment of far more psychotic and neurotic patients both in hospital and in the community.[127]

Scandals in mental illness and mental handicap hospitals

The effects of management – or lack of it – were nowhere more obvious than in the long-stay hospitals. The concentration of resources on DGH units at the expense of old psychiatric hospitals where there were too few staff and standards of care were low, added to the problems. The response to the letter Lord Strabolgi had written to *The*

Times, asking for examples of poor care, had been hundreds of letters releasing pent-up rage and misery, including many from nurses and social workers. In 1967 Barbara Robb, a signatory, published *Sans everything* on behalf of AEGIS (Aid for the Elderly in Government Institutions).[128] Its cry of distress at the undignified suffering of so many was written in careful terms, increasing the effectiveness of its attack on the care of the elderly and of elderly mentally ill people. The book consisted largely of accounts, often by staff of anonymised institutions, of random and mindless cruelty and thoughtlessness, petty fraud with patients' money and the desolation of the life in large hospitals. While paying tribute to the 'good hospitals' with excellent staff running interesting and optimistic programmes for patients, in others 'persistent staff-shortage could lead to the recruitment of 'nurses' who, knowing little or nothing about the proper care of the elderly, came to regard defenceless patients merely as sources of disagreeable hard work for themselves'.

Long before he had become Minister of Health, Kenneth Robinson knew of the bad conditions of the mental illness hospitals. He had stressed the need for improvement in the hospitals with their stark conditions, double-locked doors even in areas where patients had little tendency to wander or to abscond, and appalling sanitary conditions. There were fire hazards – 24 female patients died at Shelton Hospital, Shrewsbury, in February 1968. Knowing how difficult it was to work in these hospitals he sprang to the defence of their staff, and subsequently admitted he probably over-did it.[129] The six hospitals mentioned in *Sans everything* were identified. The regional hospital boards (RHBs) were asked to investigate. The reports were heavily edited before publication and the tenor was to dismiss the accusations as inaccurate, misinterpretation or isolated aberrations of individual staff some of whom subsequently retired. Kenneth Robinson told Parliament he deeply regretted the anxiety caused to patients, relatives and hospital staff by allegations now authoritatively discredited. The *BMJ* was pleased that staff and hospitals had been exonerated. The *Nursing Times* described *Sans everything* as an exercise in mud-slinging; the Minister, reacting to public concern, had made careful enquiries and allegations of cruelty by nurses were not proven.[130] Some thought his response smelt of a white-wash.

Richard Crossman replaced Kenneth Robinson in 1968. His interest in mental hospitals was also sincere. He discovered that the money spent on food in a district hospital was often three times that spent in a geriatric hospital and that was more than was spent in hospitals for the mentally handicapped. He asked civil servants to defend this and was told 'they wouldn't appreciate better food if they got it'. Crossman thought that good food might be one thing that elderly and mentally handicapped people really could appreciate, and that after 25 years of the NHS people in long-stay hospitals should expect equality of treatment.[131]

While the enquiry into *Sans everything* was proceeding, another was established that would have important consequences. In 1967 a nursing assistant at Ely Hospital Cardiff made specific allegations to the *News of the World* about the treatment of patients and pilfering by staff. They were forwarded to the Minister. Crossman, though Labour, comissioned an enquiry under the chairmanship of Geoffrey Howe QC, a budding Conservative politician, thereby ensuring cross-party support. Howe and his committee worked hard. The report was published in full only after some argument. Crossman came out strongly in favour of publishing the entire report. It was long, detailed and dealt with shortcomings both in the hospital and by the hospital management committee and the RHB. It spoke of the continued acceptance of old-fashioned, unduly rough and undesirably low standards of nursing care. The report laid some blame on professional isolation. The allegations had been confirmed and the most serious accusations were directed at an inert nursing administration that had victimised staff who complained.[132] Staff who, for years, had either lived with the system or got out, now sometimes spoke up, ignoring the possibility of retribution. After the publication of the Ely report in March 1969, regions were asked to examine their own services, and increased allocations of capital and revenue were made to services for the mentally handicapped.

The Hospital Advisory Service

One recommendation of the Ely Report was for a new system of regular visiting or inspection. Richard Crossman, tired of sending memoranda that nobody read, decided to establish a Hospital Advisory Service (HAS) and received the support of the medical profession. The doctors accepted that the Howe Report on Ely established good grounds for this. The team was led by Dr Alex Baker, a psychiatrist already on secondment to the DHSS.[133] It was multi-disciplinary, visiting hospitals for two to three weeks. It looked first at mental handicap hospitals, about which there was most concern, moving on to mental illness and geriatrics. Its reports went to the Secretary of State and to the regions and hospitals.[134] The first annual report drew attention to the lack of communication within hospitals, between hospitals and the community, and with management. Almost all hospitals of 1,000 or more beds had major problems, and many regions were still adding to and refurbishing old hospitals for the mentally handicapped, rather than establishing modern methods of care in smaller units.[135] Other scandals followed.

1970   While the DHSS was trying to decide how to handle the Ely report, even more serious violence was revealed at Farleigh Hospital in Somerset, a hospital for mentally handicapped boys and men. Police proceedings were brought against several nurses on charges of ill-treating patients. This led to a committee of enquiry that revealed weaknesses in hospital administration, long-standing differences between the medical superintendent and the hospital management committee (HMC), and under-staffing by nurses. It made recommendations about the need to instruct staff in how to handle disturbed or difficult patients.[136]

1971   At Whittingham Hospital police enquiries into allegations of ill-treatment and financial irregularity led to a committee of enquiry. The report said that Whittingham was a hospital of wide contrasts, some good features and some very unsatisfactory. Medical and nurse staffing was inadequate; in 1970 it had the poorest medical staffing of 108 English mental illness hospitals submitting returns. Many allegations of ill-treatment were justified, including the 'wet-towel' treatment where a towel was twisted around a patient's neck until he lost consciousness. There had been large-scale pilfering, if not organised corruption; complaints by nurses had been suppressed; the management structure was defective and there had been inadequate medical supervision in some wards. There were two standards in the hospital, one for acute mental illness and a lower standard for longer-stay – mainly elderly – patients.[137] The report was frank about the problems that occurred as mental hospitals were deprived of their short-stay patients. There was an accumulation of long-stay patients receiving no more than residual care, a system as demoralising for the staff as it was bad for the patients.[138] Dr Russell Barton had named Whittingham in 1965 as a hospital in which ill-treatment occurred. The BMA Central Ethical Committee censured him for comments capable of being construed as adverse criticisms of a member of the hospital's medical staff.[139]

1972 At Napsbury Hospital, near St Albans, an independent professional appraisal of medical and nursing practices in one part of the hospital was undertaken after an inquest on a patient who had died of severe injuries. A consultant, supported by equally enthusiastic doctors and nurses, routinely treated schizophrenics on the theory that their mental state was the result of a crisis in interpersonal relationships.[140] According to the report his methods of treatment, which included behaviour modification and the withdrawal of conventional nursing care so that conditions became dirty and unhygienic, had been pursued in an insistent and inflexible manner with at times a lack of compassion and respect for the rights of patients.

1972 At South Ockendon Hospital for the mentally handicapped, an independent committee of enquiry was set up after the death of two patients and a complaint by a nurse about low nursing standards on the ward where one had lived.

During the latter part of the 1970s there were other enquiries, the most dramatic being in 1976 at Normansfield Hospital, a hospital for the mentally handicapped in southwest London. Nursing members of COHSE went on strike when all other methods of bringing problems to management's notice had failed. The subsequent public enquiry showed an appalling quality of life of the patients and a failure of senior medical, nursing and administrative staff to co-operate with each other. The extremely low standard of patient care and the hostility between one consultant and virtually all other staff were well known to everyone at every level and all agreed that the situation was unacceptable. However, nothing was done until the nurses' action brought instant response.[141]

The inquiries devastated the morale of the hospitals, and there was much anger among the staff. It was common for more money to be given to the hospitals criticised, sometimes at the expense of others equally pressed. To overcome the lack of psychiatric leadership a task force was often assembled, and an experienced consultant and senior nurses would be drafted in to set matters right. The necessary qualities were rare. This denuded the hospitals from which they came of key staff. Of the hospitals involved in scandals, most were for mentally handicapped or elderly people. Common themes ran through the reports, the effects of professional isolation, the low expectations of custodial regimes, the dangers of corruption in closed societies and the extent to which staff and management would go to stifle criticism of the quality of patients' care. Above all they exposed the weaknesses and superficiality of the system of lay management that had failed to exert any real influence on the quality of care, and the lack of professional leadership.[142] Retrospective analysis of routine hospital returns revealed that most were badly staffed, although the returns had never been used to pinpoint hospitals where this might have made adequate care difficult to provide.[143] The BMJ contrasted the approach of the HAS with that of Florence Nightingale when facing not dissimilar conditions at Scutari. She had used her intelligence and social connections to change the system, but had personally washed wounded soldiers, scrubbed tables, boiled water and burnt maggoty dressings. Action was needed, but sadly the public and the medical profession were indifferent to long-standing problems until something went seriously wrong, a hospital burnt down or a patient was maltreated.[144] Sir George Godber also had doubts about the Hospital Advisory Service system. It involved people descending on a hospital, making a report and going away. They were not personally responsible for remedying what they had seen.

Few scandals became public after 1976. The regions and the DHSS moved fast when potential problems appeared. In the Newcastle region, a system of regional visits and continuing association was already in place. In North East Thames, in which South Ockendon was situated, it was realised that questionable practice might be widespread and a regional monitoring team was established. The team included board members and officers and visited all the mental illness and mental handicap hospitals. It had continuing responsibility for the problems discovered, and could support staff who were sometimes working under extreme difficulties.[145] Usually it spent three days and nights at the hospital, roving without warning. The reports were beautifully, indeed poetically, written by Dr Peter Camm, an officer of the authority. They were referred in confidence to the hospital and the circulation was restricted. Findings warranted this approach, for while ill-treatment was seldom found, systems of care were often ludicrously inappropriate. In one hospital the supply of towels ran out regularly each week and the nurses were forced in turn to use draw sheets, sheets and pillow-slips to dry the patients. In a ward without a clock it was explained that it would be pointless to have one, as the patients were disorientated and did not know what time it was. One hospital received regular complaints from British Rail that patients wandered across the tracks. Sadly a report was leaked to the press, the medical and nursing staff were outraged and the region ceased its visits.

White Papers

Two White Papers were subsequently published and for the first time there were authoritative and detailed statements of national policy.[146] Neither mentioned the scandals that in some measure had stimulated their publication. Keith Joseph published *Better services for the mentally handicapped* in 1971. It encouraged inpatient units in district hospitals, day hospitals, outpatient services and community care in local authority provision. Comparable guidance was issued about the mentally ill. The BMJ was sceptical. It believed that for many patients the policy was fair enough, if and when the community facilities were built. But where it was best to look after chronic schizophrenics with personality disorders and eccentric if not criminal behaviour was another matter. Perhaps the patients or their relatives might be asked. The local authority social services departments were still reeling from the implementation of Seebohm and the Local Authority Social Services Act 1970. Trust between hospital and town hall had broken down. Premature discharge of patients to social service facilities that were overloaded and creaking, or existed only on paper, did a disservice to everyone. There was a danger of patients falling through holes in the system, joining the army of the destitute.[147]

David Tidmarsh, at Horton Hospital Epsom, cared for substantial numbers of alcoholics, schizophrenics and drug addicts. On admission many were destitute, unemployed and without family ties. On discharge they ended in common lodging houses with little after-care or exchanged a hospital bed for a prison cell.[148] Tidmarsh thought that chronic disturbed schizophrenics rapidly disrupted the psychiatric units of DGHs. A committee of the BMA, the Royal College of Psychiatrists and the Society of Medical Officers of Health came to the same conclusion – that the difficulties and disadvantages of attempting to treat nearly all types of mental disorder in a small, mixed-sex ward had not been sufficiently stressed.[149] In such a setting rehabilitation was virtually impossible. Tidmarsh argued for retention of the larger mental hospitals until adequate substitutes were available.[150] Therapeutic activity was concentrated on short-stay patients in the new district psychiatric units, whilst long-stay units in the old hospitals were patched and cobbled up.

Changing the mental illness service

The government priority was to move patients from the old hospitals onto the site of the DGHs, and at first little thought was given to the development of facilities within the community or the role of the local authorities. The large hospitals were often in the country, away from the populations for which they cared. A single hospital might serve three or more districts, not necessarily even in the same region. The Epsom cluster of hospitals dealt with districts north as well as south of the Thames and the linkages were changed from time to time. Patients seldom retained contact with their home district and were accommodated at random with people from other places. If district- and community-based psychiatric services were to be established, sorting out was needed. Each district had to build up new facilities both in district hospitals and in the community. Conversion of existing facilities was generally difficult, and the facilities at hospitals such as Hackney were poor and far more crowded than the old asylums, with little space for occupational therapy and leisure activities. Spare money for new services was one thing districts did not have. The closure of the units in the shires might, in theory, provide the money but the new service had to be developed before the old one had closed. The staff of acute hospitals might be loath to host a psychiatric unit, and those at the old hospitals seldom wanted to move with the patients into the community, even if they were attuned to new treatment regimens. The gradual reduction in the number of patients in the old hospitals did not save much money, for the infrastructure had to be maintained and it was the most dependent patients who remained. In annual regional reviews the DHSS encouraged regions to make fast progress and targets were often set.

Better services for the mentally ill was published by Barbara Castle in 1975, a time of financial crisis and the year when the recommendations of the Royal Commission on

Mental Health (1957) were supposed to come to fruition.[151] It was a sober document, avoiding questions of cost, but recognising that it might be 20–30 years before a wholly new pattern of service would be in place. Regions were all too well aware of the costs of the policy. The brave new era depended on a reduction of nearly half the number of mental hospital beds and the development of a wide range of services collectively known as community care. The *BMJ* editorials, often written by Henry Rollin, were critical not of the policy but of its practicality.[152] The policy remained of local units of 100–200 beds, serving a population of no more than 250,000, as part of a comprehensive district service in which local authorities co-operated. The DHSS's *Priorities* document, published in 1976 to guide regional planning, reaffirmed this,[153] although recognising that progress would be slow because of shortage of money.

Public pressure, and groups such as the National Schizophrenia Fellowship and MIND, pressed for continuing help for people leaving mental hospitals. There was also concern about possible abuses of psychotropic drugs, ECT, psycho-surgery and compulsory administration of treatments. As time passed, fears about the policy proved justified. Support from community services might be poor and local authorities might have different priorities, for example children. Psychiatric units at district hospitals were selective about the patients they admitted and had difficulty in providing a wide range of services. Some large hospitals would be needed for a long time to come. What was to be done with existing staff in county hospitals, some of whom were as institutionalised as the patients?

Regional secure units

While hospitals had been moving to more liberal attitudes on restraint, judges and prison staff had become increasingly concerned about the number of mentally abnormal offenders in overcrowded prisons.[154] Judges believed that some prisoners were mentally ill and needed treatment under supervision, but the mental hospitals were losing the facilities, skills and desire to contain people. As locked wards disappeared, people who could not be managed with safety either to themselves or to the public without security became hard to place. Far more supervision was required and psychiatric hospitals had neither the staff nor the facilities to prevent patients from absconding. The special hospitals such as Broadmoor were filled to their limits. There was an increasing number of applications from 'normal' mental hospitals wanting to transfer problem patients to them. Most were turned down because there was no room or it was judged that really high security was not necessary. Regions faced horrendous problems with patients who, though they might rape and attack nurses and patients, were refused transfer. The special hospitals in turn needed to transfer patients into NHS hospitals at an appropriate stage of recovery. An impasse was often reached. Hospital beds were under the control of psychiatrists, who might be sceptical of how far helping psychopaths was possible. Even if psychiatrists were prepared to admit a patient, the nurses, supported by their unions, might not be. While judges could send people to prison, NHS management would have been unwise to attempt to force the admission of a patient against the wishes of the nurses and doctors. Secure facilities were also required for dangerous inpatients who had not committed any crime.

In 1974 the Glancy Report recommended that each region should provide secure inpatient facilities, and the Butler Committee, established after a mentally abnormal offender committed murder following release from Broadmoor, also proposed that each region should have a unit of 50–100 beds for convicted offenders and other mentally abnormal people who needed medical treatment in secure conditions.[155] Such units should be in centres of population, ideally on the site of a district hospital, and have access to the full range of diagnostic and therapeutic services. The DHSS accepted the recommendations but regions were slow to act. A more formal request was accompanied by a capital allocation, a target of 20 places per million and encouragement to provide interim units while permanent facilities were created. Some RHAs had little enthusiasm for the policy and spent the money on different services that they considered more important. Others found it almost impossible to obtain planning permission. Local MPs objected and nobody wanted psychiatrically disturbed criminals in their back yard. The first permanent unit did not open until 1980, others only came on stream slowly afterwards and some 'interim' units were never replaced. The initiative was an orphan; nobody particularly wanted it.[156]

General practice and primary health care

Primary care was beginning to take its place as perhaps the most important part of a *planned* health service.[157] Julian Tudor Hart, in Glyncorrwg, coined the phrase 'anticipatory health care'. He began to screen patients between 20 and 64 years of age for high blood pressure, mainly by checking people during a normal surgery attendance, supplemented by call-up and home visiting. He later applied the same approach to older patients and to other risk factors for coronary heart disease and stroke – smoking, cholesterol levels, obesity, diabetes, airways obstruction and alcohol problems. His aim was to move back from end-stage disease to its origins, improve the health of the whole practice by identifying treatable problems at an early, often pre-symptomatic stage, and to look for them systematically, building up a profile of patient information to track progress.[158]

Antibiotics had made acute infections easier to treat at home; now there was progress with the management of chronic disease. Diagnostic services such as electrocardiography and endoscopic examination became more readily available to GPs, without the need to refer first to a specialist.[159] A survey carried out by the BMA Planning Unit in 1969 revealed that the financial incentives in the GPs' charter were already producing results; general practice was entering a phase of revolutionary improvement.[160] Younger doctors were predominantly entering groups rather than smaller practices. Postgraduate centres were increasingly accessible throughout the country. Better organised and better equipped doctors questioned the need for so much home visiting; patients could be attended more quickly and probably more thoroughly at the surgery. Flexible appointment systems and better surgery organisation made same-day attendances easier. Patients more often had transport, and doctors and their receptionists attempted to reduce what they saw as unnecessary home visits, the numbers falling by at least a third.[161] Some GPs had found ways of linking their practices to large, distant 'mainframe' computers. They became enthusiastic as they explored the problems to which a computer might be a solution. The costs were so high that GPs could not fund systems personally and general introduction was not possible, but the main applications, including registers, appointment and immunisation scheduling, prescribing and recording the nature of conditions seen in the practice were soon apparent. In 1970 Dr Preece, an Exeter GP, had shown the feasibility of keeping general practice records on a computer and in 1975 an experimental project linked the practice at Ottery St Mary with the Royal Devon and Exeter Hospital.[162] It was a visionary idea but too early both in terms of computer systems and the ethos of co-operation between primary and secondary care.

The College celebrated its 20th anniversary in 1972, when it became 'Royal' and could claim substantial success for its policies. The 'College model' of general practice was widely accepted. Research units had been established in Birmingham and Dundee. Its advocacy of university departments of general practice ensured that, though few had yet been established, most medical students saw patients at home as well as in hospital. Continuing education, self-audit and the quality of vocational training schemes were issues not yet resolved.[163] In 1974 family planning services, provided previously by local health authorities, became part of the general medical services. Family doctors wished to provide them, and patients should clearly have a choice. Many clinic staff thought GPs would be inadequately trained for the work, but courses were established, fees were agreed and patients wanting contraceptive advice began to migrate to them.

Although specialist and general practitioners were often friends, inter-disciplinary friction persisted. Many specialists still felt that the problems presenting in general practice were mostly minor, that patients would really prefer to be treated at a hospital, that it did not matter much if general practice was of a low standard because the hospitals acted as a safety net, that transferring patient care to hospital did no harm and that a hospital need not be greatly concerned with the standards of primary health care in its neighbourhood.[164] Those who considered primary health care the centre point of the NHS, and that consultants supported GPs, were regarded with puzzlement.

Attachment of staff

Local authority nurse attachment schemes spread. 'Attachment' was a misnomer, for potentially it was joint medical and nursing practice. The nurses' presence affected the GPs' perception of primary health care; GPs were increasingly involved in health promotion and the long-term management of chronic disease. Alongside them were a steadily increasing number of practice nurses, employed by the GPs themselves, and now partly paid for by the NHS.[165] Where doctors and attached nurses were carefully matched, schemes might blossom from the start. Progress was hardest in small practices where accommodation was often inadequate or when there was a shortage of nurses locally. These problems were particularly acute in urban and inner city areas where senior community nurses were often unconvinced of the value of attachment. There might be a fundamental clash of attitudes. Nurses had no feel for the self-employed position of the GPs. Some GPs insisted that the nurse was 'their' nurse and failed to respect the skills of a different discipline. Nursing management had little sympathy for family doctors, nor understanding of the contribution to patient care that the joint working of nurse and doctor could make; it specified who the nurses should be, how many were available and what work they might do.

Health centres and group practice premises

In the mid-1960s John Fry estimated that 60 per cent of GP premises had been built before 1900. There were two ways of improving matters. Local authorities could build health centres to accommodate their own staff, nurses, health visitors and dentists, and rent space to family doctors. Health centres were large, costly and slow to build, yet their popularity increased and construction began to accelerate. By the early 1970s 100 or so were opening each year. By 1974 15 per cent of GPs were working from them, the numbers rising about 2.5 per cent per year.[166] They were a good basis for training young GPs. Health centre GPs were not necessarily in partnership with each other. Most centres had a manager and in 1970 a design guide was issued covering standards of accommodation. Then the oil crisis produced economic difficulties and cut the money available for building. Capital spending was limited and priority was given to deprived areas. Barbara Castle's attack on private practice alarmed GPs who thought that if they moved to a health centre they would lose freedom of action. Health centre popularity waned. Those centres under construction had been in the pipeline for many years and were not necessarily those most needed.[167] The more enthusiastic GPs had been relocated and many of the rest did not wish to leave their own premises or work closely with other doctors. Some centres, built in the expectation that GPs would move in, remained empty.

The alternative was for family doctors to design, fund and build premises for themselves. Until 1966 general practice was under-capitalised, mainly because GPs had to pay for any improvements to their premises themselves, although interest-free loans had been part of the Danckwerts settlement. The GPs' charter introduced direct payments for rent and rates and encouraged the trend towards group practice and the employment of additional staff, which in turn demanded better premises. A group practices loan scheme (subsequently operated by the General Practice Finance Corporation) made it easier to raise the money, and the system of reimbursing 'notional rent' or a 'cost rent' made the option practicable and sometimes positively desirable. Self-help became the most common way to improve premises and the cumulative effect on standards was enormous. Only in the inner cities, where there might be planning problems and the cost of land and building was often too much for the practice to bear, did the scheme fail.

Vocational training

Vocational training had been popular in the early years of the NHS and in 1957, its best year to date, there were more than 400 trainees. Then entry to general practice became less competitive and rapid partnership became the rule, for security and better pay were easily obtainable. In 1968 the trainee entry had fallen to 150. John Horder, later President of the RCGP, gave evidence to the Royal Commission on Medical Education. The College said that personal and family doctoring could survive only if it had as rigorous a training as those in specialist services. In its report the Royal Commission treated general practice like the other branches of medicine. It recommended that vocational training should be compulsory and last three years.[168] George Godber said that the question had become not 'whether' but 'how' vocational training should operate. People should not worry unduly about where the money was to come from, but get on with vocational training as an act of faith.[169] Increasingly it was realised that vocational training was coming, and the number of trainees rose to 667 in 1975. Most trainees took a newly introduced examination for membership of the College and trainees formed their own organisations and groups. The College consistently argued that mandatory vocational training was required, and in 1974 the Conference of Local Medical Committees accepted by a slim majority that it should normally be mandatory for those wishing to be principals in general practice. It was one thing to campaign for vocational training; quite another to define it. This task was undertaken by a small and senior group of doctors at the College and helped by a group of trainers working mainly in London. Their report, *The future general practitioner: learning and teaching*, showed the relationship of general practice not only with clinical science but also with such basic sciences as physiology, pathology, epidemiology, psychology, sociology and with the theory and practice of educational methods.[170] The content of training included the study of health and disease, human development, human behaviour, medicine and society, and practice management and organisation. It was a stimulating and provocative book, setting a breathtaking pace. Trainers were now selected for their ability to teach, their facilities and their qualities. They came together, region by region, to learn how to do it. 'Enthusiastic front runners in general practice,' said the *BMJ*, 'should spare an occasional glance over their shoulders to make sure that the rest of the field is still in sight.'[171]

Prescribing

After the devaluation of the pound, economies were necessary and either hospital building had to be cut or prescription charges brought in. Prescription charges were re-introduced in 1968. The number of prescriptions fell, people increasingly bought common household remedies across the counter, and GPs prescribed larger quantities. Exempt groups were established, including those with chronic diseases such as diabetes, the young, the old and people on Supplementary Benefit. Half the prescriptions issued were for these categories, reducing substantially the benefit to the exchequer.

Future primary health care policy

A vision of ideal general practice had now emerged and was often visible on the ground. The thinking of the BMA, the Royal College of General Practitioners and the DHSS was pulled together by the Harvard Davies report on the organisation of group practice.[172] It was agreed that general practice was already following the right path – well staffed and accommodated group practice. Yet there was a growing fear that some changes in general practice, though necessary for its efficiency, might have disadvantages for patients. Sir George Godber organised a working party of doctors from the RCGP and the GMC, analogous to the Cogwheel group.[173] It considered appointment systems, deputising services and access to diagnostic services. Since 1964 deputising services had developed widely and 64 were in operation by 1972. Though widely criticised to begin with, the working party now thought the services efficient, secure and generally acceptable. Such arrangements were essential to the efficient practice of medicine and should be allowed to evolve in the way that did the least injury to continuity of care.

At their annual conference in 1977 GPs passed a resolution deploring their relatively low remuneration, and asked for a completely new charter to be negotiated. A small working group was established to look to the future. This 'new charter working party' was rapidly drawn into discussions about a salaried service, security of tenure, reasonable working speeds and high standards.[174]

Local authority health services

By 1968 medical officers of health (MOsH) had a smoothly running empire, managing community nursing services, social work services, the after-care of people who were mentally ill or mentally handicapped, the ambulances, and the child and school health clinics. Relationships with general practice and the hospitals had improved and leading MOsH were at the forefront of thinking in their specialty. This effective structure now began to come to pieces. In quick succession the Seebohm Report[175] recommended the separation of social work services from medicine and directors of social services were appointed. The MOsH had lost a significant part of their work, as mental health, day centres and home helps went to the new departments. The community nurses, the district nurses, midwives and health visitors, were next, establishing a separate nursing hierarchy. The decision was taken to place ambulance services under the regions instead of the local authorities. Finally the health centre programme began to wind down.

Hospital and specialist services

The economy had been healthy and by the mid-1960s substantial development moneys were flowing into the health service. Power lay with the person signing the cheque and that person was often at the regional hospital board. The regions differed in their fields of competence. Renal transplantation prospered in Newcastle, Cambridge and Hammersmith, cardiac bypass work in Birmingham, Leeds, Hammersmith and Guy's. Newcastle and Oxford pioneered hospital building developments. Medical manpower planning and training were best developed in Wessex. Liverpool led in the better control of drugs, Sheffield in hospital libraries, Oxford on the relationship of primary health care with the hospitals, Manchester in district psychiatric units.[176] Regions got the chance to influence the policy of the centre but there were leaders and laggards.

The work of the hospitals

The hospitals were working harder and faster. Between 1969 and 1978 there was a 15 per cent drop in the number of medical beds and the length of stay fell from 16 to 11 days;[177] 22 per cent more medical patients and 10 per cent more surgical patients were being discharged. In spite of increased hospital activity, waiting times and waiting lists continued to increase. Surgeons felt they were not being given the tools they needed for the job, and growing waiting lists were

Changes in hospital admissions

Main increases	Main reductions
Kidney disease	Infectious disease
Cancer	Tuberculosis
Ischaemic heart disease	Varicose veins
Poisoning	Utero-vaginal prolapse
Osteoarthritis	Tonsils and adenoids
Strokes	Hernia
Leukaemia and Hodgkin's disease	
Fractured neck of femur	Peptic ulcer

Source: Report of a study of the acute hospital sector. DHSS 1981.[177]

the result. Beds were reallocated to reflect changes in clinical medicine. The number of beds for respiratory diseases halved and the cardiological ones increased by 50 per cent. ENT, chest, infectious disease, mental illness and general surgical beds closed, and the number allocated to surgical sub-specialties rose. Changes in treatment, for example the use of antibiotics, were having a continuing effect. In the surgical specialties, beds had fallen 5 per cent in number, and length of stay from 9.7 to 8.2 days. The number of doctors was rising faster than the number of patients they were treating, reflecting the intensity of care and new specialties such as transplant and dialysis units. Similarly, nursing staff increased 17 per cent between 1972 and 1978 compared with a 5 per cent increase in admissions (a shorter working week for nurses, 37.5 hours, accounted for a quarter of the rise). The conditions that were being treated more frequently tended to be more costly than those they were replacing, which were usually dealt with easily and quickly. There was increasing pressure to treat some diseases of elderly people, such as high blood pressure and heart disease, with expensive drugs. While some therapy, such as coronary artery bypass grafting, arguably could lead to savings on medical treatment in the long term, in others, such as kidney disease, once a patient was 'on-the-books' there were continuing and accumulating costs. Bone marrow transplantation similarly showed signs of being a growth industry, and a highly expensive one.

Hospital organisation and technology

As medical science developed, the specialties became increasingly dependent on one another. Hospital organisation had to allow for this and patients needed admission to units with the right range of facilities. When organs failed, 'organ support' might be practicable. Renal failure could be handled by dialysis, respiration by ventilation and nutrition might be intravenous – but only in centres with special expertise. Sometimes one patient required many skills; a patient in a cardiac unit who developed renal failure would be in difficulties if renal physicians were not nearby. This problem was at its most acute in early life. Few hospitals had the expertise to handle an infant with multiple problems. Similarly, badly injured people – for example road accident victims – might need a neurosurgeon for the head injury, a thoracic surgeon and an anaesthetist for chest injuries and an orthopaedic surgeon for the fractures. They needed an abdominal surgeon as well if they had a ruptured spleen. International studies showed that the outcome – life or death – was largely dependent on the size and facilities of the institution. It was better to travel 100 miles to the right place than die near one's home. Technology could be deployed to maintain life when previously that would have been impossible. Clinicians such as Brian Jennett, Professor of Neurosurgery in Glasgow, looked at the clinical, ethical and financial consequences of intensive care. Like other technologies it could help patients, but used inappropriately it showed lack of humanity and wasted resources. Sometimes simpler means could achieve the same end, or intensive care was unsuccessful because the condition was beyond influence. It might be unsafe because the risks of complications outweighed the probable benefits, or unkind because the quality of life afterwards was unacceptable. In such cases it was also unwise, because resources were diverted from more useful activities.[178]

Hospital development and design

Enoch Powell's Hospital Plan (1962)[179] had laid out a long-term blueprint and was regularly revised. Most of the money went, as intended, on district hospitals. The old voluntary hospitals had been in the city centres, and though accessible their sites were small. The municipal ones had usually been farther out and often had large grounds. When no longer required for their original purpose, they provided an incalculable asset to the NHS. Hospitals such as St George's and the Royal Free stand on the ground once occupied by London County Council fever hospitals. Increasingly, people had modern or modernised hospitals offering good acute care locally. The inclusion of geriatric and psychiatric units within general hospitals was slower, partly because they were generally in second or third phases. Because of over-ambitious planning and shortage of money, some hospitals were never finished, later phases being postponed. They were left with oversize boiler-houses and kitchens. Concentration on acute facilities sometimes undermined policy to close down large long-stay hospitals, and imposed planning and maintenance blight on small and medium sized hospitals.[180]

The huge building programme was uncharted territory. RHBs all had their own architects' departments, although some commissioned private architects, such as Llewelyn Davies, Weeks and Partners. Changes in clinical science required changes in design. Outpatient departments were ever more important, as were the service departments such as radiology and pathology. Nineteenth century hospitals had spacious ward blocks separated from one another to maintain good ventilation. Now other patterns were tried, for example a high-rise ward block sitting on a podium of service departments. The Nuffield studies had suggested a break with the 30-bed Nightingale ward in favour of single rooms combined with four- to six-bed bays. The 'racetrack' ward had patients' rooms arranged around a central core of services. 'Sister's desk' was replaced by a nursing station, where staff could sit instead of being on their feet all day by their patients. A senior architect at the Ministry, later admitted to a new ward at St Thomas', said that he had committed one of the worst architectural crimes by failing to think through what this meant to the patient. Privacy was fine for those admitted for elective surgery, but when seriously ill the constant observation and presence of the nurses were more important. As the new hospitals opened, problems became apparent. They might provide better facilities but they cost more to run than the ones they replaced. The principle of 'revenue consequences of capital spending' (RCCS) was therefore introduced. When a hospital was approved, agreed running costs for the new building were allocated to meet the additional requirements, so that those designing hospitals no longer had to be over-worried about this. RCCS inexorably swallowed nearly all the health service's growth money, leaving little for developments that were not capital led. Had the building programme been perfect, this would have mattered less, but inequalities between regions were often perpetuated and sometimes aggravated. A key problem was to use the money in the year in which it was available, but in some regions the planning staff were of poor quality and ineffective. They were late with their proposals. The money went to the southern regions that planned promptly and well, and had ready access to ministerial staff. This adversely affected Sheffield, Manchester and Leeds. To try to use the money available better, a new allocation system, the 'Crossman formula', was introduced. This allocated money partly on population size but also on bed numbers and case loads, 'need' playing only a minor part in the allocation process. The new system did not greatly improve matters; indeed it had bizarre – even biblical – results, for unto him that had was given; regions that were over-bedded were further endowed.

The hospital building bureaucracy burgeoned. To reduce the number of planning disasters, escalating costs and contracts that over-ran, a capital building code was developed (CAPRICODE), which inevitably delayed the start of building. The 'functional contents' of the hospital was determined in relation to the population size. An appraisal of alternative sites was carried out. The design had to be approved by the DHSS at each stage and by the Treasury for larger projects. Eventually it was possible to place a contract. By that time life had moved on and modifications to the original plans were needed. Redevelopment involved the planned closure of smaller, older hospitals. There was no money to keep an old hospital open once a new one had been commissioned. However, it was one thing to tell a community and its MP that a new hospital would be built on a green field nearby, quite another to shut the well-beloved institution where the locals were born and died. A new industry was established in protesting and delaying closure. Action groups with strong staff representation would demand to see ministers, who had to go through lengthy although self-imposed procedures before the hospital could be shut. The long time taken to build and open an NHS hospital, compared with a private one, was only too apparent.

The Bonham-Carter Report

In 1966 the Central Health Services Council had held a conference on district general hospitals, and decided to review the concept, now many years old. The result was the report of a subcommittee, chaired by Sir Desmond Bonham-Carter, published three years later.[181] The committee included many eminent people: nurses such as Muriel Powell and Catherine Hall, and doctors such as Tom McKeown, John Reid, Charles Fletcher and Donald Irvine. It was an example of how the application of logical principles can lead to an impracticable solution. Sometimes called the Noah's Ark report, because of the recommendation that each hospital should have at least two consultants in each specialty, it proposed much larger hospitals.[182] Economic provision of support services, such as pathology, laundries and sterile supplies led the committee to see 200,000–300,000 as the appropriate population, double that on which the Hospital Plan was based. The range of specialties to be provided, the desirability of single sites, and the provision of services for elderly people and those who were mentally ill, and sometimes regional specialties as well, increased the size further. Such hospitals clearly could support university medical schools and nurse training schools. In his preface to the report, Richard Crossman was ambivalent about hospitals with 1,000–2,000 beds. Had medical considerations had been given excessive weight? Too little consideration had been given to patient accessibility, the difficulty of managing large organisations and the possibility that economies of scale would not be realised. Indeed an unpublished study by the Department's operational research unit in 1971 concluded that the most economic size was far smaller, between 500 and 800 beds, depending on whether the site was rural or urban. Specialisation had not yet reached the point at which this measure of concentration was essential.

'It seemed a good idea at the time'

The hospital building programme provided an opportunity to test new ideas. Some worked but others did not. High-rise hospitals required banks of lifts that were expensive and slowed movement. Lifts affected the way staff met and talked. People did not meet each other as they did in, for example, the St Thomas' long corridor. Progressive patient care was a system of moving a patient during recovery from high intensity nursing and observation into a quieter environment, where there could be day rooms to which patients could go. This system could be applied to the 'racetrack' ward, which extended round four sides of a square, with nursing of different intensity. The racetrack could be combined with four-bed bays to give patients additional privacy. Greenwich was a 'test-bed' for some of these ideas. However, as the average length of hospital stay fell, patients were discharged and did not go to the low intensity area. The nurses had to walk vast distances to get things. At Truro one of the Department's operational research staff spent the night in a ward, and discovered that when the night nurses came on duty they moved the sickest patients out of the four-bed bays into the corridor, as there was no time to go into the bays to see how they were.

Central treatment areas, incorporated into the 'Best Buy' hospitals (discussed below), also misfired. Nursing treatment was centralised and staffed by specialist nurses next to the day-care unit. The additional cost of porters pushing trolleys round the hospital, the reduction in experience of the nurses remaining on the wards, and the impossibility of moving *all* the patients so the sickest had to have their procedures on wards with no facilities for preparing intravenous fluids or trolleys, brought the idea into question. New tower-block hospitals were designed in the years of low energy costs. They were large and confusing to staff, let alone patients. Charing Cross had to be closed briefly, immediately after it opened, as nobody had told the staff how to find the different departments. Tower blocks required expensive heating and air-conditioning. They had power-driven lavatories. Had the Thames flooded, those at Guy's would have ceased to work. An emergency planner suggested breaking the windows and shouting '*Gardez l'eau*'. Sometimes a project turned into a financial horror story. The Liverpool teaching hospital, expected to cost £12 million and be open by 1974, had reached a cost of £54 million by 1977 when the Public Accounts Committee investigated it, and was still not open.[183]

Standardising design

The opportunity to build anew comes once in a professional lifetime so local people were invariably inexperienced.[184] Staff had often retired before their new hospital opened. When the new Royal Free Hospital opened it was found to have large areas devoted to recovery from ECT, a form of treatment largely abandoned. The DHSS prepared hospital building notes to crystallise good practice and help architects. Standard designs were developed to avoid the cost of each RHB creating essentially similar buildings. First came the 'Best Buy' hospitals at Bury St Edmunds and Frimley, billed as 'two for the price of one'. Best Buy was a compact low-rise building, economic to build, developed in a single phase, with the wards mainly on the first floor in a band round the outside. To keep the allocation flexible, beds were not allocated to particular specialties, and there was a progression from high to low dependency areas. A 'ring-main' corridor separated the wards from the central core of highly serviced departments, theatres, central treatment rooms, intensive care and the maternity delivery suite. Supporting facilities, the laundry, sterile supply and pharmacy, were provided off-site. It was a tight design that was difficult to expand because the departments most likely to need extra space – the service departments – were in the centre. East Anglia was the only region to re-use it, building modified Best Buys at King's Lynn, Great Yarmouth and Huntingdon.[185] On the basis of epidemiological studies, the hospital was sized to provide two acute beds per 1,000 population, on the assumption that there would be full support from community care teams, local authorities and GPs, and early discharge policies.[186] The national norm was then 3.3 per 1,000, and if that standard had been adopted nationally 50,000 of the 150,000 beds allocated to acute specialties nationally would have been lost, and the Liverpool and North-West Metropolitan Hospital Regions would have had their existing beds cut by half. More rapid use of beds did not save on clinical staff, but potentially money might be released for advances in medical technology and the neglected areas of long-stay care.[187]

The needs of medicine were more varied than Best Buy permitted. Despite pleas for standardisation, most of the hospitals built were one-offs. Many followed a general fashion described as the matchbox on the muffin: a tower block containing wards (the matchbox) that stood on a low-rise building containing the service areas.[188] In 1972 it was thought that about 70 DGHs still needed building. There was a generous spirit abroad; most regions had been designing their own standard departments and the DHSS decided to co-ordinate the work, using the same set of operational policies and standard dimensions. The departments would be 'harnessed' together by a framework of communications and engineering works. The project was highly ambitious and the seeds of destruction lay in its costliness. Few were built and there was relief when the project was ditched after the oil crisis. But without 'Harness' the building programme might have suffered more than it did. 'Harness' was raided to produce 'Nucleus'.[189]

Nucleus hospitals

'Nucleus' was, in comparison, a runaway success. It was designed to provide 300 beds at a works cost of less than £6 million at 1975 prices. The basic pattern was not rigidly standard and provided a range of departments to suit most needs. It was viable as a first phase and could be expanded later to 600–900 beds. Designed as a low-rise building, there were never more than three floors, reducing the need for lifts. Windows could be opened for ventilation. It resembled a Lego set of interchangeable 'templates', each the shape of the Red Cross emblem. The templates might be wards, a laboratory or an outpatient department. The use of the same template for all functions made for flexibility, but in some places the squeezing showed. The space for patients was ample, but for staff was not. The modules could be piled on each other three high and coupled at the ends or sides. The Department's building division produced a small 'build your own Nucleus' package with movable pieces that made a good party game. Modules could be arranged to suit sites of different shapes and gradients. The order of phases was a local decision; acute care might come first, the psychogeriatric unit later. Regions could use standard and tested designs, or create their own internal arrangements and modify the external appearance as they chose.[190] The first was built at top speed from 1976 onwards, partly to satisfy the local lobby that had opposed the closure of the Poplar Hospital near David Owen's home. Maidstone opened shortly afterwards, and had the reputation of being one of the prettiest. The design was modified to reduce the energy requirement, and the first low energy Nucleus was built at St Mary's on the Isle of Wight.

Hospital management and clinical budgeting

Cogwheel was an early attempt to involve hospital doctors in management and ensure that power and responsibility rested in the same place. The Cogwheel reports had suggested that consultants should form clinical divisions, each with a chairman, to decide how they would work with each other to produce the best outcome for patients. Although staff were not always enthusiastic, Cogwheel divisions were progressively organised and quite a lot was achieved. More information was available to clinicians, decisions were taken sooner than before, and all specialties had a voice, although the links with public health and general practice were often inadequate. By 1972 consultants in half the hospitals of the country had revised the organisation of medical work in a quiet revolution.[191]

Bed usage was a perennial problem.[192] Hospitals forever seemed under pressure yet nationally there were always tens of thousands of beds unoccupied at any one time. Statistical systems such as hospital activity analysis (HAA) showed that the intensity of bed use varied widely from hospital to hospital and many methods were used to improve efficiency. Progressive patient care, programmed investigation units, admission wards, pre-discharge wards, pooling of beds and better hospital information systems were all tried.

Medical science raced ahead with new discoveries, leading to fresh and often expensive treatments. Deciding which 'advances' should be introduced widely, used on an experimental basis only or rejected was given less attention.[193] Iden Wickings at the Westminster Hospital in 1973/4 experimented by giving clinicians responsibility for the budgets. Doctors were involved in agreeing service and expenditure plans, providing an incentive for them to screen out unnecessary or expensive prescriptions and to scrutinise clinical demands more closely. Although there were expenses in setting up costing systems and in the time of the doctors involved, those who had experienced the process came to support it. It made it easier to review priorities and spend money to best effect.[194]

Health service information and computing

Planning and managing the NHS, and forecasting expenditure, was an imprecise affair because the information systems in existence had been designed for accounting rather than management purposes. In 1970 the King's Fund established a working party on the application of economic principles to health service management. In its report, *Accounting for health*, the group considered that major changes would be needed if an information system were to be medically useful, outcome orientated and provide a basis for management and planning.[195] Linking clinical activity and the costs incurred would be essential, and the only way would be to build up from data for each individual patient. Brian Abel-Smith, who chaired the group, proposed an individual patient identifier, perhaps a unique number, so that all activities could be linked. The starting point would be data from hospitals, GPs and the prescriptions that they issued. Scotland also saw a need for more broadly based health service information systems and commissioned SCICON to explore the requirements. SCICON similarly believed that the key was the collation of information about patients, their illnesses and their environment. The report stressed the need for a basic register of people in each area, based on a unique identification number, which would link activities such as hospital discharges, the immunisation programme and special disabilities or risks. SCICON envisaged a major interlinked information system covering nearly all health service activities, including finance, personnel and supplies, which would also provide a basis for health services research.[196]

The experimental computer programme

In 1966 Robert Rowe and Don White, two DHSS officers, toured US hospitals, to look at computer systems. The following year the 'experimental programme' began, to explore the use of computers in hospital management. The *BMJ* said that the practice of medicine by every individual doctor was going to be influenced over the next few years by computer developments, but was worried about costs and confidentiality, and that the unsolicited generosity of government might be intended to serve a national computer industry rather than the interests of the NHS.[197]

Computers were already being used by RHBs for paying staff and running their finances. They were also processing the 10 per cent sample of admissions (the Hospital In-patient Enquiry) and the 100 per cent HAA. It was decided to standardise these functions to minimise the costs of each RHB writing its own software. Several clinical scientists, for example Professor Whitehead in Birmingham and Professor Flynn at University College Hospital, were connecting auto-analysers to small computers and developing systems to calculate the results and print reports. Medical officers of health such as Tom Galloway in West Sussex were using local authority machines to run immunisation programmes. A few general practices were using distant computers to list their patients, maintain records of contacts and run immunisation programmes. Some hospitals were also beginning to consider the possibility of computerisation.

At first the experimental programme was funded generously. It explored unknown territory, attracted people of vision, and was based on real-time computing compared with the batch processing then standard. The administrators at the hospitals chosen were often high-flyers and many did well in their later careers. Twelve sites were chosen, each exploring different applications. Most systems dealt with administrative rather than clinical problems, reducing the commitment of the professionals. All projects discovered that the starting point had to be a master index of patients. King's College Hospital attempted to develop computer-based medical records. The project failed to accomplish this, but important lessons were learned about how doctors took histories and came to a diagnosis. The London Hospital believed it was better to computerise a single activity across the entire hospital than to go deeply into an activity in one department only, and began with admissions and discharges. At Exeter an attempt was made to link a practice in Ottery St Mary and the Royal Devon and Exeter Hospital. Four teaching hospitals worked on a co-ordinated project; the main lesson to emerge was the difficulty of co-ordinating teaching hospitals.

Substantial expenditure needed to be justified. Sizeable evaluation teams were engaged who faced immense problems. How did you show that computers were saving money, time or lives? Systems analysis revealed poor organisation and lack of management information that had to be sorted out before computerisation – a benefit, but not one attributable to the computer. So inefficient was one hospital that the systems analysts declared it was impossible for it to be functioning at all! 'Before and after' comparison would not work because hospitals were continually changing. They could not easily be compared with each other – would Charing Cross ever admit that it was comparable with the Royal Free or vice versa? The main achievement of one team was to show that they could divide variables into those that could be costed, those that could be counted but not costed, and those such as patient satisfaction that one could neither count nor cost.

It was too early for success. British hospitals lacked the need to invoice patients, which underpinned all USA hospital computer systems. Software and the hardware were primitive. Mainframe computers cost so much that they could not be duplicated; they had to be taken off-line at night to update the files, so the systems could not be used round the clock. As hospitals worked day and night, this was a substantial problem. The Public Accounts Committee in 1976 had harsh things to say about some projects,[198] but the debacle was no greater than often occurred in industry. Ultimately the experiments were bequeathed, with a moderate dowry, to the RHAs. Yet visits to the USA showed that effective systems could be developed and that hospitals such as El Camino, in California, which were well organised and had defined their information requirements, could introduce hospital-wide systems.[199] By the mid-1970s, more mundane systems were clearly going to be worthwhile. National standard immunisation and child surveillance systems, and systems to support the functions of family practitioner committees (FPCs), were going ahead. The expertise in computing, though dearly bought, was an asset to the service.

The special problems of London

London presented a particular problem. The pattern of hospitals inherited in 1948 included a heavy concentration of acute hospital beds in inner London that subsequent development had done little to improve.[200] Substantial rebuilding of teaching hospitals had accentuated the imbalance and alone among the regions the specialised services of the four Thames regions were eccentrically placed, all cheek by jowl in the centre of London. Elsewhere the teaching centres were near the geographic centre of their region. The four regional health authorities made co-ordinated planning difficult and the presence of the postgraduate hospitals, still directly responsible to the Department of Health, added to the conceptual difficulties. In 1975 a London Co-ordinating Committee was established to assist in solving the problems, run by Albertine Winner, a recently retired deputy CMO of the Department of Health. The regions differed widely in their views and their ethos, and the committee lacked the power to make contentious decisions bite, highlighting the problems of developing generally acceptable London-wide strategies.

The policy of financial reallocation from the southeast to the north of the country made action imperative for hospitals and medical schools in London. A second attempt was made in 1977 and an officers' group was established, the London Health Planning

Consortium (LHPC).[201] It faced two main problems. First was the need to reduce the level of acute hospital services in central London to bring it in line with the population and the money likely to be available in the future. Second, it was widely accepted that there were too many small and medium sized units in specialties such as radiotherapy and cardiac surgery, and a degree of rationalisation was clinically desirable.

Medical education and staffing

The Royal Commission on Medical Education

Royal Commission on Medical Education (1968)[202]
• Medical education a university responsibility
• Three years' general professional education after qualification
• Further professional education thereafter, continuing education for life
• Substantial increases in medical school intake; new medical schools
• Teaching hospitals to be placed under regions
• Great change in London; pairing medical schools

Chaired by Lord Todd and appointed in 1965, the Commission reported in April 1968.[202] There were two underlying themes. First, the undergraduate course produced not a finished doctor but a person who could become one with further training. (There was, in comparison with Goodenough, little new here.) Second, medical education should continue throughout professional life. The Commission made recommendations on the structure and organisation of postgraduate training, proposing general professional training followed by more specialised posts and vocational registration both for hospital specialties and for general practice. It saw the future NHS as fewer but larger hospitals in association with large groups of GPs working, possibly, in health centres. The Commission suggested the abolition of boards of governors, placing teaching hospitals within the regional hospital service. Each group of teaching hospitals should be under the immediate charge of a governing body with strong university representation and should be an integral part of a wider structure, again with appropriate representation. Teaching hospitals and their medical schools opposed these recommendations. Todd personally favoured salaried general practice and his vision was similar to the Kaiser-Permanente system of health maintenance organisations in the USA.

The Commission differed from Willink in assuming continued emigration, at a higher level than in fact proved to be the case. It also believed that with economic growth there would be an increase in the doctor/patient ratio. Both reports assumed that there would be no fundamental change in the organisation and delivery of health care or that other disciplines might take over work traditionally done by doctors.[203] The Commission also differed from Willink in recommending an early increase in the medical school intake to 3,500 and to 5,000 by 1985, a new undergraduate clinical school at Cambridge, and further new medical schools at Leicester, Swansea, and possibly at Keele, Hull and Warwick in the future. It favoured large schools with an average intake of 200 students and insisted that they should be part of a multi-faculty university. The *BMJ* welcomed this 'new look in medicine'.[204] The government agreed that student numbers should be increased, partly by the expansion of existing schools and partly by the new schools. Two were in the Sheffield region, at Leicester and

Nottingham, the first Nottingham students graduating in 1975. The third was in Southampton, where the first students graduated in 1976. In the new schools the curriculum was designed to blur the distinction between teaching and non-teaching hospitals and between hospitals and the community. Students saw the full impact of illness in the home, the community and the hospital from early in their course. The first Dean at Southampton was Donald Acheson (later Chief Medical Officer). With a population of 200,000, that city was too small to support an annual intake of 130 students. However, Wessex region had a population of 2,000,000, a highly developed system of postgraduate education and a regional authority keen to work with the university. Many hospitals in the region were therefore involved in clinical teaching.[205]

In London, where many big problems lay, the Commission made six major recommendations:

- The intake should be increased from 800 to 1,200 to allow maximal educational use to be made of the country's largest concentration of medical resources.
- The schools should be reduced in number from 12 to 6 by pairing them, so each school could have a full range of clinical departments with academic staff.
- Paired medical schools should be associated with a multi-faculty college, to enable contact with teachers in other disciplines.
- Postgraduate institutes should associate with the paired medical schools.
- Money should be provided to fill academic gaps.
- Implementation should be in the hands of a committee able to ensure that short-term convenience did not nullify long-term planning.

The essence of pairing was the formation of joint academic units, often in emerging subjects. Many schools resisted closer association. Postgraduate institutes in particular were united and effective in their resolve to resist the proposal to associate them with a general medical school. Most pairing schemes proved costly or led to an inappropriate pattern of services and, once the economic crisis was obvious, the Commission's proposals were increasingly seen as unrealistic.

Medical staffing

Hospital specialist care for patients had improved substantially, but often at the cost of sacrificing the postgraduate training of young doctors, a dangerous reliance on overseas doctors, who might not always want to come to Britain for training, and an excessive workload for regional consultants.[206] Britain trained more doctors than was needed to replace the 2,500 GPs and consultants who died or retired each year, but far too few to staff the hospitals. Medical immigration from the Indian sub-continent had provided many hospitals with their junior staff. The central problem was that hospital doctors took about ten years to train, in house officer, registrar and senior registrar posts. If appointed as a consultant they then remained in a career grade for thirty years until they retired at 65; so in theory having three consultants to one junior doctor was desirable, or at most two to one. As it was, fully trained doctors waited years for dead men's shoes or for a vacancy often in an area that did not appeal to them. To create a system that provided an effective service, in which training and career posts were balanced and that provided an effective and forward-thinking consultant body was a formidable task. A consultant grade lacking people in their early thirties also lacks a degree of initiative, and the influence of clinical advances.

The responsibilities of the consultant grade (1969)[207]

- Increase the number of consultants faster than trainees
- Adjust the geographical balance
- No permanent sub-consultant grade
- Training about 8 years, no longer than necessary
- Provide a responsible post for trained specialists

Juniors were vocal about their career prospects, the length and quality of the training they received and the hours of duty. Three ways of solving the problem had been canvassed: first a permanent sub-consultant grade such as the old senior hospital medical officers or a newly created medical assistant grade; secondly a part-time sub-consultant grade drawn from general practice such as the hospital practitioner posts some GPs occupied; and thirdly an expansion of the consultant establishment compared with training grades. Discussions began with the medical profession, in a group appointed by ministers and chaired by Sir George Godber. To the puzzlement of the consultants, two junior doctors were included. The group's proposals were set out in *The responsibilities of the consultant grade*[207] and were accepted by the Secretary of State, Richard Crossman. The idea of a permanent sub-consultant grade was dismissed. Instead it was proposed that training in a specialty should take no more time than necessary, ordinarily about eight years. Immediately training was completed the opportunity should be given to assume responsibility, instead of waiting a further six or seven years for a consultant post. Training and career posts would have to be brought into line with each other, and it was proposed to increase the number of consultants more rapidly than the training grades, 4 per cent as against 2.5 per cent. Adjusting the distribution of doctors across the country would also be necessary. The metropolitan regions had far more juniors than regions such as Birmingham, Sheffield and East Anglia. Established consultants would lose some of their juniors, as would hospitals in the south. Consultants in regional hospitals, in which 90 per cent of the work of the NHS was carried out, saw the proposals differently from their medico-political colleagues in London and the teaching hospitals. A series of articles written by 'unheard voices' appeared in the *BMJ*.[208] Buildings were decaying, staff were poorly paid and morale was low. Quality junior staff were scarce, making delegation difficult. Merit awards that seemed routine at teaching hospitals were elsewhere as unexpected as winning a premium bond prize. A physician said 'Consultants have been told that they'll have to make do with fewer registrars and housemen than at present; they must roll up their sleeves and do more of the humdrum work. This patronising directive has infuriated doctors in the periphery. We're already fully stretched. The whole division is always short of one registrar or houseman away on study leave.' 'Like most of my friends,' said an orthopaedic surgeon, 'we've read all these reports, Godber, Cogwheel and so on. We're all agreed that they show a total lack of any idea of what actually goes on in a district hospital, and the sheer problems of our workload. When I'm on my way between one hospital and another and it's my registrar's day off, I'm constantly on tenterhooks that an emergency, say a multiple road smash, will come into one of the hospitals that nobody is competent to cope with. We're taking unjustifiable risks with our patients.'[209] Once consultants seemed to inhabit paradise compared with the junior doctors. Regional consultants, seeing the progress made by the juniors and GPs, became increasingly vocal, convinced that the proposals were unfair and that the establishment at BMA House had dominated and mismanaged their affairs. The leaders of the profession backed off from proposals that would have balanced the workforce, but to the detriment of regional consultants.

Michael Freeman, an orthopaedic surgeon and one of the authors of *The responsibilities of the consultant grade*, said that consultants had three objections to the solution proposed. First, they would see fewer cases of interest and have to do more routine work; secondly they would have to share out the beds, operating time and outpatient sessions with more consultants; and thirdly their earnings from private practice would probably fall. Though complaining of overwork, they might be reluctant to solve the problem by the appointment of a colleague.[210] Any radical change in the balance of consultant work was resisted, while the Treasury hampered expansion of the consultant grade for financial reasons. To some it seemed that what was at issue was rewarding and satisfying lives for doctors rather than an effective patient-orientated health service. Although there was agreement that the existing system was wrong, there was none on how to put it right. The suggestions in George Godber's report were delayed, opposed and undermined by the profession's representatives both centrally and in the regions. The opportunity was lost and would not come again until the mid-1980s. The regions spent years struggling, to little avail and with less support, to move registrar posts out of the teaching hospitals, and from London to the north.[211] In 1972 a new Central Manpower Committee was established; it had a long haul ahead.

In April 1970 the Labour government held up the publication of the doctors' 12th Review Body report and its recommendation of increases of 30 per cent. The government referred half the award to the National Board of Prices and Incomes, criticising some of the reasoning behind recommendations. The Chairman of the Review Body, Lord Kindersley, and his fellow members resigned. The BMA applied sanctions. After the 1970 election the newly elected Conservative government led by Edward Heath withdrew the reference.[212] A new review body was announced and the BMA sanctions were lifted. The new body could work as it chose and review pay any time, asking for any information it needed. Although the doctors remained suspicious of government, the combination of an independent body and a vociferous, strong and united (over the question of pay) profession seemed as invulnerable to the whims of government as anything could be.

The aspirations of seniors and juniors were different. Young doctors wanted more senior posts to be available, better training and not to be used simply as 'pairs of hands'. Junior hospital doctors were gaining power and better representation, and they pressed for a contract that recognised the long hours they worked. An extra duty allowance was introduced in 1970. In 1973 the juniors were granted an independent 'craft committee' within the BMA, and with it a stronger voice in negotiation. In 1975 a new contract, in the wake of industrial action, gave them a basic 40-hour week, while ensuring that they would still work whatever extra hours their posts required. They were paid overtime and although this was at a lower hourly rate it increased their earnings by a third. The changes were moving junior doctors away from a professional system of remuneration and closer to an industrial one.[213] Slowly shift systems were introduced, particularly at night. Junior doctors might have only short-term responsibilities for patients whom they would never see again. They would find themselves on call with consultants with whom they never did a ward round, working relationships were less close and the mutual support within the team was diminished.[214] The traditional 'firm' system began to break down.

Nursing

Nurse education and staffing

Nurses and midwives were the largest group of NHS staff and their numbers had grown steadily over the previous decade; only community midwives were getting fewer. The demand from specialised units was rising. There were fewer school leavers, student entry was static and there were never enough recruits of high quality. The post-war expansion of higher education provided wider opportunities for young women, and nursing had to compete. Degree courses were introduced, for the small minority of students with the necessary academic qualifications who wanted them, so that such people were not lost to the profession. They had time to go more deeply into a subject and relate it to other areas of knowledge.[215] A Scottish study showed that the better the educational qualifications of the entrants, the less likely they were to give up. Some students were now married. By the time they took the final state examination, nurses were often planning a family, travel or a new career. Wastage remained high – 36 per cent at the Central Middlesex, where a careful study showed that the cause was not just the hard work; most entrants were attracted to nursing precisely because it involved looking after people in a practical way. Anxiety about the responsibility, being away from home, emotional involvement with patients, problems in studying and lack of confidence in their own skills played a part as well.[216] The problems identified by nurses on the wards had hardly changed over the years. They did not relate directly to quality of care, but to shortages of nursing, ancillary and secretarial staff, questions of status between various groups, travelling, accommodation, working hours and retraining.[217] The Department of Health issued a hospital memorandum. It was a pink one, which meant it was for action, not information. Richard Crossman sent it to chairmen of boards of governors and HMCs, and the CMO to medical advisory committees.[218] Because nurses were scarce, they should nurse, and not spend valuable time on non-nursing duties, chores that others could do, such as sterilising, distributing meals and taking messages. Intensive care units should be brought together in one place. Nearly everything doctors decided to do for their patients had nursing implications. The best way to help was to bring nurses fully into management.

Hospital nursing staff (England and Wales)		
	1949	*1968*
Total*	137,636	255,641
Registered nurses	46,300	85,898
Student nurses	46,386	53,148
Enrolled nurses	16,076	38,725
Pupil nurses	1,515	18,406
Other	27,355	59,464

*Excludes hospital midwives
Source: NHS Executive

The need for a second grade of practical nurse remained. Over the first 20 years of the NHS the number of nursing auxiliaries more than doubled, a greater increase than students or registered nurses, and the numbers continued to grow. To the nursing profession this was seen as a threat to standards and a continuing dilution of the profession, and there was a move to remove the word 'nursing' from their title. To management it was the answer to many staffing problems. Not only were auxiliaries making a major contribution to patient care but they were increasingly holding positions of responsibility, carrying out a wide range of nursing that registered nurses were either unable or unwilling to do in some areas of the country.[219] After 1974 health authorities had many local authority members, some of whom saw political as well as practical reasons for recruiting widely from ethnic minority groups and the pacific rim; often they funnelled these recruits into the auxiliary grades. The nursing profession in the USA had constantly upgraded its educational requirements, creating a role for a support worker. The same process in the UK maintained the need for the auxiliary, the state-enrolled nurse (SEN), distinguishable by badge and uniform.

Conflicts within nursing

Exclusive profession	:	Extensive workforce
Profession	:	Trade union
Pure nursing	:	Management responsibilities
Holistic practice	:	Specialist practice
Senior clinicians	:	Senior managers
Female	:	Male

Source: Owens and Glennerster (1990)[220]

The development of a more open society, a larger group of nursing academics and unionisation intensified the conflicts. Should senior nurses concern themselves with nursing alone or become involved in the wider environment of health care? Militant trade unionism and professional aspirations clashed. Nurses were seen in street protests. The *Nursing Times* carried a poem on 'Thoroughly Militant Millie' whose reward was a post first at Region and then the Ministry.[221] There was also the gender issue; male nurses had dominated the mental illness and mental handicap hospitals, and reorganisation in 1974 saw a substantial increase in the number of male chief nursing officers particularly in the north. In tune with the times, discipline was relaxed. The nurse's 'mystery' was diminishing and at times patients were encouraged to use the nurse's first name. To maintain recruitment and morale, attempts were made to give nurses off-duty convenient to their social life; when planning duty rotas ward sisters had to bear in mind the requests the nurses had made for time off as well as ward staffing requirements. The question of uniform would always stimulate debate among nurses; apart from a shorter hemline, nurses' and sisters' uniforms had changed little in some hospitals since the times of Florence Nightingale. Rules governing dress were less strictly applied; sometimes caps were not worn. Now nurses rushed home in their uniform it could hardly protect patients against cross-infection, although it still made clear the occupation and status of the wearer.[222]

Prices and Incomes Report no. 60

- Lower entry age to 17
- Larger training schools independent of hospital management
- Modify off-duty restrictions
- Implement Salmon in January 1969
- Replace RHBs/HMCs with single-tier authorities
- A general increase of 9 per cent in pay with many other improvements including enhanced overtime, mental and geriatric 'leads'

In 1968 the Prices and Incomes Board was asked to examine nurse pay structure, levels of pay and conditions of service. The Board frequently strayed far outside its terms of reference. In its report it considered nurse training and management and suggested a new salary structure as an incentive to efficiency, translating existing posts into Salmon grades.[223] Higher rates would be paid where staff shortages existed. The RCN initially welcomed the report for it offered the chance to revolutionise training. Later there were criticisms of its proposals and the size of the pay award. The government recognised that nurses were 'an exceptional case' and recommended the report to the Whitley Council negotiating body. In a subsequent debate in the Lords, Lord Amulree suggested that there should be a review body for nurses, as there was for doctors. The *BMJ* said that nurses had been exploited for a century; their medical colleagues should help them achieve economic justice. [224]

The Briggs Report

In 1970, when health service reorganisation was clearly coming, Professor Asa Briggs was asked to review the roles, education and training of nurses and midwives.[225] The driving forces were the problem of recruitment, education and the conditions of work in nursing; there was little feminist pressure at that time. It was immediately apparent that many recommendations of past studies had not been followed through. The Committee chose to address issues that had immediate topical importance and to be forward looking. It reported the following year and was not the easiest report to understand. Though produced by an eminent historian, there was little reference to the past; Briggs wrote in a desire to obtain action. The most immediate problems were often long standing; no solution was offered for some of them. Pointing to the changing social and medical context, Briggs thought nursing must also change and would be judged by the quality of care individuals received. Dividing lines between hospital and community services would have to be crossed if reorganisation was to improve patient care. In future, hospital beds would be used only when necessary, and be linked with outpatient and domiciliary services based on group practices and health centres. Nurse attachment to practices was commonplace and health centres were spreading. Services for the mentally ill and handicapped were increasingly based in the community.

The Briggs Report (1971)[225]

- Two 18-month modules
- Relate theory to practice in four clinical areas: medicine, surgery, psychiatry and community
- A continuous process of education within a profession in the process of change
- Colleges of nursing
- More undergraduate nursing degree courses
- Creation of a unified statutory body for nursing

The recommendations were concerned more with the structure and organisation of nurse education than with the role of nurses and the nature of nursing. Asa Briggs thought the current system of training inadequate and did not always provide a satisfying range of opportunities for nurses. He proposed fewer but larger colleges of nursing and midwifery, which should recruit from a wide range of intelligence. It was, however, NHS reorganisation in 1974 that provided an opportunity to halve the number of schools to about 200, each usually relating to one of the new area health authorities (AHAs). The report said that basic nursing could be learnt thoroughly only in clinical settings and theoretical instruction should be related step by step to this. The course should be in two stages, each of 18 months' duration. Continuing education, specialist and back-to-nursing courses should be developed and there should be a drive to produce more teachers. Conditions of work should be improved and the hospital and community services should work more closely. The *Nursing Times* commented on the extent to which Briggs followed Miss Nightingale's ideas, that nursing could only be taught at the bedside, that students should be encouraged to have an *ésprit de corps*, that education was a continuing process, and students needed library facilities.[226]

Asa Briggs wished that his report had appeared before Salmon and Seebohm. He felt that Salmon's elaborate grading structure took little account of the varied aspects of the nursing profession, and Seebohm dealt with matters that affected some nursing roles, particularly health visitors. The report was presented before Britain joined the European Community, but it subsequently became muddled up with the EC directives and its implementation was repeatedly delayed. The Treaty of Rome meant that the UK had to be in compliance with the directives. Important Briggs recommendations could be implemented only if there was a single body controlling nurse education – and there were 13 or 14. Briggs proposed changes in the statutory framework of the profession and a single central body responsible for professional standards, education and discipline. This meant lengthy discussions with the many nursing professional bodies, each of which had a desire to fight its corner. Roland Moyle, the Labour Minister, not fully realising what he was letting himself in for, agreed to chair a group bringing the conflicting interests together. Each had its own ethos and the loss of individual statutory bodies was therefore a cause for anxiety. Each wanted maximal representation on the new United Kingdom Central Council for Nursing, Midwifery and Health Visiting (UKCC) so horse trading led to a top-heavy organisation and accusations that the representation of some countries and nursing disciplines was inappropriate. Financial and legislative problems delayed action on Briggs, which was allowed to mature until Barbara Castle, in May 1974, announced that she would accept the main recommendations concerning training: £18 million would be found for tutors, clinical teachers and ward sisters; in the event, it was put off again because of an economic crisis. It took seven years before the legislation set up the statutory framework; every time legislation reached the House of Commons a general election was called, to the despair of those responsible.

Nursing practice

Theories of nursing

Developments in medicine were forcing changes onto nursing, and there was a greater advance in medical than in nursing knowledge. Over the years nursing had followed medicine in the pursuit of cure, and hospital nursing was largely synonymous with tasks associated with diagnosis and treatment. Much in nursing depended on the relationship of patient and nurse, and that took time to develop. Patients, however, now left hospital more rapidly; what could be done to maintain this central feature of the profession? High technology, the development of intensive care units and electronic monitoring placed new burdens on nurses' shoulders. There was little room in hospital for the ambulant patient. In a crisis nurses needed both to diagnose and to act in a way outside the traditional nursing role, and in the process developed skills and knowledge in specialised fields beyond the competence of nursing management and not covered in student training, becoming an integral part of medical teams.[227]

The first English university department of nursing studies was established in 1970 in Manchester, although there were university degrees available elsewhere (as at Southampton) associated with nursing or health visitor registration. Nurse educationalists looked for autonomy and a role less dependent on the processes of diagnosis and treatment of the acutely ill. Doctors who had traditionally taught student nurses were invited to do so less often. A partnership of trust, working to a common purpose, began to be replaced by mutual wariness and attempts to define territory. New ideas in nursing were sometimes unattributed adaptations of sociological or educational concepts, or medical systems of history taking, diagnosis and record keeping. Many came from the USA.[228] Technical concepts often transferred well but those relating to how people thought and behaved were culturally based. The fundamental assumptions on which the ideas were founded might not fit the culture into which they were being transferred. For example, in the USA nurses had long distinguished between 'nursing therapy' and 'patient care', the latter often not being the nurse's concern but something left to non-professional workers.[229] Nursing was more technical, and nurses worked within a context of defensive medicine. New theories of nursing, for example the nursing process, were developed at least partly by American nurses in an attempt to retake some of the basic nursing territory occupied by nursing assistants. They were not ideally suited to the UK, with its tradition of bedside nursing. Virginia Henderson, the American nursing academic and for 25 years editor of *The principles and practice of nursing*, published her definition of nursing in 1955, which gave the nurse a role as the authority on the maintenance of daily living activities, the doctor the authority on the diagnosis and treatment of disease, and stressed partnership between the two.

> *The unique function of the nurse is to assist the individual, sick or well, in the performance of those activities contributing to health or its recovery (or to peaceful death) that he would perform unaided had he the necessary strength, will, or knowledge. And to do this in such a way as to help him gain independence as rapidly as possible. This aspect of her work, this part of her function, she initiates and controls; of this she is master. In addition she helps the patient to carry out the therapeutic plan as initiated by the physician. She also, as a member of the medical team, helps other members, as they in turn help her, to plan and carry out the total program whether it be for the improvement of health, or the recovery from illness, or support in death.*[230]

Divisions

Changes in the way health care was provided altered the way doctors and nurses interacted. Because patients were discharged with ever greater rapidity, and beds were allocated more flexibly, a consultant would have patients on many wards, and each ward would be visited by many consultants. The traditional ward teams were disappearing. Formal ward rounds by 'the chief' became less a feature of ward life; some sisters ceased to accompany the consultants when they were there, and where team nursing had been introduced it was the staff nurse leading the team who was best informed. Continuity of care seemed fractured beyond repair. A consultant wrote 'I turned to ask sister a question during my regular ward round and she had gone – off duty, I was told; "Miss Nightingale" had fled and the long admired dedication with her. Similarly, the younger doctors were good competent professionals when on duty, but when they were off, they were off.'[231] Doctors and nurses were beginning to speak different languages, not necessarily to the advantage of patients. Doctors could never understand why those who taught nursing did not practise it; or why there was so much concentration on nursing as a profession, its education and structure, and so little research on patient care.

Virginia Henderson was critical of some developments, believing that too much time was being spent on theoretical approaches, and that nurses were using terminology that was both vague and could not be understood. She wished that some theoreticians were at least part-time practitioners.[232] She thought the distinction between the role of doctors and nurses was 'pretty absurd' considering the varying patterns of clinical practice in different parts of the world. In her textbook of nursing she placed equal emphasis on the technical and the holistic. Nursing, always an amalgamation of different groups with different values, was dividing. On the one hand were nurses who were claiming professional autonomy. On the other were those who enjoyed the challenge of intensive care, dialysis and transplantation, and active clinical work in all disciplines. Doctors, recognising the contribution that nurses made, encouraged them and trained them. The nurses saw themselves as valued partners who often substituted for the doctor and key people in a unit run under protocols agreed by all professionals.

Community Nursing Staff (England and Wales)

	1949	1959	1968
Home nurses	5,776	7,087	8,803
Health visitors	3,753	4,278	5,409
Midwives	ND	4,820	4,861

ND, no data
Source: NHS Digest of Statstics

Community nursing was also altering. The growing numbers of elderly people made increasing demands on district nurses, who were enjoying the experience of working with the better general practices. Domiciliary midwives saw their home deliveries disappearing and from 1967 onwards their numbers fell rapidly. Health visitors, with their background in social and environmental issues, and a concept of health linked to local authority social services and voluntary organisations, had greater readjustments to make. The place of health visiting within primary health care, the health visitor's role in relation to general practice and how – within the attachment schemes – she could maintain her public health role were constant topics of debate. The supporting structure of the MOH's department had been lost. Health visitors were now fully part of the NHS, part of a group of community nursing services.

Nursing administration

The Salmon Report

Brian Salmon's Committee had recommended an organisational structure for nursing with a nurse at every level in the hospital hierarchy, and this reduced the historic power of the matrons of the large acute hospitals. Salmon wanted to pilot implementation gradually over a period of years, so that the new structure would be well understood. Instead, in 1968, shortly after pilots had begun, the DHSS responded to the report of the Prices and Incomes Board and decided to implement the new structure nationally. Nurses' pay would be increased at all levels, and simultaneous implementation of the staffing structure was required to avoid the anomalies of two parallel pay structures. In Salmon's view, 80 per cent of senior nurses were placed in the new structure with no management training, a foolish way of introducing a new system. By 1970 approvals had been given to 166 Salmon schemes and the comparable Mayston Report on community nursing was implemented simultaneously.

The interpolation of additional levels of management reduced the traditional supervision of the wards by 'matron's office', ultimately to the detriment of patients' care. Problems on the ward were no longer instantly known to hospital management. Chief nursing officers (grade 10) were in a weak and lonely position with few contacts and without the intimate hospital involvement matrons previously had. Their tasks were recruitment, finance, the appointment of senior staff and the representation of nursing at the highest levels.[233]

The Salmon Report aroused many passions. The two senior nursing grades (10 and 9) concerned with policy decisions, two middle grades (8 and 7) dealing with programmes to apply policies and two front line grades (6 and 5) at the bedside had, according to the *BMJ*, emerged like a trident with one prong amputated. There were beckoning heights for nurses who became administrators, but for ward sisters who preferred nursing patients (the Salmon no. 6s) prospects appeared depressingly flat.[234] A follow-up report, *Progress on Salmon*,[235] was confident that the proposals were right, while admitting that there was lack of understanding of the tasks of the different grades, particularly grade 7, the new nursing officer. Those in grade 7 were to be experienced clinical nurses able to take responsibility for the standards of nursing. They would combine clinical and managerial roles and be based in the unit, not in matron's office. Sometimes grade 7s had to cover units with mixed functions, such as general medicine, coronary care, renal dialysis and children's surgery. They were unlikely to have expertise in all these fields. Salmon resulted in the promotion of experienced ward sisters to grade 7, leaving many wards with younger, less experienced staff. Consultants noticed the change and complained that the most highly trained clinical nurses were being promoted away from patients and into management. Salmon said that expertise should stay on the ward – and ward sisters should be properly rewarded for their work.[236] The new structure did not survive for long because NHS reorganisation in 1974, and subsequent management changes, killed the concept of Salmon and ruined the morale of senior nurses. Simultaneously Cogwheel was changing the organisation of the medical staff. Nursing was hierarchical but medicine was not and frictions developed between the professions.

The path to NHS reorganisation

Industrial unrest

Industrial action had been rare in the NHS and no more than 3,000 staff had been involved in any year until 1971. Thereafter inflation and industrial action became significant. Union power was strong. Income policies affected hospital ancillary staff, and management might concede unnecessary overtime to increase earnings. Previously a small pay award might last two or three years but it did so no longer. The introduction of strict government control of wages at a time of high inflation and the breaking of traditional links with local government workers who had agreed terms just before the start of a pay freeze led to the first major national dispute, the ancillary workers' strike in 1972. The numbers involved in industrial action rose to 97,000.[237] The last months of 1973 saw the Yom Kippur war and the decision by the oil producing and exporting countries (OPEC) to raise the price of oil substantially. This produced a financial crisis and in December 1973 the Conservative Chancellor, Anthony Barber, introduced a package of cuts concentrated on capital projects, supplies and services.[238] Attempts to resist wage demands led to further industrial unrest. In January 1974 a ban on overtime working by the miners led the government to take emergency powers and impose a three-day week throughout industry. The *Lancet* (which had to fly copies into the country from the USA) thought the time was now ripe for a governmental retreat with dignity, by giving the miners a large increase of pay in compensation for the injuries and ill-health associated with mining.[239] The crisis led to the fall of the government.

Organisational issues

Alongside the economic problems there was increasing concern about the division of the NHS into three parts – hospital, GP and local authority services – which organisationally and financially seemed to have little to do with each other.[240] Because so many people with long-term problems required both the NHS and social services, co-operation between the two was desirable. Within the NHS the medical profession, critical from the time of the Porritt Report, argued increasingly for structural change to improve co-operation and co-ordination. A hospital-orientated NHS was said to be anti-GP and out of contact with the community services run by the local authority.[241] Past planning had been based on consultant numbers or on hospital building, taking little account of developments in primary health care or objective criteria of patients' needs. Yet the diseases with which the NHS dealt increasingly had multiple causes and required long-term care, mostly outside hospital. Health education, hospital services, GP and community services all needed to be brought together. Walter Holland, Professor of Public Health Medicine at St Thomas', believed that a planning process was necessary, considering the ideal future, forming an objective, setting a target, allocating resources and implementing a programme that was followed up and evaluated. This would provide a clear and coherent framework for all the myriad decisions, small and large, within the new organisational structure on the horizon.[242] From the patient's perspective, or from that of the GP, the problems were less apparent. At 'grass roots' people were blissfully unaware that the tripartite nature of the service was considered unsatisfactory. John Reid, the MOH for Buckinghamshire, himself an advocate for unification, was planning the new health services for the future Milton Keynes effectively, even though the managerial division into hospital, local authority and GP services was deemed to make co-ordination impossible.[243]

A multitude of reports and proposals

The pace was set by the existence of the Royal Commission on Local Government and the Seebohm Committee on Local Authority Social Services. Local government boundaries were going to change. In principle Labour and Conservative parties were agreed that a unified health and local authority system would be ideal but was not practical politics. Both the medical profession and the local authorities had, in effect, a veto. Similarly there was tacit agreement that, if amalgamation was not possible, alignment of the boundaries of health authorities and the local authorities was desirable. Between 1968 and 1972 there were several attempts to create a better organisational structure. The plethora of reports was itself confusing. In November 1967 Kenneth Robinson announced that he intended to review the administrative machinery of the NHS, looking particularly at the tripartite structure. In 1968 the report of the Royal Commission on Medical Education and the Seebohm Report were published.[244] Robinson's Green Paper on NHS structure was published after them, in July 1968. Its central theme was the unified administration of services in each area in place of the nearly 700 separate authorities currently existing. Regions would go and there would be 40–50 area boards in England and Wales, a proposal criticised on the grounds that they would be too remote from the field and too many for the Ministry to handle effectively.

In 1968 Richard Crossman succeeded Kenneth Robinson to head a newly merged Department of Health and Social Security. As Secretary of State he appointed Brian Abel-Smith, the economist who had worked on the Guillebaud Committee, as a special adviser. Abel-Smith maintained close contacts with Professor Jerry Morris, at the London School of Hygiene and Tropical Medicine. Crossman had to conduct the negotiations on Kenneth Robinson's proposals and to deal with the additional criticisms that the hospital service would dominate the area boards and the advantages of regional planning would be lost. He established a committee to examine possible regional functions, and favoured a bottom–up system in which regions would essentially be a federation of district representatives. In March 1969 he announced that a new Green Paper would be issued, that there would be a two-tier system with some 200 district committees and above them a second tier of about 20 regional authorities.[245] The report of the Royal Commission on Local Government, published in June 1969, recommended that consideration be given to unifying responsibility for the NHS within a new system of local government, proposing 58 unitary local authorities and a two-tier system for Birmingham, Liverpool and Manchester similar to that in Greater London.[246] Crossman's Green Paper of February 1970 set out the two main objectives of integration. The first was to establish a unified administration at all levels of the service, to facilitate distribution of resources between the three sectors of the NHS and to secure better balance between hospital and community. The second was to promote continuity of care, better communication between health service personnel and more flexible use of staff to secure a better quality of service from existing expenditures.[247]

Neither of two obvious solutions for reorganising the NHS would work:

- One could integrate all the local authority community services that were even marginally connected with health into the NHS, for example home help services and old people's homes. This was the BMA solution but it would continue a hospital orientation and increase neither local authority nor GP influence. It might increase the aloofness of the service.

- One could integrate the whole NHS into the new large local authorities. There were two problems with this.[248] First, local authorities would need a new and growing source of finance. Was there a Chancellor who would allocate a tax that naturally expands, like income tax, to the local authorities? There was also the medical veto, for the doctors had made it clear that they would not permit it to happen, fearing that local authorities might give health a lower priority than other services, for example education, and that standards would differ from place to place. To work under a local authority was seen as an end to clinical freedom and the doctors' standing in society.

Crossman thought government was being forced into a 'miserable middle way' and local authorities would be alienated if the boundaries for health authorities and local government were not the same. He believed the NHS would wobble between the two simple options.[249] George Godber opposed coterminosity, as it might open the door to a future take-over of the NHS by local government; he thought their boundaries were all wrong for the NHS. However, he argued for an elected component to health authorities. In the event, the reorganised NHS neither took over those local government services that were essentially community services nor was it taken into local government. Crossman tried to wobble it as near the local authorities as he could. Area authorities were proposed that would match the local authorities. They would have a substantial membership of local people, partly councillors, partly representatives of local doctors with GPs strongly represented, and nurses and others who would want to develop community services. There would be regional councils to co-ordinate the areas, but they would have little power as the areas would be directly accountable to the centre.

Conservatives' proposals for NHS reorganisation

The Conservative victory in the 1970 election stopped consultation on the second Green Paper. The BMJ wasted no time in reminding Keith Joseph, the new Secretary of State, that the fundamental problem was a shortage of resources, not the organisation of the service.[250] Keith Joseph spoke of a search for alternative sources of money but said that the NHS would continue to be paid for very largely out of taxes and contributions. Although the service would be reorganised under health authorities and outside local government, he did not think Richard Crossman's system would be efficient. The regional tier would be maintained with its power intact, and there would be new areas that would match the local authorities. This added another tier and in retrospect it was a major error, inevitable given the extent of local authority influence and the absence of anyone as tough as Nye Bevan to say 'No'. Keith Joseph issued a further consultative document in May 1971.[251] It was brief and largely confined to issues where his views differed from those of Crossman. The objective was a unified and efficient management, and members of authorities would be chosen for their management ability, not because they represented different interests. The BMA supported the continuation of regions as it would favour proper organisation of hospital services. Line management and chains of command now became dominant. Much attention was paid to recommendations from the management consultants, McKinsey's, and Brunel University; the Lancet thought they were given far too much attention. Both bodies added greatly to the richness of the jargon used in the NHS. 'The exclusion of representatives,' said the Lancet, 'is defended on the ground that management should not be confused with the community's reaction to management – administering the health service is too serious a matter to be shared with the citizenry.'[252] Crossman believed that Keith Joseph did not appreciate that one problem of the service was its remoteness from the public and Joseph's ideas would maintain the self-perpetuating regional oligarchy.

The White Paper appeared in August 1972.[253] It was full of management jargon of which the medical profession was becoming tired and sceptical. The sections on private practice would certainly have been different had it been Richard Crossman's rather than Joseph's document, because private practice was seen as 'giving people an opportunity to exercise personal choice'. The *Lancet* had now mellowed; Theodore Fox had retired and the journal was less radical.

> This week's White Paper on the reorganisation of the NHS (in England) is welcome
> and wise . . . the picture is emerging and it looks none too bad. The call for integration
> has been heard for so long that some forceful utterance such as this was needed to save
> the plea from becoming a dim echo . . . Ever since 1948, the imperfections of the NHS
> have sprung mainly from three faults: lack of money; shortage of skilled staff in many
> areas (partly the result of fault no.1); and too little enthusiasm among some of the
> service's members – enthusiasm to make it really work. The White Paper, should it
> become the foundation of a new NHS structure, backed by ample resources, should
> revivify the whole scene. Some critics will regret the dearth of research and experiment
> before action; others will rightly point to the scarcity of able administrators; others to
> the continuing separation of health and social services . . . Yet all these will be in a
> minority . . . The future looks brighter.[254]

NHS reorganisation

Shortly before reorganisation Sir George Godber retired as CMO at the Department of Health; it was the end of an era. A professional civil servant since the late 1930s, he had taken part in the shaping of the service and, with his close contacts in the profession, increasing seniority and unswerving loyalty to a succession of governments, he had used his influence to mould and improve the NHS. The *BMJ* said that his unceasing effort to make the NHS a harmonious organisation for doctors and patients, his knowledge, fair judgement, patience and courtesy had endeared him to a profession not notably tolerant of bureaucracy.[255] The quality of CMOs could now be measured in units known as the godber; none exceeded 1.0. The power he exercised was not permitted to his successors.

More work and consultation took place in the run up to the 1974 reorganisation than on any structural change before or since. Public interest was virtually nil and there were no fanfares from doctors. There had been no bitter political battles and no threats of doctors walking out. Neither the health needs of the population nor the staffing of the service were going to change. Perhaps the absence of drama accounted for the general lack of enthusiasm for the first major face-lift in 25 years.[256] The failure of TV and radio 'to fulfil their duty to stimulate informed public debate on important issues' was raised by the Social Morality Council, which pointed to the absence of any serious television programme on the topic in the two years after May 1971 when government's intentions became clear. The BBC replied that there had been a programme on Radio 4 in September 1972.[257]

Community medicine

Increasingly, the term 'community medicine' was used to describe the branch of social medicine that dealt with matters relating to the health of groups rather than individuals. Such doctors were anxious and in a state of uncertainty. Reorganisation was moving the MOH out of local government, and there was a wish to form a single specialty to include the public health doctors, the medical administrators and the epidemiologists in academic departments. There were debates about the definition, aims and methods of their disciplines.[258] Professor JN Morris, influential at the London School of Hygiene and Tropical Medicine, believed that public health practice should be firmly based in epidemiology, advocacy, health promotion and the control of disease. The community physician 'should be teacher, watchdog and trouble-maker . . . In promoting the people's health, the community physician must be directly concerned with the mass problems of today and be able to draw on the community's resources to deal with these, not be limited to the categories of need or service that history happens to have deposited in his office.'[259] Others emphasised planning and management, in a service crying out for the evaluation of services and prioritisation. The groups came together and established the Faculty of Community Medicine, uniting the factions as recommended by the Royal Commission on Medical Education. Max Rosenheim, a great leader of the RCP, helped the creation of the faculty within the Colleges of Physicians of London, Edinburgh and Glasgow. Archibald Cochrane became its first President. Crossman had established a working party to look at the work of medical administrators in the reorganised health service, chaired by Dr RB Hunter, Vice-Chancellor of the University of Birmingham. Keith Joseph continued it and in 1972 the report suggested a pattern of training and staked out a place for the community physician of the future at region, area and district levels.[260] The future community physicians would be key in assessing the health needs of the population, assisting integration of the health services, linking administrators with clinicians and co-ordinating the work of the NHS with that of the local authorities. 'Community' came to have two meanings; those in the new specialty saw it as meaning the whole population, while others increasingly spoke of the community as the non-hospital services. Many were uncertain about the role of the new community physicians; they seemed to be involved in decisions affecting the curative work of clinicians, just as the MOH had been before the NHS began. The crux of it appeared to be health service planning, priorities and the interpretation of statistical and epidemiological information.[261]

The structure of the reorganised NHS

Key features of NHS reorganisation

- 14 RHAs, 90 AHAs and FPCs, 192 districts
- Coterminosity of health and local authorities
- Integration of health services in districts with a population of 250,000–300,000
- Participation of clinicians in management
- Clear allocation of responsibilities of an authority and its officers
- Consensus decision-making
- A planning system with decentralisation of decision-making balanced by national and regional strategies
- Better use of resources by greater efficiency

Adapted from the *BMJ* 1975[268]

The English RHBs were reconstituted, with minor boundary changes, as 14 regional health authorities (RHAs). Their role was strengthened and they were responsible for strategy, the building programme, staffing matters and the allocation of resources to their 90 subordinate area health authorities (AHAs). Local authority health departments, hospital management committees and the teaching hospital boards of governors were replaced by the AHAs, each coterminous with one of the 90 new local authorities. Universities with medical schools could nominate the area within which they mainly worked, which became teaching area health authorities (AHA(T)s) with modified membership to reflect their academic role. Where the new areas encompassed two or more major district general hospitals, each with its own territory, a multi-district area was established, each district having its own district management team. There were 192 districts, each of which was divided, in turn, into sectors. There were acute hospital sectors, and community sectors that were generally seen as lower in status. The boundaries of the London areas were bitterly contested for here there was little relationship between the realities of health service provision and local authority boundaries.[262] Reorganisation had little effect on general practice, and once GPs realised this they took little interest in it. The executive councils that had dealt with family practitioners – the doctors, dentists, pharmacists and opticians – were abolished. In their place were 90 family practitioner committees (FPCs) coterminous with the AHAs and, in theory but not in practice, subordinate to them. They still dealt directly with the DHSS. A clearly defined pyramid now existed, with the Secretary of State for Social Services at the top. 'Maximum delegation downwards' was matched by 'accountability upwards'.

Membership of area health authorities

- Chairman – appointed by the Secretary of State
- 15 members; 16 in teaching areas.
- 4 members representative of local authorities
- Others appointed by RHAs after consultation with universities associated with the region, bodies representative of the professions and any federation of workers' organisations

---

The responsibilities of the disciplines involved, the administrators, doctors, nurses and finance officers, were analysed. Detailed role specifications and job descriptions were prepared in an attempt to reflect the clinical autonomy of professionals and the need for effective management. The results appeared in *Management arrangements for the reorganised NHS* (the 'Grey Book').[263] For the first time the NHS officers had clearly defined duties. There was no flexibility to meet local circumstances. It was all down in the Grey Book in black and white. Consensus management was introduced, an idea derived from the work of Elliot Jaques, a management scientist and psychoanalyst who was on the steering committee of the reorganisation management study. There was inadequate emphasis on the need for someone to bring the disciplines to consensus, or if that were not possible to report the failure to the authority. If one member of the team did not like a proposal or decision, that tended to be the end of the matter; agreement was at the lowest common denominator. The officer teams consisted of an administrator, a community physician, a nurse, a finance officer and, at district and area, a consultant and a GP. The consultants, recruited from the greatest pool of experience and talent in the NHS, rapidly learned the managerial game. To co-ordinate health authorities with local authorities there were joint consultative committees. Then there were joint care planning teams, responsible for part of the AHA allocation earmarked for local authority schemes that would benefit both the health and the local authorities. In response to the criticism that patients had little influence on the new system, community health councils (CHCs) were created in the hope that, if they were involved in planning, it would reduce pressure on ministers. A gesture to consumer participation, they were regarded with suspicion by members of authorities and the medical profession. Appearing just as Schumacher published *Small is beautiful*, the new structure was, to quote *The Times* 20 years later, a bureaucratic structure of mind-boggling complexity.[264]

1974 shared one characteristic with 1948: the outcome was the best available compromise. Many groups had to be placated by the addition of another tier, committee or special interest group. Attempts were made to be fair to the staff who were having to apply, if not for their own jobs, for something like them. MOsH who, in 1948, had stayed in their posts now had to compete to be area medical officers. The number of top posts was smaller, many moved to new areas and much talent was lost. There were personal tragedies and at least one suicide. There was similar turbulence among nursing and administrative officers.

Some were converts; one quoted Peter Drucker as saying that the NHS was grotesquely over-administered and dangerously under-managed.[265] Most, including clinicians, probably agreed with a writer in the *Lancet* who said

> We are at last coming in sight of the Great Day when, according to the prophets, a second coming of the NHS is going to cause the rooting out of all that is bad in the present system and lead us into some therapeutic Heaven, where all will be perfection, peace and light. But the whole business is being viewed with much less than fervent optimism by many of us who actually come into contact with patients – the 'grass roots' of the service. And let's face it, grass roots puts us in our place, as low down as you can get. From our lowly viewpoint the NHS looks like a particularly nervous colony of ants which has just had a particularly large garden fork shoved in and stirred around. Individuals race hither and thither, carrying little schemes with them and giving them to others, who carry them a little further and pass them on in their turn. Of course the trouble is we don't understand. We are unable to share the enthusiasm of our administrative colleagues as, with the schoolboy eagerness of modern Druids waiting for the midsummer sun to rise at Stonehenge, they prepare for the New Day.[266]

Florence Nightingale said that hospital management was important and difficult to learn, requiring experience.[267] Senior staff whose length of service had given them pride and loyalty to their institution now either left or became disillusioned. Expertise in the management of outbreaks of infectious disease was lost, as over 100 MOsH left the NHS. Few of the new managers were committed to the hospitals, regarding their jobs as stepping stones to something better. They were so busy with paper work and meetings that they were never seen about the place. Their future lay at the upper levels of an over-heavy bureaucracy and they deserted their posts in droves, leaving huge general hospitals to be run by a succession of juniors, to the dismay of medical staff. Merely to run a hospital did not seem of significance. It was the 'big picture' that mattered, strategic planning at region, area or district. A few trouble-shooters, walking round their hospital, inviting complaints and criticisms and pointing out possible improvements would have helped morale. Instead, to the clinician's eye, there were unrealistic committees run by grey people of second-rate ability with a natural reaction to say 'no'.[268] Already there was a common and rational belief that only two tiers were really necessary and that in time one of the three would dwindle in importance; in applying for new jobs officers could only make their own guesses.[269] It was the night of the long knives; the joke was repeated of the old administrator, displaced by a young manager, who left three sealed envelopes containing advice to use when crises broke. The young man, confident in his ability, nevertheless ran into trouble. The first read 'blame your predecessor', a strategy that worked. The second read 'reorganise', and this was also successful for a time. The third merely said 'prepare three envelopes'.

A failed solution

The new Labour administration

A snap election in March 1974 saw the election of a minority Labour administration led by Harold Wilson and a new Secretary of State, Barbara Castle. The economic situation was grim and consultants were discontented to the point of considering sanctions. They felt that they were being expected to do more work in deteriorating physical facilities with diminishing support, reducing living standards, all the time beset by an unimaginative and over-centralized administration.[270] Labour had made its priorities clear, ending prescription charges, banning private practice in NHS hospitals, reducing the bias towards hospital medicine, encouraging consultants to work full-time for the NHS and strengthening local democratic control of the NHS.[271] The ranks of health service workers were sown with the seeds of mutiny. Clive Jenkins, leading ASTMS, said he intended to raise hell in the health service about the highly qualified and poorly remunerated people who worked in it. In May 1974 nurses marched with banners from the RCN to Hyde Park and Barbara Castle acknowledged their grievance, saying that everyone accepted that they deserved priority. She announced a rapid independent inquiry into the pay of nurses and the professions supplementary to medicine. It was chaired by Lord Halsbury and recommended an average increase of 30 per cent. But the hospital ancillaries also had a strong case and could not be held back for long. Bleak times, said the *Lancet*, for strikes were also taking place throughout industry. The NHS stood in more peril than ever before.[272] In August Mr Wilson pledged that more money would be found for pay awards.

Although the new NHS structure had never seemed satisfactory to the Labour Party, to tamper with it carried a danger of damaging patient care. For all its manifest faults, wrote David Owen the Labour junior minister, the structure of the reorganised NHS could provide a framework for achieving good health care, sensitive to the consumer and at reasonable cost. The new administration's policy was therefore to make changes in an evolutionary way. The objective would be to devolve more power, only possible, to Labour thinking, if there was a strong democratic element locally.[273] A paper on *Democracy in the NHS* was published in May 1974 that added local government representatives to the new RHAs and increased their proportion on the AHAs to a third.[274] It also proposed to extend the role and influence of CHCs by aiming for a high calibre of secretary and seeking to give them better access to information and planning processes.[275] The equitable distribution of money was moved higher on the agenda. Two initiatives flowed from this – a new method of allocating resources nationally and a further attempt to tackle the organisation of health care in London.

Private practice

An increasingly unionised nursing staff resented the time spent on caring for private patients, although money received for the patient's stay fed back centrally into NHS funds.[276] Matters came to a head at the Charing Cross Hospital. Led by Mrs Esther Brookstone, a NUPE branch secretary, staff went on strike in an attempt to close private facilities. The medical profession had seen union power wielded the previous year with disruptive effect to demand politically motivated changes, and believed that they too would be heard only if they were prepared to back their views with action. The BMA at once threatened to withdraw from contractual discussions with the Department and to impose sanctions from midnight on 8 July 1974 unless Mrs Castle intervened. Immediate talks took place and the unions backed off.[277] Private practice, ideologically significant to Barbara Castle and of fundamental importance to the consultants, was far less important to the health of the public than many other issues that could only be solved in co-operation with the doctors. The nurses chose this moment to strike for more pay and the NHS was sinking into chaos.

In October 1974 another election was called and Labour was returned with a slim majority. In parallel was a change in the professional power structure. In 1947/8 the Royal Colleges had acted as mediators between Bevan and the profession, receiving little thanks for their efforts. Subsequently there was a deliberate reduction in the Colleges' medico-political role because of the risk to their recognition as 'charities' for tax purposes. This coincided with a stiffening of resolve in the BMA leadership to maintain the position of the profession, just as the political left was becoming more militant.

Labour moved to phase out pay-beds from NHS hospitals and to negotiate a new consultant contract. The existence of pay-beds had been part of a concordat between Bevan and the consultants from the beginning of the NHS. It had advantages for all concerned: if consultants were going to undertake private practice, it was better for NHS patients for them to be in the main hospital rather than at a private unit down the road. Nevertheless, strong opposition to private practice was traditional Labour Party policy and phasing it out had twice been a manifesto commitment. It was an ideological blot on an otherwise pure NHS landscape and at times it allowed queue-jumping while NHS patients waited months or years for treatment.[278] Barbara Castle believed that the facilities of the NHS should be available on medical priority alone and not made available to those able to pay.

Consultants work to rule

Matters were made yet worse by the simultaneous attempt to negotiate a new consultant contract, a process that had begun under the Conservative administration. The consultants believed that they were over-worked and under-paid, and wanted a work-sensitive contract or item of service payment. Barbara Castle saw an opportunity to achieve her own goals and proposed a joint working party between the profession and the Department, chaired by David Owen.[279] Doctors hoped their discontents would be resolved peacefully, and were in for a shock. Barbara Castle was prepared to offer an extra 18 per cent pay to consultants who took whole-time contracts, which would have reduced private practice and placed consultants under tighter control. The consultants rejected the proposals. In addition it was proposed that merit awards, which went disproportionately to high-tech medicine and the staff of teaching hospitals, should increasingly recognise service in unfashionable specialties and unfashionable places. The distribution of merit awards was a long-standing problem to which a solution was required, but in the atmosphere prevailing consultants saw Barbara Castle's move as an unacceptable intrusion into professional territory. Meetings between ministers and the medical profession ended in acrimony and broke down dramatically.[280] In December 1974 consultants took industrial action and for 16 weeks many 'worked to contract.' Restrictions were placed on the numbers seen in outpatient clinics and waiting lists rose. Clinics became a pleasure rather than a chore for the doctors, and there was little prospect of a return to the old ways of rush and scramble, working long hours at a frantic pace.[281] Doctors began to feel less personal responsibility for the NHS. Chaos was all around. GPs were signing undated resignations; junior doctors were preparing for battle. However, several small improvements were made to the consultant contract and the Review Body made a pay award of more than 30 per cent. Mrs Castle honoured the recommendation and the medical profession settled.

Immediately after, in May 1975, Mrs Castle announced that the government would not only phase out pay-beds but would also seek powers to regulate private practice more closely. The medical profession rejected Mrs Castle's proposals.[282] The BMA felt that patients had a right to chose private medicine; that government should maintain the right that consultants had under their contract to private practice, if it did not encroach on their NHS duties; and that the availability of private practice was essential because it made it possible for consultants to achieve incomes above the comparatively low salaries that the NHS was prepared to pay. An alliance was formed between the BMA, the Royal Colleges, the Hospital Consultants and Specialists Association and the private insurers to oppose the proposals, employing Lord Goodman, an eminent lawyer, as adviser. In November a Royal Commission on the NHS was announced. Barbara Castle had looked to Harold Wilson for support on a manifesto commitment, but her fierce commitment had come into conflict with the cold determination of Anthony Grabham, the consultants' leader. To attempt to resolve the deadlock over private practice Lord Goodman was asked to mediate. Wilson met the leaders of the profession, with Lord Goodman and Barbara Castle. During the meeting an attempt was made to entice individual College presidents into debate and break the impression of professional unity. It failed, Anthony Grabham presenting the united views of the profession.[283] A compromise followed that radically altered Labour's proposals for private practice. Facilities would be maintained where they were needed, although some unoccupied private beds would be shut. The dispute slowly subsided but the issue of principle had not been resolved. Labour maintained that it had never wished to abolish private practice, but merely to separate it from the NHS. There were no winners; the medical profession was seen to be prepared to strike, waiting lists had risen, the government had been forced to compromise and the NHS as a whole had been undermined. Barbara Castle believed that some senior medical civil servants supported the profession rather than her and barred them from key meetings. The damage she inflicted on the NHS is hard to over-estimate and when James Callaghan became Prime Minister in April 1976 David Ennals succeeded her.[284] Pay restraint, introduced in July 1975, increased the doctors' sense of grievance.

A Bill to begin to phase out private practice more slowly, still opposed by the BMA, received Royal assent in November 1976. Private beds and outpatient facilities would remain if there was a reasonable demand for them, facilities would be withdrawn only if there were reasonable alternatives, and continued authorisation would depend on steps having been taken to meet reasonable demands outside the NHS. Within six months 1,000 private beds would be eliminated and a Board would be established to consider further proposals.[285] Labour policy achieved the opposite of what was intended; there were only small reductions in NHS private beds, but the alarm led to a substantial increase in the number of private hospitals throughout the country. The numbers taking out private medical insurance (including some in the trades unions) rose, as did the demand from foreigners for treatment.[286] London already had private hospitals that were 'disclaimed' under the original 1946 legislation because they were religious foundations or hospitals associated with a particular group such as the Royal Masonic, King Edward VII's Hospital for Officers, or the trades unions' Manor Hospital. Nuffield Nursing Homes ran others with charitable status. The new expansion came from the commercial sector. Some were started with American investment (e.g. the Princess Grace Hospital). The Wellington Hospital, opened in 1974, became American-owned. Others had Middle-Eastern financial backing. The Cromwell aimed to become the home of the super-specialties and the Portland Hospital was developed on the site of the old Royal National Orthopaedic Hospital to provide services for women and children. The proximity of these developments to Harley Street was no coincidence; the development of the special hospitals a century earlier had the same *raison d'être*. In the territory of the Kensington, Chelsea and Westminster Area Authority 25 per cent of the beds were in the private sector.

Two further years of incomes policy brought the medical profession to the point of rebellion again. Doctors had acquiesced for a time to government policy, believing that bringing inflation under control was vital. By 1977 the Review Body reported that doctors had fallen 15 per cent behind comparable groups in the previous two years. Others could take advantage of increased productivity and overtime to an extent that doctors could not.[287] Pay policy was still in place and an appeal to the Prime Minister was fruitless. Morale, said the BMJ, was lower 12 months after Mrs Castle had left office than when she was Secretary of State. There was growing hopelessness that the medical profession would ever be treated fairly again.[288] The new consultant contract, the product of years of work, was not agreed until 1978, and in the event was never implemented.[289]

Planning and priorities

Increasingly the way money was spent was driven by planning processes. The DHSS issued guidelines on the staffing and organisation of services, guidance that was expensive to follow and, in the wake of the problems in mental illness and mental handicap, taken seriously. The NHS had suffered from a surfeit of reports on how services should be staffed and organised, calling attention to unmet need and pressing for more money. These optimal standards, published in good faith and often with political support, left regions with an impossible bill. At the sharp end of exhortation, they rebelled. When Keith Joseph, as Secretary of State, visited the South-East Metropolitan RHB in 1973, he challenged the assertion that the money available would not pay for his policies. Malcolm Forsythe and his colleagues assembled the detailed guidance that had been issued on staffing levels and calculated the costs of implementation for their population of 3.5 million. The region would have needed two and a half times the revenue and five times the capital allocation to do everything required of them, even over a ten-year period. David Crouch MP, a member of the RHB, asked to see Keith Joseph, and the findings were presented. The region thought that instead of normative planning it would be better to give the money available to the health authorities with the fewest possible strings attached and expect them to produce the best mix of services possible.

The Priorities document

Priorities for health and personal social services in England (1976)[290]

	Indicative change in funding
Services for elderly people	3.2 per cent
Services for mentally ill people	1.8 per cent
Services for mentally handicapped people	2.8 per cent
Services for children	2.2 per cent
Acute and general hospital services	1.2 per cent
Hospital maternity services	−1.8 per cent

The high point for RHAs and for corporate planning was 1976. The Resource Allocation Working Party Report appeared, as did *Prevention and health: everybody's business*. Barbara Castle published *Priorities for health and personal social services in England*, which made it clear that, because of the economic limitations, choices had to be made.[290] The *BMJ* referred it as a document of despair. At a time of economic recession current expenditure would continue to increase in real terms but the capital programme would be halved.[291] It was increasingly clear, said the journal, that the NHS could not balance its books and stood no chance of doing so. Growth was concentrated on primary care, health promotion and services for children, the elderly and the mentally ill and handicapped, putting 'people before buildings', and ignoring the decaying hospitals and their effect on staff morale. The *Priorities* document translated general objectives into specific financial policies. It looked coldly at the money likely to be available, calculated programme budgets and named the winners and losers. It was a mine of information about what was happening, reviewing virtually all NHS policies, looking at costs and trends, and taking account of local authority services. Although consultative, it was intended that the strategy would provide authorities with a basis for planning and was to be applied at once. Low-cost solutions must be sought, levels of provision examined and redeployment of resources, in discussion with the professions, would be required in the acute sector. Yet the acute services were to reduce waiting times and geographical disparity, and facilitate medical advance. The priorities, the Royal Commission on the NHS was later to say, were not the result of objective analysis but of subjective judgement; they were not the only possible choices but were broadly correct.[292]

The planning system became a central feature of the reorganised NHS. It required good information and in spite of the effort that had gone into HAA there were well-founded criticisms of the accuracy and timeliness of the information available to management. Planning was all-embracing and of a new order of complexity. The system swept into action just as growth money was disappearing, so 'planning for negative growth' and 'zero based planning' became watchwords. Ten-year strategic plans aimed to redress the perceived imbalance between hospital and the community, acute medicine and the long-stay services. Almost immediately, further reduction in the funds likely to be available forced some regions to rewrite their proposals. Sir George Godber rightly predicted that planning would be a shambles for some time. He thought the procedure was too formalised, allowing little for the change inherent within the service. It failed to recognise that what happened was a continuous moulding exercise and elaborate production of new plans each year was wasteful of time and money.

The system aimed to produce ten-year strategic plans every three years and a shorter term operational plan. District, Area, Region and the Department all had to interdigitate, the 'superior' authority providing priorities and an indication of the resources for the next four years, the 'inferior' authority producing plans after consultation. Clinical staff spent long hours constructing ideal paediatric or mental handicap services that were generally impracticable or unaffordable. Some regions, like North East Thames, produced a central plan and imposed it on their areas. South East Thames RHA pointed to the difficulty in planning ten years ahead without clear guidance about the money likely to be available. Many existing policy commitments were unattainable, given existing budgetary constraints. Areas such as Medway, where the population was expanding rapidly, had problems both with general practice and the hospital sector and there were no funds available to help. The aims in the *Priorities* document could be achieved only by putting acute services in jeopardy, and in South East Thames that would mean closing one of its three central London teaching hospitals. The *BMJ* thought that regional strategic plans, though variable in quality, should be welcomed for they prompted a debate about fundamental issues.[293]

The results of consultation on the *Priorities* document were published in 1977 by David Ennals in *The way forward*.[294] Though less explicit, it maintained the same general principles and programme budgets. Ennals was convinced that with skilled planning faster progress could be made. Regions, particularly those losing money, were less convinced and the losing RHAs in the south maintained that money first had to be spent to rationalise the acute services before funds could be released for transfer to the priority sectors. North East Thames gave priority for capital spending to five acute hospital projects, such as Homerton Hospital and The London.

Complaints about the complexity of the planning system spurred review but the modifications increased its complexity. Consensus management did not work out as planned. Unless a strong leader emerged locally – often the administrator – matters tended to drift. Within the consensus teams some disciplines flourished. Many consultants, in management for the first time, learned the necessary lessons. Community physicians varied widely in their impact; some made their mark but many did not. GPs were unable to speak authoritatively for their colleagues who were independent contractors; nurses could speak for their own discipline but seldom showed much interest in matters of wider policy.

Financial problems

In July 1974 the BMA, the Royal Colleges of Nursing and Midwives and the British Dental Association met the Prime Minister and asked for £500 million extra for the NHS and for an independent inquiry into its financing. Harold Wilson promised that extra money would be provided to meet the cost of pay claims and inflation but refused an inquiry.[295] In October 1974 the Royal Colleges and Faculties took an unprecedented step and sent a joint statement to the government, again asking for careful scrutiny of NHS funding and clear recognition of the extent of the shortfall. The gap between the care provided for patients and what might now be achieved was widening and, denied the resources they needed, the morale of doctors was low.[296] The time, said the BMJ, had come for realism. If the NHS was to remain short of money, intelligent use must be made of what there was. The medical profession itself, at a conference held in Winchester in 1974, recognised the effects of economic stringency and the importance of cost-effectiveness.[297] There was certainly waste – unnecessary drugs prescribed and investigations performed. Much conventional practice, for example the length of stay in hospital after operation, was governed more by custom and convenience than by efficient use of scarce resources. If each area were given a budget and told it could keep the savings from economies, said the BMJ, there would be a real incentive.[298] It would, however, be necessary to rectify the regional disparities. The claim that every patient could be offered all available treatments had always been something of a fraud. It was no longer possible even to go on pretending. Choices would have to be made. What advances in treatment could be afforded and how many doctors were needed?

BMJ's proposals for reform (1975)[299]

- Prune the extravagant and elaborate administrative structure
- Doctors should take a critical look at the costs of their treatment
- Better use could be made of skilled staff, for example outpatient surgery
- Health education should be encouraged

Reorganisation was losing its sparkle. The BMJ said it had suffered from a failure to define what 'delegation downwards' meant; there were fights for power between regions, areas and districts. The NHS was trying to operate with too few staff in hospitals scheduled for rebuilding 25 years previously, in an atmosphere of resentment and despair.[299] Social services had, in effect, been excluded from the integrated health service. GPs, valuing their status as independent contractors, had maintained independence through the creation of family practitioner committees. Disastrously, in 1974 the oil crisis pitched the nation into retrenchment, so all plans for expansion had to be frozen or cut. Clinicians found that the new structure had led to a plethora of reciprocating committees. 'Take the simple matter of getting approval for a new registrar – in the old days it went straight to the Department of Health. Now it has to go through at least 14 stages – it's a sort of mad administrators' Monopoly.'[300] In October 1975 Harold Wilson announced the setting up of a Royal Commission to consider the best use and management of the financial and staff resources of the NHS. Sceptics saw it as a public relations exercise to pacify doctors angered by the private health care issue. It was, however, just the sort of enquiry that the profession had been demanding. The BMA began to prepare its submission, drew attention to the dangerous state of doctors' morale, and argued for the abolition of area health authorities.[301]

Resource reallocation

Health service funds had always been distributed unfairly. When the NHS was established in 1948 the regional hospital boards and the boards of governors were allocated the expenditure of the previous year. For 20 years, estimates and forward looks operated largely from that baseline.[302] The resources available were far higher in the south than in the north of England, although this was not clear from publications that usually presented revenue allocations on a functional rather than a geographic basis. The significant exceptions were Wales, which had caught up a 25 per cent deficit on England, and Scotland, which had moved from a deficit to a substantial surplus on a population basis.

From 1969 it became policy to attempt to achieve equity over ten years but progress was slow. Richard Crossman introduced a new formula but, as this took into account existing services, redistribution did not occur. He despairingly said,[303]

> In order to fulfil this demand for equality, in England for example, you have to have a revolutionary change in the relationship between the health services provided in the south east and the services provided in the rest of the country. If we look, for instance, at the standard of service which a Londoner can get and which somebody in Sheffield can get, they are poles apart. Measured in terms of access to a GP, access to hospital, or standards of nursing, London does far better. The reason is that when we took over the health service the London hospitals were the dominant hospitals of the country because the wealthy lived in the south east and the GPs and hospitals were therefore concentrated in that area. The standard of service has indeed gone up outside the south east but the gap, judged even by the money they receive in their annual budget, is not much better than it was.

Crossman showed that fair shares would mean taking 10 per cent away from London, in which case wards would be closed and there would be a political problem. It could only be done on an expanding budget from which a higher percentage of the gross domestic product was allocated to the NHS. That was why there had been virtually no change in 25 years. Successive governments had given reallocation no priority and seemed to have been pulled between the vociferous claims of the regions and the teaching hospitals.[304]

The grouping of teaching hospitals under the new regional health authorities made the extent of the problem more obvious. 'District profiles', produced to help new AHAs, showed that the crude variations between areas were even bigger than between regions. Within Trent RHA one area was 39 per cent above the regional average and another 62 per cent below.[305] The incoming Labour government in 1974 was keen to redress inequality but could hardly have chosen a worse time. David Owen, Minister for Health, believed that the NHS should be a tool to achieve a more uniform standard of medical care. He commissioned studies by the Department's economists, first appointed in 1970. His worst fears were reinforced for, even allowing for approximations, there were quite horrendous differences in the level of provision in different parts of the country that could not be explained by differences in need. In the mid-1960s the expenditure per head on the hospital service varied from £9.32 in Trent to £15.33 in North East Thames. In 1971/2 the spread was as big as ever.

By the end of 1975 there was a political imperative to redress the inequalities in provision. A system to do so had to be created, so that planning in the reorganised NHS could be on an equitable basis. Answers had to be found that did not require massive injections of additional cash or jeopardise developments already under way. Above all, the solutions had to be acceptable to everyone concerned as a fair way of achieving, over time, more equitable distribution. Forsythe and Gentle, from South East Thames RHA, suggested that revenue should in future be allocated on the basis of population, with weighting to take account of the size, age and sex of the population, teaching commitments and cross-boundary flow.[306]

The Resource Allocation Working Party

The formation of the Resource Allocation Working Party (RAWP) was announced in July 1975, and its membership included Walter Holland, Malcolm Forsythe, and economists. The BMA agitated in favour of resource reallocation, because consultants outside the southeast were tired of seeing all the money going to London. The task of the working party was to devise a formula for England that would allocate regional resources in relation to health care need, rather than supply, demand and historical factors; be robust and relatively stable from year to year; be dependent on valid, reliable and readily available health data; and be understood by most of those affected. The working party accepted that major determinants of health included deprivation and poverty in all its aspects (e.g. housing). However, the formula was based on health data to ensure that the health service was not seen by government as a means of correcting deprivation. It published its report in 1976.[307] RAWP, as the policy became known, was concerned with allocations rather than the way money was used – that was a matter for the authorities locally. The system was based on the residential populations adjusted for differences in age, gender and death rates. There was no simple way of taking account of the costs of long-term morbidity that were often higher than mortal illness. Mortality was used as a proxy for morbidity. Calculations included allowances for patients who lived in one area but received treatment in another, and for the cost of teaching and research, which had an impact on hospitals that was not spread evenly over the country. Some problems were impossible to solve. There was little information about the cost of individual procedures (e.g. heart surgery), which made it difficult to be fair to districts that collected complex and expensive cases. A national system was established for the central funding of 'supra-regional' units in fields such as paediatric liver transplantation, in which only three or four units were either necessary or desirable. The major weakness was that no link was created between resource allocation and medical staffing policy. The *BMJ* criticised the report as dealing only with resources and not the reasons for high expenditure in London. The fantasy solution would be to move some of the London teaching hospitals to the underprivileged regions of the north and west; that was improbable but the survival of centres of excellence in London and the transfer of resources would be possible only if the number of major hospitals were reduced.[308]

The RAWP formula set target allocations that showed the distance of each region's allocation from what it would be if equity were to rule. The Thames regions were considerably over-target. Trent, Northern and North Western were well below it. Additional 'growth' money available each year would be used to move regions nearer to equality of treatment. Barbara Castle thought that the policy of redistribution was possible even at a time of world recession for public expenditure, and a high public sector deficit would help to sustain employment.[309] The broad principles of RAWP were introduced in the 1977/8 allocations. Targets were recalculated each year and growth money gradually used to redress the situation. Each region was asked to apply the same principles to its areas, so that in a gaining region some areas would gain more than average. Provincial regions, and particularly North Western and Trent, could expect to do well. There was ill-disguised glee in the north at the difficulties facing clinical staff in the metropolis. In a losing region some areas would lose proportionately more if their resources seemed large compared with their resident population. Central London teaching areas were hit three ways: by national redistribution, by regional redistribution and by the need to move funds away from acute services towards long-stay specialties. The priority services for people who were elderly, mentally ill or mentally handicapped were now unambiguously the responsibility of the same district authorities that ran the teaching hospitals and came into direct conflict with new initiatives in acute treatment.

RAWP remained contentious and much intellectual effort was spent on proving that justice was not being served in particular districts. The annual meetings of regional chairmen with the Secretary of State to learn of their allocations were tense affairs. Allocations aimed to bring the poorer regions closer to their target while giving headroom to the richer Thames regions to help them switch funds to their poorer areas. David Ennals was told by the Chairman of the Northern Region that he could not go back to Newcastle with only 3 per cent. 'Living in London is very expensive,' Ennals told him. Sir Frances Avery Jones said that inequality was the price of progress, a comment that had a kernel of truth as far as teaching districts were concerned.

The University of London and its medical schools, themselves under financial pressure, rapidly appreciated the potential effect on acute hospital services and medical education, and established a working party to look at the problem. The financial pressures on London teaching districts were severe but their ability to react was constrained by the need for public consultation and local opposition to any reduction in services. Some of the districts with the greatest problems were matched by left-wing local authorities that considered any reduction in service to be anathema.

The state of the NHS

A decade that had started well ended in disarray. NHS reorganisation was not a success. The oil crisis had led to recession and the building programme was cut to save jobs. Devolution downwards was long in coming. Far more rapid was the increasing centralisation of powers and the issue of immense amounts of detailed guidance, epitomised by a turkey circular that advised hospitals to cook the Christmas fowl fully. In 1976 lack of enthusiasm for NHS reorganisation, its cumbersome nature and the costs of management led David Ennals to ask three RHA chairmen to comment on the relationship of the regions with the Department, and to invite area health authorities to comment on AHA/RHA relationships.[310] They believed that the DHSS had become too large and complicated and the absence of a clear division between the Department and NHS resulted in duplication of activities. The *BMJ* was pessimistic.

> *Any future historian looking at the National Health Service is likely to see the 1970s as the decade of the decline of the hospital service. Mrs Barbara Castle shattered the political confidence of consultants as effectively as Henry II slighted his opponents' strongholds. Next came the war of attrition in which the hospital unions undermined medical authority, a long-drawn-out and covert process helped by the administrators' appeasing tactics which kept as many incidents hidden as possible. Finally, freedom itself was eroded, not only by the clamour of numerous pressure groups and watchdog associations but also by the intrusion of an ombudsman into areas where he had neither knowledge nor competence.*[311]

Yet clinical care continued to develop apace. Enoch Powell's contrast of the ever-expanding demand and the limitation of resources was more and more relevant. The public recognised that much had been achieved and prized the NHS. However, politicians and the media fuelled public expectations and the sums did not add up. The gap between what was possible and what was provided seemed to be widening all the time.

References

1. Toffler A. *Future shock*. London: Bodley Head, 1970.
2. *Report of the committee on local authority and allied personal social services*. (Chairman: F Seebohm.) Cmnd 3703. London: HMSO, 1968.
3. Twenty years on [leading article]. *BMJ* 1968; 1: 195–6.
4. Department of Health and Social Security. *NHS twentieth anniversary conference*. London: HMSO, 1968.
5. Drain GA. Manning the service. In: *Report of the NHS twentieth anniversary conference*. London: DHSS/HMSO, 1968, 74.
6. Ministry of Supply and Services, Canada. *A new perspective on the health of Canadians*. (Minister M Lalonde.) Ottawa: Ministry of Supply and Services, 1974.
7. Department of Health and Social Security. *Prevention and health: everybody's business*. London: HMSO, 1976.
   Owen D. Chairman's introduction. In: *Prevention and health: everybody's business. Report of a symposium*. London: DHSS, 1976.

8. Morris JN. The case for prevention. In: *Prevention and health: everybody's business: Report of a symposium*. London: DHSS, 1976.
Parliament. *First report from the Expenditure Committee, session 1976/7, Preventive medicine*, vol 1. London: HMSO, 1977.
DHSS/DES. *Prevention and health*. Cmnd 7047. London: HMSO, 1977.

9. Doll R. Prospects for prevention. *BMJ* 1983; 286: 445–53.

10. McKeown T. A historical appraisal of the medical task. In: McLachlan G, McKeown T, editors. *Medical history and medical care*. London: Nuffield Provincial Hospitals Trust, 1971.
McKeown T. *The role of medicine: dream, mirage or nemesis*. London: Nuffield Provincial Hospitals Trust, 1976.

11. Ashton J, Howard S. *The new public health*. Milton Keynes: Open University Press, 1988.

12. Miller H. A contemporary view of historical influences on medicine. In: McLachlan G, McKeown T, editors. *Medical history and medical care*. London: Nuffield Provincial Hospitals Trust. 1971.

13. Tudor Hart J. The inverse care law. *Lancet* 1971; 1: 405–12.

14. Cochrane AL. *Effectiveness and efficiency*. London: Nuffield Provincial Hospitals Trust, 1972.
McLachlan G, editor. *A question of quality?* London: Nuffield Provincial Hospitals Trust, 1976.

15. Irvine D, Donaldson L. Quality and standards in health care. *Proceedings of the Royal Society, Edinburgh* 1993; 101B: 1–30.

16. Brook RH, Appel FA. Quality of care assesment: choosing a method for peer review. *New England Journal of Medicine* 1973; 288: 1323–9.

17. Rutstein DD, Berenberg W, Chalmers TC et al. Measuring the quality of medical care. *New England Journal of Medicine* 1976; 294: 582–8 and [letter from same authors] 1980; 302: 1146.

18. Donabedian A. Evaluating the quality of medical care. *Milbank Memorial Fund Quarterly* 1966; 44, no 3 part 2: 166–202.

19. Towards medical audit [leading article]. *BMJ* 1974; 1: 255–7.

20. McColl I. Observations on the quality of surgical care. In: McLachlan G, editor. *A question of quality?* London: Nuffield Provincial Hospitals Trust, 1976.

21. Priorities in medicine. Statement prepared by the BMA Planning Unit. *BMJ* 1969; 1: 106–8.

22. Challenging clinical judgement [leading article]. *BMJ* 1977; 2: 1498.

23. Finance for the NHS [from the Council]. *BMJ* 1977; 2: 1165.
Falling standards and dangers to patients [from the JCC]. *BMJ* 1977; 2: 1234–5.

24. *Second report from the select committee on the parliamentary commissioner for administration*. London: HMSO, 1971.
Clinical judgement [leading article]. *BMJ* 1971; 3: 389.

25. Health Commissioner starts work [leading article]. *BMJ* 1973; 4: 5.

26. Levens LK, Durham JE. Pop music festivals: some medical aspects. *BMJ* 1971; 1: 218–20.

27. Field service [leading article]. *BMJ* 1971; 3: 494.

28. Williams DG, Truelove SC, Gear MWL et al. Gastroscopy with biopsy and cytological sampling under direct vision. *BMJ* 1968; 1: 535–9.
Cotton B. Fibreoptic endoscopy. *BMJ* 1973; 2: 161–5.

29. Browse N. Spare-part surgery. *BMJ* 1967; 4: 157–61.

30. Intensive cardiac care [leading article]. *BMJ* 1968; 1: 782–3.
Tanser AR, Wetten BG. Multipurpose intensive care unit in a district general hospital. *BMJ* 1973; 3: 227–9.

31. Fearnley GR. Changing face of medical practice. *BMJ* 1970; 1: 46.

32. Lehrman S. Stanford seeks life after Cohen–Boyer patent expires. *Nature* 1993; 363: 574.

33. Whitehead JEM. Bacterial resistance: changing patterns of some common pathogens. *BMJ* 1973; 2: 224–8.

34. Clinical progress: in peptic ulcer. *BMJ* 1969; 4: 99–105.

35. Cimetidine and ulcers [leading article]. *BMJ* 1976; 2: 1275–6.
    Cimetidine for ever (and ever and ever)? [leading article] *BMJ* 1978; 1: 1435–6.
    Price BJ, Dodds MG. The quest for new medicines. In: Morris PGT et al., editors, *Milestones in 150 years of the chemical industry*. London: Royal Society of Chemistry, 1991.

36. Pride NG. Asthma: treatment. *BMJ* 1969; 4: 359–61.

37. Prichard BNC, Gillam PMS. Treatment of hypertension with propranolol. *BMJ* 1969; 1: 7–16.

38. Ellwood P, Cochrane AL, Burr ML et al. A randomized controlled trial of acetyl salicylic acid in the secondary prevention of mortality from myocardial infarction. *BMJ* 1974; 1: 436–40.

39. Huckisson EC, Woolf DL, Balme HW et al. Four new anti-inflammatory drugs: responses and variations. *BMJ* 1976; 1: 1048–9.

40. Oral contraceptives and thromboembolism [leading article]. *BMJ* 1968; 2: 187–8.
    Inman WHW, Vessey MP. Investigation of deaths from pulmonary, coronary and cerebral thrombosis and embolism in woman of child-bearing age. *BMJ* 1968; 2: 193–9.
    Vessey MP, Doll R. Investigation of relation between use of oral contraceptives and thromboembolic disease. *BMJ* 1968; 2: 199–205.

41. Thalidomide's long shadow [leading article]. *BMJ* 1976; 2: 1155–6.

42. Control of amphetamine preparations. *BMJ* 1968; 4: 572–3.
    Restrictions on amphetamines? [leading article] *Lancet* 1971; 1: 332.

43. Barbiturates on the way out [leading article]. *BMJ* 1975; 3: 725–6.

44. Whitfield AGW. Iatrogenic misadventure. *BMJ* 1972; 1: 733–4.

45. Johns MW. Self poisoning with barbiturates in England and Wales during 1959–74. *BMJ* 1977; 1: 1128–30.

46. Headaches and coffee [leading article]. *BMJ* 1977; 2: 284.

47. Hounsfield GN. Computerised transverse axial scanning (tomography). I. Description of the system. *British Journal of Radiology* 1973; 46: 1016–22.
    Computer assisted tomography [leading article]. *BMJ* 1974; 2: 623–4.

48. Isherwood I. Diagnostic radiology. *International Journal of Radiation Biology* 1987; 51: 855–72.

49. Non-invasive investigations of the brain [leading article]. *BMJ* 1975; 2: 295–6.

50. And now the whole body [leading article]. *BMJ* 1975; 2: 300.
    Kreel L, Meire HB. The diagnostic process: a comparison of scanning techniques. *BMJ* 1977; 2: 809–11.

51. Imaging in radiology. *BMJ* 1975; 3: 605–6.

52. Reidy JF. Stopping bleeding by embolisation. *BMJ* 1987; 294: 592–3.
    Allison DJ, Wallace S, Machan LA. Interventional radiology. In: Allison DJ, Granger AG [Editors]. *Diagnostic radiology*, vol 3. Edinburgh: Churchill Livingstone, 1992.
    Taylor W, Rodesch G. Interventional neuroradiology. *BMJ* 1995; 311: 789–92.

53. Howie J. The pattern of communicable diseases in the UK and abroad. *BMJ* 1976; 2: 217–19.

54. Slow virus infections [leading article]. *BMJ* 1973; 1: 129–30.
    Slow virus infections [leading article]. *BMJ* 1974; 2: 343–4.

55. Preventing animal diseases [leading article]. *BMJ* 1976; 1: 355–6.

56. Department of Health and Social Security. *On the state of the public health*. Report of the CMO for 1971. London: HMSO, 1972.

57. Parliament. *Report of the committee of inquiry into the smallpox outbreak in London in 1973*. Cmnd 5626. London: HMSO, 1974.

58. Emond RTD, Evans B, Bowen ETW, Lloyd G. A case of Ebola virus infection. *BMJ* 1977; 2: 541–4.

59. Epidemiology; note compiled by the CDSC for the Public Health Laboratory Services. Legionnaires' disease. First cases identified in England. *BMJ* 1977; 2: 1425.

60. Ministry of Health. *On the state of the public health*. Report of the CMO for 1968. London: HMSO, 1969.

61. King A. Failure to control venereal disease. *BMJ* 1970; 1: 451–7.

62. Total replacement of the hip [leading article]. *BMJ* 1972; 2: 177–8.

63. Total replacement of the knee. *BMJ* 1967; 2: 525.
New knees now [leading article]. *BMJ* 1979; 1: 1586.

64. New knees for old [leading article]. *BMJ* 1972; 2: 363–4.
Freeman MAR. Current state of total joint replacement. *BMJ* 1976; 2: 1301–4.

65. Diet and coronary disease [leading article]. *BMJ* 1972; 3: 539–40.
Prevention of coronary heart disease [leading article]. *BMJ* 1976; 1: 853–4.

66. White NM, Parker WS, Binning RA et al. Mobile coronary care provided by ambulance personnel. *BMJ* 1973; 3: 618–22.

67. Mobilisation after myocardial infarction [leading article]. *BMJ* 1977; 2: 651.

68. Mitral stenosis: the picture changes [leading article]. *BMJ* 1984; 288: 167–8.

69. Oakley CM. Long term complications of valve replacement. *BMJ* 1982; 284: 995–6.

70. Saphenous vein bypass for coronary artery disease [leading article]. *BMJ* 1972; 2: 603–4.

71. Criteria for heart transplants. *BMJ* 1968; 1: 762.

72. Invasion of privacy [leading article]. *BMJ* 1969; 2: 526–7.

73. Hoffenberg R. *Clinical freedom*. Rock Carling Fellowship 1986. London: Nuffield Provincial Hospitals Trust, 1987.

74. Cardiac transplantation today [leading article]. *BMJ* 1971; 4: 377–8.
Cardiac transplantation 1979 [leading article]. *BMJ* 1979; 1: 69–70.
Jamieson SW, Stinson EB, Shumway N. Cardiac transplantation in 150 patients at Stanford University. *BMJ* 1979; 1: 93–5.
Jennett B. *High technology medicine*. Oxford: Oxford University Press, 1986.

75. Calne RY. Organ transplantation: from laboratory to clinic. *BMJ* 1985; 291: 1751–4.

76. Calne RY. Organ transplantation. In: Dawson AM, Compston N, Besser GM, editors. *Recent advances in medicine – 18*. London: Churchill Livingstone, 1981, 253.

77. Calne RY, Williams R. Liver transplantation in man. *BMJ* 1968; 4: 535–42.

78. Present state of liver transplantation [leading article]. *BMJ* 1979; 1: 1441–2.
Liver transplantation comes of age [leading article]. *BMJ* 1981; 283: 87–8.

79. Prentice HG. Bone marrow transplantatin. In: Dawson AM, Compston N, Besser GM, editors. *Recent advances in medicine – 18*. London: Churchill Livingstone, 1981, 235–51.

80. Calne RY, Evans DB, Herbertson BM et al. Survival after renal transplantation in man: an interim report on 54 consecutive transplants. *BMJ* 1968; 2: 404–7.
Facilities for treating terminal renal failure. *BMJ* 1971; 1: 301.

81. PHLS. Hepatitis B in retreat from dialysis units in 1973. *BMJ* 1976; 1: 1579–81.

82. Renal transplantation from cadavers [editorial]. *BMJ* 1972; 3: 251–2.
Nelson SD, Tovey GH. National organ matching and distribution service. *BMJ* 1974; 1: 622–4.

83. Kidneys from living donors [leading article]. *BMJ* 1974; 2: 344–5.

84. Wing AJ. Prospects for the treatment of renal disease. *BMJ* 1977; 2: 881–4.

85. Assessment of kidney transplantation [leading article]. *BMJ* 1974; 1: 588–9.

86. London Health Planning Consortium. *Report of the study group on ophthalmology services*. London: DHSS, 1980.

87. Kelman CD. Phaecoemulsification and aspiration. A new technique of cataract removal. *American Journal of Ophthalmology* 1967; 64: 23–5.

88. Cataract management today [leading article]. *BMJ* 1977; 1: 1616–17
89. New ways with diabetic retinopathy [leading article]. *BMJ* 1972; 3: 781.
90. Galton DAG. In my own time: Hodgkin's disease. *BMJ* 1979; 2: 587–9.
    Calne RY. Organ transplantation. In: Dawson AM, Compston N, Besser GM, editors. *Recent advances in medicine* – 18. London: Churchill Livingstone, 1981, 253–9.
91. Long survival from acute leukaemia in childhood [leading article]. *BMJ* 1975; 1: 111.
92. Informing the public about cancer [leading article]. *BMJ* 1975; 3: 119–20.
93. Ward HWC. Anti-oestrogen therapy for breast cancer: a trial of tamoxifen at two dose levels. *BMJ* 1973; 1: 13–14.
94. Primary cancer of the breast [leading article]. *BMJ* 1970; 1: 579–80.
    Treatment of early carcinoma of breast [leading article]. *BMJ* 1972; 2: 417–18.
95. Screening for cervical cancer [leading article]. *BMJ* 1976; 2: 659–60.
96. Royal College of Physicians of London. *Smoking and health now.* London: RCP, 1971.
    The smoking disease [leading article]. *BMJ* 1971; 1: 61–2.
97. Maternal deaths [leading article]. *BMJ* 1972; 3: 714–15.
98. Home or hospital confinement? [leading article] *BMJ* 1977; 2: 845–6.
99. Lloyd G. The general practitioner and changes in obstetric practice. *BMJ* 1975; 1: 79–82.
100. Department of Health and Social Security. *Domiciliary midwifery and maternity bed needs.* (Chairman: Sir John Peel). London: HMSO, 1970.
101. Allison J. *Delivered at home.* London: Chapman & Hall, 1996.
102. Changing maternity services [leading article]. *BMJ* 1968; 4: 468–9.
103. Beard RW. Medicine in the 1970s: changes in obstetrics. *BMJ* 1977; 2: 251–3.
104. Lewis TLT. The Abortion Act. *BMJ* 1969; 1: 241–2.
105. Munday D, Francome C, Savage W. Twenty one years of legal abortion. *BMJ* 1989; 298: 1231–4.
106. Fowkes FGR, Catford JC, Logan RFL. Abortion and the NHS: the first decade. *BMJ* 1979; 1: 217–19.
107. Lewis TLT. Legal abortion in England and Wales 1968–78. *BMJ* 1980; 1: 295–6.
108. *Report of the committee on the working of the Abortion Act.* (Chair: The Hon Mrs Justice Lane.) London: HMSO, 1974.
    Attitudes to abortion [leading article]. *BMJ* 1974; 2: 69–70.
109. Abortion or contraception? [leading article] *BMJ* 1971; 3: 261–2.
110. The therapeutic pendulum and the special care baby unit [leading article]. *BMJ* 1979; 1: 575.
111. Chiswick M, Davies P, Bate R et al. Regional organisation of neonatal intensive care in the north-west. *BMJ* 1979; 2: 247–50.
    Blake A, Pollitzer MJ, Reynolds EOR. Referral of mothers and infants for intensive care. *BMJ* 1979; 2: 414–16.
112. House of Commons. *Second report from the Social Services Committee: session 1979–80. Perinatal and neonatal mortality.* (Chairman: Mrs Renée Short.) London: HMSO, 1980.
113. Clarke CA. Prevention of Rh-haemolytic disease. *BMJ* 1967; 4: 7–12.
    Tovey LAD. Haemolytic disease of the newborn and its prevention. *BMJ* 1990; 300: 313.
114. Human growth hormone [leading article]. *BMJ* 1971; 2: 236–7.
    Treatment with growth hormone [leading article]. *BMJ* 1971; 3: 547–8.
115. *Fit for the future: report of the committee on the child health services.* (Chairman: SDM Court.) Cmnd 6684. London: HMSO, 1976.
116. Grimley Evans J. Integration of geriatric with general medical services in Newcastle. *Lancet* 1983; 1: 1430–3.
117. O'Brien TD, Joshi DM, Warren EM. No apology for geriatrics. *BMJ* 1973; 4: 277–80.
118. Hodkinson HM, Jeffreys PM. Making hospital geriatrics work. *BMJ* 1972; 4: 536–9.
119. Parnell RW, Cross KW, Wall M. Changing use of hospital beds by the elderly. *BMJ* 1968; 4: 763–5.

120. Geriatric day hospitals. *BMJ* 1971; 1: 130.
Brocklehurst JC. *The geriatric day hospital.* London: King's Fund, 1970.

121. Tooth GC, Brooke EM. Trends in mental hospital population and their effect on future planning. *Lancet* 1961; 1: 710–13.
Eason RJ, Grimes JA. In-patient care of the mentally ill: a statistical study of future provision. *Health Trends* 1976; 8: 13–18.

122. Mental hospital revolution [leading article]. *BMJ* 1971; 4: 249.
Mixture as before [leading article]. *BMJ* 1971; 4: 700.

123. Department of Health and Social Security and Welsh Office, Central Health Services Council. *The functions of the district general hospital.* London: HMSO, 1969.

124. Mayou R. The history of general hospital psychiatry. *British Journal of Psychiatry* 1989; 155: 764–76.

125. Brothwood J. The development of national policy. In: Cawley R, McLachlan G, editors. *Policy for action.* London: Nuffield Provincial Hospitals Trust, 1973.

126. Rollin HR. Treatment by committees. *BMJ* 1973; 1: 363.

127. Marks IM, Connolly J, Hallam RS. Psychiatric nurse as therapist. *BMJ* 1973; 4: 173.

128. Robb B. *Sans everything.* London: Nelson, 1967.

129. Kenneth Robinson on BBC2, *The New Jerusalem*, July 1995.

130. *Findings and recommendations following enquiries into allegations concerning the care of elderly patients in certain hospitals.* Cmnd 3687. London: HMSO, 1968.
Old people in hospital [leading article]. *BMJ* 1968; 3: 135.
Mudslinging or whitewashing. *Nursing Times* 1968; Jul 19: 953.

131. Crossman RHS. A *politician's view of health service planning.* Maurice Bloch lecture. Glasgow: University of Glasgow, 1972.

132. Martin JP. *Hospitals in trouble.* Oxford: Basil Blackwell, 1984.
Parliament. *Report of the committee of inquiry into allegations of ill-treatment of patients and other irregularities at the Ely Hospital, Cardiff.* Cmnd 3975. London: HMSO, 1969.

133. Baker A. The hospital advisory service. In: McLachlan G, editor. *A question of quality?* London: Nuffield Provincial Hospitals Trust, 1976.

134. Department of Health and Social Security. *Annual report for the year 1969.* Cmnd 4462. London: HMSO, 1970.

135. Failure to communicate [leading article]. *Lancet* 1971; 1: 1112.

136. Department of Health. *Annual report for 1972.* Cmnd 5019. London: HMSO, 1972.
Parliament. *Report on Farleigh.* Cmnd 4557. London: HMSO, 1971.

137. Department of Health. *Annual report for 1971.* Cmnd 5019. London: HMSO, 1972.
Parliament. *Report on Whittingham Hospital.* Cmnd 4861. London: HMSO, 1972.

138. Staffing our asylums [leading article]. *BMJ* 1972; 1: 523–4.

139. Extracts from the minutes of the BMA Central Ethical Committee. 11 November 1965.

140. Constraints on consultants [leading article]. *BMJ* 1973; 1: 501–2.

141. Parliament. *Report of the committee of inquiry into Normansfield Hospital.* Cmnd 7357. London: HMSO, 1978.

142. Martin JP. *Hospitals in trouble.* Oxford: Basil Blackwell, 1984.
Reed J. Leadership in the mental health service. Address to the Royal College of Psychiatry, 1994.

143. Yates J. Who's ever heard of form SBH112? *Health and Social Service Journal* 1982; Nov 18: 1378–9.
Yates J. Saved from the scrapheap? *Health and Social Service Journal* 1982; Nov 25: 1410–11.

144. The unpleasant reality. *BMJ* 1971; 2: 415–420.

145. The British National Health Service. *Conversations with Sir George Godber.* JE Fogarty International Center. Washington DC: US Department of Health, Education and Welfare, 1976, 78.

146. Department of Health and Social Security and Welsh Office. *Better services for the mentally handicapped.* Cmnd 4683. London: HMSO, 1971.
     Department of Health and Social Security. *Better services for the mentally ill.* Cmnd 6233. London: HMSO, 1975.
147. Mixture as before [leading article]. *BMJ* 1971; 4: 700.
     Wing JK. Problems of a developing psychiatric service. In: Cawley R, McLachlan G, editors. *Policy for action.* London: Nuffield Provincial Hospitals Trust, 1973.
148. Rootless wanderers [leading article]. *BMJ* 1973; 3: 1–2.
149. Royal College of Psychiatrists, BMA and Society of Medical Officers of Health. *The mental health service after unification.* London: BMA, 1972.
150. Hostels for the mentally ill. *Lancet* 1971; 1: 403–4.
     The need for mental hospitals [editorial]. *Lancet* 1971; 1: 438–9.
151. Department of Health and Social Security. *Better services for the mentally ill.* Cmnd 6233. London: HMSO, 1975.
152. Asylums are still needed [leading article]. *BMJ* 1976; 1: 111–12.
153. Department of Health and Social Security. *Priorities for health and personal social services in England.* London: HMSO, 1976.
154. Secure hospital units [leading article]. *BMJ* 1974; 3: 215.
155. Home Office and Department of Health and Social Security. *Interim report of the committee on mentally abnormal offenders.* Cmnd 5698. London: HMSO, 1974.
156. NHS security beds [leading article]. *BMJ* 1979; 1: 1585–6.
     Stocking B. *Initiative and inertia.* London: Nuffield Provincial Hospitals Trust, 1985.
157. Department of Health and Social Security. *On the state of the public health.* Report of the CMO for 1972. London: HMSO, 1973.
158. Tudor Hart J, Thomas C, Gibbons B et al. Twenty five years of case finding and audit in a socially deprived community. *BMJ* 1991; 302: 1509–13.
159. Holdstock G, Wiseman M, Loehry CA et al. Open access endoscopy service for general practitioners. *BMJ* 1979; 1: 457–9.
160. Irvine D, Jeffreys M. BMA planning unit survey of general practice 1969. *BMJ* 1971; 4: 535–43.
161. Whewell J, Marsh CN, Angus McNay R. Changing patterns of home visiting in the north of England. *BMJ* 1983; 286: 1259–61.
162. Bradshaw-Smith JH. A computer record-keeping system for general practice. *BMJ* 1976; 1: 1395–7.
163. RCGP comes of age [leading article]. *BMJ* 1972; 4: 187–8.
164. Horder JP. Physicians and family doctors: a new relationship. *Journal of the Royal College of Physicians* 1977; 11: 311–22.
165. Reedy BLEC, Philips PR, Newell DJ. Nurses and nursing in primary medical care in England. *BMJ* 1976; 2: 1304–6.
166. Department of Health and Social Security. *On the state of the public health.* Report of the CMO for 1974. London: HMSO, 1975.
167. General practice premises [briefing]. *BMJ* 1977; 2: 1432–3.
168. Parliament. *Royal Commission on medical education 1965–68.* (Chairman: Lord Todd.) Cmnd 3569. London: HMSO, 1968.
169. Conference on vocational training for GPs. *BMJ* 1968; 2: 758–60.
170. Royal College of General Practitioners. *The future general practitioner: learning and teaching.* London: RCGP, 1972.
171. General practice observed [leading article]. *BMJ* 1972; 3: 781–2.
172. Department of Health and Social Security and Welsh Office. Central Health Services Council. *The organisation of group practice.* (Chairman: R Harvard Davies.) London: HMSO, 1971.

173. Department of Health and Social Security. *Report of the joint working party on general medical services 1973.* London: HMSO, 1974.
    A look at practice organisation [leading article]. *BMJ* 1972; 4: 747–8.

174. Debate on the new GP charter [GMS Committee]. *BMJ* 1978; 1: 58–9.

175. *Royal Commission on local authority and allied personal social services.* (Chairman: F Seebohm.) Cmnd 3703. London: HMSO, 1968.

176. The British National Health Service. *Conversations with Sir George Godber.* JE Fogarty International Center. Washington DC: US Department of Health, Education and Welfare, 1976, 95–6.

177. Department of Health and Social Security. *Report of a study of the acute hospital sector.* London: DHSS, 1981.

178. Jennett B. Inappropriate use of intensive care. *BMJ* 1984; 289: 1709–10.

179. National Health Service. *A hospital plan for England and Wales.* Cmnd 1604. London: HMSO, 1962.

180. Smith J. Hospital building in the NHS. Policy II: reduced expectations. *BMJ* 1984; 289: 1368–70.

181. Department of Health and Social Security and Welsh Office. Central Health Services Council. *The functions of the district general hospital.* (Chairman: Sir Desmond Bonham-Carter.) London: HMSO, 1969.

182. Smith J. Hospital building in the NHS. *BMJ* 1984; 289: 1289–300.

183. Inquest on extravagance [leading article]. *BMJ* 1977; 2: 1108.

184. Smith J. Hospital building in the NHS. How hospitals are built. *BMJ* 1984; 289: 1679–81.

185. Smith J. Hospital building in the NHS. Ideas and designs. I: From Greenwich to best buy. *BMJ* 1984; 289: 1437–40.

186. Tomorrow's buildings: two for the price of one. *BMJ* 1968; 2: 113.

187. Wheeler M. How many acute beds do we really need? *BMJ* 1972; 4: 220–23.

188. Smith J. Hospital building in the NHS. Ideas and designs. II: Harness and Nucleus. *BMJ* 1984; 289: 1513–16.

189. Smith J. Hospital building in the NHS. Ideas and designs. II: Harness and Nucleus. *BMJ* 1984; 289: 1513–16.

190. Smith J. Hospital building in the NHS. Policy II: reduced expectations. *BMJ* 1984; 289: 1368–70.

191. The quiet revolution [leading article]. *BMJ* 1972; 4: 688.

192. Yates J. *Hospital beds: a problem for diagnosis and management?* London: Heinemann, 1982.

193. 'Challenges for change' [leading article]. *BMJ* 1971; 4: 443–4.

194. Wickings I, Coles JM, Flux R, Howard L. Review of clinical budgeting and costing experiments. *BMJ* 1983: 286: 575–7.

195. *Accounting for health.* Report of a working group. (Chairman: Brian Abel-Smith.) London: King's Fund, 1973.

196. Bodenham KE, Wellman F. *Foundations for health service management.* London: SCICON/Nuffield Provincial Hospitals Trust, 1972.

197. Computers on the march [leading article]. *BMJ* 1969; 4: 123–4.

198. Committee of Public Accounts. *Sixth Report (1975/6 session).* London: HMSO, 1976.

199. Department of Health and Social Security. Internal report of a multidisciplinary visit to examine US progress in medical computerisation. 1974.

200. Owen D. *In sickness and in health.* London: Quartet Books, 1976.

201. Rivett GC. *The development of the London hospital system, 1823–1982.* London: King's Fund, 1986.

202. Parliament. *Royal Commission on medical education 1965–68.* (Chairman: Lord Todd.) Cmnd 3569. London: HMSO, 1968.
    Royal Commission on medical education. *BMJ* 1968; 2: 109–11.

203. Klein R. The tale of two committees or the perils of prediction. *BMJ* 1976; 1: 25–6.
204. New look in medicine [leading article]. *BMJ* 1968; 2: 65–6.
205. Acheson ED. Medical school at Southampton. *BMJ* 1969; 3: 749–51.
206. Five years hard labour [leading article]. *BMJ* 1972; 3: 429–30.
207. Department of Health and Social Security and Department of Health for Scotland. *The responsibilities of the consultant grade.* (Chairman: Sir George Godber.) London: HMSO, 1969.
208. The surgeon. *BMJ* 1970; 1: 358–9.
     The consultant physician. *BMJ* 1970; 1: 421–3.
     The pathologist. *BMJ* 1970; 1: 492–3.
     The obstetrician. *BMJ* 1970; 1: 559–60.
     Central Committee for Hospital Medical Services. *BMJ* 1970; 1: 39–40.
209. The orthopaedic surgeon. *BMJ* 1970; 1: 748–9.
210. Freeman MAR. Possible future trends of medical staffing in the hospitals of England and Wales. *BMJ* 1969; 4: 612–15.
211. Transfer of registrars [leading article]. *BMJ* 1973; 4: 369–70.
212. Review Body [briefing]. *BMJ* 1977; 1: 1228–9.
213. New contract priced [leading article]. *BMJ* 1975; 3: 726.
214. *The consultant physician: responding to change.* A report of the Royal College of Physicians. London: RCP, 1996.
215. Loss of student nurses. *BMJ* 1968; 4: 596–7.
     Wilson KJW. British nursing and the universities. *Nursing Times* 1968; Feb 9: 175–7.
216. Garland TO. Student nurses. *Nursing Times* 1968; Feb 23: 249–50.
217. Hockey L. *Women in nursing.* Nursing Research Unit, University of Edinburgh. London: Hodder & Stoughton, 1976.
218. Department of Health and Social Security. *Action to improve the nursing situation.* HM(70)35 and HM(70)36. 1970. London: HMSO
219. Carr AJ. When is a nursing auxiliary not a 'nursing' auxiliary? *Nursing Times* 1968; Jun 28: 863–4.
220. Owens P, Glennerster H. *Nursing in conflict.* London: Macmillan, 1990.
221. Thoroughly militant Millie. *Nursing Times* 1968; Oct 4: 135.
222. McCarrick H. Figleaves or farthingales. *Nursing Times* 1968; Jan 12: 61.
223. Ministry of Health and Scottish Home and Health Department. *Report of the committee on senior nursing staff structure.* (Chairman: Brian Salmon.) London: HMSO, 1966.
224. Review body suggested for nurses' pay [parliamentary notes]. *BMJ* 1969; 2: 521–2.
     Exploitation of nurses [leading article]. *BMJ* 1969; 4: 320.
225. *Report of the committee on nursing.* (Chairman: Professor Asa Briggs.) London: HMSO, 1971
226. By Briggs out of Nightingale [leading article]. *Nursing Times* 1972; Nov 9: 1401.
227. Raven Dame Kathleen. Nursing. In: Department of Health and Social Security. *The state of the public health.* Report of the CMO on the state of the public health for 1970. London: HMSO, 1971.
228. McFarlane JK, Castledine G. *A guide to the practice of nursing using the nursing process.* London: Mosby, 1982.
229. Altschul AT. Trends in psychiatric nursing. In: Freeman H, Farndale J, editors. *Trends in the mental health services.* Oxford: Pergamon Press, 1963.
230. Smith JP. *Virginia Henderson: the first ninety years.* Harrow: Scutari Press, 1989.
     Henderson V, Nite G. *Principles and practice of nursing.* New York: Macmillan, 1978.
231. Miss Nightingale has fled. *BMJ* 1975; 2: 267–8.
232. Smith JP. Theories, models, concepts. In: Smith JP. *Virginia Henderson: the first ninety years.* Harrow: Scutari Press, 1989.
233. In the balance – 1980 v Salmon [conference report]. *Nursing Times* 1968; Apr 19: 536.

234. Salmon – a two-pronged trident? [leading article] *BMJ* 1972; 4: 125–6.

235. Department of Health and Social Security and Welsh Office. *Progress report on the implementation of Salmon proposals on nursing administration.* London: HMSO, 1972.

236. Salmon and Cogwheel [leading article]. *BMJ* 1970; 4: 635.
Is Salmon a scapegoat? [leading article] *BMJ* 1974; 4: 550–1.

237. Parliament. *Royal Commission on the NHS.* (Chairman: Sir Alec Merrison.) Cmnd 7615. London: HMSO, 1979, para 12.10.

238. NHS economies [leading article]. *BMJ* 1974; 1: 47.

239. The miners: a special case? [editorial] *Lancet* 1974; 1: 81.

240. Klein R. *The politics of the National Health Service.* London: Longman. 1983, 90 ff.
Office of Health Economics. *The NHS reorganisation.* London: OHE, 1974.

241. Owen D. *A unified health service.* Oxford and London: Pergamon Press, 1968.

242. The planning process [leading article]. *Lancet* 1971; 1: 846–7.
Bispham K, Holland WW, Stringer J. Planning for health. *Hospital* 1971; 67: 82–7.

243. Reid JJA. Milton Keynes. A joint approach to planning. *BMJ* 1969; 1: 628–32.

244. *Royal Commission on medical education 1965–68. Report.* (Chairman: Baron RA Todd.) Cmnd 3569. London: HMSO, 1968.
Royal Commission on local authority and allied personal social services. (Chairman: F Seebohm.) Cmnd 3703. London: HMSO, 1968.

245. Another green paper [leading article]. *BMJ* 1969; 1: 590–1.

246. *Royal Commission on local government in England.* (Chairman: Lord Redcliffe-Maud.) Cmnd 4040. London: HMSO, 1969.

247. Department of Health and Social Security. *NHS: the future structure of the National Health Service.* London: HMSO, 1970.
Accounting for health. Report of a working group. (Chairman: Brian Abel-Smith.) London: King's Fund, 1973.

248. Webster C. Local government and health care: the historical perspective. *BMJ* 1995; 310: 1584–7.

249. Crossman RHS. *A politician's view of health service planning.* Maurice Bloch Lecture. Glasgow: University of Glasgow, 1972.

250. Priorities [leading article]. *BMJ* 1970; 3: 175–6.

251. Department of Health and Social Security. *National Health Service reorganisation consultative document.* London: HMSO, 1971.
The NHS reorganisation – mark III [leading article]. *BMJ* 1971; 2: 420.
The managerial revolution [leading article]. *BMJ* 1971; 2: 481–2.

252. Invitation to consult [leading article]. *Lancet* 1971; 1: 1056.

253. Parliament. *National health service reorganisation: England.* London: HMSO, 1972.

254. Come 1974 [editorial]. *Lancet* 1972; 2: 265–6.

255. Sir George Godber retires [leading article]. *BMJ* 1973; 4: 442.

256. No fanfares for 1 April [leading article]. *BMJ* 1974; 1: 587–8.
Fair shares in the new NHS [editorial]. *Lancet* 1974; 1: 544–5.

257. Broadcasting and the NHS. *Lancet* 1974; 1: 126.

258. Holland WW. Changing names. *Scandinavian Journal of Social Medicine* 1994; 22: 1–6.
Warren MD. *The genesis of the Faculty of Community Medicine.* Canterbury: University of Kent, 1997.

259. Morris JN. Tomorrow's community physician. *Lancet* 1969; 2: 811–16.

260. Department of Health and Social Security. *Report of the working party on medical administrators.* (Chairman: RB Hunter.) London: HMSO, 1972.

261. What is community medicine? [leading article] *BMJ* 1974; 2: 186–7.

262. Rivett GC. *The development of the London hospital system, 1823–1982.* London: King's Fund, 1986.
Holland WW. Health services in London. *BMJ* 1972; 2: 233.

263. Department of Health and Social Security. *Management arrangements for the reorganised NHS*. London: HMSO, 1972.
264. Obituary of Lord Joseph. *The Times* 1994; Dec 12.
265. Cooper P. What will reorganisation do for the patient? *Lancet* 1974; 1: 670–1.
266. In England now. *Lancet* 1974; 1: 61.
267. Nightingale F. *Notes on nursing*. London: Harrison, 1860.
268. Paton A. Reorganisation: the first year. How it strikes a contemporary. *BMJ* 1975; 2: 729–30.
269. Editorial. *Hospitals Year Book for 1974*. London: IHSA, 1974.
270. Ready for sanctions. *BMJ* 1974; 1: 630–1.
    Standards in jeopardy [leading article]. *BMJ* 1974; 2: 292.
271. Labour Party health plans [parliamentary notes]. *BMJ* 1973; 4: 119.
272. Nothing much for the nurses [editorial]. *Lancet* 1974; 1: 971.
    McKie D. The nurses – and others. *Lancet* 1974; 1: 1103.
    Bleak times [editorial]. *Lancet* 1974; 1: 1263.
273. McKie D. Democratising the health service. *Lancet* 1974; 1: 1279.
274. Department of Health and Social Security. *Democracy in the National Health Service: a consultative document*. London: HMSO, 1974.
275. Owen D. *In sickness and in health*. London: Quartet Books, 1976.
276. Grabham AH. A message to senior hospital doctors. *BMJ* 1975; 4: 298–9.
    Debate on the Queen's Speech [parliamentary notes]. *BMJ* 1974; 4: 354.
    Owen D. *In sickness and in health*. London: Quartet Books, 1976.
    Klein R. *The politics of the National Health Service*. London: Longman, 1983.
277. Private practice and the NHS [leading article]. *BMJ* 1974; 3: 71–2.
    Private practice. *BMJ* 1974; 3: 188–9.
    Damaging and needless collision [leading article]. *BMJ* 1974; 4: 305–6.
278. Labour's NHS plans win mixed reviews from health workers. *The Times* 1994; Aug 10.
    Timmins N. *The five giants*. London: HarperCollins, 1995.
279. Crisis working party [leading article]. *BMJ* 1974; 1: 532.
280. Grave threat to the NHS [leading article]. *BMJ* 1975; 1: 4.
    Timmins N. *The five giants*. London: HarperCollins, 1995.
281. Falling standards and sagging morale. *BMJ* 1975; 1: 675–6.
282. Private practice and the NHS – BMA's message to the profession. *BMJ* 1976; 1: 1291.
283. Grabham T. Divided we fall (yet again). *BMJ* 1994; 309: 1100–1.
284. Private practice and NHS: a chronology. *BMJ* 1976; 1: 1290.
285. Health Services Act 1976. *BMJ* 1977; 1: 185.
286. For those who pay. *The Economist* 1981; Jun 20: 64.
287. Doctors' incomes [briefing]. *BMJ* 1978; 1: 734–5.
288. Incomes policy: Annual Representatives Meeting speeches. *BMJ* 1977; 2: 333–5
    One-day industrial action proposed. *BMJ* 1977; 2: 397–400.
    Prime Minister unsympathetic about doctors' pay. *BMJ* 1977; 2: 397, 401.
    BMA evidence to Review Body. *BMJ* 1978; 1: 125.
289. CCHMS. Overwhelming approval for new contract. *BMJ* 1978; 1: 1297.
290. Department of Health and Social Security. *Priorities for health and personal social services in England*. London: HMSO, 1976.
291. A policy of despair [leading article]. *BMJ* 1976; 1: 787–8.
292. Parliament. *Royal Commission on the NHS*. (Chairman: Sir Alec Merrison.) Cmnd 7615. London: HMSO, 1979, para 6.61.
293. Problems of NHS planning [leading article]. *BMJ* 1977; 2: 214.
294. *Priorities in the health and social services: the way forward*. London: HMSO, 1977.
295. The financing of the NHS [leading article]. *BMJ* 1974; 4: 297–300.
296. NHS finances: Royal Colleges' statement. *BMJ* 1974; 4: 237.

297. Conference on cost-effectiveness in the NHS. *BMJ* 1974; 4: 272–9, 327–33, 389–96.
298. New alternatives for the NHS [leading article]. *BMJ* 1974; 4: 247–8.
299. Looking at reorganization [leading article]. *BMJ* 1975; 2: 705–6.
      Diagnosis clear; treatment for debate [leading article]. *BMJ* 1975; 4: 185–6.
300. Falling standards and sagging morale. *BMJ* 1975; 1: 675–6.
301. Evidence to the Royal Commission from the BMA. *BMJ* 1977; 1: 299–334
      Sombre diagnosis: conservative treatment [leading article]. *BMJ* 1977; 1: 794.
      The Royal Commission on the NHS: the background [briefing]. *BMJ* 1979; 2: 288–9.
302. Royal Commission on the NHS. *Management of financial resources in the NHS*. Research Paper no. 2. London: HMSO, 1978. 22–3.
303. Crossman RHS. *A politician's view of health service planning*. Maurice Bloch lecture. Glasgow: University of Glasgow, 1952.
304. Owen D. *In sickness and in health*. London: Quartet Books, 1976.
305. Buxton MJ, Klein RE. Distribution of hospital provision: policy themes and resource variations. *BMJ* 1975; 1: 345–7.
306. Gentle PH, Forsythe MH. Revenue allocation in the reorganised health service. *BMJ* 1975; 3: 382–4.
      Rationing NHS resources [leading article]. *BMJ* 1975; 3: 122.
307. Painful redistribution [leading article]. *BMJ* 1975; 4: 66–7.
      Department of Health and Social Security. *Sharing resources for health in England*. Report of the Resource Allocation Working Party. London: HMSO, 1976.
      RAWP [briefing]. *BMJ* 1977; 1: 460–1.
308. The end of excellence? [leading article] *BMJ* 1976; 2: 779–80.
309. Department of Health and Social Security. *Priorities for health and personal social services in England*. London: HMSO, 1976.
310. Ennals DH. Secretary of State's reply to the *BMJ*. *BMJ* 1976; 2: 735–6.
311. Appeasement 1977 style [leading article]. *BMJ* 1977; 2: 1619.

Chapter 4

1978–1987

Clinical advance and financial crisis

Chapter 4

1978–1987

Clinical advance and financial crisis

Chronology: the fourth decade

Background	Year	NHS events
Winter of discontent	1978	Alma-Ata declaration: Health for All First test-tube baby Medical manpower – the next 20 years
Conservative election victory (1st term) Margaret Thatcher Prime Minister	1979	Royal Commission on the NHS reported *Patients first* (a priorities document) Industrial action
Kennedy's Reith lectures SAS storm Iranian embassy	1980	Black Report on inequalities in health WHO announce eradication of smallpox Flowers and LHPC Reports on London Compulsory vocational training for GPs Körner steering group established on information Magnetic resonance imaging (MRI) Clegg report – nursing pay *Panorama* programme on brain death
Humber Bridge Charles and Diana marry	1981	*Care in action* (a priorities document) Cost improvement programmes Primary health care in inner London (Acheson)
Falklands War Barbican centre opened in London Tylenol deaths from cyanide sabotage	1982	First reported case of AIDS Körner Reports on information Industrial action NHS restructuring; abolition of areas Warnock inquiry Mandatory GP vocational training

Background	Year	NHS events
Conservative election victory (2nd term) Seat belts compulsory Compact discs	1983	NHS management enquiry (Griffiths) UKCC established Mental Health Act Pay review body established for nurses Binder Hamlyn report on cash limits for family practitioner services completed, but not published
Miners' strike British Telecom privatisation Band Aid concert for Ethiopian famine Data Protection Act	1984	Warnock Report Implementation of general management function Limited List
Word processors increasingly common Mikhail Gorbachev takes power	1985	Enthoven's review of NHS FPCs gain independent status WHO (Europe) *Targets for health for all* Stanley Royd salmonellosis outbreak
Chernobyl nuclear disaster British Gas privatisation Stock market 'big bang'	1986	BSE identified in cattle Project 2000 *Primary health care* (Green Paper) Neighbourhood nursing: Cumberlege Report
Conservative election victory (3rd term) Black Wednesday on stock market King's Cross tube station fire	1987	*Promoting better health* (White Paper) *Achieving a balance* (medical manpower) Financial crises Health Education Authority

Thirty years on

The thirtieth anniversary of the NHS in 1978 brought self-congratulatory noises from the Department of Health and Social Security (DHSS).[1] The medical profession took a different view and dissociated itself from celebrations.

> In 1948 the NHS may have been an example to the rest of the world, but 30 years later it measures poorly against many alternative methods of providing health care, and its medical and nursing staff are disillusioned and depressed. Yet only ten years ago the same staff were enthusiastic and optimistic. There is nothing wrong with the concept of the NHS . . . What has gone wrong?[2]

Two experienced commentators, Sir Francis Avery Jones, a clinician, and Professor Rudolf Klein, an academic, thought NHS reorganisation had put too great a distance between administrators and clinicians, breaking up the partnership and trust between those working in and those running the service. Economists, civil servants and administrators with no recent clinical contact had written three major documents of the previous decade, the *Report of the Resource Allocation Working Party*, the *Priorities* document (*Priorities for health and personal social services*), and *The way forward*. The combination of an administration remote from practical realities and abrasive labour relations had made the NHS vulnerable to financial stresses, when all over the world medical services had been struggling to reconcile economic stagnation with a period of remarkable technical and pharmacological innovation. A major cause of low morale was the dangerous delays in decision-making that NHS reorganisation had produced. An environment free from internal dissension and outside interference was needed.

There was increasing scepticism about the idea of an all-embracing welfare state. Not even prosperous economies (and Britain's was not that) could slake medicine's insatiable thirst for resources and skilled staff. 'There has been a lot of wild talk recently about the NHS being in danger of collapse through lack of funds,' said David Ennals, Secretary of State. 'The fact is that current spending in real terms has gone up every year under this government.'[3] Staff were not convinced. The managerial response to low morale seemed to be to demand better information systems. The cult of arithmetic waxed. The workforce was counted, cash was limited, budgets were set and indicators of performance were calculated. Less attention seemed to be paid to the organisation and development of clinical services. The direct access between staff and management enjoyed pre-reorganisation was sadly missed.[4] Large-scale organisations were increasingly seen as out-of-date monuments to the optimistic belief in rational planning that dominated the 1960s and early 1970s. The reorganisations of 1974 and 1982 epitomised the change. In 1974 the emphasis was on the centralisation of planning and the centre could reasonably claim credit for growth. In 1982 the emphasis was on decentralisation of responsibility; governments were well advised to diffuse the blame for bad news.[5]

Overshadowing the health service was the financial pressure after the oil crisis. Spending on the NHS had previously grown faster than the economy. In the earlier decades, staff believed that if they did not get the money they wanted one year, they would do so in the next. The reduction of growth in real terms, from 3–4 per cent in earlier decades to little more than 1 per cent, now meant that some dreams would never come true. The Labour government had tried to constrain NHS costs by income policies and cash limits, and to shift more resources to the care of people who were elderly, mentally ill or mentally handicapped. It proved difficult to change spending patterns at a local level. The search for a new national solution began.

Social change

Public mood had swung away from unquestioning admiration of science and technology. Ian Kennedy's Reith Lectures in 1980 were a watershed in public perception of medicine. Kennedy suggested that there should be a new relationship between doctor and patient, with people taking greater responsibility for their lives, challenging the power that doctors exercised.[6] Nuclear energy was seen as a threat, the car was evil and jet aircraft were noisy and polluting. Films were concerned with doom, disaster and the paranormal. Much could no longer be taken for granted; violence might be random and meaningless. In September 1982 a schoolgirl in Chicago woke with a sore throat, took an analgesic at her father's suggestion and dropped dead on the floor. Six more people died within a day and, by a wild guess, two firemen noticed an association with Tylenol. By the following morning tests had shown that capsules, all from one lot, each contained some 65 mg of potassium cyanide. There was panic and copycat crimes. Johnson & Johnson were devastated by the industrial sabotage. They introduced new tamper-proof packages.[7] Patients and health care were not immune from evil.

The *BMJ* felt that there was a flight from science. Increasingly patients were being treated by alternative medicine – meditation, acupuncture, ginseng and a galaxy of special diets. Much of the appeal of alternative medicine lay in the setting in which it was given. Practitioners gave their patients time, courtesy, individual attention, and they listened. Healing was not necessarily the same as curing, and a compassionate healer who did nothing to arrest the disease process could relieve symptoms.[8] Whatever the merits of alternative medicine, those seeking it were seldom cranks; they were well-informed people seeking a solution to an unresolved long-term problem. They had not lost confidence in conventional medicine. Young doctors showed more interest in the techniques than their seniors.[9] Nevertheless, for medicine there was a down-side. While the media gave massive publicity to the hazards and side effects of orthodox medicine, the proponents of alternative medicine such as chiropractic did not follow the same standards of proof when it came to assessing their favoured alternatives. The British Medical Association (BMA) Board of Science and Education examined how far it was possible to assess the effectiveness of alternative medicine. Although not totally impossible it was nearly so, partly because with some therapies no two patients were treated alike. While alternative medicine comforted many, and some might be 'healed', the responsibility of the medical profession, said the BMA, was to types of care that could be assessed scientifically.[10]

Television was now deeply involved in health service affairs. Since *Your life in their hands* was first screened in 1958, ever more programmes had been produced, sometimes sensitive and deserving acclaim, occasionally a travesty of medicine. Ian McColl,

Professor of Surgery at Guy's, advised the BBC on request, and the requests were frequent. Most doctors now accepted that the public needed information to form a view of important but undecided medical issues, and to co-operate in treatment. However, producers did not seem to feel that a balanced approach necessarily mattered.[11] When Channel 4 was set up the *BMJ* urged the new programme makers to increase public awareness about the influence of life styles on health, the limitations of what medicine could do and the need to debate medical priorities.[12] In October 1980 BBC's *Panorama* broadcast a programme on brain death. It centred on four American patients, said to have been declared brain dead, who subsequently recovered. In none of the cases were the criteria for certifying brain death, set out by the Royal Colleges,[13] satisfied even approximately. The Director General of the BBC, Ian Trethowan, was told in advance that damage would be done to the renal transplant programme and patients would die as a result. The BBC edited out the comments of British doctors whom they interviewed. The Secretary of State told Parliament it had been a disturbing broadcast and his department had received torn-up donor cards from people worried by what they had seen. In a single night *Panorama* virtually destroyed trust between television and the medical profession. Transplantation numbers remained static for two years. While the BBC proposed to return to the topic subsequently, it and the Royal Colleges failed to agree on the arrangements for a reply. The BMA and the Colleges held their own press conference in an attempt to allay public anxiety.[14]

Rudolf Klein said that it was easy to forget one startling fact. Throughout its history the NHS had enjoyed popular support. The NHS was probably the most popular institution in Britain.[15] Its finances might be precarious, its staff on the edge of revolt and its facilities threadbare. Yet whenever pollsters asked the public, four out of five declared themselves satisfied, a figure remarkably steady over the decades. The contrast between public support for the health service and increasing cynicism about other national institutions such as Parliament was striking. However, general satisfaction was combined with specific grievances, such as the organisational routines of hospitals and the personal attitudes of staff. There was also a generational effect. People who grew up in the pre-NHS era had lower expectations. Dissatisfaction was therefore likely to increase.[16]

The NHS and the private sector

The introduction of the NHS had greatly reduced the role of private health care, and what little persisted was essentially in the hospital sector. Following Barbara Castle's forays, however, health care had moved hesitatingly and haphazardly towards a mixed economy. The assumption that health care policy could be equated with what was happening in the NHS was no longer valid.[17] Private care was performing two main functions. First was the elective (non-emergency) treatment of acute self-limiting illness, paid for predominantly by insurance, mostly in the south where the NHS itself was best funded, and undertaken by consultants also working in the NHS. Secondly, there was the long-term care of elderly people in residential and nursing homes, paid for partly by the individuals concerned but increasingly by social security – private provision of publicly financed care. There was, according to Rudolf Klein, no clear explanation for the growth; was it 'overspill', an excess of demand over supply creating

a private sector? Were the attractions of private health care making it tl
pattern when payment was no great problem? Could the blame be laid at La
whose wages policy provided an incentive for employers to offer health insu
whose assault on private practice had lessened the commitment of some con
the NHS? The General Household Survey in 1982 showed that 7 per cent of both sexes
had some form of private insurance. The number of operations performed privately was
also rising, to 17 per cent in the Oxford region in the early 1980s.[18] Previously, private
work was often carried out in the evenings or at weekends. Increasingly it was
undertaken during the normal working day, nearly all by consultants working for the
NHS, which created an awkward relationship seldom found in the commercial world
or the public service, although accepted by Bevan from the beginning.[19]

Private health care was particularly common in some surgical specialties, such as
ophthalmology, heart disease and orthopaedics. Waiting times for an NHS outpatient
appointment in these specialties were usually lengthy, and further time was spent
waiting for admission. The NHS workload of surgeons who also engaged in private
practice varied widely, and the specialties with the longest waiting times were also
those with the highest earnings from private practice. Two-thirds of private work was
undertaken by 20 per cent of NHS consultants, and doubling their income was
comparatively easy in some fields. Many reasons for NHS waiting lists could be quoted.
There might be a shortage of consultant staff, although the local surgeons were
sometimes loath to see an additional colleague appointed. Shortage of money might
mean the curtailment of operating sessions. Often the only way for patients to avoid a
long wait was to pay, when the problem disappeared.

Medical progress

Health promotion and Alma-Ata

Developing countries could not even start to emulate the patterns of health care
common in the West. Increasingly they looked to primary health care, the use of semi-
skilled workers based in the community, and collaboration between different sectors –
agriculture, water, sanitation and education. In September 1978 the World Health
Organization (WHO) and UNICEF called a conference at Alma-Ata in the USSR.
The resulting declaration stressed that primary care was the route to Health for all, this
was achievable by the year 2000 and could be attained at affordable cost.[20] The
definition of health was idealistic: health was a state of complete physical, mental and
social well-being, not simply the absence of disease or infirmity. The Alma-Ata
declaration pointed to unacceptable gross inequality of health status, the right of
people to participate in the planning and implementation of their health care, and the
need to switch expenditure from armaments and conflicts to social and economic
development, of which primary health care was an essential part. Primary health care
was not primary medical care; it was far broader. It was universal, based on homes and
families rather than clinics, provided according to need, culturally acceptable with an
accent on health promotion, housing and education, and involving the community in
the planning process. It demanded redistribution of resources, between and within
nations, radical change in medical priorities and passing power from the professional to

the community. The European countries did not immediately recognise the 'health for all' movement as relevant to them; they saw it largely as a call to the richer countries to provide greater help to the third world.

The 'new' public health, based on these ideas, was in some respects a rediscovery of old traditions. Previously health promotion had been conducted in an earnest and worthy way. Now it became a mass movement with various schools of thought. The nature and style of health promotion broadened from disease prevention by providing information, and programmes with clear objectives and outcomes that could be measured, to community-based intervention based on alliances and pressure for legislative activity. Some argued that, alongside simple intervention such as immunisation, educating public opinion was essential and legislation would then follow. Others felt that legislative action, regulation and changes in taxation could be introduced irrespective of a public demand for them. Most believed that government, health promotion agencies, the media, educational institutions, local authorities, health authorities and industry all had a role to play, together and individually. Money, co-ordinated action, programme planning, research and evaluation were needed. Changes in life style were required, particularly in smoking, diet, exercise, alcohol consumption, sexual activity and behaviour on the roads. Nationwide health promotion strategies were called for.[21] Sometimes it took a disaster to shift public attitudes. Restrictions were increasingly placed on smoking in public places after the disastrous fire at King's Cross underground station in 1987, when 31 people died.

The Americans produced *Health for the year 2000* shortly afterwards. In 1985 the European office of the WHO published *Targets for health for all*. In 1986 the Ottawa charter for health promotion, the outcome of a joint conference organised by the European regional office of WHO and the Canadian Public Health Association, set out a broad conceptual policy for the direction that health promotion and 'the new public health' might take.[22] The WHO launched its 'Healthy Cities' project in 1986, which aimed to build up a strong lobby for public health at local and city level. Early participants in Britain were Glasgow, Liverpool and the London Borough of Camden. The 'Healthy Cities' project reflected the increasing importance of the green movement, and health promotion was becoming increasingly politicised. Should organisations concerned with health promotion continue to restrict themselves to education or be more active in promoting healthy life styles, arguing for changes in society and the social, economic and legislative environment desirable for healthy living? Should health education encompass the socio-economic factors relating to health? In 1977, when David Ennals commissioned the Black Report on inequalities in health, there was a broad consensus that the welfare state was a good thing, even if worryingly expensive. Published three years later, the Report showed that the association of health and socio-economic status was not trivial; the standardised mortality rate was more than twice as high in social class V as in social class I. The association was universal. Wherever there was social disparity there was disparity in health, and disparity was to be found in a wide range of conditions from obesity to accident rates, arthritis and stroke. By the time of publication in 1980 things had changed and the Conservative government issued the report as duplicated copies of the typescript, without a press conference. The report was allowed to mature undisturbed, although it was updated in 1987 by the Health Education Council.[23] By then, government had become unhappy with the HEC. The Health Education Authority (HEA) replaced it in 1987. A body less independent of government, it was given the task of health education on AIDS.

Strong though British primary health care was, it had not been particularly successful in the incorporation of health promotion. Social workers were seldom integrated into primary health care teams. Priority was not always given to people with the greatest need, and patient participation was rare. Alma-Ata challenged professionals to be more 'patient-centred' and government to give higher priority to primary care.[24] Nevertheless, save in public health circles, Alma-Ata was barely mentioned throughout the management changes to come.

The quality and effectiveness of health care

The Maxwell six[25]

- Access to services
- Relevance to need
- Effectiveness
- Equity
- Social acceptability
- Efficiency

International concern with the rising cost of health care, and increasing awareness that not all treatment was helpful, was leading to closer examination of what professionals were doing. Robert Maxwell at the King's Fund proposed six criteria that defined health care quality.[25] Maxwell's 'six' were drawn in part from American sources, for example the work of Donabedian and the US Joint Commission on Hospital Accreditation. They proved influential in Britain because they encompassed population aspects as well as those relating to individuals.

Retrospective review had led to the improvement of some forms of care, for example the confidential enquiry into maternal deaths. In 1979/80 the Association of Anaesthetists undertook a study based on over one million operations in five regions, associated with over 6,000 deaths within six days after surgery. The report by JN Lunn and WW Mushin showed that, although anaesthesia was remarkably safe, mistakes and avoidable deaths did occur.[26] Trainee anaesthetists might be left unsupervised, and monitoring equipment might be inadequate or not used. In 1982 the Association of Surgeons and Anaesthetists set up a confidential enquiry into perioperative deaths (CEPOD) related to operations in the Northern, South Western and North East Thames regions. Immunity from prosecution was obtained from the DHSS and all deaths that occurred within 30 days of any operation were studied. Probably the most vigorous self-appraisal ever undertaken by the profession, it was financed by the King's Fund and the Nuffield Provincial Hospitals Trust. There were about 4,000 deaths among 555,000 operations. Widely differing standards of care were found and several problems were apparent. Surgeons might be operating outside their field of expertise, or there might be inappropriate surgery on patients known to be dying. Consultants were not always involved in serious decisions their trainees were making about patients, and some trainees were going far beyond their competence. The quality of hospital notes might be poor. Few deaths were reviewed as a routine. Sometimes elderly and sick patients were subjected to long operations when already in a poor medical condition.[27] Two regions began a prospective review of neonatal deaths.

Walter Holland, at St Thomas', followed Rutstein in looking at conditions in which it was generally accepted that appropriate and timely intervention could prevent death, and at the variation in mortality in different districts for ten conditions, including cancer of the cervix, tuberculosis, high blood pressure and asthma. Substantial variations that persisted over time were apparent. In one district it was found that the screening process for cancer of the cervix failed to reach high-risk individuals; in another there was failure to follow up abnormalities.[28]

In the USA workers concentrated on the process of health care, variations in practice and the number of procedures undertaken. Clinical practice varied from place to place. John E Wennberg at Dartmouth, New Hampshire, showed that apparently similar groups of people in Vermont and Maine were treated for conditions such as enlargement of the prostate, carotid stenosis and coronary artery disease at widely varying rates, and even when far more operations were done there seemed to be no apparent difference in the outcome for the patient.[29] Similar variations were found in the UK by Klim Macpherson. Wennberg believed that the different rates occurred because different decisions were being made about the need for aggressive treatment. Doctors were not equally well informed, and were motivated by factors other than pure science. Patients were seldom given enough information to make a rational choice and their preferences were not always sought. The more doubt there was about the indications for treatment, the wider the variation from clinician to clinician. Wennberg believed that some procedures were of little worth and that if they were abandoned the increasing cost of health care would lessen, and rationing would probably not be required.

To underpin decisions on priorities, measurements of outcome rather than process were required. Systems to assess health status were developed in the USA and in the UK. Questionnaires, sometimes self-administered, took account of pain, disability and emotional factors. They could be used on a regular basis to track the effect of clinical care. An economic perspective led to the development of the 'quality adjusted life years' (QALYs), which attempted to measure life expectancy and quality of life. Devised by the US Senate Office of Technology Assessment, QALY was popularised in the UK by Williams and Maynard, economists at the University of York.[30] A year of healthy life was taken to be worth one; the value was lower if health was poorer or life expectation shorter. It might be possible to cost treatment that changed the QALY and produce a 'cost/QALY'. For example, advice to give up smoking was cheap to give and, although comparatively few people took it, enough gave up smoking to generate a substantial benefit. Complex surgery might rate poorly, for the costs were high and life expectancy might not change dramatically. These techniques challenged the clinical freedom to carry out any treatment, however costly and slim the possibility of success.[31] QALYs did not solve the problems facing clinicians. How did one value death or the quality of life enjoyed by people with widely disparate conditions – needing hip replacement or renal dialysis or suffering from dementia? At a crude national level QALYs might provide a new insight, but to doctors caring for patients it was like comparing apples and oranges.

Robert Brook, Medical Director of the Rand Corporation in the USA, described the appropriateness of clinical practice as 'the next frontier' in clinical development.[32] The

Rand Corporation had long been interested in whether different patterns of health care organisation, or different forms of treatment, improved patients' health.[33] Everyone agreed that new drugs should be tested before their introduction. A similar consensus developed over surgical procedures. The phrases 'health technology' and 'technology assessment' were coined to cover new types of treatment and their scientific assessment. David Eddy, of Duke University, wrote about the creation of clinical guidelines.[34] Paul Ellwood's consultancy firm, Interstudy, developed questionnaires on patient health status. In his Shattuck Lecture on 'outcomes management' in 1988 he brought these ideas together.[35] Guidelines, outcome management and evidence-based medicine (as the concept later became known in the UK) were much the same idea. As health costs rose, consumer groups became more powerful and widely varying patterns of practice persisted, could management remain on the sidelines? In the USA audit and quality assurance were generally introduced by management and backed by sanctions. When so much was being spent on care that was of doubtful efficacy, management had an incentive to examine the processes and the outcomes. This approach was not to the liking of the British medical profession, which preferred an educational approach. Government chose to keep out of the professional minefield. In 1948 the profession had been given an assurance that it would be free from outside intervention in clinical work, and British doctors were cautious about medical audit with its implied threat to clinical freedom. If the professionals wanted no outside interference, said the *BMJ*, would they ensure that patients had no need to be concerned about the quality of care? Jargon obscured the simple idea that doctors should look at their day-to-day work to see if they could improve it.[36]

Regular clinical review of routine work was not regarded as part of the day-to-day activity of a doctor. Don Berwick, who ran quality assurance at the Harvard Community Health Plan, a health maintenance organisation (HMO)* in Boston, argued that it should be, and that clinicians should be educated and encouraged, not policed.[37] In the USA the Agency for Health Care Policy and Research (AHCPR), an agency within the US Public Health Service, was well financed to develop a wide-ranging programme of evaluative research to produce treatment guidelines and stimulate research on the effectiveness of established treatment. Well-established operations, such as transurethral resection of the prostate, might have a complication and re-operation rate far higher than had been thought. Priority was therefore given to major problems common in health services, which involved many people and cost much money, rather than rare conditions at the forefront of medicine.

The drug treatment of disease

Increasingly, new drugs were produced by techniques that manipulated DNA. The first drug for human use produced by genetic engineering reached the market in 1982, human insulin. New drugs were often designed to act on DNA or intercalate with it. Interferon, initially discovered in 1957 as a protein that interfered with viral infection,

---

*HMOs, a US system of health care delivery first emerging in the second world war but becoming popular in the 1980s, were increasingly seen as an interesting organisational development. They provided an integrated health service for 'members', usually on a local basis and financed through capitation payments. Varying in pattern, they might own their own facilities or contract for them. They aimed to offer quality care more cheaply by restricting the choice of doctors, providing secondary care only in selected hospitals, encouraging clinical guidelines and sometimes placing an accent on primary health care. They competed with each other and with fee-for-service medicine.

was the focus of much research. It proved to be a group of compounds, with several varieties – alpha, beta and gamma – that were produced in small quantities by recombinant methods. Although they caused regression in some types of tumours, their side effects limited the dose that could be given and interferon never was to cancer what penicillin had been to bacterial infection.[38] A new antiviral drug of remarkably low toxicity, acyclovir, was introduced in the early 1980s, active against the herpes simplex virus that causes cold sores and varicella-zoster virus. It was immediately applied to eye infections, cold sores and viral encephalitis.[39] The pharmaceutical industry undertook less work on cardiovascular drugs, where there had previously been great activity, to concentrate on cancer chemotherapy.

Diabetic control was improved by the introduction, in the late 1970s, of self-monitoring of blood glucose. It allowed patients to make spot checks before driving, exercising or sleeping, and enabled patients to build up a profile of their blood glucose concentrations to establish the best insulin dose. Combined with continuous subcutaneous infusion or multiple daily injections almost normal levels of blood glucose could be achieved.[40] In dermatology the outlook for patients with psoriasis was improved by the introduction of ultraviolet light in combination with a skin sensitiser, and for those with acne by retinoid drugs derived from vitamin A.

The relief of pain had long been part of a doctor's role. However, patients' analgesic requirements differed and the dosage had to be adjusted to match individuals. New forms of equipment such as infusion pumps allowed patients to control their own pain and proved to be safe and effective when used for postoperative and obstetric pain, coronary pain and pain in terminal disease. No longer was there a need for patients in discomfort to wait until a doctor or nurse had time to ask the necessary questions and decide if another dose was required.[41]

The popularity of oral contraceptives peaked in the mid-1970s when about 3 million women were using them. Then usage fell a little, as women became aware of clinical studies showing complications and occasional deaths from thrombo-embolism. Lower-dosage pills restored some of their popularity. Increasingly, people turned to sterilisation, in particular vasectomy, as a safe and effective alternative.[42]

In the 1960s the benzodiazepines had replaced barbiturates in the symptomatic treatment of minor neuroses and anxiety states. The public and the profession embraced them with enthusiasm, and consumption continued to increase during the 1970s. Then it was noticed that some patients tended to ask for them for unduly long periods and they were shown unequivocally to produce pharmacological dependence. It was accepted that they were usually unsuitable for anything more than short-term use and their use began to decline.[43]

The establishment of the Committee on Safety of Drugs in 1962 had helped to keep unsafe drugs off the market. Sometimes, however, because adverse reactions were uncommon they became apparent only when drugs were in wide use. Opren (benoxaprofen) was an example. There were concerns about its safety from an early date. The manufacturers, however, promoted it as a useful drug in the rheumatic diseases: it suppressed inflammation and was effective in controlling symptoms when given only once a day. In 1982 eight elderly women were reported to have developed jaundice, and six died. At that time over 500,000 people in Britain had taken it. Other reports of adverse reactions followed and the drug was quickly withdrawn. The BBC programme *Panorama* suggested that the company had made deceptive claims, obscured important information and did not act quickly enough when the drug evidently caused problems; faults in the approval procedure were uncovered.[44] The need for post-marketing surveillance was becoming clear. But this was costly and difficult – how did one establish a control group? For which drugs would it be most important – perhaps those for disorders that were not life-threatening and for which reasonably safe alternatives were already available?[45] Not only might an individual drug have side effects, but there was also a danger of interaction between powerful remedies.[46] Two drugs might alter each other's absorption, metabolism or excretion. Drugs might be additive, and be potentiated by alcohol. So complex were the interactions that wall charts, cardboard slide-rules and computer systems were developed to alert the doctor or pharmacist to dangers.

Radiology and diagnostic imaging

Much of the achievement of high technology radiology was the result of advances in microprocessors and processing power. CT scanning revolutionised investigative practice, improved diagnostic accuracy and rapidly became the method of choice for imaging the brain. A new phenomenon originally identified in 1945, nuclear magnetic resonance, was also applied to imaging. It did not use ionising radiation but strong magnetic fields and radio-frequency pulses. The hydrogen protons of water and fat were imaged, their concentration and settling down behaviour when stimulated determining the contrast of the images. Computing systems, central to the display of images, had already been developed for CT scanners, and magnetic resonance imaging (MRI) could piggy-back on the technology. Workers in Nottingham and Aberdeen, aided by EMI, showed its potential and in 1978 a contract was placed for the development of the first serious clinical instrument. It was installed at the Hammersmith Hospital in 1980, at a time when EMI was seeking to leave the field of imaging. Unlike CT scanning, which was immediately successful, there were many teething problems with MRI and a phase of disillusion in the UK, if not in the USA. The resolution of the images was poor, there were problems with contrast so that some tumours could not be seen, and the speed of the scans was in no way comparable with CT scanning. There were even doubts as to its safety, for example in epilepsy. However, in 1981 the first patient studies began and the first series of patients was published from the Hammersmith in 1982. After that, development was rapid. Many workers contributed to the success of MRI and there is no doubt that the British teams were the first to produce good usable pictures. They established the basic principles, which have changed little over the years. In 1983 there were five clinical MRI systems in the world, of which four were in Britain.[47] The technique was non-invasive, doing patients no harm although the noise and the isolation in the scanner were found by some people to be frightening. Development of MRI depended largely on improvements in the technology of powerful magnets and was incredibly rapid. Scans were soon at least comparable with the quality of CT images. The new system excelled in the head and spine, distinguishing the brain's white and grey matter better than any previous system and improving diagnostic accuracy. Varying the pulse sequence enabled blood vessels to be displayed. MRI was clearly destined to be a further 'quantum leap'.[48] In joint disease it seemed likely to replace arthroscopy and arthrography. There was an expectation that CT scanning would be replaced by MRI, but CT scanning itself improved and provided much faster, simple and reliable images all over the body with less error from movement.

Another new approach, positron emission tomography (PET), used radioactive atoms that emitted positrons. These could be introduced into compounds such as the sugars that are metabolised by the body, and injected into the blood stream. The PET scanner could then measure the gamma rays being emitted, and create an image of the tissues and the chemical changes that were taking place. This technique was rapidly applied to the study of brain disorders.

By 1980 the application of computing to digitised images was changing the face of diagnostic imaging. In 1985 Professor David Allison, at the Hammersmith, knowing of experimental work elsewhere, raised the possibility of creating a filmless department of imaging. He began to interest the DHSS, charitable trusts and manufacturers in the idea.

Infectious disease

Between 1983 and 1985 the DHSS reviewed the Public Health Laboratory Service (PHLS), an essential part of the country's protection against infectious disease. The review recommended that the responsibility for the administration and funding of peripheral laboratories be passed to health authorities. The government consulted on the recommendation and accepted the arguments in favour of the *status quo*, an integrated laboratory and epidemiological network as a protection for the public health.

Emerging diseases

The pattern of infectious diseases was changing. Traditional diseases such as diphtheria, poliomyelitis and smallpox were less common or had even disappeared. Brucellosis, dysentery, measles, tetanus and tuberculosis had also declined.[49] Others were emerging. Pathogens such as *Campylobacter* enteritis, *Cryptosporidium*, enteropathogenic *E. coli* and Norwalk-like viruses (responsible for winter vomiting disease) had new opportunities. Giardiasis producing diarrhoea and the emergence of typhoid strains showing resistance to antibiotics added to problems.[50] A worldwide perspective had to be taken. Even cholera might on occasion reappear in the UK, after an absence of many years. Nowhere was further away than a 36-hour flight, as business and leisure travel increased. Demographic patterns influenced infectious disease, with the rapidly expanding, young urbanising populations in the developing countries, and ageing ones in the West. There were serious public and political concerns about food-borne and water-borne disease. Innovative ways of processing food introduced new hazards. In the past much of a nation's food had been produced locally; now with an open market in food manufacture, faults in one country could lead to outbreaks throughout Europe. An outbreak of *Salmonella* poisoning in 1982 was traced to small chocolate bars imported from Italy. After a public warning, 3 million bars were recalled and the outbreak quickly came to an end. Another *Salmonella* outbreak in 1987 was traced to small sticks of German salami, popular with children.[51] The cost of such outbreaks was considerable. Poultry were becoming an increasingly common food, but when reared intensively are readily infected with *Salmonella*. In the mid-1980s a particular strain, *Salmonella enteritidis* phage type 4, acquired the ability to pass through the hen to infect the developing egg. Human infections with this strain increased rapidly.

In the early 1980s cross-infection in hospital by methicillin-resistant *Staphylococcus aureus* (MRSA) was becoming increasingly serious. New strains were resistant to many antibiotics and revealed an increased ability to spread within and between hospitals. An outbreak of food poisoning at Stanley Royd Hospital in 1986 showed the poor quality of hygiene in hospital kitchens, a widespread problem often known to management but sometimes not remedied. New kitchens were expensive, there were other priorities, and the NHS could claim Crown immunity, to the irritation of environmental health inspectors. The Stanley Royd outbreak also revealed management failures and the lack of anyone clearly identified as responsible for the handling of outbreaks.[52]

In the mid-1980s the incidence of meningococcal septicaemia rose in the UK, and, although fluctuating year on year, remained high. Chiefly affecting the young, it had a fatality rate around 10 per cent; there were 1,000–2,000 cases annually, of whom 150–200 might die. People no longer expected a healthy child to sicken and die rapidly from an infection and cases attracted national publicity. Legionnaires' disease became better recognised, the infecting organism was identified, and cases were now regularly reported. One outbreak in 1981, occurring among men working on a power station site, was traced to a water system in a cooling tower. A larger one in April 1985 occurred at the Stafford District General Hospital. It affected 101 patients, 28 of them dying. Again it was related to the design of the air-conditioning system and shortcomings in maintenance of water-spray cooling systems. In November 1986 a new disease in cattle, bovine spongiform encephalopathy (BSE), was identified by the Central Veterinary Laboratory. The condition was thought to have been transferred through the consumption of sheep offal infected by the disease scrapie, and epidemiological studies were begun.

Malaria

In the 1970s mosquitoes were becoming insecticide-resistant and the number of cases of malaria rose substantially. In 1980 there were 1,670 with nine deaths, a number that fell slightly with improving mosquito control in the Indian sub-continent. Usually the disease appeared in travellers within a month of their return to the UK but occasionally the delay would be much longer. The tropical disease hospitals in Liverpool and London saw few cases in the early stages, and GPs, faced by patients with an unexplained fever, were sometimes slow to make the diagnosis, particularly if malarial prophylaxis had been taken.[53]

Sexually transmitted disease and AIDS

The incidence of gonorrhoea fell steadily during the decade and more than halved to about 20,000. The decline in syphilis was even steeper, from more than 2,500 to fewer than 200 cases. Cases of herpes infection, *Chlamydia* and genital warts increased in numbers and, until the arrival of AIDS, were the major cause for public concern. Genital herpes, in particular, received enormous attention. Emotive articles in the press suggested that herpes sounded the death knell of an individual's sex-life.[54] The increasing size of the problem, the incurable and untreatable nature of the condition, neonatal infection and the association with carcinoma of the cervix were all discussed.

The disease of the decade was acquired immune deficiency syndrome (AIDS).[55] It was unusual in that from the outset it was highly politicised, and the policies adopted owed much to the activities of those initially most affected, the gay community, and its network of friendships. An uncommon form of pneumonia in five homosexual men was reported in the USA by the Center for Communicable Disease in 1981, rapidly followed by reports of cases in the UK and an increase a previously rare form of cancer, Kaposi's sarcoma. As experience was gained, it was appreciated that infection was seldom diagnosed immediately. Many had poor immunological resistance to infection before developing severe illness. AIDS was part of a spectrum of disease and produced a wide range of symptoms, including neurological defects. The gay community in the UK learned rapidly from the experience of friends in the USA, organised itself to obtain government help, spread the message about reducing the number of partners and safer sexual behaviour, and developed systems to support sufferers. In 1982 the Communicable Disease Surveillance Centre (CDSC) began to monitor death certificates. From 1983 other groups were recognised as at risk, recipients of blood transfusion, intravenous drug abusers, people with haemophilia and children of infected parents. The cause was not known until 1983 when the human immunodeficiency virus (HIV) was identified in France. BBC TV's *Horizon* ran a programme about the problem in New York, but in contrast to the size of the epidemic in the USA there were only 15 cases in the UK in 1983 and 74 in 1984. Lacking effective treatment, public health measures were the only way the spread of infection might be reduced. There was no evidence that the virus was spread by casual or social contact but the abandonment of promiscuity, homosexuality and drug abuse, while it might have been effective, hardly seemed a practical control measure.[56] The safety of blood and blood products then became an issue; there was initial scepticism about the extent of the risk. People with haemophilia, who had gained greatly from treatment with Factor VIII, were afraid not only of AIDS but also that withdrawal of treatment could take them back to the early 1960s when the disease produced joint damage and pain, and greatly shortened life expectancy. From 1984 heat treatment was available in the USA to eliminate transmission from blood products, and from October 1985 transfusion centres routinely screened donors for HIV.

A test for the virus was developed in 1984. It was discovered that there was a high incidence of AIDS in Central Africa, and people who had been sick in the late 1970s could be identified retrospectively as suffering from AIDS.[57] The test was used to screen blood donations in 1985. Not until the middle of that year were heat-treated, and therefore safer, blood products available in the UK. In the early 1980s large quantities of cheap heroin arrived in Edinburgh. The police arrested drug dealers and confiscated needles; the result was that drug abusers simply shared needles and by 1985 half the drug abusers tested were HIV-positive. An outbreak among adolescents at a school near Edinburgh, in 1984/5, showed how appalling were the consequences for these young patients and the babies a few of them bore. AIDS was a catalyst in refocusing drug abuse policy on minimising harm. The homosexual and the drug-using cultures were different, although some links were formed.

AIDS involved just about every contentious aspect of human behaviour and, given the voyeurism of the press, individuals would be regarded as unimportant compared with the story that they could tell. Merely by contracting the disease, against their own wishes, the early cases might become public figures about whom the press felt people had a right to know. Anxiety, even hysteria, came to surround the disease as sufferers lost their jobs, were evicted from housing, children of patients were expelled from their schools and one with AIDS as a result of treatment for haemophilia became the centre of media attention.[58] The press covered cases in which doctors with AIDS continued at work and guidelines were developed by the medical profession and the DHSS to safeguard the public. An injunction was granted against the *News of the World*, banning it from revealing the identity of two doctors undergoing treatment.[59] Much that was learnt about the disease was the result of open discussion with gay men. When these were patients it was essential to maintain confidentiality, even though it meant narrowing the number of professionals with knowledge of individual cases. Confidentiality might be seen not only as a personal issue but also as a public health one: only by safeguarding confidentiality could essential information on the epidemiology of AIDS be obtained.

Between 1981 and 1985 policy was developed from below; little was known about the disease and most of that came from the gay press, gay men and patients. Key people in the UK saw what was happening, listened to the clinical specialties involved and the gay community, developed their ideas and relayed them through Donald Acheson, the Chief Medical Officer (CMO), to ministers. By 1984 Acheson was referring to AIDS as the greatest challenge in communicable disease for many decades. He established and oversaw an Expert Advisory Group on AIDS, ensuring that government had the best advice available and could move rapidly when prepared to do so. By 1985/6 AIDS was generally recognised as a major issue and collective fear developed. Nobody knew what would happen next, and what clinical or ethical problems would emerge. Some believed that AIDS should be treated like other grave communicable diseases, for example by notification, a view opposed on the ground that this would prevent sufferers from seeking help. Gay pressure groups painted AIDS as a human rights issue. While doctors regularly tested patients for other diseases without fully discussing all possibilities, patient consent here was necessary and pre-test counselling became almost mandatory. Informing sexual partners of infectivity was left to the patient. Prevalence studies were more difficult to mount, for epidemiology could not be conducted without considering the human rights aspects. Important questions were also raised for the blood transfusion service.

The number of British patients, who mostly lived in London, was in no way comparable to those in the USA or Africa. Over the first few years the number of cases doubled every year, but by the end of the decade the numbers were rising less fast. By September 1986 more than 500 cases had been reported in Britain compared with 30,000 in the USA, where many were children, the offspring of drug-abusing parents. The pattern of the epidemic, not just in the UK but worldwide, was determined in part by sexual habits, the numbers of contacts and the prevalence of the disease among particular groups. In Africa it crossed rapidly into the heterosexual population; in the UK it did so to a far smaller extent. A liberal and scientific consensus developed. One early result was a government publicity campaign on 'safe sex' in explicit terms that Whitehall would not normally contemplate. In 1986/7 the government, strongly urged by Donald Acheson, Kenneth Stowe (the Permanent Secretary) and Robert Armstrong (Cabinet Secretary), launched a major, sustained and consistent publicity campaign, the TV adverts using a tombstone theme and subsequently an iceberg. The message concentrated on minimising risk, the danger of ignorance and the fact that AIDS could affect everyone. The gay community was not directly targeted, in part to avoid increasing public feeling that AIDS was a 'gay plague' and in part because this was the advice of the advertising agency. The following year the campaign concentrated on the danger to drug users of sharing syringes, and was deliberately designed to shock. One poster showed a body in a plastic bag; another a blood-stained syringe. TV companies were encouraged to make their own documentaries, widening the information available to the public and dealing with questions such as needle exchange schemes for drug abusers. The *Daily Telegraph* asked its readers for indulgence, saying that by its nature the epidemic could only be discussed and countered in terms more explicit than normal.[60] HRH The Princess of Wales took a personal interest in people who were dying, and by her presence reduced the fears that normal social contact was risky. The first major breakthrough in treatment came in 1986 when Wellcome introduced zidovudine (Retrovir). Trials showed that it prolonged life, stopped weight loss and increased the well-being of patients with AIDS. Drug treatment, like the disease itself, became a political issue.

Genetic medicine

Knowledge in clinical genetics exploded as it began to be possible to map the fine structure of human genes. How genes controlled the structure of a single protein could be defined in molecular terms. Monoclonal antibodies, discovered in the mid-1970s, were specific for one antigen and produced from a pure single-cell culture line. They revolutionised the study of immunity and opened the possibility of many new diagnostic tests, and perhaps even therapy. Genetic disorders accounted for a substantial fraction of human disease. Single-gene defects such as Huntington's chorea, cystic fibrosis, phenylketonuria, thalassaemia and haemophilia were rare, but severe in their effects. Chromosomal abnormalities such as Down's syndrome were more common, and there were even more conditions such as spina bifida and congenital heart disease with a genetic component. The first practical application was prenatal diagnosis for congenital and genetic defects. Methods included amniocentesis, visual examination of the fetus by endoscopy, measurement of alpha-fetoprotein in maternal serum and removal of placental tissue for examination (chorionic villus sampling).[61] Diagnosis as early as 8–10 weeks made it possible to consider the likely outcome when deciding whether a pregnancy should be terminated. There was a tantalising possibility of replacing a missing enzyme or a defective gene, for example by destroying the bone marrow by irradiation and replacing it with health marrow from a compatible relative.[62]

Gastroenterology

Technology and pharmacy drove developments in gastroenterology. Videochip cameras and better endoscopes made the assessment of stomach, duodenal and colonic disease swifter and easier for both doctor and patient. The diagnosis and treatment of benign tumours of the colon that might later become malignant could be carried out on a day-patient basis. There was resistance to the new technology among the older specialists, and sizeable endoscopic units were slower to develop in the UK than in other countries.

From the 1950s onwards, the number of deaths and admissions for gastric and duodenal ulcers had been falling. Changes were taking place in what had been one of the commonest causes of admission to hospital. It was hard to know whether diagnosis was now more accurate, or treatment was better or that changing social conditions and diet were responsible. H₂-antagonists relieved symptoms so effectively that some people were given them as a 'diagnostic test': if a patient's condition improved after taking an H₂-antagonist, it was considered unnecessary for radiology or endoscopy to be done.[63] Then workers in Perth suggested that peptic ulcer was an infectious disease caused by bacteria. In 1983 Robin Warren (a pathologist) and Barry Marshall (a physician), reported the presence of bacteria in the stomach wall and suggested that there might be a causal link between them and peptic ulcer, gastric cancer and other bowel diseases. When the theory was presented at a conference in Brussels it was regarded as preposterous, and Marshall gained a dubious notoriety. Scientists set out to prove him wrong, and could not do so. Believing that antibiotics might be capable of curing the infection, Marshall swallowed the bacteria himself, rapidly becoming sick.[64]

Inflammatory bowel disease, such as chronic Crohn's disease, could be treated by artificial nutrition, which varied from supplementing the normal diet to intravenous feeding. Improving the general state of health substantially was possible.[65]

Surgical workload and surgical progress

Top 20 general surgical and urological operations in 1978	
Appendicectomy	70,480
Inguinal hernia	63,650
Benign breast disease	37,100
Cholecystectomy	36,310
All anal operations	35,160
Cystoscopy	30,620
Varicose veins	26,880
Malignant skin lesion	25,330
Circumcision	21,920
Prostatectomy	17,420
Mastectomy	14,670
Orchidopexy	11,580
Colectomy	10,570
Rectal carcinoma	9,240
Thyroidectomy	8,500
Vagotomy	8,280
Hydrocele	5,730
Femoral hernia	5,720
Amputation of leg	4,250
Defunctioning colostomy	3,940

Source: BMJ 1983[66]

Since the start of the NHS, surgery had been dividing into ever-more sub-specialties but in district hospitals 'general surgery' remained central to surgical activity. The most commonly performed operations were long established. Roughly 645,000 general surgical operations were performed during 1978 in England and Wales.[66] Sometimes, sub-specialty expertise offered patients a substantially better outcome. For example, one man in ten would eventually need an operation for benign enlargement of the prostate: 80 per cent were done by general surgeons, who used a major abdominal procedure. There was an alternative method, resection by an instrument passed up the urethra, virtually painless, needing half the time in hospital and with a mortality less than half that of the open techniques. The argument for the specialist urological surgeon was now clear although it was no procedure for the occasional operator. The technique was not easy to learn.[67]

Day surgery had long been encouraged, to provide good care at less cost. Day wards did not need to be staffed at night and at week-ends; shorter time in hospital meant that more patients could be treated if theatres were available; and there were savings on 'hotel facilities'. The practicability was established and many hospitals had excellent day surgical units. Yet even in hospitals committed to day surgery, the full potential was seldom exploited. In Southampton it was estimated that, excepting cardiac and neurological surgery, every surgical specialty needed day surgical facilities and the proportion of cases suitable lay between 40 and 80 per cent.[68]

Minimal access surgery

Minimal access surgery (often called colloquially 'keyhole surgery') was a major advance applicable to many more common procedures. It was the result of spectacular developments in the technology of operating instruments.[69] Operative mortality and morbidity had been accepted as unavoidable for 150 years, but in the early 1980s it became apparent that less invasive methods could reduce complications and risks. Reducing surgical trauma reduced morbidity and mortality. Urologists had been in the forefront with transurethral prostatic resection. Between 1979 and 1983 there were radical changes in the treatment of kidney stones. First came their removal through tiny 1 cm tracks from the body surface, percutaneous nephrolithotomy.[70] Secondly there was shockwave extracorporeal lithotripsy, a completely new form of treatment, developed by the German engineering firm Dornier. Focused shock waves, either sound or electrical, were passed through soft tissue to break the kidney stone into fragments. These then passed along the natural urinary passages to the outside. The first UK machine was installed in London at the Devonshire Hospital lithotripter centre in 1984. In the first 50 patients treated the average length of stay was 3.7 days; within two years 1000 patients had been treated, with a high success rate.[71]

Endoscopic appendicectomy had been performed in Germany and medical gastroscopists and colonoscopists were rapidly relieving surgeons of the responsibility of treating ulcers and polyps. Vascular surgeons were doing endoscopic endarterectomies, using lasers to treat coronary artery obstruction. Orthopaedic surgeons were undertaking intra-articular operations of the knee and many other joints. Neurosurgeons, ENT surgeons and gynaecologists were also adopting the new techniques. With the development of CT scanning and ultrasound, endoscopes could be passed into the bile ducts making it possible to deal with stones even in elderly and medically sick people. Some types of obstructive jaundice could also be treated.[72] By 1987 it seemed possible to predict the elegant and less traumatic way in which surgery would develop in the next decade.[73] How dangerous the techniques might be in unskilled hands was not, at first, appreciated.

Microsurgery made possible the successful reattachment of an amputated limb. At first the scope of the technique was limited by the size of the blood vessels that could be joined reliably. Developments in optical technology, micro-instruments, sutures and needles made it possible for surgeons to join small vessels and nerves, so that finger reattachment became practicable. Internal fixation would stabilise bones, joints might need repair, vessels and nerves were joined, and adequate skin cover obtained. Such surgery was extremely demanding of time and practicable only in specialised units. The younger the patient, the better the result.[74]

Orthopaedics and trauma

Although fitting seat belts to new cars was compulsory, people were under no obligation to use them. The evidence that they would save lives was not seriously challenged, but there were questions of civil liberty. From 1983, however, wearing belts became compulsory. All regions now had major accident plans. The absence of such plans in the early years of the health service had been responsible for confusion at the time of the Harrow and Lewisham crashes. Regular training exercises paid dividends at Manchester airport in 1985: a fire occurred on a Boeing 737 at take-off, with 137 on board. Toxic smoke inhalation was a major problem; 52 died on the aircraft, 85 escaped. Wythenshawe Hospital was rapidly warned, the consultant in charge was there within minutes, triage began and as patients arrived they were handled systematically.[75]

The growing need for surgical treatment of fractured neck of the femur and for arthritis of the hip, reaching almost epidemic proportions, overwhelmed the wards allocated to the trauma service and spilled into the beds needed for general surgery and elective orthopaedics. By 1987 total hip replacements for arthritis numbered 35,000 per year, and total knee replacements 10,000. In the 1950s there had been a substantial failure rate with total hip replacement, but by the 1970s it was recognised as one of the outstanding surgical successes of the previous 20 years.[76] Charnley's own cases, now counted in their thousands, showed that less than 1 per cent a year needed revision because of loosening. Acrylic cement used to glue the new head into the shaft of the femur was well accepted. Operative complications – infection and pulmonary embolism – were few and patients were discharged in days rather than weeks. Initially most patients were elderly and many had to wait; the first operation lasted them all their lives. Increasingly, however, younger and more energetic patients were operated on, and the revision rate within five years might be as high as 25 per cent. A repeat operation took twice as long and patients required longer in bed afterwards. More than 100 different patterns of hip replacement became available, varying widely in price. Despite the Charnley hip being one of the first to be used in large numbers, after 25 years none of the newer ones had been shown to match it.[77] However, the high molecular weight polyethylene used for the Charnley cups wore slowly, at about 0.1 mm per year. Revision operations were necessary and the cement used to fix the components was suspected.[78] Other methods of fixation were tried, for example porous metal components into which bone cells might grow, and prostheses coated with bone salts before implantation. Then the possibility was suggested that the particles produced by polyethylene wear might be to blame. Some of McKee's original metal-on-metal hip replacements were still giving good service and showing little signs of wear after many years. Surgeons began to experiment again with metal components, now excellently engineered.

Arthroscopy became increasingly important in orthopaedics, particularly for disorders of the knee. Minimal access surgery was applied to the treatment of lumbar disc prolapse. Using an operating microscope the disc could be dealt with through a 2 cm incision, and the surgeon could see inside the disc space. The operation could be completed in half an hour, and most patients could leave hospital within two or three days instead of two or three weeks.[79]

Cardiology and cardiac surgery

Cardiac ultrasound began to be a useful clinical tool in the mid-1970s. The development in the 1980s of cross-sectional echocardiography revolutionised non-invasive diagnosis, particularly for congenital heart disease, and was capable of supplanting cardiac catheterisation for most purposes apart from coronary angiography. It produced good anatomical images, and the introduction of pulsed, continuous wave and colour Doppler flow mapping improved the knowledge of heart function, providing an accurate method of looking at spatial information about the velocity of blood flow within the heart and major vessels.[80]

It was clear that much heart disease could be traced to smoking. Advances in therapy were merely repairing the effects of a preventable disease. The Royal College of Physicians (RCP) refined estimates of the relationship of diseases to smoking. It was causing 100,000 deaths annually, and a third of deaths in middle age.[81] Cigarette smoking fell steadily in the 1970s and early 1980s, especially in men; for example, the proportion of adults who smoked fell from 51 per cent of men and 41 per cent of women in 1974 to 36 and 32 per cent, respectively, in 1984. Thereafter, though, the decline became slower, particularly in younger adults. A clear relationship existed between price and consumption. Passive smoking also appeared to increase the risk of disease. Pressure for the introduction of widespread screening of blood cholesterol levels was, however, resisted by the Standing Medical Advisory Committee. Evidence did not exist to justify the cost of screening in terms of any benefits that might result.

The treatment of angina improved with the introduction of beta-blocking drugs (e.g. propranolol), which increased the capacity for pain-free exercise. An important new class of drugs, calcium-channel-blocking agents, were introduced for angina. They reduced the strength of cardiac muscle contraction and the work the heart did, altering heart rhythm and dilating blood vessels. They were soon used for abnormal cardiac rhythms and for high blood pressure as well.[82]

The ability to resuscitate people suddenly and severely ill, if the breathing and the circulation could be maintained, was behind the creation of a new discipline, the paramedics.[83] There was no evidence that doctors were any better at preserving life in these emergencies. The US city of Seattle was early to develop the idea, basing paramedics with the fire service because, by its nature, a fire service has few routine commitments and fire stations are well distributed. The Seattle paramedics received 1,600 hours' training and could administer any of the 40 drugs they carried. Because roughly a third of the community was also trained in cardiopulmonary resuscitation, the efficacy of the whole service was increased. In Belfast and Brighton coronary ambulances had been introduced and it was shown that, with advanced life support skills, many victims of heart attacks could be saved.[84] Hampton, in Nottingham, was critical of services such as that in Belfast where doctors were used. Paradoxically, if a GP had been called, an accurate diagnosis would be made but at the cost of delay; Hampton thought a mobile unit was unnecessary because the most dangerous moments had passed and the risk of death before being admitted to hospital was lessening. Progress could not be made on the basis of a few special vehicles. A complete restructuring of the ambulance service was needed, separating the 10 per cent of real emergency work from the 90 per cent that was no more life-saving than a good taxi or bus service. He believed that all emergency vehicles should carry a defibrillator and be staffed by crews who had received advanced training.[85] Some ambulance services, such as those in Nottingham, introduced this for some of their crews, and in 1984 a national training programme for paramedics was adopted on government recommendation.[86] Groups of GPs also banded together, equipped themselves properly and worked with the ambulance service to provide early help and resuscitation as well as to road accident victims (BASICS, the British Association of Immediate Care Schemes).

In the early 1960s, pilot schemes had shown that fibrinolytics (clot-busters), though expensive, could be used safely in patients with acute myocardial infarction. A succession of clinical trials suggested that mortality could be reduced by their early administration, immediately on admission to hospital or, if there was going to be a delay, by the GP.[87] Oral anticoagulants, popular in the 1950s, had suffered a decline in use because of problems with serious episodes of bleeding and doubts about their efficacy. As methods of controlling the dosage improved, anticoagulants were reassessed to see if there was any benefit from their long-term administration. Exercise regimens were also introduced as people recovered from a heart attack.[88]

Effective drugs had been available for the treatment of high blood pressure since the 1950s. Because of their uncomfortable side effects, though, only the most severe cases were treated until better drugs became available. By the 1970s they were. There was debate about the advantages in treating people with mild hypertension, the level at which treatment should begin and the extent to which pressure should be reduced. With 175 general practices, the MRC set up an experiment to examine the benefits of treating mild hypertension. It was found there was a reduction in the incidence of strokes, with a much smaller effect on heart attacks, from both diuretics and beta-blockers.[89] In the ten years since the trial began there had been further advance in the treatment of raised blood pressure, but the question of whether to treat had now been settled.

If a patient had chronic angina from coronary artery disease that did not respond to drug treatment, and the vessels were anatomically suitable, there was no longer any dispute that surgery, coronary artery bypass, was effective. Coronary artery bypass grafting secured a firm foothold. In 1978 the units in the Thames regions did 1,720 operations and the numbers steadily rose, making exceptionally heavy demands on nursing staff. With elective operation there was a better than 95 per cent chance of surviving the operation, with a 90 per cent chance of improvement; 70–80 per cent of patients were cured of their symptoms.[90] There was also a place, not clearly determined, for emergency surgery after acute myocardial infarction.[91] The number of coronary artery bypass grafts undertaken nationally rose from 2,297 in 1977 to 6,008 five years later.[92] Some units operated on few patients and a joint report of the Royal Colleges of Physicians and Surgeons recommended that, to maintain expertise, centres investigating and operating on the heart should have at least three cardiac surgeons each performing not fewer than 200 open heart operations a year.[93] Coronary artery bypass grafting was the topic of the first consensus conference in the UK, organised by the King's Fund. Economic studies of the procedure were presented. Alan Williams, from York, costed the operations and calculated the cost per quality adjusted life year (QALY) gained. Particularly in severe cases of angina it compared well with valve replacement for aortic stenosis and the insertion of pacemakers for heart block. It was probably less cost-effective than hip replacement.[94] In 1976 another surgical technique was developed, percutaneous transluminal ('balloon') angioplasty. The coronary arteries were displayed radiologically (coronary arteriogram) and a fine double-lumen balloon catheter was passed down the coronary artery to the site of the obstruction. The balloon was then inflated and the atheroma squashed, increasing the blood flow to the heart.[95] Lasers and high-speed revolving cutters could also be introduced into the coronary arteries. These were, however, difficult techniques best performed by the experienced. They might result in acute and abrupt occlusion, when emergency open-heart surgery would be needed, at increased risk. In one patient in three there was re-stenosis, which meant that angioplasty might need to be repeated.

Organ transplantation

In 1978 Roy Calne confirmed the potency of cyclosporin A (discovered in 1976 at the Sandoz laboratories) in the prevention of rejection. When it became commercially available in 1983 this largely replaced azathioprine.[96] With the improved drug regimens, patients previously with no hope could expect a good chance of restoration to near normality. The capacity to perform transplants was limited both by the size of the units and by the limited supply of organs.

Heart transplants, suspended after the early failures, were resumed in 1979 at Papworth by Terence English, and in 1980 at Harefield by Magdi Yacoub, a brilliant and charismatic surgeon who worked round the clock and inspired great devotion among his staff. Both centres were equipped for advanced cardiac surgery, with sufficient medical, nursing and technical personnel, and support in pathology, immunology and microbiology. There were three reasons for resumption. First the Stanford Medical Center had produced convincing evidence that heart transplantation could be an effective form of treatment. Secondly there had been a change in the public's attitude towards the concept of brain death, which made heart donation easier. Thirdly there had been improvements in preserving hearts between removal and re-implantation.[97] Private donations of £300,000 to both units met part of the costs. An evaluation undertaken in 1984 showed a three-year survival of 54 per cent and a cost of about £12,700 for the operation and six months' postoperative care. The programme expanded, further units being established in Newcastle and Manchester with the ultimate aim of providing this service on a regional rather than a national basis. By 1987 combined heart–lung transplantation, first reported in 1982, was also moving out of the experimental phase.

Liver transplantation, though a great ordeal for a patient who was already sick and often grossly malnourished, became steadily more effective. About 70 per cent of children and 60 per cent of adults would be alive a year later. Bone marrow transplantation was also increasingly successful, though costly. The centres treating patients were few and almost entirely in London. Sir Douglas Black, the DHSS's chief scientist, recommended further centres in the regions to make the service more widely available. About three patients a week were having a transplant in 1982, most commonly for leukaemia, both myeloid and acute lymphoblastic in type. A few people with aplastic anaemia, or with a liability to infection from a deficient immune system, were also treated.[98]

Renal replacement therapy

Transplant operations performed in NHS hospitals in the UK 1979–1988

Year	Kidney	Heart	Heart/lung	Liver
1979	842	3		
1980	988	25		
1981	905	24		
1982	1,033	36		21
1983	1,144	53	1	20
1984	1,443	116	10	51
1985	1,366	137	37	88
1986	1,493	176	51	127
1987	1,485	243	72	172
1988	1,575	274	101	241
total	12,244	1,087	272	720

Source: DHSS. On the state of the public health 1988.[99]

By the early 1980s young patients with renal failure and no complicating factors had an excellent outlook. Most felt well and many were in full-time employment. The pattern of treatment that emerged under the restraints of the NHS was strikingly different from that in other countries. The UK strategy was to restrain hospital dialysis, using home dialysis followed by renal transplantation, the single most important therapy in numerical terms from 1977.[100] Implicit was the attitude that people incapable of performing independent dialysis or who were unlikely to receive a transplant would be rejected by the units, which were hard-pressed and short of money. Physicians in the selection and referral chain sensed this, so high-risk patients such as elderly people and those with diabetes tended to be excluded. Increasingly, though, it was shown that people in these categories too had reasonable survival rates.[101] As the transplantation programmes grew, so did public concern about the criteria for determining death. A conference of the medical Royal Colleges had agreed these, but the *Panorama* programme on 'black Monday' led to a fall for several months in the number of kidneys available from patients diagnosed as 'brain dead'.[102]

There were other ethical problems. How could the state keep a controlling hand on public expenditure when it concerned matters of health? How could the profession safeguard the interests of individual patients when, because of restricted resources, one patient's transplant was another's hip replacement? Antony Wing showed that, although the acceptance rate for treatment up to the age of 45 was much the same in Britain, France, Germany and Italy, far fewer older patients were accepted in Britain than in the other countries. There was no rule about acceptance; that was just what happened when doctors had to ration scarce resources. A research study revealed that British and American nephrologists had different standards of acceptance for treatment. Were British doctors acting against the interests of patients by rejecting many because of shortage of resources? Or were US doctors motivated in part by financial factors, accepting more patients for treatment and choosing the most profitable form of care – regular dialysis in a hospital unit?[103] In 1980 the use of continuous ambulatory peritoneal dialysis (CAPD) became widespread. Instead of removing the patient's blood and passing it through an external dialysis system, dialysis fluid was introduced into the patient's abdominal cavity, and then removed along with the waste products that, in health, would have been removed by the kidneys. No large capital expenditure was required for this form of therapy, and there was a rapid and radical change in the upper age-limit of patients accepted for treatment.[104] By the end of the decade twice as many patients were on CAPD than haemodialysis at home. Units increasingly ran an integrated approach, offering patients CAPD, haemodialysis or renal transplantation, as appropriate. In December 1984 the government announced, for the first time, a target for the number of new acceptances annually: 40 new patients per million per year. Britain remained far behind Europe where, because of the existence of insurance-based health care, targets were never required.

Neurology and neurosurgery

Advances in biochemistry, immunology and molecular genetics improved the recognition and understanding of neurological diseases. An increasing number were found to have an autoimmune basis, for example myasthenia gravis, peripheral neuropathies and multiple sclerosis. This suggested possible methods of treatment, by corticosteroids, high dosage human immunoglobulin, plasma exchange and immunosuppressive drugs. CT and MRI scans provided new ways of looking at the nervous system. Not only could tissues could be seen in outline, but their function could be studied as well. During relapses, MRI could demonstrate the appearance and disappearance of plaques of multiple sclerosis, making it possible to monitor treatment. Positron emission tomography (PET) made it possible to determine the rate of oxygen utilisation, and the distribution and utilisation of chemicals responsible for the transmission of nerve impulses. Patients with paralysis from a stroke could be scanned with little discomfort to determine whether haemorrhage or thrombosis was responsible.

ENT surgery

Surgery was now firmly established for deafness when the problem was sound conduction by the bones of the middle ear. There was, however, still no medical or surgical help when the problem was damage to the sound receptors of the inner ear, sensori-neural deafness. Although there had been dramatic advance in the design of hearing aids, many people suffered from such profound deafness that even the most powerful aids provided little help. However, there were nearly always some surviving fibres in the auditory nerve, even when the sensory hair cells in the inner ear that respond mechanically to sound had disappeared. It now became possible to stimulate the surviving nerve fibres by tiny electrodes inserted into the cochlea. In 1978 a report was submitted to the DHSS on a visit to the only centres world-wide where cochlear implants were being done, Los Angeles, San Francisco and Stanford.[105] Roughly 20 implants had been done by that time. The implants became increasingly sophisticated and reliable, and the results were so promising that the technique was extended from adults to children.

Major developments were made in surgery for cancer of the head and neck. Improvements in plastic surgery and reconstruction meant that ENT surgeons could now confidently expect their colleagues to retrieve the situation they had created by wide excision of the tumour.

Ophthalmology

Corneal grafting had become a well-established operation and many more could have been undertaken had the supply of corneas been plentiful. However, the doctors most often present when patients died suddenly were the house officers, and few thought of eye donations, even when they asked for permission to use kidneys. For a while it was thought unnecessary to tissue type recipients, but this eventually was found to be desirable. In 1986 corneal banks were opened in Bristol and Manchester.

Cancer

Patients with cancer often required long-term care both in and out of hospital. The hospice movement and the Macmillan and the Marie Curie nurses increasingly linked with nurses in the hospital. Oncology wards might now organise regular meetings with them, community nursing staff and the social services, to discuss the care of individual patients. The best way to treat even common cancers was not always clear. Tom Stamey, a respected American urologist, wrote in 1982 'I do not know how to treat carcinoma of the prostate.' The cancer was common and most men would survive a normal life span without treatment. Some forms of treatment such as radical surgery, though popular, were disabling. A major study showed that hormone treatment, also common, had at best doubtful benefits. The scientific foundation of treatment was insecure.[106] In the rarer cancers there was increasing recognition of the importance of specialised centres; the greater the experience, the better the results. Staff were aware of the complications that could occur, and how to manage them. Testicular cancer, bone cancer in children and neuroblastoma were examples of such conditions.[107]

New cytotoxic drugs for chemotherapy continued to be developed, often related to an existing one, in an attempt to increase efficacy and reduce toxicity. Cisplatin, which acted on DNA strands, was useful though toxic, and analogues were sought.[108] By the late 1970s cancer of the testis could be treated, with an 85 per cent cure rate, as CT scanning allowed accurate 'staging'. Two main types of leukaemia were the result of disorderly growth of the precursors of two sorts of white blood cell. Survival after treatment of acute lymphoblastic leukaemia in childhood improved substantially; the outlook for myelogenous leukaemia was more discouraging.

Radiotherapy departments were now switching from radioactive cobalt machines because radio-cobalt slowly decayed, lengthening treatment times and needing replacement every three to four years at considerable cost. Linear accelerators, introduced in the 1950s, were now usually specified when new equipment was required. They might cost more but they could treat more patients.

Breast cancer claimed 12,000 lives a year but there had been few advances in its treatment. There were two approaches to early diagnosis: screening by mammography of an asymptomatic 'at-risk' population; and careful instruction of women in breast self-examination, which was highly publicised. Clinical trials in both were established.[109]

Early results apparently showed a substantial reduction in mortality in screened populations and there was strong public demand for screening. An advisory group, chaired by Sir Patrick Forrest, was established in 1985 and its proposals were accepted. In 1987 a national breast screening service was announced; within two years there would be a screening service in each region calling women between 50 and 64 years of age every three years.[110] Attention was also focused on the early diagnosis of cervical cancer. From 1983 it was decided to replace the national cervical cytology recall system, which dealt largely with women who had already been tested, with a locally based scheme. This would call all women for a smear every five years from the age of 35, and would be based on computerised family practitioner committee records.

During the decade lung cancer decreased for men but increased for women; men were giving up smoking to a greater extent than women. The risk of passive smoking was also now clear; breathing other people's tobacco smoke was a cause of lung cancer.[111]

Obstetrics and gynaecology

The ninth report of the confidential enquiry, covering 1976–1978, showed a continuing fall in maternal deaths, and attention increasingly centred on the infant. Abortion was no longer among the leading causes of death but the other causes were the same – pulmonary embolism, inexpert anaesthesia, high blood pressure and haemorrhage, ectopic pregnancy and sepsis. Nearly all births now took place in hospital. High technology was seen as imperative in the interest of mothers and their babies. Ultrasound was now used regularly around the 18th week to scan the fetus for anomalies. With the reduction in home deliveries, emergency flying squad calls were few, and it was hard to provide a good service staffed by professionals accustomed to working under domiciliary conditions. The management of problems became conservative, the accent being on transfer to hospital.[112] District midwives were restricted to antenatal care and postnatal visiting, unless they were allowed to manage their own cases in hospital, alongside hospital midwives. Increasingly, GPs were content just to supervise the antenatal and postnatal periods.[113]

In the 1980s a consumer movement developed, challenging the policy of encouraging all women to give birth in hospital, and the loss of small and sometimes isolated maternity units serving rural communities. Clear differences were emerging between the professional groups, the midwives believing that an increased number of births could take place at home to the satisfaction of mothers, and with safety. Technology and intervention were seen as dehumanising a natural process, childbirth. The movement drew support from the National Childbirth Trust, the feminist movements and some politicians. It criticised the crowding of clinics and the lack of sensitivity sometimes found.[114] Labour was increasingly induced, sometimes in as many as 40 per cent of cases. There was wider use of epidural anaesthesia and the caesarean section rate was steadily increasing throughout the developed world. Was it impossible to achieve better results without ever more obstetric operations?[115] A Labour MP made parliamentary history by nursing her baby in the House of Commons. Emotions ran high; midwives argued that greater attention should be paid to the wishes and needs of the mother, and home delivery should be available. Obstetricians stressed the risks of giving birth at home, far from the emergency facilities of a consultant unit.

Fertility treatment

From 1968 Patrick Steptoe in Oldham and Robert Edwards in Cambridge made a series of technical advances that raised the possibility of successful in-vitro fertilisation in the human. These included the demonstration that spermatozoa would penetrate oocytes in vitro, that oocytes could be recovered by laparoscopy, and that embryos could be grown to the early stage of development in vitro. The procedure was refined and the birth of the first 'test-tube' baby took place in Steptoe's unit in Oldham General Hospital in 1978. They then turned to simplification of the procedure, but never by taking dangerous short cuts. Everything was checked and rechecked, within good scientific rules and the strictest possible ethical guidelines.[116] Major alterations to the procedure, including the stimulation of ovulation by drugs, increased the success rate and the technique clearly had an important place in the treatment of human infertility. There was debate about ethics, the major concern of opponents being the manipulation and survival of human embryos, the concept of a human person and when a human could be said to exist.[117]

In 1982 the government decided to set up a wide-ranging inquiry to consider the social, ethical and legal aspects of techniques that modified human fertilisation and embryology. The chair was taken by Mary Warnock, who was asked *not* to recommend the establishment of any new organisation or authority. The membership encompassed several professions with a concern in such matters, and a variety of religious traditions. The members had to look in many directions of medicine and science, and take into account public opinion that varied from the elegantly argued and cogent to the frankly ludicrous. The report, published in 1984, was timely and thoughtful but did not provide a detailed prescription of what should be done. Although there were three notes of dissent on surrogacy and research on human embryos, it was agreed that *some* principles should rule, and *some* barriers should not to be crossed. The logic of their discussions led to the need for a controlling body, and the report proposed a new statutory authority to regulate fertility services, monitor developments and vet individual research projects. It proposed that spare human embryos could be frozen and stored for repeated attempts, with an upper limit for storage. There was a division within the committee on the issue of experimentation with spare embryos.[118]

In an attempt to reduce the number of unwanted pregnancies, family planning services tried to reach the younger age groups. DHSS guidance, that parental consent could in some circumstances be dispensed with for someone under 16 years of age, was challenged in the courts by Victoria Gillick. The presiding Law Lord considered that the only practicable course was to entrust the doctor with a discretion to act in accordance with his view of what was best in the interests of the young woman who was the patient.[119]

As the use of cervical cytology increased, more disease was identified and more women required follow-up to exclude carcinoma of the cervix. Colposcopy, magnifying the cervix, made it easier to spot lesions, and to remove them accurately and more safely.[120] The new imaging systems found gynaecological applications. Laparoscopic surgery was at first used mainly for diagnostic purposes. However, it was increasingly applied to the treatment of endometriosis, and the polycystic ovary syndrome.

Hormone replacement therapy was introduced for women past the menopause. A reduction in fractures associated with osteoporosis and in coronary artery disease were claimed as its benefits, though there was a possibility of an increase in cancer of the breast in the longer term. It rapidly became a popular form of treatment.

Paediatrics

The fight to allow parental access to children in hospital had been won. Some facilities were provided for resident parents, but although modern wards had mother and child cubicles, the increasing numbers of parents meant that many would be sleeping on mattresses on the floor beside the child, and in the morning the ward kitchen might be full of parents trying to prepare their child's favourite breakfast.[121] The pattern of childhood disease continued to change; accidents were by far the most frequent cause of death after the first year, and sudden unexpected death was increasingly seen as a problem.

Developments in the medical specialties had a ripple effect on paediatrics. Increasingly, paediatrics divided into sub-specialty areas mainly in regional referral centres: paediatric oncology, cardiology, immunology, genetics and haematology.[122] The care of mothers and their babies was the subject of a Social Services Committee report in 1980. Concerned at the perinatal death rate, further concentration on large maternity units and the phasing out of home delivery were key recommendations. The safety of mother and baby was paramount, and the labour ward should be regarded an intensive care area with better access to neonatal intensive care.[123] Neonatal units could now use cerebral ultrasonography to image the brain, and the accent changed from respiratory distress to the prevention and treatment of intracranial damage from delivery.

The 1980s saw two major improvements in the treatment of thalassaemia. Initially although one could determine by amniocentesis whether a baby was likely to be affected, this was only possible late on. The introduction of chorionic villus sampling made it possible to determine whether a fetus was affected as early as the 11th week of pregnancy, allowing the mother to be offered selective abortion. Second, in 1983/4 Guido Lucarelli in Pesaro, who had many patients with the disease, started a large programme of bone marrow transplantation, with substantial success. Bone marrow transplantation was also offered selectively to patients with severe sickle-cell disease, but the initial results were not so good, because patients were ill and supportive care of the highest order was required. Prophylactic treatment with penicillin by mouth was found to reduce the death rate substantially, and became routine treatment.[124]

Human growth hormone (HGH) had been used since 1959 to treat children with short stature who were deficient in it. There were probably 100–150 children each year for whom it was indicated and those started early on treatment made good progress. Supplies were short, because HGH was derived from pituitaries specially removed during postmortem examinations.[125] Some children died of a recurrence of the condition that had led to their treatment in the first place, for example intracranial tumours, but it was reported that three patients in their 20s and 30s had died of an illness resembling Creutzfeldt–Jakob disease (CJD), a progressive and fatal brain disease probably caused by a 'slow' virus present in the preparation. Human growth hormone was withdrawn from use in 1985. Subsequently a further 14 died from CJD, out of a total of about 1,900 receiving HGH between 1959 and 1985.[126] Within about a year, synthetic hormone was available.

Geriatrics

Increasingly the patients in general hospital wards were in the upper age groups. Nearly all district hospitals now had a geriatric service and a day hospital. Of growing concern was the problem of psychiatric problems among the elderly. Between half a million and a million old people suffered from some degree of dementia, the commonest mental disorder in that age group. Special psychiatric services for elderly people were developed, and about half the geriatric services had such a facility. The Health Advisory Service made psychogeriatric services a special interest, and published a report, *The rising tide*, bringing together hard-won experience on how such services could be established.[127]

Demand for hospital beds and the need to reduce the length of stay emphasised the importance of rehabilitation and support from social services. It became common for geriatricians to undertake domiciliary consultations to reduce inappropriate admission; perhaps one in three admissions could be avoided in this way. With the development of rapid assessment, effective treatment and early discharge came questioning of how far the NHS should be responsible for long-term provision when medical conditions had been treated as far as possible. Enlightened local authorities had developed personalised systems of care management. Some NHS chronic wards still existed, and the quantity of local authority residential accommodation was falling. There were, however, huge increases in the provision of private residential and nursing homes that more than matched the reduction of NHS and local authority places. Commercial companies entered the field, in retirement areas the homes competed with each other and the quality of care available improved. Day care had increased, but domiciliary services such as home helps and health visitor visits to elderly people barely kept pace with the growing elderly population. Joint finance, a system by which part of a health authority's allocation was earmarked for co-operative ventures with the local authorities, might be used to encourage the transfer of patients from the NHS to local authority provision. The NHS was ceasing to see, as part of its function, the provision of accommodation for frail elderly people.

Mental illness

The development of mental health services was now government's top health priority. The number of beds continued to fall. This should have freed resources for community-based services, but regions and districts sometimes subverted the money for acute care. However, in the early 1980s there was increasing government pressure on regions to dispose of under-used or surplus property. The old mental hospitals stood on large sites. Financial incentives, and a booming property market, made them marketable. Local authorities were seeking land for housing, and property developers were seeking sites for hypermarkets and shopping centres. It became easier to find the capital to fund new and local facilities.

Fewer beds in the old asylums, coupled with the adoption of open wards, increased the problem of managing patients with dangerous, violent or criminal propensities. It remained difficult to transfer patients from secure hospitals into NHS provision when the time was right. Unions such as COHSE often took a tough line, and the courts sometimes found that no place could be found for a criminal who seemed more in need of health care than of a prison regime. Lack of staffed beds, the patient's characteristics and refusal by staff to admit a person were the reasons commonly advanced.[128] Difficulties remained in the establishment of the regional secure units, the longer term solution to the problem. Even the regions keen to do so experienced opposition from staff, unions and local communities. Some regions, not having a forensic psychiatrist available to help, moved ahead but experienced problems with the siting and design of the buildings, which needed to form links with the probation service, prisons and the district psychiatric services. Some regions established a single unit; others a more complicated pattern of central and satellite provision.[129]

Twenty-five years after the Mental Health Act 1959, which marked a new era of enlightened mental health provision, a further liberalising Act increased the rights of patients on 28-day observation orders to appeal, discouraging the use of emergency orders. The Mental Health Act 1983 restored formal legal safeguards to a central place in mental health legislation.[130] It was successful in its aims; more patients appealed, but the number discharged by tribunals remained small.[131] Few of the large mental illness hospitals had as yet closed; comprehensive community health and mental handicap services were uncommon. Few community mental health teams existed. Those attempting to orchestrate change faced obstacles from lack of money and lack of will to make the change come about, from professionals and the community itself.[132] There was increasing criticism of the mental health services. Had such de-institutionalisation as there had been, gone too far? The House of Commons instituted a large-scale inquiry on the community care of the mentally ill and handicapped, reporting that the pace of removal of facilities for mental illness had far outrun their replacement in the community, and that it had been blithely over-optimistic to believe that modern treatment would lead to a massive reduction in the need for long-term care.[133]

General practice and primary health care

The changing tasks of general practice

Following the GPs' charter in 1965 the standard of general practice continued to improve, but patchily. Reorganisation in 1974 and restructuring in 1982 changed little for the GPs, although family practitioner committees (FPCs) were promised greater independence. Bosanquet in York showed that practices differed in their philosophy, young doctors investing highly in their practices often at a cost to their personal income, while older ones were often being more 'traditional' in their approach though showing a greater willingness to undertake home visiting.[134] According to the 1981 morbidity survey, GPs were doing more preventive work. More time was being spent on psychiatric disorder, ten patients consulting GPs for every one attending a psychiatric outpatient department. Depression, potential suicide and marital problems were brought to the surgery. An increasing number of doctors not only undertook counselling themselves but also employed counsellors to whom they could refer their patients, raising questions about its effectiveness and the training and qualifications of the counsellors themselves.[135] Increasing access to sophisticated investigations began to move general medicine out of the hospital; not every difficult case had to be referred. Increasingly it was the norm for GPs to use peak flow meters, to assess the severity of asthma, and electrocardiographs. Well-woman clinics and blood pressure screening were no longer the sign of a fanatic. The literature of general practice not only expanded rapidly but also yielded several classics. A significant change in the vision of general practice was taking place.

One potential of the British primary health care system was little explored; GPs were too busy dealing with illness to worry much about health.[136] Health promotion was the subject of a series of special reports published by the Royal College of General Practitioners (RCGP).[137] Godfrey Fowler, an academic GP in Oxford, looked at the evidence for its effectiveness. Cardiovascular disease, heart disease and stroke seemed to be promising, although GPs would have to become more active in education on change in life style.[138] Elaine Fullard, who had a background in health visiting and worked with Fowler, believed that many GPs would practise preventive medicine if they were helped to organise their practices to make it easier. A 'facilitator' was provided, a trained nurse experienced in general practice to help interested practices to set up programmes that included advice on smoking and diet, and checking blood pressure.[139] The idea became popular; increasingly, health promotion became a task for practice nurses and health visitors.

The management of chronic diseases – diabetes, high blood pressure and asthma – were also areas in which nurses could work effectively. Julian Tudor Hart thought the GPs' charter (1965) had provided immense opportunities.[140] GPs were capable of much of the care of chronic disease currently carried out by the hospitals, if they would only do so. They were in the right place and had the right training. GPs should anticipate future deterioration in health and act early with the weapons now to hand. With office and nursing staff available, a good records system, and making use of direct access to the hospital laboratory, imaging departments and postgraduate centre, GPs could undertake much of the work currently done in medical outpatients. Tudor Hart saw the way ahead as the salaried community GP, accountable to patients and local democratic organisations in which patients participated. He influenced the policies of both the Labour Party and the Medical Practitioners' Union (MPU). His view on the transfer of care from the hospital to the community was accepted by the Conservatives for financial and professional reasons. Some forward-looking local medical committees (LMCs) such as the Northumberland LMC also developed visionary proposals for future general practice.[141]

The number of GPs and the proportion working in groups continued to rise. List sizes fell and teamwork was more common although the nurse's role in the surgery was mainly limited to treatment room work. General practice now attracted more than its share of the best medical students. Vocational training that had existed on a voluntary basis for many years became mandatory in 1982. Young doctors entered a three-year course, one year in general practice with a suitably experienced trainer and two years in appropriate hospital posts. Training schemes were popular because they provided stability in one area, good posts and a passport to general practice if that later seemed the best option. Premises also improved; about 17 per cent of doctors now worked in health centres, fewer, though, in the conurbations. However, health centre running costs were escalating and maintenance was poor. In 1979 the DHSS told regions that they no longer had to allocate specific amounts of capital to health centre building and the programme slowed. GPs were encouraged to improve their facilities by their own endeavours, often with money from the General Practice Finance Corporation. The Royal Commission on the NHS in 1979 saw the advantages of health centres but thought it would be foolish and unprofitable to try to force general practice into one mould.[142] Some matters continued to rankle, in particular the commitment to issue certificates for short-term sickness. Year after year the issue was raised at GP conferences until at length, in 1982, self-certification for the first seven days of incapacity was introduced.

Inner city primary health care

It had long been believed that general practice in inner cities, and London in particular, was not as good as elsewhere. The central problem was its varying quality. London's difficulties were found elsewhere, but London seemed unique in its failure to resolve them. Its size encouraged isolation, lack of awareness of good practice elsewhere and a feeling of impotence. The mobile young, a multitude of ethnic groups, an intelligentsia, users of drugs and alcohol – they all congregated in London. With a few exceptions, academic general practice developed late in London. London had fewer innovative GPs, and incentives offered nationally were not readily taken up. Modern premises were largely non-existent. Compared with the rest of the country, team working was poor with fewer practice nurses and attachment schemes. Without reasonable accommodation it was hard to develop teams. The combination of high land values, unsavoury locations and planning problems made it almost impossible to find a good site in the right place. Recruiting young doctors of high quality was a perennial problem. The archetypal inner city doctor faced a high morbidity and a dismissive attitude on the part of the nearby teaching hospitals, which were slow to provide access to laboratory and X-ray facilities, and were not greatly interested in vocational training and postgraduate centres. Inner city GPs were thought to send too many people to hospital, if only because that was what the patients expected and demanded. They were, on average, older. More were single-handed and had trained overseas. Fewer had purpose-built premises and staff attached to the practice. Young doctors seldom wished to enter such practices, and when single-handed vacancies became available energetic young GPs often lost to those with experience rather than expertise. 'Better' doctors went to greener pastures. Because they were further from specialised services, they themselves provided a wider range of care and the task of developing a good practice was intrinsically easier. Such practices seldom had problems recruiting the colleagues they wanted. David Morrell, based at St Thomas', toured his inner city area to see what might be done. Most of the premises were totally inadequate and many GPs saw no way of improving matters. There was an impression that the doctors had been lulled into accepting second best, and were not inclined to rise up and demand something better.[143] One innovation in London was a new community care centre in Lambeth, opened by HRH The Princess of Wales, to help those who needed medical and nursing help of a non-specialist nature, but who for lack of suitable home circumstances might end in a specialist unit not designed for their needs.[144]

If the domination of London's health services by acute hospital-based medicine was to be reduced, primary health care had to play its part, as it did elsewhere. A study group was therefore established by the London Health Planning Consortium as part of its work on rationalising London's health services. The choice of chairman was difficult, for most eminent people would appear biased to one or another of the interest groups whose co-operation was essential. The choice fell on Donald Acheson, then Dean of the Southampton Medical School. Acheson's report provided a clear analysis of the problems.[145] It made 115 recommendations, some directed towards government. Kenneth Clarke said they were a maze and a minefield, difficult to handle.[146] Among those providing evidence was Professor Brian Jarman, of St Mary's Hospital Medical School. He had developed a measure of the social characteristics that in London GPs' opinion most increased their workload or the pressure on their services. His index used eight census variables and correlated with other indices that attempted to measure deprivation or the levels of illness in different areas. The index was subsequently accepted by the BMA and used by the DHSS as part of the payment system, to compensate inner city doctors for the additional work in deprived areas.[147]

Indicators of deprivation in the Jarman index[148]

- Pensioners living alone
- Children under five
- One-parent families
- Unskilled breadwinners
- Unemployed
- Over-crowding
- Mobile population
- Ethnic minorities

Computers in general practice

By the early 1980s a few GPs were beginning to install practice-based microcomputers, smaller, more powerful, faster and cheaper though lacking in tailor-made software.[148] There were perhaps 100 practices using computers seriously although the market was unstable and firms tended to merge or go bankrupt. 1982 was Information Technology year. After discussion with the profession, practices were invited to volunteer for a trial, 'Micros for GPs', in which 150 practices would be helped to buy microcomputers with £2.5 million from the Department of Industry. Almost 2,000 applied, the practices were selected and an evaluation was set in hand. The main benefits seemed to lie in the ability to aggregate and analyse information, so that practices could assess what they were doing, plan, review their activities and introduce change. From then on computerisation proceeded apace. By 1985 more commercial systems designed for GPs were available and these were also assessed.[149]

Changing the rules

The DHSS had traditionally done nothing to alter the framework of general practice without the full agreement of the profession. To the doctors' puzzlement it ceased to be quite so supine. In 1984, after TV programmes about the quality of deputising services, Kenneth Clarke, the Minister, proposed regulations to control their use. No longer could a doctor pass the practice over to a service every night and every week-end, as some did, providing no out-of-hours cover personally. FPCs were given a role in the supervision of the quality of deputising services. GPs, 45 per cent of whom used them, thought the imposition of a limit on their use unacceptable. The General Medical Services Committee (GMSC) said that the draft circular from the DHSS

> would destroy most deputising services and stretch or damage those remaining. It employed an Orwellian way to monitor deputising doctors, and was a threatening document based on misinformation and ignorance. It had produced a reaction from the profession not seen since the 1960s.[150]

John Ball, the GMSC Chairman, and Kenneth Clarke respected each other and could do business. Both sides backed off and an agreement was negotiated to tighten up the conduct of deputising services in a way acceptable to most GPs. Barely had the dust settled than there was a more serious confrontation.

Since the earliest years of the health service there had been concern over the large and growing sums spent on medicines. Educational material such as *Prescribers' notes* and bar-charts showing the costs had been sent to GPs. Regular statements analysed their prescribing. DHSS regional medical officers visited GPs whose prescribing substantially exceeded local costs, after which their costs usually fell spectacularly. Nevertheless, expenditure continued to rise. Different companies marketed the same drug under different names for different costs. Less expensive but effective alternatives often existed. Some GPs had introduced practice formularies and audited their prescription costs. In the view of the DHSS, safe and effective prescribing was often economical prescribing as well. In November 1984, with little warning, Norman Fowler, the Secretary of State, announced that certain groups of medicines would no longer be available for prescription on the NHS.[151] The groups had been carefully chosen and were generally those for minor and self-limiting ailments including tonics, antacids, mild pain relievers, cold cures and laxatives.

The reaction from the profession to the 'limited list' was immediate, intense and critical.[152] Both the RCGP and the GMSC rejected the proposals. Doctors should decide on prescribing, not the DHSS; it was the thin end of a rather thick wedge. Patients would have to take medicines that were unpalatable and less acceptable or pay the price. The drug industry launched an advertising campaign showing a happy pensioner who could afford her drugs and a sad one who could not; Roche sent GPs pre-printed letters of complaint to sign and forward to their MPs. The thrust of the argument was that patients would suffer to save the government £100 million, and the new mandate was an encroachment on clinical freedom to prescribe whatever particular preparation the GP deemed most appropriate. Kenneth Clarke's views were clear: there were better ways of spending the £100 million that would be saved by more prudent prescribing. There was no passion in Parliament against the limited list. Raymond Hoffenberg, President of the RCP, said that the profession had chosen a weak issue on which to defend its rights.[153] Many hospitals had long operated hospital formularies that imposed some kind of restriction on prescribing. There were educational and financial advantages in examining the drugs to be used. Doctors were fighting the issue as a matter of principle, rather than because they had scientific reasons for their choices. An expert advisory group was established to oversee the list. Within a year or so, substantial sums were being saved and few believed that patients' health care was the worse.

New charter working group – 1979

- Overall development of general practice backed by greater investment
- Improved undergraduate, vocational and postgraduate education
- Average list sizes to be reduced to 1700 by early 1990s
- Identification of payment for normal working hours, work-sensitive payments for out-of-hours, and 'continuity' payments for chronic disorders
- Incentives to increase the number of young doctors in the inner cities and the establishment of supernumerary doctors in rural areas
- Profession should take responsibility for audit and clinical standards

---

Towards a new GP contract

There was a ferment of ideas about the improvement of primary health care. From 1977 to 1979 a working group of the GMSC, concerned at the much smaller increase in spending on general practice than on other parts of the health service, assembled proposals for a 'New Charter'. From the GPs' angle, pay was a major consideration: it should be comparable with that in Europe and reflect widening responsibilities in the continuing care of all age groups, including preventive and curative medicine and health education.[154] Out-of-hours payments were a central issue. A salaried service was considered but the group thought a single contract, rather than several options, was the best approach. The MPU proposed an alternative left-wing solution. Community GPs, with extra training in epidemiology and research, should be salaried and work from neighbourhood health units, usually health centres, with the support of a deputising service. They should help to define local health needs and implement national programmes to reduce heart and arterial disease, cancer and other illnesses that might in some degree be preventable. The GPs should relate more closely to local authorities and the community to which they were accountable. Medical education should change substantially. The community itself should be directly involved in the selection of medical students to ensure that selection was non-racist, non-sexist and non-class biased.[155] At the other political extreme, Michael Goldsmith's Harrow Health Centre sought to provide good primary health care and to do so at a reasonable cost outside the NHS.

In the RCGP and academic circles there was also radical thinking about the future of general practice. Thinking was based on assessment of changes in society, demography and medical specialisation, and on medical problems themselves including chronic disease management and health promotion.[156] Issues of quality appeared on the RCGP agenda. What was quality, and how could it be encouraged and measured? In 1983 Donald Irvine, Chairman of Council of the RCGP, argued that variation in quality was the outstanding problem in general practice. He said that each GP should be able to describe his current work and the services the practice provided for patients, should define specific objectives for patient care and monitor the extent to which they were met. The RCGP 'Quality Initiative' was an attempt to give leadership to the increasing number of doctors concerned with their performance.[157] *What sort of doctor?* analysed the nature of good practice and listed four fundamental attributes of the good GP – professional values, accessibility, clinical competence and ability to communicate.[158] Avedis Donabedian was invited to visit the College and comment on activities that stemmed from the College's initiative. Doctors, particularly those involved in vocational training, were visiting each other and entire practices became willing to expose themselves to outside professional scrutiny. In 1985 the RCGP published a radical document setting out its strategy for maintaining and raising quality.[159] It proposed that GPs should have passed the RCGP membership examination before becoming principals. It stressed the need for continuing medical education and argued for protected time for this. Computerisation should be universal, and the GP contract should be altered so that unacceptable levels of performance were reflected in a GP's pay. With a wide variation of GP performance, general practice had to reform itself or be reformed. *The Times* welcomed the RCGP policy to lobby for payment by results as a welcome sign of modern economic reality in one part of the medical profession. Perhaps the RCGP would use local muscle in local pay bargaining.[160] The GMSC, whose task it was represent all NHS GPs, was not amused, and invited the College to take its guns off the GMSC's lawn.

The two main challenges to the status quo were the wide diversity in the quality of care with little incentive other than professional pride to strive for the highest standards, and secondly the general acceptance that the NHS must prove that society was receiving value for money. Alan Maynard, an economist, thought that general practice was difficult to define, highly variable and anti-competitive in its delivery, hard for patients to assess and was resulting in ever-increasing bills for the tax-payer.[161] Conservative think-tanks, such as the Centre for Policy Studies (CPS), founded by Keith Joseph and Margaret Thatcher, were increasingly interested in NHS reform in general, and primary health care in particular. From government's perspective, spending on the family practitioner services was growing fast. It was hard to forecast accurately what would be spent on a service that was not cash limited, and to control that spending. In 1982 the DHSS commissioned accountants, Binder Hamlyn, to examine and review arrangements for financial forecasting and control, including the possibility of cash limits. A year later their report was on the verge of being published when there was a political decision not to do so. Its contents never became public. But embedded in the Binder Hamlyn report were the suggestions that if all payments to GPs were payments per patient, a cap on spending on prescribing was possible; and if capitation was 100 per cent, controlling spending would be easier.

In April 1984 Norman Fowler announced plans to review primary health care. The review was a way out of having to do anything precipitate about the proposals in the Acheson report on inner city general practice, the unpublished Binder Hamlyn report, the ability of GPs to continue to practise into their 80s if they wished, and so on. John Ball, Chairman of the GMSC, believed the process would take several years and resigned to ensure that there was continuity of professional leadership. Michael Wilson, not a man to whom compromise came easily, replaced him. Kenneth Clarke, as Minister of Health, took a personal interest, and a small and junior departmental team was created, outside the normal hierarchy and unmarked by yesterday's thinking, to distil emerging ideas. The new GMSC Chairman described the idea that the future of general practice might be determined by this young team as a rather bad joke.

The confidential ministry proposals went through many revisions, while Kenneth

Clarke moved to another Department. Downing Street suggested that GP–hospital links were important, and the best arrangement might be to allow GPs to select services for their patients from hospitals of their choice and for the district health authority's funds to follow. GPs might also be given a fixed drugs budget. While the BMA equated quality of care with small GP lists, there was little evidence that small-list GPs provided a better service. The suggestion that GPs might be given a budget to purchase hospital services for their patients, and a section about American HMOs, appeared in drafts but were removed by older and wiser hands. A Green Paper, *Primary health care – an agenda for discussion*, was published for consultation in April 1986.[162] The profession initially welcomed the commitment by government to comprehensive primary health care and its willingness to negotiate on the development of services to patients.[163] Naively, ministers thought they might have a happy tour round the country, presenting their ideas before entering into genuine consultation with the profession. Believing that an informed professional debate would be helpful, a DHSS officer quietly suggested to Marshall Marinker, Alan Maynard and Denis Pereira Gray that articles might be written for the *BMJ*, to appear immediately after the publication of the Green Paper, outlining the pros and cons of different types of incentive systems and contracts.[164] GPs, content with the existing contract, ignored them. The authors were later accused of putting ideas in the government's mind, and the profession, by ignoring them, of getting its just deserts.[165] The BMA, seeing an election over the horizon, thought it could kick the ball into touch, that the profession had a veto and that the government was weak.

The Green Paper

Central was the government belief that primary health care mattered and that financial incentives could be used to get it right. The proposals aimed to improve services, to make them more responsive to the public and to centre them increasingly on health promotion. Managerially, clearer priorities would be set for the family health services in relation to the rest of the NHS. The consultative document echoed much RCGP thinking and its Secretary innocently told a medical newspaper that opening the package 'was just like Christmas'. The more the GMSC examined the proposals, the less it liked them. The Minister, when meeting the GMSC, said he was more interested in hearing its views on improving primary health care than in answering detailed questions.[166] Ten ministerial 'road shows' took soundings on various aspects of the Green Paper. A good practice allowance was proposed to reward GPs giving the highest standards of care and to provide an incentive to others.[167] Direct linkage of pay with quality would have broken new ground. There were inevitably questions about how assessments could be fair and, as in 1966, the profession rejected them. Who should judge, how could rigidity in assessment and interference in clinical freedom be avoided? Those aspects of health care most easily measured might not be those of most importance, or ones that mattered to patients. GPs felt that it would be impossible to devise a scheme that would be fair to practices with a greater than average number of problems, for example those in areas of social deprivation. The good practice allowance was seen as a merit award, given by management to doctors who did as they were told and awarded on foggy criteria possibly in the teeth of natural justice. It clearly was not going to fly. In December 1986 Michael Wilson and the GMSC sent the profession's response to the Secretary of State. Most of the government's ideas were rejected;

Main points of *Promoting better health*[169]

- New payments to encourage preventive medicine and greater efficiency
- Set clearer priorities for family practitioner services
- Increase competition and give public greater choice
- Compulsory retirement at 70 and abolition of '24-hour retirement'
- Cash limits on funds for direct reimbursement for ancillary staff and premises, but an extended scheme
- General Practice Finance Corporation to be privatised
- Incentives for inner city practice
- Nurses given limited powers to prescribe
- Pharmacists given financial incentives to widen their services

---

instead the GPs wanted to discuss their own proposals.[168]

Officials looked at other ways of achieving the same objectives, and in November 1987 a White Paper outlining government proposals was published, *Promoting better health*.[169] It presented the profession with a package that left room for negotiation only at the margins. Instead of the good practice allowance, financial incentives would be used to encourage specific services such as immunisation, cervical cytology, comprehensive care for elderly people, postgraduate education and practice in the inner cities. Other proposals included freedom of GPs to advertise their services, practice information sheets, greater emphasis on training, retirement at 70 years, help for inner city doctors and an increase in the proportion of GP pay related to list size (then 45 per cent) to 'provide a greater incentive to doctors to practice in ways that will encourage patients to join their lists'. The devil with the GPs' contract was in the details. These were left to be worked out in discussion. Some incentives, including those for postgraduate education, had hardly been considered. The 1965 GPs' charter had linked seniority awards to postgraduate medical education but Barbara Castle had let this go, at the request of the profession. Additional money for the doctors might be available, but that depended on the progress of negotiations. Initially some GPs saw advantages in some proposals: the accent on primary health care and health promotion, the delegation to nurses and increased staff. However, there would be more work and a risk that the new dispensation would again improve the better but not the poorer practices.[170] Before long the profession's attitudes hardened. Julian Tudor Hart dubbed leading GPs who had supported the need for change as 'the gang of four' (Dennis Pereira Gray, Donald Irvine, Marshall Marinker and Colin Waine), though his own ideas had been as influential as anybody's. The stage was set for a battle royal out of which few emerged unscathed.

The community nursing review

In parallel with the Green Paper a review of community nursing was taking place. The Health Visitors' Association wanted one because of uncertainties about their role but Kenneth Clarke, decided that all three nursing professions should be included, and set the terms of reference. Julia Cumberlege, then Chairman of Brighton District Health Authority, was asked to chair the review, with a small team and a six-month deadline. This irritated the nursing organisations, which considered the time-scale unrealistic.

By the early 1980s it had become clear that hospitals should be concentrating their resources on curative medicine. Patients whose needs were for long-term care would increasingly receive this at home. The review team wanted to make this easier, give a new impetus to nursing in the community, create better links with social services and explore the role of nurse-practitioners. The subliminal feminist agenda, appealing to nurses, was of nurse prescribing, nurses managing their own services and nurses negotiating with GPs as equals within primary health care teams. The trend to organisation on a neighbourhood basis had developed in local authorities. Many had been organising services such as housing from a locally based unit rather than a distant and centralised office. Local centres were more accessible and put problems right more quickly and sensitively. Similar patterns of care were developing for the mentally ill and handicapped. GPs had, themselves, always worked within and for a local population. The Cumberlege Report, published at the same time as the Green Paper on primary health care, proposed the organisation of community nursing on a neighbourhood basis.

The report called for a switch of resources from hospital into the community. It supported nurse prescribing, the nurse-practitioner approach (undefined) and a common core training with substantial community experience for all nurses. Crucially it recommended that neighbourhood nursing services, covering 10,000–25,000 people, should be established in each district, locally managed and near to the consumer. It maintained that nurses were at their most effective when they and GPs worked together in an active primary health care team, but found that close working relationships were often lacking. To improve this, the Cumberlege team suggested formal agreements between GPs and community nurses. The team did not approve of the 'fragmented nursing' in the community, and the way in which GPs employed practice nurses while districts ran more broadly based community nursing, midwifery and health visiting. All should be brought together within the neighbourhood nursing context. Brian Jarman, Professor of Primary Health Care at St Mary's, and Julia Cumberlege wrote a joint article pointing out the advantages to everyone if the best traditions of all disciplines were combined and professionals worked together, preferably from one building, to provide the full range of medical, nursing and social services to an area of 10,000–25,000.[171] Their carefully drafted appeal to sweet reason, from a socialist GP and a conservative authority chairman, fell on deaf ears. It had little appeal to extremists on either side.

GPs vigorously opposed the report, feeling that, while it paid tribute to the *idea* of primary health care teams, in reality it was dismissive of practice nurses, apparently because they worked alongside doctors. GPs had had experience of the intrusion of nurse managers into the relationship of doctor, nurse and patient, and were wholly opposed to any plan to zone GPs to fit in with a tidy system of neighbourhood services. Nursing organisations, on the other hand, gave an almost unqualified welcome to the proposals. There appeared to be a surprising inability of doctors and nurses to understand each other's position.[172] While the proposals were never formally implemented, they influenced the organisation of services in many districts and later some community trusts were based on neighbourhood nursing units.

Hospital and specialist services

Hospital development and design

The Bonham-Carter Report of 1969 had recommended bigger hospitals serving a population of 200,000–300,000.[173] Although never formally accepted by the DHSS, this idea had taken root and many hospitals on the drawing board or under construction exceeded 1,000 beds. The disadvantages of these hospitals were now becoming apparent. There might be impersonality and problems of staffing and management, and of accessibility to the community. Were larger hospitals needed when shorter length of stay in hospital would lead to fewer beds in total?

The quadrupling of oil prices by 1978 effectively finished the ambitious programme of hospital building. Sir Francis Avery Jones suggested that existing hospitals should be surveyed, and capital money should be spent on refitting older ones, especially those built before 1914, which were well built and generously proportioned.[174] Dr Gerard Vaughan, then the Minister of Health, issued a consultation document in 1980 suggesting less emphasis on centralising services and more on retaining a wider range of facilities in small hospitals, which were more accessible, popular and conducive to high staff morale.[175] DGHs should not normally have more than 600 beds, and some beds in acute specialties should be provided outside the main DGH. More of the geriatric and psychiatric beds than originally envisaged should be sited away from the main hospital because there would be no room within it. Gerard Vaughan reviewed plans for new hospitals against these criteria, although the BMA and the Joint Consultants Committee severely criticised them. They thought his proposals were woolly on questions of safety in small acute hospitals, and that relegation of geriatric and psychiatric patients to peripheral hospitals was undesirable. The proposals were seen as an ill-disguised attempt to justify the status quo; in many places groups of hospitals had not been brought together on one site as had been the intention of the Hospital Plan, large asylums had not been shut, single-specialty hospitals continued, and staff still worked in inefficient and decrepit surroundings.[176] As a result, no formal guidance was ever issued. Staff had been willing to put up with substandard and ill-maintained buildings with the promise of a replacement on the horizon. Now they had less hope of any improvement. The proposed policies were, however, realistic. The shortage of money meant that the country would be relying for years on existing buildings, and planning had to allow for this. In future there would need to be more careful appraisal of all options, including the option to do nothing.

If there would be less new building, better estate management and refurbishment were called for. Avery Jones' suggestion was taken up by the King's Fund Jubilee project, which showed what could be done to upgrade older hospitals. There was an alternative, the 'Nucleus' hospital introduced in 1974 as a result of the oil crisis, and the culmination of all the work on standardisation since the 1950s. The doctors' reaction towards Nucleus was one of resignation; it was often that or nothing. At least it improved the facilities for the vital new technology now being introduced. Before long there were 50 Nucleus projects on the drawing board – some totally new, others expansions of an existing hospital.

Hospital management and clinical budgeting

The work on clinical budgeting undertaken by Iden Wickings at the Westminster was slowly taking root. Merely giving doctors financial information did not alter their behaviour, but when clinicians controlled the expenditure, for example the replacement of equipment, they might make savings that could be used for better purposes. Management budgeting focused on the use of money at unit level, involving clinicians in management.[177] Virtually nothing was known about the expense of individual clinical procedures, although research projects had attempted to find out how much some, such as hip replacement, cost. In 1979 the Financial Information Project was established to examine the need for financial information for health planning, and for clinicians in the management and organisation of their units. The project concluded that costing at the level of the individual patient would be needed, but would probably be prohibitively expensive. Doctors did not like the phrase 'clinical budgeting' so 'resource management' was substituted. Four schemes were set up in demonstration districts in 1985 in Basingstoke, Ealing, North Tees and Southmead. Shortly after, the programme was expanded as the 'Resource Management Initiative', in six hospitals and six community sites. Their aim was to help clinicians and other managers to make better-informed judgements about how the resources they controlled could be used to maximum effect. It was an ambitious programme of management change, following on Cogwheel. The programme was steadily expanded to more than 100 sites, the single biggest co-ordinated investment in computing in the NHS. The £300 million programme was rushed forward but came to be seen as ill-conceived, often based on poor quality data. Only a minority of the case-mix management systems worked, and even when they did they seldom proved much help to the staff.[178]

In the hope that managers would compare the performance of their units with similar ones, the DHSS and the NHS developed a series of performance indicators. They initially covered clinical activity and finance. Often, however, the information was not available to answer the interesting questions that arose – precisely why were lengths of hospital stay continuing to fall, and why were there substantial differences between regions? Statistics did not deal with the problem of readmission; patients discharged rapidly who were sent back to the same or a different hospital were counted twice, making it hard to assess the effectiveness of care. There was almost no research to show which admission policy yielded the greatest benefits as to health outcome – though if a patient were discharged quickly hospital costs rose, for another would immediately be admitted in his place.[179] In 1984, in response to a severe financial crisis, Guy's decided to adopt a method of management pioneered at Johns Hopkins Hospital in Baltimore, which was a more sophisticated version of Cogwheel.[180] The medical staff, together with the nurses, took over much of the management responsibility for running the hospital. Sixteen clinical directorates were established, each headed by a senior clinician, who together formed a hospital management board. Each clinical director held a budget and delegated responsibility for a wide range of activities, including waiting lists and outpatient management.[181]

Health service information and computing

The 1974 reorganisation, with the introduction of the planning system, highlighted the paucity of NHS information, its availability, relevance, quality and timeliness. A new information system to replace hospital activity analysis (HAA) seemed essential. In 1980 a steering group was established, chaired by Mrs Edith Körner, an ex-vice-chairman of the South Western RHA, to agree, implement and keep under review the principles to guide future developments, and to propose changes. The working group ignored 'the siren calls of enthusiasts inviting it to run before those who would have to implement the proposals were able to walk, or who suggested collecting the uncollectible'.[182] It ignored *Accounting for health* and the SCICON Report.[183] The group issued a series of reports that set out a common spine of information, a minimum data set to which other items could be added. A major problem was that the finance subcommittee consisted only of finance officers; the addition of people able to link money and clinical activity was rejected. The system was implemented in 1987. From the outset there were criticisms, for Körner's work was strongly directed towards supporting management, and the functions of the district general manager in particular.[184] The minimum data set contained no information required solely for the care of individual patients. The emphasis was on aggregated data, cost and numbers. Information needed by health professionals to evaluate the results of their care and information about the occurrence of disease or the health needs of populations were excluded. Partly on the grounds of confidentiality, the need for access to information about patients' identities, doctors' identities, diagnoses and major components of treatment (which HAA had provided) was denied. There was inadequate recognition of the need to compile and maintain registers to schedule, control and evaluate primary and secondary health care. As the costs of the NHS are largely incurred by the treatment of individual people for specific problems, the basic data necessary for the intelligent management or the professional assessment of health services were missing. There was also little emphasis on the use and feedback of information. Körner was implemented at substantial cost and produced little benefit.

London hospital planning

The attempt by Albertine Winner's London Co-ordinating Committee in the mid-1970s, to co-ordinate the planning of the metropolitan regional boards, had been clinically based. In several specialties there were too many units too small in size for the best performance. Now London's hospital service was increasingly affected by RAWP (1976)[185] and the economic problems after the oil crisis. Health authorities had less growth money and a wider range of responsibilities. London was losing to the north, to shire counties such as Essex and Sussex who were demanding fair play, and money also had to be transferred from acute services into the care of people who were elderly, mentally ill or mentally handicapped. Faced with financial crisis there was an attempt to remould the capitals' health services to ensure high quality and accessible services for the population; and to provide appropriate support for the medical schools' clinical and research activities.

Re-examination began under Labour. Although the offices of three of the four Thames regions were in the same building in Eastbourne Terrace, intercommunication was almost non-existent. Ministers believed that London's health services could be reshaped only if they were brought together within a single strategic framework. This they were unlikely to organise for themselves. The London Health Planning Consortium (LHPC) was therefore established in 1977 as an officer group of the four regions, the postgraduate hospitals, the University of London, the University Grants Committee (UGC) and the DHSS itself.[186] It was not an executive body, and decisions continued to lie with the statutory health and academic bodies, and where necessary with the Minister. It was, however, excellently serviced and chaired by John Smith, a DHSS officer of great drive who had also chaired the Resource Allocation Working Party, which gave him an excellent background. It was continued under the Conservative administration.

Main LHPC reports

- Methodology for projecting bed needs (1978)
- Profile of acute hospital services in London (1979)
- *Towards a balance* (1980)
- Reports on specialties (1979–1980):
    cardiology and cardiothoracic surgery
    neurology and neurosurgery
    radiotherapy and oncology
    ophthalmology
    otology and laryngology
- Primary health care in inner London (Acheson Report) (1981)

The level of acute services likely to be available in the future was examined, starting with the demographic change predicted over ten years. London's population had fallen from 8.5 million during the second world war to 6.9 million in 1977 and was likely to fall to 6.3 million by 1988. Inner London had fallen from 4.8 million in 1931 to 2.7 million in 1977 and would be 2.3 million in 1988. Account was taken of the changing age structure, level of hospital utilisation, the differences in turnover and length of stay compared with other parts of the country, the need to compensate for social deprivation, and the shortcomings of London's non-acute services. The study undermined the myth that the extra beds were mainly used by people from outside London; comparatively few were. It showed how the progressive outward movement of the population from central London had led to a marked inequality of access to acute services and to an over-concentration in central London.[187] The Report concluded that there might need to be reductions of 20–25 per cent in the number of acute beds in inner London. If the reductions were not made, resources would not be available to improve the standards of geriatric, mental illness and mental handicap care. The Consortium commissioned the Acheson Report on primary health care.

Calculating the number of acute hospital beds likely to be available was an essential preliminary to an examination of the clinical facilities for undergraduate medical education and the intake of the London medical schools. If the number of beds fell, the medical schools would need to rethink the way they provided clinical experience. All the schools were visited and the problem was analysed in *Towards a balance*.[188] It was proposed that teaching hospitals, each of which lay at the apex of a wedge radiating outwards from inner London, should relate to major hospitals further out, as in the wartime emergency hospital service. Such an arrangement could provide a good clinical service and a sound basis for teaching. This structure left four teaching hospitals in the centre without many people around them; the movement into them of some postgraduate hospitals and their institutes was suggested. There was close co-operation with a university working party, chaired by Lord Flowers, considering the use of university resources for medical and dental education. The Flowers Report, published on the same day as *Towards a balance*, proposed a series of amalgamations for the same reasons that had led to the Todd pairings in 1968.[189] The plan was no better received, and students from the Westminster Hospital paraded with coffins outside Senate House.

Everyone agreed that there were too many units providing services such as radiotherapy and heart surgery. There was no consensus on which should close. Existing provision and the likely needs over the next decade were examined by groups with an independent chairman. Specialists in the field under examination came from outside the Thames regions to avoid special pleading. The reports recommended substantial rationalisation of units that were often too small to be viable and provide the best opportunities for service, teaching and research.[190]

The outcome of planning

Faced with proposals that offended almost every powerful lobby in sight, Patrick Jenkin took refuge in an advisory body.[191] In May 1980 he asked Sir John Habakkuk, Principal of Jesus College Oxford, to chair a London Advisory Group and act as an honest broker. Habakkuk agreed that a reduction of 15 per cent in the number of acute beds in London was correct and that services should be concentrated on major hospitals rather than maintaining an acute service role for many more. This would free resources for the elderly, the mentally ill and mentally handicapped, and for primary health care.[192] The LHPC work was planning at its best – logical, intellectually appealing, backed by analyses and the facts to win the argument, and taking on board as far as possible all stakeholders. When the work was complete, the DHSS dismantled the team that by then had great expertise. Implementation was left to the regions, the opponents of change breathed a sigh of relief and little was done. The Flowers proposals for a smaller, leaner but well-organised pattern for London medical education had been talked to death. There had been little consensus and no single body had both the will and the power to act. Later some London teaching hospitals had cause to regret their intransigence and inability to see where their long-term interests lay.

Who, asked the BMJ, would have the courage to bell the cat?[193] Rationalisation began during the 1982 restructuring of the NHS, spurred by financial pressure that demanded major mergers across existing authority boundaries. Amalgamation was a time-honoured way of reducing the number of hospitals, and the medical schools of UCH and the Middlesex Hospital had for some time been working with each other. Patrick Jenkin took the decision to unite two districts as Bloomsbury, encouraging the University of London to merge the medical schools of UCH and the Middlesex. The schools at Guy's and St Thomas' also merged as the United Medical and Dental Schools. The process of change continued. In 1984 the medical schools of Charing Cross and Westminster hospitals united, and in the following year the districts in which they were situated were merged into one authority, Riverside, with plans to rebuild and reduce the number of hospitals to two. Brent and Paddington were also considering merger; 'we're huddling together for strength and warmth,' said the district manager.[194]

Postgraduate hospitals and institutes

London, unlike the rest of the country, had single-specialty hospitals with associated academic institutes. They varied from large ones such as Great Ormond Street and the Royal Marsden, to small ones such as St John's Hospital for Diseases of the Skin. Many were in need of redevelopment and some of their institutes were academically dubious. They had survived the logic of the Hospital Plan (1962) and Sir George Pickering's examination. They had survived the 1974 reorganisation and remained outwith the regional structure, directly responsible to the DHSS. The civil servants had a soft spot for them and their devotion to clinical medicine. A Labour proposal to bring them into a single postgraduate group for management purposes was vetoed by Patrick Jenkin in 1979 when the Conservatives took office.[195] An alternative was sought and the London Advisory Group distinguished between six where either the hospitals needed rebuilding or the future of the matching university institute was in question, and six larger ones that could rationally continue in their current form for the foreseeable future. The first group were amalgamated with general medical schools and managed by DHAs. The second group were managed by new special health authorities (SHAs), replacing the existing boards of governors. The Hammersmith Hospital was also to be managed by a SHA.[196]

Stringency in London's hospitals

As economic problems began to bite it was easy to run the argument that there were too many acute beds in London but long-stay services were often sadly lacking.[197] Some areas took draconian measures whereas others used creative accounting to postpone ward closures, but the longer the delay, the deeper the cuts had to be. Capital was converted to revenue; bills were left for payment in the next financial year. Staff represented 70 per cent of the NHS budget, so reduction in numbers through natural wastage and redeployment was inevitable. Patrick Jenkin, as Secretary of State, insisted that authorities should live with their cash limits but Lambeth, Southwark and Lewisham Area Health Authority refused to make cuts of £3.5 million to balance the books. Mr Jenkin appointed five commissioners to take over management.

Closing single wards did not solve problems for the infrastructure costs still had to be borne. Even the closure of an entire hospital, such as the Connaught, did not help greatly as facilities at hospitals nearby were used more intensively, and the savings fell short of those predicted. The most efficient districts were the hardest hit for they had the least fat. High technology specialties had, in recent years, often outpaced growth in more ordinary ones and were candidates for cutbacks. Faced with the unpalatable decision of whether to cut local acute or regional services, most authorities settled for cuts to both. Hospital closure was vociferously opposed. It was the smaller institutions such as the Poplar, the Metropolitan and the South London Hospital for Women that were selected. Although these were often housed in buildings with a huge backlog of maintenance work they provided services that were greatly valued locally. Closures began under Labour whose ministers were in a cleft stick. They could not simultaneously impose RAWP and deny regions the right to balance the books. Each was delayed for months while the community health council had its say. Closures continued under the Conservatives, although the Elizabeth Garrett Anderson Hospital had astutely obtained a written statement of support from Mrs Thatcher, while in opposition. Because the Thames regions planned in different ways, after the demise of the London Health Planning Consortium the chairmen of the twelve teaching districts jointly examined what was happening. They found it impossible to say with any confidence what London medicine might look like in a few years.[198]

Medical education and staffing

Medical education

The oil crisis also hit the medical schools. In 1981 the University Grants Committee wrote to the universities to say that it would no longer be able to offer to clinical medicine the protection it had previously enjoyed. The total grant to universities fell 17 per cent between 1980/1 and 1983/4.[199] How, asked the University of London, were their schools going to spend the money they were not going to have? Medical education had grown fast as new medical schools had opened and the numbers of students and medical academics had risen in line with the recommendations of the Todd Report. Faced with a cutback, medical schools were loath to reduce student numbers. Instead vacant posts were left unfilled, redundancies were considered and departments were at risk of closure. If the attempt was made to preserve those of highest quality, how was excellence measured? Could charitable moneys be raised? One option was to try to get districts to fund more of the service work carried out by university employees. In many medical schools research projects culminated in the introduction of new investigations at the cutting edge of medicine and university laboratories would find themselves providing a diagnostic service. Since the NHS began there had been a 'knock-for-knock' arrangement, NHS employees doing some of the teaching and academic ones providing a measure of service. The partnership was under threat.

Medical staffing

It had taken several years, under Labour, to negotiate a new consultant contract. Once it was agreed it had to be priced under the Income Policy. The additional money was minimal and after the Conservatives took office in 1979 the proposals were abandoned, It was quickly decided to increase the income of part-time consultants roughly 10 per cent and to allow whole-timers to earn an additional 10 per cent from private practice. The two groups of consultants had previously fought each other; their interests were now much closer.

Further attempts were made to forecast the future demand for medical staff. Over the first 30 years of the NHS the number of hospital doctors had more than doubled at a growth rate more than 3 per cent a year; the number of GPs had increased by only a third. Although changes in health policy influenced the numbers required, for example *Better services for the mentally ill* (1975), the increase had broadly paralleled the growth in the money available to the NHS. Perhaps the key factors were the number of doctors trained and that the NHS could afford to employ, rather than an abstract view of what was 'needed'. In 1978 the UK health departments published a 20-year prediction of the requirement for doctors, and Maynard and Walker made a 'best guess'.[200] The estimates for the number of doctors required in 2000 AD ranged from 72,000 to 100,000, and both groups said they lacked data and research was needed. The Royal College of Surgeons said that previous forecasts, Willink (1957) and the Royal Commission on Medical Education (1968), had not met with conspicuous success. The most important lesson was that the future was unpredictable. The *BMJ* believed that such exercises showed how insubstantial was the work of even reputable groups studying manpower and that the health service could not survive another 30 years of ad hoc policies.[201] In October 1981 the House of Commons Social Services Committee, chaired by Mrs Renée Short, reported on medical staffing, recommending an increase in the number of consultants and a freeze on junior posts. That had been policy for 12 years, during which time the numbers of juniors had increased by 62 per cent while consultant posts had risen by only 29 per cent.[202] By 1983 the profession, though arguing for consultant expansion, was again coming to believe that too many students might be entering medicine. By the year 2000 there might be 25,000–30,000 extra doctors, and without enormous capital investment they would be unable to find employment.[203] The Advisory Committee on Medical Manpower Planning, despite intensive statistical work, was unable to reach any conclusion about whether the country would need more or fewer doctors over the next 30 years – but concluded that existing policies would maintain a reasonable balance. Doctors would grow in numbers by about 1.1 per cent a year.[204] Members of the BMA Council were not reassured: Anthony Grabham said that the provision of as many doctors as the government wanted, and a few more, would make the profession's negotiating position weaker; John Marks declared that nothing would suit the Secretary of State more than 2,000 hungry doctors.[205]

Hospital career structure

Although the geographical distribution of doctors was more even, there were still major variations between regions, and between teaching hospitals and the others. There was a mismatch between training and career posts, and between UK doctors and those from overseas. The opportunity to balance the senior and junior staffing of hospitals had been lost time and again.[206] In 1981 the DHSS tried once more to improve the hospital career structure by proposals to double the number of consultants and halve the number of senior house officers over the next 15 years, changing the pattern of consultant work, and reversing the ratio of consultants to juniors from 1 : 1.8 to 1.8 : 1. Addressing the consultants, Sir Henry Yellowlees, the CMO, said he did not think that consultants need necessarily be resident, nor did he favour shift medicine, but he refused to guarantee that consultants would never be required to sleep in the hospital.[207] There was a tart response from the consultants who said that the Department's calculations were flawed and proposals were being put forward that had not been discussed, let alone agreed, with the profession. A service *led* by consultants was one thing; a consultant-*provided* service quite another.[208]

Mrs Renée Short's committee looked at staffing again in 1985; Kenneth Clarke told the committee that the Royal Colleges and he were in total agreement in support for consultant expansion, but the Colleges tended to believe that the reduction of junior posts was a difficult problem that might be deferred. Consultants found it hard to accept that they should share in the simpler work, with fewer juniors and more in their own grade. They resisted the proposals in their locality, and making changes proceeded with the ease of extracting teeth from a non-anaesthetised animal.[209]

Achieving a balance (1986)[210]

- Increase the number of consultant posts
- Restrict the number of training posts
- Introduce a new career staff grade for doctors who do not wish, or are unable, to progress to the consultant grade

In 1986 a joint group of the profession, the NHS and the DHSS was established, and a further and detailed examination of staffing issues began. The group's report, published as *Achieving a balance*, was a carefully crafted and politically sensitive compromise; each group both achieved something and conceded something.[210] Juniors would work a few years more than was absolutely necessary to achieve specialist status, and longer hours than was necessary for their training; consultants would do a little more on-call than they would have liked; there would be some consultant expansion; and there would be a new intermediate service grade with little prospects of a consultant post. After long and acrimonious debate the juniors accepted it. The following year *Achieving a balance: a plan for action* was published, a ten-year programme.[211] There would be more consultant posts, consultants would be appointed at an earlier age, there would be fewer registrars and the new staff grade would be introduced. It also introduced the idea of career registrars and visiting registrars; career registrars expected a career in the UK but the visiting ones would return home after training. Virtually every review of medical staffing and training had called for an increase in the number of consultants of about 4 per cent a year; the rate achieved was nearer an average of 2 per cent. *Achieving a balance: a plan for action* proposed a more realistic increase of at least 2 per cent annually over ten years.[212] Arguments rumbled on; for example, there were many training posts in the academic hierarchy, the lecturers and senior lecturers who combined research and teaching with their service activities and yet expected in time to become NHS consultants. Earlier proposals had foundered in the objections of the regional consultants; now it was the academics, and particularly the academic physicians, who delayed the implementation of the proposals.

In 1948 junior doctors had largely been male, unmarried and had lived in the hospital. Now many had family responsibilities and wished to live out. Rota systems were invariable, but 36-hour shifts were common. There were *causes célèbres* in which patients' deaths were associated with tired juniors. The BMA wanted hours reduced, and in 1979 the MPU, now a section of Clive Jenkins' ASTMS, took up the cause. Not only their patients but their families, too, suffered. It was reported that when a surgical registrar came home early one evening his two-year-old daughter ran terrified to her mother crying 'Mummy there's a man here'. Shorter hours, however, meant more juniors (not sensible from the point of view of the career structure), or more intense work at night if one junior covered several jobs, or more involvement of the consultants who were unenthusiastic about night shifts.[213] In 1982 the DHSS asked health authorities to eliminate rotas more onerous than one night in two on duty.

Nursing

Nurse education and staffing

NHS nurses and midwives (annual movements)

Entering training/year	27,000
Total in training (3 years)	90,000
Qualifying/year	21,000
Returning/year	9,000
Wastage of qualified staff/year	30,000
Total qualified staff	300,000
Total unqualified staff	120,000

Adapted from Price Waterhouse (1987).[214]

Nursing and midwifery staff (including those in training) represented nearly half the NHS workforce, accounting for a third of NHS revenue and nearly 3 per cent of public expenditure. Even allowing for the reduction in working week in 1980, down to 37.5 hours from 48 hours in 1948, the number employed was rising after the 1974 Halsbury pay award. Yet in the priority specialties, mental illness and geriatrics, staffing was often unacceptably low and there were also critical shortages in dialysis units, paediatric intensive care and leukaemia units.[215] In 1987, 40 years after the Wood Report on the recruitment and training of nurses (1947), nursing remained a high recruitment but high wastage profession, massively dependent on new student intakes. Nursing was the largest single recruiter of women school leavers with between five 'O' and two 'A' levels, taking 17,000 out of a total of 70,000, a number that demography was likely to reduce. Student wastage was much greater than in higher education, where it was nearer 10 per cent. Over the decade the number of inpatients, day cases and outpatients all increased. Earlier discharge, medical advance, potent drugs, monitoring equipment and intravenous treatment added to the nursing burden.[216] The situation reached desperate proportions with shortages of 20–25 per cent. Untrained staff were increasingly employed. Straight eight-hour shifts and part-time working had been introduced to reflect the needs of married and non-resident nurses, and with more married nurses came greater use of statutory maternity leave. Unit meetings, time off for study and union meetings added to the demands on nurses without necessarily improving patient care. Health authorities were instructed in 1983 to put domestic, catering and laundry services out to tender and money was saved, but this meant fewer staff employed for fewer hours for the same workload. Sometimes nurses had to fill the gaps, washing, cleaning and apologising as meals and laundry failed to materialise.[217] The morale of the nurses fell and by 1987 both qualified and student nurses were leaving in droves. As money became tighter, nursing budgets were often cut, both in hospital and in the community, to deal with over-spending in other parts of the service. Obtaining firm staffing figures was difficult, and determining the numbers to be employed was more an art than a science.[218] Several nurse–patient dependency systems had been developed after early work by Barr in Oxford. One of the simplest was to allocate a set number of nursing hours per patient per day to each ward. Some systems worked top–down, trying to relate numbers to measures of output or activity. Others worked bottom–up, planning from ward level. All gave different results and none achieved widespread acceptance. This resulted in wide differences between the numbers employed. The DHSS felt nursing staffing was primarily a local responsibility that required local knowledge.

Nurses complained of being unable to get on with their job and not gaining the respect they felt they should enjoy. Students thought they were being used as 'pairs of hands', that there was a gap between theory and practice and that they were thrown in at the deep end.[219] More rapid patient discharge and more time off for nurses meant that students could not get to know patients and their background properly. Changes in the syllabus meant rapid rotation between specialties, without time to learn each thoroughly, or to revise their knowledge.[220] In the search for solutions, education became the focal point. There was conviction that the time for tinkering was over and this was nursing's last chance. Nurse education was a vast and complicated patchwork of provision with 200 nurse training schools and little linkage with other educational systems.

The UK was one of the last major English-speaking countries to conduct its basic nursing education within hospitals on an apprenticeship basis. One reason for suggesting that nurses should be prepared through higher education, rather than in hospital schools, was the hope that this would reduce wastage. The Royal College of Nursing (RCN) established a commission, chaired by Dr Henry Judge, Director of the Department of Educational Studies at Oxford, who had written extensively on the professions that, like nursing and teaching, were largely staffed by women. He believed that the NHS still relied on the 'easy come, easy go' system that Revans had described in the 1950s, and recommended the transfer of nurses' education into the higher education system, uncoupling education and service. There should be a foundation course followed by suitable supervised clinical practice and a staff development programme.[221] Student bursaries would be needed, and the cost would fall on the Treasury. The qualification gained should be a diploma.

The United Kingdom Central Council (UKCC) was established in 1982 after the Nurses, Midwives and Health Visitors Act 1979, replacing the many autonomous statutory bodies, several of which had been active in practice development. The national boards, such as the English National Board (ENB) were then created, after further disputes about reserved seats for 'minorities' – midwives, health visitors and psychiatric nurses – in which the nursing unions played a part. The UKCC and the ENB examined the problem of basic nurse education simultaneously. There was friction between them. The UKCC's proposals were formulated by its Education Policy Committee, not by a group specially established. The Committee consisted in part of nurses in management or educational positions, with four 'outsiders', also educationalists. There were no practising nurses or doctors. The proposals were driven by Celia Davies, the project officer, a sociologist by training, and a forceful person with a deep commitment to women's issues.[222] Leadership was passing from clinical nurses, who were inevitably involved in medical development, to a group more in tune with educational theory, sociology and community issues.

Project 2000

In May 1986 the UKCC published proposals for reform: *Project 2000 – a new preparation for practice*. The key proposal, advocated by every review of nursing education since the 1940s, was to end the dependence of hospitals on student labour. June Clark, later President of the RCN, said that education would be much broader,

Project 2000

- A threefold division of labour:
  a single level of registered nurse (the 'second level nurse' to be phased out)
  a more advanced specialist grade, e.g. health visiting and district nursing
  a support worker
- The registered nurse to be a 'knowledgeable doer'
- A common foundation programme of 18 months followed by a second 18 months in a 'branch programme' (adult, child, mentally ill or mentally handicapped)
- Reorientation from acute towards community care
- Schools of nursing to link with higher education
- Supernumerary status for 80 per cent of the time
- Students to receive training grants
- Academic recognition of professional qualifications

more community orientated, and based on a health-orientated nursing model instead of the disease-orientated medical model.[223] When submitted to the DHSS, *Project 2000* contained no costings; it was returned for these to be incorporated. The timing was good, for nurses were arguing for change in the run-up to the 1987 general election, at a time when there was a substantial shortage of nurses and when they were yet again angry about pay, barracking ministers at their College conference.[224] It was a moment at which it would have been foolish of MPs to show indifference. Professional status was involved but the case for a new system was argued on educational and service grounds. There were too many schools, some of doubtful quality. Students' studies suffered from their ward work, so they should be supernumerary to ward establishments. Educating nurses alongside other students would increase the academic content of their education and their experience of the outside world, and might decrease wastage, then 7–20 per cent with a further 15–20 per cent failing exams. On service grounds it was said that the needs of the NHS were changing, that a high proportion of nurses worked in the community, or in mental illness and mental handicap, and the current training was inappropriately hospital-based. It was said to be difficult to manage a flow of learners and that wards suffered from 'constant replacement' as groups moved on. Sometimes it seemed to ward staff as if the students, allocated by tutors for educational reasons, were more trouble than they were worth. *Project 2000* appeared to regard the case for the abolition of pupil nurse training and the State Enrolled Nurse as self-evident, although it would create difficulties in the less popular aspects of care where SENs made a vital contribution. Phasing them out was likely to increase reliance on nursing auxiliaries with even less training.[225] Consultation took place. There was widespread concern about the cost and staffing implications of the proposals, the care of an ageing population and a shortage of recruits. In May 1988 John Moore, then Secretary of State, announced, to the cheers of the nurses, that the government had accepted the broad thrust of the proposals. There were two conditions to acceptance – further work on widening entry into nursing, and concrete proposals for the new support worker and the framework of training.[226]

Nursing practice

Nursing was affected by the rapid discharge of patients, which made it impossible to plan work on the ward days ahead. The increasing numbers of specialists made it harder for a ward sister to discuss patient care with the medical staff. Sisters were younger, frequently less experienced. Sometimes there was more than one. They were not nearly so often on duty, less pre-eminent on the ward and less able to censure junior medical staff when it was warranted.[227] In 1953, the Nuffield work study report had suggested that team nursing might be better than task allocation, in which all the nurses worked together and tasks were allocated to individual nurses, a medicine round, meals, the doctor's round, and bed-making. Team nursing was increasingly used, the nurses being divided into groups, each responsible for particular patients, perhaps in four- to six-bed bays. Nursing academics pressed for a further stage – the introduction of primary nursing, the delivery of nursing care by an individual nurse assigned to an individual patient. Such a nurse was responsible for the overall assessment of need, planning action and evaluating the effectiveness of the plan made for the patient. Others would carry out the programme and report their observations and any changes made in her absence.[228]

The nursing process

Nurses undertook a wide variety of activities, which made it difficult to define nursing. Academics sought a unifying philosophy, and one result was the nursing process. Winging its way across the Atlantic, it was seized on as a solution to problems both in education and in practice. It drew on decision-making theory, and simplified it. Larry Weed, Professor of Medicine in Vermont, was arguing for medical records that were structured differently, around the patient's medical problems; and a systematic approach to the history, its analysis and the consequent treatment. Social workers were developing 'client care' plans. Using these ideas, it was suggested that nursing was a 'process' that should relate to a patient's 'problem'. Nursing was offered a new starting point.[229] Introduced to the UK by the Department of Nursing, University of Manchester, the nursing process adopted Henderson's promotion of self-care as the basic aim of nursing. It proposed a systematic approach to individual patients, collecting information by taking a nursing history, identifying patients' nursing needs, planning the nursing methods to use and assessing the results. Midwives, who were far clearer about what they were trying to do, rapidly found the new approach unproductive. Systematic methods of problem solving were neither new nor unique to nursing, being the same logical approach to decision-making used by managers, or anyone faced by a personal decision such as the purchase of a car.[230] The nursing process was based on the assumption that a nursing diagnosis and care plan could be independent of the medical diagnosis; that individual nurses could be accountable for carrying out and reviewing care plans and evaluating their outcomes; and that the patients had an active part to play. It implied that nursing was a distinct activity not subordinate to medicine and challenged inter-occupational relationships in hospitals.[231] Patient-orientated care had long been an aim and the nursing process aimed to supplant task assignment. Properly undertaken, it needed time not always available in a busy ward; if applied by rote the results were of little value. It had not evolved upwards from ward nursing and patients' needs, but descended from schools of nursing often forced on unwilling or uncomprehending staff by enthusiastic nurse-managers, who saw it as a way of giving nurses autonomy and freeing them from medical constraints.

The nursing process was followed by 'nursing models' that provided a theoretical basis for how individual nurses and groups of nurses perceived and organised nursing, and were part of the call for nurses to assert themselves. Some British nursing models, for example those patterned on the activities of daily living, were straightforward and were used to structure basic textbooks on nursing. Others were weird and verged on alternative medicine. The development of an additional 'model' appeared to be an initiative test for a new department of nursing. Nursing models were sharply differentiated from the 'medical model' that was somehow bad, seldom defined and always rejected. In nurses' eyes medicine was disease orientated rather than holistic; analytical rather than integrational; scientific rather than orientated in a psycho-social way; and autocratic rather than an activity in which the patient was a partner. Nurses criticised 'the overwhelming dominance of medicine and the medical model of illness.'[232] Doctors were unaware of the existence of a medical model, and when it was explained to them did not recognise it. The accusation that they were interested only in diseases and not in people seemed wrong and offensive. Doctors preferred traditional formulations of the medical role, for example that attributed to Ambroise Paré, 'to cure sometimes, to relieve often and to comfort always'.[233]

Professor Mitchell, Professor of Medicine in Nottingham, thought the nursing process was based on a false dichotomy between the cause, treatment and clinical course of the disease, and the resultant problems of daily living. Some nursing texts placed an impenetrable barrier of educational, sociological and psychological jargon between themselves and their readers. He thought that the nursing process was complex and encouraged the completion of time-consuming checklists that were often inappropriate and sometimes bizarre.[234] In reply a nurse, herself responsible for one of the more common models adopted in the UK, wrote that many nurses were concerned with people who did not have a disease, for example midwives, health visitors and those caring for the mentally, physically and visually handicapped. Many people were not receiving medical treatment but did require help. Nurses did not reject the relevance of medical diagnosis and treatment to nursing; instead the nursing process encouraged them to place an emphasis on health, normality and individuality.[235]

A feminist and political agenda became more apparent. Several groups of nurses emerged who described themselves as 'radical': radical midwives, radical health visitors and radical nurses. The groups had informal contacts and joint conferences. All wanted sweeping changes in health care, linking its improvement to improvement in the nurses' lot.[236] For the midwives 'radical' meant returning to their roots as independent practitioners. Did nurses act as the patient's advocate? In the case of hospital scandals many had remained silent out of fear, or loyalty to the hospital. Were nurses educated to fit a preconceived pattern, or to develop particular skills? Did they receive a fit training, or were they trained to fit? Textbooks on holistic nursing appeared, some with a 'new age' flavour, broad in scope and with their ideas packaged in verbal cotton-wool. The RCN published a booklet, *Towards standards*, suggesting that the nurses' responsibility should be extended further, their accountability should be independent of cover by medical staff, that doctors' and nurses' goals for a patient might differ or even conflict and a patient might need a nurse as advocate against the doctor.[237] Some in both professions believed that the divergence had extended too far and lasted too long.[238] The difficulty of believing simultaneously in a holistic approach to patients' problems and in professional autonomy with independence from medicine was largely ignored. Nurses reduced their contact with the medical profession at just the time when they would have benefited from a powerful professional ally in the fight to maintain standards and establishments.

In the community, matters were different. District nurses were now almost invariably part of a primary health care team, working closely with GPs who increasingly were employing practice nurses to handle the work within the surgery. Relationships within the practices became closer as nurses and doctors came to understand each others' pattern of work. Health visitors were also part of the teams. In the 1960s they had been encouraged to regard themselves as 'family' visitors, and had worked increasingly with elderly people. In the wake of several well publicised cases of child abuse they pulled back, to concentrate on child protection.

Nursing development units

Nursing development units emerged, in which patient care was a nursing, rather than a medical/nursing, responsibility. In 1981 a small group of nurses working in Burford, an Oxfordshire village with a GP-staffed cottage hospital, explored a new method of organising nursing care. They adopted primary nursing and tried to work with patients in partnership in a 'patient-centred' way. Nursing was seen as therapy, caring for people whose prime need was rehabilitation, and doing so without consultant cover. Two groups of patients who needed rehabilitation after a fractured neck of the femur had been pinned were compared, one remaining in the acute hospital, the others transferring to Burford. A second experiment began in 1985 in Beeson ward, at the Radcliffe Infirmary, Oxford, funded by the Sainsbury Trusts. The patients admitted were sicker and medically less stable. The ward routine was informal and individualised, managed by the nurses. An attempt was made to compare the results of traditional medical with nursing supervision but the randomisation was faulty. The nurses were in charge, as at Burford, and summoned help only when they believed that medical care was required. The junior doctors, however, reported that there might be a delay when medical care was urgently required, as for a patient with hypoglycaemia. They threatened to withdraw cover as it was not clear who was ultimately responsible. The health authority was alarmed and ended the experiment, which had by then attracted considerable interest in the nursing profession.[239]

Nurse-practitioners

The tasks at one end of the spectrum of nursing's responsibilities are medical and technical, covering work sometimes undertaken by doctors. For example, as day surgery developed, the main clinical decisions were taken in the outpatient department, and when the patient arrived for operation it might be a nurse, not a house officer, who 'clerked' the patients and was responsible for much of the subsequent care. At the other end the responsibilities shaded off into domestic work.[240]

As with many other nursing innovations, nurse-practitioners originated in the USA, where nursing expanded into the grey area between the two professions. In 1971

Kaiser-Permanente, a large HMO in California, pioneered the establishment of a nurse-practitioner training programme. Originally a means of meeting a shortage of doctors, it was soon realised that effective and satisfactory primary care for patients could be provided by carefully selected nurses trained to perform expanded roles in physician–nurse teams. Kaiser-Permanente hoped that the additional career opportunity would encourage some of the best nurses to remain involved with patient care. Programmes were developed in paediatrics, medicine, and obstetrics and gynaecology.[241] Encouraged by medical staff, nurses went to college for 1–2 years to train in their new field, learning to take a history, make a diagnosis and prescribe. Then they worked as part of a clinical team headed by doctors, often being the first point of contact. Nurse-practitioners often proved better than doctors at continuing supervision of patients with long-standing conditions, and at working in a consistent and empathetic way.

The role proved appealing to a few British nurses. Barbara Stilwell began work in a north Birmingham practice connected to the university medical school in 1982. Strongly supported by her medical colleagues, she felt her work to be a natural extension of nursing and health visiting, and was awarded a bursary to study in the USA. The conditions she handled fell into all categories, although many were related to preventive medicine and health education. Barbara Burke-Masters, in London's East End, worked with homeless and destitute patients who had difficulty in obtaining normal care. With the support of a local GP she diagnosed and prescribed, and referred patients to specialists when necessary. As in the USA, British nurse-practitioners received little support from the medical or nursing establishment, but more help was forthcoming from medicine than nursing. Both had to organise their own training, because courses, though widely available in the USA, were non-existent in the UK. Both showed that it was possible to extend substantially the role of a nurse in primary health care, and they provided role models for many practice nurses who had traditionally acted as treatment-room nurses rather than as points of first contact.[242] Julian Tudor Hart believed that nurse-practitioners and practice nurses were the key to effective anticipatory primary health care; the need was for in-service training and credible teachers who had themselves tackled the job. Higher up the nursing hierarchy, he wrote, there seemed to be many botanists but few gardeners.[243]

In 1946 the Wood Working Party had been asked what was the proper task of the nurse. Now nurses were increasingly interested in what was their proper image. 'We're not angels, we're workers' declared a nurse at a pay protest meeting. The public had an image of nursing, perhaps dating back to its religious roots, and, in the views of some, to masculine stereotypes of women generally. In Mills & Boon romances nurses were docile, compliant, tender, dedicated, the doctors' devoted handmaidens whose virtue was rewarded by marriage. There was increasing resentment at this stereotype, and at the others – the naughty nurse in the *Sun*, the battle-axe matron or the limp-wristed gay. Sir Roy Griffiths was said to have described them as 'doe-eyed and dangerous'. Trades unions created their own stereotypes, sometimes militant and black. Nurses might collude in the process. Just who were the nurses?[244]

Nursing administration

The restructuring of 1982, with the concept of strong locally based management able to take decisions, provided an opportunity to eliminate the multiple tiers of nurse management that made it difficult to take decisions.[245] In many forms of patient care, including midwifery, mental illness and mental handicap, and the care of elderly people, effective local management could have been advantageous. However, there was a desire to fit as many middle management nurses as possible into the new structure, which remained top heavy.

Industrial action

Financially 1978 was a turning point. Inflation was rampant, government was attempting to control pay awards with an incomes policy and industrial unrest was widespread. As strikes in the NHS became more frequent, David Ennals, the Secretary of State, agreed procedures with the unions that would reduce unnecessary industrial action. These were published in October 1978. The rules covered issues that would previously have been determined by management without any kind of negotiation, such as the parking of bicycles. Management, in advance, had conceded arbitration on such matters, greatly weakening itself in the process.[246] In January 1979 the Secretary of COHSE, Britain's biggest health union, was angered that government had treated doctors, but not nurses, as a special pay case. In a telegram to the Prime Minister he demanded the resignation of David Ennals. Porters, cleaners and laundry workers were demanding a rise. The nurses sought 18 per cent to restore them to their 1974 post-Halsbury award earnings. 'Pay not Peanuts' was their slogan at a mass meeting on January 18 when, despite a rail strike, 2,000 angry nurses heckled politicians at an emotionally charged meeting. Although nurses would stop short of all-out strike action, some worked to rule.

Over the next two months there was anarchy in the NHS. Ambulancemen went on strike and military ambulances were brought into service. Faced with substantial disruption by intermittent and variable action throughout the country, the government encouraged a low profile approach by management in an attempt to maintain a semblance of service. Unions sometimes made the continuation of emergency services dependent on the cancellation of other admissions; doctors resented their intrusion into clinical matters, and in Northampton three operating theatres were blacked and surgeons could operate on emergencies only by bringing in supplies themselves. At times the question emerged 'who is responsible for taking decisions to ensure that urgent treatment of patients takes place?' Hospitals that were running normally might confirm union claims that they had brought the health service to a standstill. To avoid making matters worse, union members were frequently paid even when they had withdrawn their labour. A firm local stand received no support higher up the hierarchy. The unions drew up a code of practice to try to ensure that cardiac, dialysis, intensive care, accident and emergency, and cancer patients were treated; deaths that could be laid directly at their door would not have helped them. Nevertheless, patients in general suffered, and in large numbers.[247]

Most staff returned to work in early March after accepting a 9 per cent increase in pay and the offer of a comparability study, the Clegg reports published in 1980. Roger Dyson wrote that the unions could feel pleased. They were faced with a pay limit of 5 per cent, achieved 9 per cent and defeated the government at little cost to themselves. Few members suffered much loss of earnings. But the NHS had seen a rapid growth in waiting lists. Dyson criticised the inconsistency of the government's approach that damaged the morale of local management. There should be standard rules about withdrawing pay from staff refusing to work as directed. If the overriding aim was to maintain patient services in the short term irrespective of longer term consequences, the NHS was doomed to future industrial strife.[248]

1979 – the Conservatives in power

The victory of Mrs Thatcher and the Conservatives was a watershed. 'At some bleary-eyed hour during Friday morning's election marathon,' wrote a contributor to the *BMJ*, 'I was awakened by one expert's comments about the new administration's likely spending plans. There would be no cut in the NHS budget. One advantage, I hope, will be a drop in the quantity of legislation affecting health care, leaving doctors and other health care workers with a little more time to treat patients.'[249]

Before he became Secretary of State, Patrick Jenkin had been enthusiastic about insurance to raise additional money for the NHS. The idea was quietly shelved; it would require a new bureaucracy to administer it, and how did one ensure that those genuinely unable to pay still received the treatment needed?[250] Speaking to the BMA, Mr Jenkin said that the main thrust of policy must be to make the NHS more of a local service. Doctors were trained to take professional decisions off their own bat and did not need the torrent of advice that had poured out of the DHSS. The voice of the doctor should not be drowned by the clamour of competing interests in local management. People came to the health service to be treated by doctors and nurses, and other professions and disciplines needed to be reminded of that.[251] The Conservatives rapidly came to an agreement on the consultants' contract. The phasing out of private beds would cease and the Health Services Board would be abolished. Six principles governing private practice in NHS hospitals were agreed with the profession. Labour, now in opposition, saw them as a private patients' charter and a first step on the road towards a two-tier health service.[252] Nor were the doctors enthusiastic. The new moves might undermine the private facilities that had blossomed under Labour, and that were perhaps the best assurance of the safety of private practice.[253] For a while Conservative health policy was virtually the same as Labour's. Priding themselves on the ability to manage the economy better, the Conservatives would have more money available for the health service. It was, however, with some surprise that it was discovered that Patrick Jenkin did not seem to believe in the planning that had dominated the previous decade.

The Royal Commission on the NHS

In July 1979 the Royal Commission reported.[254] It had been appointed by Labour against a background of a good deal of emotion, worry about lack of finance, pay beds, industrial action and the 1974 reorganisation. It provided a careful and well-documented account of patient services and the problems of the staff providing them. It made 117 recommendations, many of which were simple and sensible and were implemented in the years to come. Like Guillebaud, the report gave the NHS a reasonably clean bill of health. The NHS was not suffering from a mortal disease susceptible only to heroic surgery. There was no crisis but neither were there dramatic solutions. Improvement was possible but it would be a long slog. As to value for money and patient satisfaction the NHS was doing well. There was no evidence that other or radically new schemes of financing would do better. In terms of staff morale and renewal of buildings the NHS was not doing so well and the latter could be solved only by more money. The 1974 reorganisation, though it might have been correct in principle, had led to a byzantine system of administration in need of simplification, and the service lacked leadership at all levels.

The Conservatives judged the report good in parts. A major recommendation, that RHAs should be accountable to Parliament for matters within their competence, was rejected as inconsistent with the responsibility of the Secretary of State to Parliament. The incoming Ministers, Patrick Jenkin and Gerard Vaughan, had done much homework while in opposition. The government decided to tidy things up and iron out the obvious problems, rather than reorganise yet again. Recommendations about the improvement and simplification of the management and organisational structure of the NHS were welcome and within months Patrick Jenkin produced his own consultative paper, *Patients first*.[255] Summarising the Commission's report as showing that the problems were too many tiers, too many administrators, a failure to take quick decisions and a waste of money, the remedies suggested were

- Strengthening local management with greater delegation.
- Simplification of the structure by removing the area tier.
- Simplification of professional advisory machinery.
- Simplification of the planning system.

NHS restructuring

Restructuring – 1982

- 14 regional health authorities (RHAs)
- 192 district health authorities (DHAs) replaced 90 area health authorities
- 7 special health authorities (SHAs) replaced the boards of governors of postgraduate teaching hospitals
- 90 family practitioner committees (FPCs)

Patients first attracted many comments, largely favourable. The *BMJ* thought Mr Jenkin was determined to fulfil his pledge that decisions should be taken as close to the patient as possible.[256] In August 1980 ministers announced their plans, the key one being abolition of AHAs. To replace them 192 district health authorities (DHAs) were established, usually on the basis of the previous districts and organised like the old single-district areas. If 1974 had been a triumph for coterminosity between health authorities and local government, the restructuring of April 1982, outlined in health circular HC(80)8, restored the district as the functional and key tier.[257] The circular read:

> Districts should be established for the smallest geographical areas within which it is possible to carry out the integrated planning, provision and development of primary care and other community health services, together with those services normally associated with a district general hospital, including those for the elderly, mentally ill and mentally handicapped. The new authorities should not necessarily be self-sufficient in all these services. They should as far as possible comprise natural communities.

The determination of boundaries was particularly difficult in central London where the wish for coterminosity had to be balanced against organisational requirements and managerial practicabilities. Considerable flexibility was allowed for regions to determine the district pattern, and the districts their administrative structure. Although the process had to be complete by April 1982, regions could set their own pace. A major shift of power was taking place: issues previously settled centrally would now be handled at local level, and most people were broadly content.[258] Districts would be responsible for the planning, development and management of services. They would have management teams of six, including two clinicians (a consultant and a GP) and a community physician. They would continue to operate by consensus, but a new feature was introduced by HC(80)8 – the primacy of the district administrator.

> There must be clear arrangements for administrative co-ordination which are understood and accepted by all. This will be the responsibility of the district administrator. This does not give him any managerial authority over other chief officers, but it does impose on him a responsibility to see that an account is provided to the authority on how its policies and priorities are being implemented.

The first task would be to organise districts' services into units of management, each with its administrator, director of nursing services and a senior doctor. There were hospital units and community units, concerned with nursing services, welfare clinics, health promotion, chiropody and the like. The government wanted units to have their own budgets.[259] Area health authorities had never been interested in FPCs, which were now to gain independence on condition they were more active in planning and developing primary health care. In 1974 there had been turmoil and pain as staff had to find new jobs, and the process was repeated in 1982. Once more there was a night of long knives, but with fewer jobs to go round. Early retirements were necessary and among the big losses were area medical officers, some of them the best of the ex-medical officers of health. Far more left than anyone had predicted, at a cost of £54 million to a disgruntled Treasury. Consultants were anxious that their contracts should be held by the RHA, and not locally, and that doctors' role as advisers to health authorities should not be lost. After discussion with the profession, details of how this might work at district level were sent out, but the arrangements at region were never agreed.[260]

With the new region/district structure in place, the planning system needed modification. An attempt was made to simplify it and to make it more flexible.[261] How much money would be available in the future was uncertain, so planning would not simply be a method of allocating growth money. Zero-based planning was introduced;

existing services would have to be scrutinised. When Mr Jenkin's priorities document, *Care in action*, appeared its priorities were general aspirations.[262] Policy objectives were no longer linked with specific financial targets. As there could be no certainty that money would be available, and much would have to be financed from efficiency savings, this was just as well. In times of economic recession the new document was realistic, rational and fitted the policy of devolving power to local level.[263]

The NHS was labour intensive, with 827,000 employees. Numbers had risen 80 per cent in 20 years and staffing targets were given to the regions in an attempt to control the trend. In January 1982 Norman Fowler, the next Secretary of State, announced new arrangements to ensure better accountability to Parliament. Ministers would lead annual departmental reviews of the RHAs' long-term plans, objectives and effectiveness with each regional chairman and the chief officers. Regions saw the reviews differently; one regional officer produced a list of over 40 departmental priorities, only a few of which would have consumed all spare money. They were viewed as another instance of central interference with local autonomy and not quite the thing to be expected of a Conservative administration.[264]

More industrial action

1982 was to produce the longest industrial dispute the NHS had yet seen. Thirteen health service unions, which were seeking a uniform rise of 12 per cent, rejected a pay award that would have given a 6.4 per cent rise to the nurses and 4 per cent to other workers. Five thousand angry nurses rallied outside the RCN headquarters, and were told by June Clark (a senior official) that they might have to reconsider their position on industrial action. The dispute was overshadowed in the early days by the Falklands crisis, but once that was over the unions embarked on selective one-day stoppages that increased in length and intensity. Throughout the dispute the nurses stuck to their long-standing policy that they would not strike. Consultants were advised by the BMA to do nothing that might inflame the dispute, but held that the decision about what was and what was not an emergency should be entirely for the doctor. The disruption grew. Boiler-men left hospitals without hot water; the police had to provide emergency ambulance services. The suffering of patients was clearly shown on the media. The government remained firm, Norman Fowler, the Secretary of State saying 'we simply do not have that kind of money available. It could only be provided by cutting services to patients.' A higher offer, of 7.5 per cent, was made to the nurses to try to split the unions. It was one thing to be the hammer of hospital porters; to be harsh to nurses was quite another. Some saw the RCN as lambs loose in a world populated by wolves.[265] The RCN press office was not so naive; its staff said that 1982 showed that the College could hold its own with Arthur Scargill and the mineworkers when it came to newsworthiness. The press was favourably disposed to the RCN, which was adept at locating 'a nice nurse, young and attractive' for the media.[266] The tactics of the unions of getting nurses on to the picket lines muddied their image as dedicated servants of the sick, making them seem a bit too much like other people seeking more pay.

Mrs Thatcher said that the unions were damaging patient care and she did not believe that was what trades unionism was for. The dispute dragged on and in September

60,000 people took to London's streets, and most pits and ports stopped working. Enough is enough, said the BMJ.[267] Patients had suffered, waiting lists had become much longer, personal relationships had been damaged and the NHS was in danger of being politicised by outside unions. The NHS, now 40 years old, was saddled with some of the less attractive features of Britain's industries: outdated plant, poor management, and too many workers who believed that they were guaranteed a job for life. Should it not be more vigorous in the pursuit of efficiency, finding out where 'privatisation' of laundry, maintenance and catering would save money? Should it ignore such promising developments as HMOs, an increasingly popular method of delivering health care in the USA with built-in incentives for efficiency? The union tactics had turned the press and public, and drove a wedge between them and the RCN. The government held firm and in December the unions settled for a lower offer over two years. The nurses got their reward for moderation, their own independent pay review body, announced in July 1983. Its establishment recognised their special position within the NHS, and in particular the fact that most of the staff had not engaged in industrial action. The government reserved the right to exclude from the scope of the review body any groups that did resort to industrial action.[268]

The NHS could not cope with everything that was being thrown at it. There was a continuous increase in demand, fanned partly by political encouragement to deliver ever higher standards and partly by the rising costs of medical advance. From 1982 onwards cash limits bit, nearly all improvements had to come from greater efficiency, and financial allocations included an assumption that authorities would save 0.5–1.0 per cent of their cash limit each year. It was not enough. In the 1983 election the issue of the NHS suddenly surfaced, with accusations from Labour that if the Tories got their way the NHS would cease to be a national service and would be more concerned with money than health. There was a good old slanging match, Mrs Thatcher saying she had no more intention of dismantling the NHS than of Britain's defences.[269] Once she had won the election it was decided to cut £1 billion from public sector spending, and regional workforce targets were imposed, a reduction of 0.75–1.0 per cent in directly employed staff, including doctors and nurses.

The management review

For 15 years successive ministers had pursued the vision of stretching scarce resources by improving the quality of management.[270] The 1968 Green Paper had proposed area authorities with four or five directors under a chief administrative officer. The 1974 reorganisation had been managerial in nature. The 1982 restructuring had aimed to flatten the hierarchy and devolve powers. Now it was Norman Fowler's decision to turn to business for advice. In 1983 he asked a small team of businessmen under the leadership of a senior manager in the food marketing industry, Sir Roy Griffiths, to advise on the effective use and management of manpower and related resources in the NHS.[271] While preparing his report he met many people and regularly dined with senior staff at St Thomas', on whom he tried out his ideas. Nevertheless, coming from business, it was hard for him to avoid the criticism that he was unused to the idea of professional responsibility, and that his definition of management excluded the informal systems that existed in the NHS. It is probably true that the NHS did not, at the time, devote enough of its resources to proper and disciplined management, but it would have been surprising if Griffiths had not immediately identified the absence of general management as the main difference between the NHS and the business world. In a memorable sentence he said, 'if Florence Nightingale was carrying her lamp through the corridors of the NHS today, she would almost certainly be searching for the people in charge'. It was not the first time a chief executive had been proposed; Bradbeer had suggested it for hospital management committees.

Recommendations of the management review

- A small, strong general management board should exist at the centre, to ensure that power was pushed as far down the line as possible
- All day-to-day decisions should be taken *in* the main hospitals and other units
- Clinicians should be involved more closely in management decisions, should have a fully developed management budget and the necessary administrative support. This should prompt some measurement of output in terms of patient care. Service objectives and workload would relate to staffing and financial allocations
- There should be an accountability review system starting centrally and establishing a chain right through to unit managers
- A general manager should be identified (regardless of discipline) at each level and authorities should have greater freedom to organise the management structure suited to their needs (in contrast with the dirigiste approach of 1974)
- There should be a reduction in the number and levels of staff involved in decision-making and implementation
- The role of the regions should be strengthened (while ensuring that districts and hospitals were liberated to get on and manage the service)

Whether or not general management is appropriate in health services, where much of the talent is professional and on the shop floor, Griffiths believed that the lack in the NHS (and indeed in the DHSS) of a clearly defined general management function was responsible for many of its problems. Early on the team felt that the development of management budgets was vital, and commissioned demonstration projects in four districts.

The government rapidly accepted the general thrust of the report. The *BMJ* was, at first, guardedly welcoming.[272] The recommendations were not based on an analysis from which they could be logically deduced. Perhaps the more that was known of the reasons for them, the easier they would be to criticise and the less likely it would be that any action would be taken. Klein described the change as moving from a system based on the mobilisation of consent, to one based on the management of conflict. Like all newcomers to the health service, Griffiths was dismissive of the differences between the NHS and private industry. Private industry was about competition in conditions of surplus, while the NHS was all about rationing scarce resources on criteria of *needs*, as defined by professionals, rather than *demands*, as expressed by consumers.[273] The NHS did not have a single pyramidal structure, with Parliament, a Minister or the district management team at the apex. Clinical freedom created a political dimension outside any normal managerial framework. As quickly as efficient management reduced long-established queues, medical science opened new ones. Clinical freedom allowed consultants to make decisions affecting resources, and consultants had to be persuaded if they were to make their clinical demands more modest. A long and divisive conflict was in prospect if management was to going to be autocratic, challenge clinical decisions and overturn the 1948 agreement between Bevan and the consultants about clinical freedom.[274]

Opposition to general management was not long in coming. If there were to be executive managers who took decisions in isolation that were harmful to patients, consultants would not feel bound to co-operate with them. Community physicians were also opposed to the concept. They had seen themselves as having a key role, determining the needs of the area, setting priorities, leading the planning process and giving the service direction. It had been a flawed strategy because they seldom carried the prestige to deal with the senior and often brilliant consultants in the acute sector.[275] In contrast there was no doubt from the gleeful shouts of triumph from administrators that they thought they had entered the promised land.[276] The RCN attacked 'the exclusion of nurses from any meaningful management role' and spent £250,000 on advertising and publicity. The matter was raised in the Lords. Matrons were being transformed into the ghastly hybrid post of 'quality assurance manager'. Would not Florence Nightingale turn in her grave at that? Ministers were surprised at the nurses' reaction, but unprepared to intervene in local management structures, believing that the nurses were after their own management hierarchy – incompatible with Griffiths – and that management arrangements would sooner or later include all professional groups.[277] Nurses had fought for involvement in policy formation since 1946 and were incensed by the initial failure to give the DHSS's Chief Nursing Officer (CNO) a place at the top table. Their campaign was emotional but soundly based. Although many senior nurses had proved ineffective in management, their demotion from managers to advisers was detrimental to the quality of patient service. Nurses lost a guaranteed path of access, through nursing line management, to the employing authority. In theory a chief executive was in charge of everything; in practice nobody would now control the quality of nursing care.[278] After Griffiths the CNO was replaced by a district nursing *adviser* to the newly created district general manager.[279] Clinical units, often headed by a doctor, were established. Senior nurses found posts within this structure, sometimes in quality assurance or as a unit business manager, but not as part of a single hospital-wide nursing workforce. Florence Nightingale had fought for the control of nurses by a nursing head; Griffiths had brought this to an end. Clinical leadership in nursing was in decline, nationally, regionally and at ward level.

It took a year for the DHSS to change its own structure and recruit a suitable chief executive. The job was not widely sought after. The first person to chair the NHS Management Board was Victor Paige who soon left, in June 1986, because he could not carry through the changes he wished in the face of Ministerial opposition. Shortly before his resignation there was a proposal to 'rationalise hospital accommodation'; the process was begun, but vetoed because it would have meant selling nurses' homes, a proposal that was clearly not a vote winner. The members of the central Supervisory Board, having little health service background, needed educating and their influence was hardly perceptible. Changes at regional level were more important and there were sitting tenants with a claim to the new post of regional general manager (RGM) – the administrator, medical officer, nurse and treasurer. There was wry amusement as some regional administrators, who had raised the inability to take decisions to an art form, were appointed. One doctor, one nurse and one treasurer got RGM appointments;

otherwise administrators got the job, the power and the money. Was it satisfactory that the chairmen of the regions reported to the Secretary of State who had appointed them, while the RGMs reported to the Chief Executive? Would the quality of the service be improved by downgrading the status of professional officers? Some RGMs did not want professionals at management board level. As the general management function was implemented, first at region and then at district and hospital level, protests grew. The Griffiths changes were introduced before the 1982 restructuring had shaken down; they were set to a political timetable that was managerially unrealistic. Neither were general management skills widely available; a management development programme was needed.[280] The implementation of the general management function, however, opened a door to further changes.

There were other small but significant management changes. In 1983 government announced that, to improve the use of resources, health authorities would have to develop systems of competitive tendering for services such as laundry, cleaning and catering. The policy of contracting-out was established, ensuring that private contractors could compete on equal terms with in-house services, possibly an attempt to reduce the power of the unions.[281] The preparation of contracts and tenders was a new field for health service management and the Nuffield Provincial Hospitals Trust helped to define the necessary procedures.[282] The principle was established that the NHS did not have to provide all hospital services by a salaried direct-labour force. Hospitals could also seek income from new sources; for example, income-generation schemes led to the rapid development of shopping arcades in unused areas of hospitals.[283]

Recurrent financial crises

Year by year the cost of providing services was increasing. In the mid-1970s Barbara Castle had argued in Cabinet that the changing age structure of the population, with more old people, meant that an extra 1 per cent was required every year just to provide the same level of service, and that a further 1 per cent was required to cover the costs of the new technology that was continually being introduced. In spite of the pain, the policy of reallocation was pursued and ten years later (1977–1987) the gap between the richest and the poorest regions had narrowed from 26 percentage points to 11 points – the most over-provided being 7 per cent above target and the most under-provided 4 per cent below.[284] In absolute terms the NHS was getting better year by year, but staff saw deterioration in what was offered compared with what was possible. In *Health care and its costs* the DHSS produced statistics showing a rising number of doctors, nurses and admissions, and more money being spent on the NHS in real terms.[285] Professionals, however, looked at the NHS in a different way, asking about the quality of care received by individual patients and how the potentials of modern diagnosis and treatment could be mobilised. Crude totals of service activity did not provide a picture of how the service was changing, and its accessibility in different parts of the country. The figures showed what was being done, not what was not done in a health service increasingly dominated by the problems of people over 65. Tension between politicians and professionals was built into the structure of the NHS.[286] Labour had capitalised on the future of the NHS during the 1983 election campaign – it was the one issue it got right. Some student nurse intakes were cut to save money, and in September 1983 the RCN launched a 'Nurse Alert' campaign, holding a press conference in front of a backcloth emblazoned 'Stop killing the NHS'.[287] Doctors were frustrated at having to explain to patients why services could not be provided. Morale was said to be dropping; it was hard to identify whether it was RAWP, government cuts, reorganisation, technical advances or changes in management that were causing problems.[288] The presidents of the Royal Colleges wrote to *The Times* on 21 March 1984 expressing dismay. No relief was in sight.

The BMA, the Institute of Health Services Management and the RCN began statistical analyses of the trends and the likely medium and long-term prospects for the health service. They launched a report prepared for them by Bosanquet, from the Centre for Health Economics at York.[289] It called for a commitment to maintain the minimum annual rate of growth for hospital and community services at 2 per cent, to fund pay awards fully and to give health authorities greater freedom to plan their spending over time. Ministers pointed to rising amount of money going in to the health service, and the fall in acute sector costs as a result of greater efficiency that allowed more patients to be treated. The organisations were unconvinced, and continued to hammer home the message that the NHS was seriously under-funded.[290]

Twelve consultants, representing all the London teaching hospitals, also wrote in protest to *The Times* in 1986.

> *We are consultants working in the health districts of inner London and have been monitoring the deterioration of the hospital services in our area . . . during the last five years over £35 million has been cut from our district budgets and . . . has caused the closure of 20 hospitals and more than 2,500 acute beds . . . It is no exaggeration to say that the care of the sick and the proper training of tomorrow's doctors are now being jeopardised in our hospitals . . . The inner London population is no longer receiving an adequate acute medical service. The future of hospital medical services in London looks grim.[291]*

The 12 had formed a small group and the letter was followed by a press conference in the House of Lords chaired by Lord Ennals. There was a subsequent meeting between some consultants and Norman Fowler, Secretary of State, and additional funding to 'ease transitional problems from regions receiving the lowest increases under RAWP' was announced, North East Thames RHA receiving £4.6 million.[292] In the House of Lords the medical peers hijacked a debate to discuss standards of clinical care. Lord Smith said he felt that the NHS provided less and less for patients year by year. In 1948 a patient with angina would have been given medicine costing a few shillings; now there would be invasive tests and probably cardiac surgery costing thousands of pounds. Lord Porritt said governments could face up to the health bill only by cutting standards or raising taxation; he favoured a mixture of state, private enterprise, insurance, charity and even lotteries to finance medical care. It had become a dire necessity to practice selective medicine and the selection was made by the wrong people, politicians for financial reasons instead of doctors for medical ones.[293]

Health authorities had used stratagems to cope with the growing squeeze on their budgets. They had closed beds towards the end of the financial year and delayed paying their suppliers. Creative accounting kept them in balance but their debts slowly mounted. In 1987, as another election approached, it was made clear to authorities that bed closures were out. The 'good news' about the NHS proclaimed by Norman Fowler began to jar with the public perception of problems. Frank Dobson, Labour's health spokesman, said that over the last year there had been a new epidemic – an epidemic of hospitals short of beds, an epidemic of doctors hunting for beds, an epidemic of patients turned away.[294] June 1987 brought John Moore to the DHSS in Norman Fowler's place. Moore did not appreciate the dire financial situation of the NHS and failed to extract extra money from the Treasury. Communications failed and the message from the health service did not get through to ministers. Then the unpaid bills were presented and by September 1987 health authorities, realising that no more money was forthcoming, began to close beds by the score. Closures in January had been common enough, but not in October and November. A string of unrelated problems hit the NHS. Proposals for a new pay structure brought the nurses out on strike, and as nurses marched, doctors petitioned Downing Street. Blood transfusion staff took action. In October 1987 a hurricane ripped roofs off the hospitals, symbolising everything happening to the NHS.[295] Medicine and the NHS were caught between the need to concentrate on what was effective and essential, and the temptation to embark on exciting developments that were costly, marginal in their benefit but of great interest to the media. A shortage of intensive care beds was blamed for the death of a baby whose heart operation had been cancelled five times in six weeks.

The NHS was becoming a political, statistical and managerial battleground.[296] Norman Fowler spoke of 'seven years' progress' with rising numbers of nurses, doctors and dentists, more cases being treated, and more outpatient attendances. Why, asked the BMJ, were the professions not impressed by this rosy scene? The answer lay in the complexity of the NHS, the largest organisation in Europe outside the Red Army. This unwieldy organisation was responsible for one of the few growth areas in the British economy, and one that would keep growing. The reality was that there would never be sufficient money and someone, somewhere, would be short of treatment they might reasonably expect. Much of the additional money had gone to absorb the large Clegg pay award inherited by Mrs Thatcher. More was absorbed by the reduction in the working hours of nurses. Demographic growth and technical developments required extra money merely to maintain the status quo. The rate of inflation of health service costs (pay, equipment and costs) was higher than the increase in the retail price index more generally. Closing beds, not because they were unnecessary but to save money, produced a ripple effect. Expectations had risen. More was demanded than was provided. More could be done than resources permitted. This message was percolating through to the public; the Conservative government was not winning the argument about the successes of the NHS.

The approach to NHS reform

Neither NHS reorganisation in 1974 nor restructuring in 1982 had altered the basic structure of the NHS. Society, however, had changed. A command economy can accomplish much, but it may not do it in a timely and sensitive way. People who increasingly expected attentive help in other fields could hardly fail to notice the absence of 'customer-led' services in the NHS. In the 1980s the Conservative government explicitly repudiated consensus and partnership with the professions in policy making. The public interest was no longer seen as achievable in this way and the professions were increasingly regarded as just another lobby, rather than carrying a special imprimatur derived from the nature of its expertise and values.[297] The broadly bipartisan approach to the NHS ended after the Conservative victory in 1987. It was said that, if there was a third term, Mrs Thatcher's motto would be 'the customer comes first'.[298] John Peet, a journalist and a member of a right wing think-tank, thought there was a simple and quick way of increasing efficiency built on competition.[299] Among the political beliefs underpinning the coming changes were: the paramount importance of a sound economy and strong currency, without which public services could not be funded; the view that there was little the public sector could do that the private sector could not do better; and that managerial inefficiency was rife throughout the public sector, whether in the utilities, the schools or the health service.[300] The changing approach in the NHS was only part of a wider ideological battle about society, industry and public services, although many in the NHS did not appreciate this. Maurice Shock later said that professionals failed to read social and political signs and were slow to press for the changes needed to adapt the NHS to rapidly altering circumstances. The once dominant Co-op had been virtually obliterated by stores such as Marks & Spencer, and a vacuum had been left in the direction of one of the largest and most expensive organisations in Europe.[301] The profession was thrown into confusion when it was struck by the blitzkrieg from the right, which believed that efficiency would be driven only by a market or some modification of one. The left believed that the market had many benefits but could not do certain things – prevent pollution or exploitation, nor generate the economic security of social harmony. Julian Tudor Hart thought there was a fundamental misunderstanding of health care and consultations. Health care was not something that patients consumed; patients and health professions produced it jointly. Patients participating in their own care – by managing their diabetes or high blood pressure, for example – made for better, more rational and cost-effective decisions. But they needed to be given professional time, something not encouraged by a market-place.[302]

Health service reform had been on the Conservative agenda for a while but other issues had priority. In 1982 the Cabinet had been presented with a paper prepared by the Central Policy Review Staff, proposing the replacement of the NHS with a system of private insurance as one way to cut public expenditure. Leaked to *The Economist*, there was an immediate outcry.[303] The proposals were killed by Mrs Thatcher as electoral suicide but left fears that there was a hidden agenda.[304] John Redwood and David Willetts at the Centre for Policy Studies had been considering how a market might work within a national health service. Willetts, later a member of the No. 10 Downing Street think-tank on health, argued that the government was getting the worst of all possible worlds. No credit was being given for the ever-increasing sums spent on the NHS. There was anxiety that the NHS was heading for the worst features of American medicine, with care provided only if your credit card was good. There could be advantages in radical but *public* proposals that did not threaten free patient care yet were consistent with the radical Thatcherite philosophy. If an insurance-based system was ruled out, because of the additional overheads, reform had to be on the supply side. GP budgets had already been considered in the context of the review of primary health care. Redwood and Willetts lunched at the Nuffield Provincial Hospitals Trust with Alain Enthoven, a leading expert on the economics of health care, who was on a preliminary visit to Britain before holding a fellowship funded by the Trust. The thinking of the Centre for Policy Studies was discussed, but all the main ideas that later appeared in Enthoven's *Reflections on the management of the NHS* were current in radical-right circles.[305]

Enthoven was involved in the reshaping of US health care organisations, in particular HMOs. His public statement of the ideas was useful to the Centre for Policy Studies. He noted that 'bureaucratic forces in the NHS drove for uniformity'. Variation was equated with inequality and injustice. The idea of a district trying something distinctly new and different, other than in response to orders from the DHSS, was perceived as a threat to the Minister. Enthoven believed there would be increasing problems for a service without incentives to provide either better quality care or services at a lower cost. There seemed little indication of a desire for radical reform, even though the service was approaching gridlock. He was particularly concerned that teaching hospitals were not getting adequate recompense for the work that they did. One approach, he thought, would be to create an internal market as a way forward, with each district receiving a RAWP-based per-capita revenue and capital allocation from which it would pay for and provide health services for its own residents and for others at negotiated prices. Each district would resemble a nationalised company that would buy and sell services from other districts and trade with the private sector. A more radical alternative, which Enthoven preferred, would be competitive HMOs, an idea also favoured by the Adam Smith Institute.[306] The *BMJ* thought that, although North America was a fertile source of flying critics of the NHS, Enthoven was knowledgeable and constructive. His analysis was sharp and his solutions radical. That the NHS was approaching gridlock was in tune with professional thinking; the NHS did seem held in a grip of interlocked forces making real change difficult. It would be a tragedy, said the *BMJ*, if his ideas were not taken seriously, weighed in the balance and tested in the small pilot schemes he advocated.[307]

The end of the rainbow

Alongside a political belief about how services were best provided there was continual evidence that, pressed as it was, the health service could not continue on its current basis. Sir Bryan Thwaites, a mathematician and Chairman of the Wessex RHA, believed that the public was sophisticated enough to recognise that the NHS could not do everything medically possible and that bounds had to be set.[308] Applying hard science to soft data, he calculated that expectations were rising at 5 per cent a year, because of public awareness of what could be provided, the absence of any charge at the point of delivery, lowered tolerance of discomfort, doctors' attitudes and expectations, advances in medical treatment, more research, more GPs leading to more treatment and more consultants leading to more research. Government might be proud of a 2.5 per cent growth rate, but the public was disenchanted that it was not getting what it wanted. The health service needed rethinking; perhaps some services should be outside its range of provision, and more consideration had to be given to costs and outcomes. He gave examples of what the NHS might – and might not – cover. Safely within his vision of NHS services would be the average man with arthritis, and a young wife expecting her first baby; just outside was the married woman wanting in vitro fertilisation; well outside the NHS was the fiancé with a voluptuous nude tattoo impeding his latest courtship, and an elderly and unlikely survivor of heroic surgery. *The Economist* thought that choice, competition and cost-effectiveness would settle the matter; managers and clinical staff required incentives. Sir Bryan Thwaites disagreed; each step forward in efficiency was frustrated by two steps backwards in the face of the onrush of expectation.[309] Bounds and limits were needed. He did not, however, explain who would make the choices, and how. The problems experienced in the front line were presented graphically in an article about the King's College Hospital accident and emergency department. More were attending and more needed admission. Beds were short and patients waited on trolleys until one was found. If Mrs Thatcher was to retire to her home in Dulwich, that was where a sudden illness would bring her. The conditions were third-world. Nurses rather than domestic staff cleaned up the vomit and blood. 'If you don't get it while its wet it's twice as hard to clean up afterwards and if anybody slips over then it's you who answers for it.' Patients bled onto the floor; lumps of plaster fell from the ceiling. The picture was Hogarth. How long were people prepared to stick it?[310]

At the Conservative Party conference in October 1987, John Moore, the Secretary of State, pledged reform of the NHS. A slaughter of sacred cows was promised, which seemed to involve better economic policies to generate wealth, an extension of competitive tendering and more co-operation with the private sector. During the winter of 1987/8 the media began producing horror stories about the NHS on a daily basis.[311] In December 1987 the presidents of three Royal Colleges – Physicians, Surgeons, and Obstetricians and Gynaecologists – issued a terse statement. Giving a press conference on the steps of the DHSS, their message was clear. An immediate overall review of acute hospital services was mandatory and additional alternative funding must be found. Something had to be done to save the health service, once the envy of the world.[312] The view took hold on the Conservative back benches that health care was too important to be left to the DHSS. The pressure to provide more money for the NHS was almost irresistible. Critics argued that the real growth in the NHS budget was not enough to match growing demand from demographic change and the introduction of new costly medical techniques and planned improvements in services. The government believed that a system reflecting a command economy was never going to deal adequately with the demand within the resources available. The next managerial drama, and the greatest since 1946, was about to begin.

References

1. Department of Health and Social Security. *NHS and Social Services: thirtieth anniversary.* London: DHSS, 1978.
2. The disalienation of the NHS [leading article]. *BMJ* 1978; 2: 1–2.
3. Additional £50 million for NHS [parliamentary notes]. *BMJ* 1978; 1: 1062.
4. Regional rides – 'We doubt that we can cope'. *BMJ* 1978; 1: 866–7.
5. Klein R. Health care in the age of disillusionment. *BMJ* 150th anniversary issue. 1982; Jul 5: A2–4.

6. Kennedy I. *The unmasking of medicine*. London: George Allen & Unwin, 1981.
7. Dunea G. Death over the counter. *BMJ* 1983; 286: 211–12.
8. Smith T. Alternative medicine. *BMJ* 1983; 287: 307.
9. Taylor Reilly D. Young doctors' views on alternative medicine. *BMJ* 1983; 287: 337–9.
   Moore J, Phipps K, Marcer D. Why do people seek treatment by alternative medicine? *BMJ* 1985; 290: 28–9.
10. The flight from science [leading article]. *BMJ* 1980; 280: 1–2.
    Alternative therapy. Report of the Board of Science and Education. London: BMA, 1986.
11. Doctors and television. *BMJ* 1978; 1: 348–50.
12. An opportunity for Channel 4 [leading article]. *BMJ* 1980; 1: 504.
13. Diagnosis of brain death. [Conference of the medical royal colleges and their faculties.] *BMJ* 1976, 2: 1187–8.
14. An appalling *Panorama* [leading article]. *BMJ* 1980; 281: 1028.
    Medical news. *BMJ* 1980; 281: 1221, 1291.
    Medicine and the media. *BMJ* 1980; 281: 1485.
15. Klein R. Public opinion and the NHS. *BMJ* 1979; 278: 1296–7.
16. Harrison A, Gretton J, editors. Is the NHS safe with anyone? Attitudes to public and private health. In: *Health care UK*. London: CIPFA, 1985.
17. Day P, Klein R. Towards a new health care system. *BMJ* 1985; 291: 1291–3.
18. McPherson K, Coulter A, Stratton I. Increasing use of private practice. *BMJ* 1985; 291: 797–9.
19. Yates J. *Private eye, heart and hip*. Edinburgh: Churchill Livingstone, 1995.
20. World Health Organization. *From Alma-Ata to the year 2000: reflections at the midpoint*. Geneva: WHO, 1988.
21. Jacobson B, Smith A, Whitehead M, editors.*The nation's health: a strategy for the 1990s*. A report from an independent multidisciplinary committee. London: King's Fund, 1991.
22. World Health Organization/Health and Welfare Canada/Canadian Public Health Association. Ottawa Charter for health promotion. *Ottawa Health Promotion* 1986; 1(4): iii–v.
    WHO Regional office for Europe. *Targets for health for all*. Copenhagen: WHO, 1986.
23. Black D, chairman. *Inequalities in health: the Black report*. Harmondsworth: Penguin Books, 1982.
    Whitehead M. *The health divide: inequalities in health in the 1980s*. London: Health Education Council, 1987.
24. Horder J. Alma-Ata declaration. *BMJ* 1983; 286: 191–4.
25. Maxwell RJ. Quality assessment in health. *BMJ* 1984; 288: 1470–2.
26. Lunn LN, Mushin WW. *Mortality associated with anaesthesia*. London: Nuffield Provincial Hospitals Trust, 1982.
27. Devlin HB, Lunn JN. Confidential enquiry into perioperative deaths. *BMJ* 1986; 292: 1622–3.
    Buck N, Devlin HB, Lunn JN. *The report of a confidential enquiry into perioperative deaths*. London: Nuffield Provincial Hospitals Trust, 1987.
28. Holland W. Avoidable death as a measure of quality. *Quality Assurance in Health Care* 1990; 2: 227–33.
29. Wennberg JE. Better policy to promote the evaluative clinical sciences. *Quality Assurance in Health Care* 1990; 2(1): 21–9.
30. Williams A.The value of QALYS. *Health and Social Services Journal* 1985; Jul 18: C3–5.
31. Hampton JR. The end of clinical freedom. *BMJ* 1983; 287: 1237–8.
32. Brook RH, Appel FA. Quality-of-care assessment. *New England Journal of Medicine* 1973; 288: 1323.
    Hicks NR. Some observations on attempts to measure appropriateness of care. *BMJ* 1994: 309; 730–2.

Brook RH Appropriateness; the next frontier. *BMJ* 1994, 308: 218–19.

33. Ware J, Brook RH et al. *Health outcomes for adults in prepaid and fee-for service systems of care; results from the health insurance experiment.* Santa Monica: Rand Corporation, 1987.

34. Eddy DM. Clinical decision making: from theory to practice. *Journal of the American Medical Association* 1990; 263: 287–90, 441–3, 877–80, 1265–75, 1839–41, 2493–505, 3077–84; 264: 389–91; 265: 782–8, 2399–406.

35. Ellwood PM. Outcomes management, a technology of patient experience. Shattuck Lecture. *New England Journal of Medicine* 1988; 318: 1549–56.

36. A decade for the patient [leading article]. *BMJ* 1980; 1: 65–6.
Shaw CD. Aspects of audit. 1. The background. *BMJ* 1980; 1: 1256–8.
Audit in general practice [leading article]. *BMJ* 1980; 2: 1375, 1440–1.

37. Berwick D. Continuous improvement as an ideal in health care. *New England Journal of Medicine* 1989; 320: 53–6.

38. Sikora K, Smedeley H. Interferon and cancer. *BMJ* 1983; 286: 739–40.

39. Jeffries DJ. Clinical use of acyclovir. *BMJ* 1985; 290: 177–8.

40. Bell PM, Walshe K. Benefits of self monitoring of blood glucose. *BMJ* 1983; 286: 1230–1.

41. Rosen M. Patient controlled analgesia. *BMJ* 1984; 289: 640–1.

42. Wellings K, Mills A. Contraceptive trends. *BMJ* 1984; 289: 939–40.

43. Tyrer PJ. Benzodiazepines on trial. *BMJ* 1984; 288: 1101–2.

44. Benoxaprofen [leading article]. *BMJ* 1982; 285: 459–6.
Medicine and the media. *BMJ* 1983; 286: 218–19.

45. Rawlings MD. Postmarketing surveillance of adverse reactions to drugs. *BMJ* 1984; 288: 879–80.

46. Aronson JK, Grahame-Smith DG. Adverse drug interactions. *BMJ* 1981; 282: 288–91.

47. Isherwood I. Recent advances and future prospects in clinical radiology. In: Ashton D, editor. *Future trends in medicine*. London: Royal Society of Medicine, 1993.

48. Nuclear magnetic resonance imaging and neurology [leading article]. *BMJ* 1982; 284: 1359–60.
Steiner RE. Nuclear magnetic resonance imaging. *BMJ* 1987; 294: 1570–2.

49. Galbraith NS, Forbes P, Mayon-White RT. Changing patterns of communicable disease in England and Wales. II. Disappearing and declining diseases. *BMJ* 1980; 2: 489–92.

50. Galbraith NS, Forbes P, Mayon-White RT. Changing patterns of communicable disease in England and Wales. *BMJ* 1980; 2: 427–30.

51. Gill ON, Bartlett CLR, Sockett PN et al. Outbreak of *Salmonella napoli* infection caused by contaminated chocolate bars. *Lancet* 1983; 1: 574–7.
Cowden JM, O'Mahoney M, Bartlett CL et al. A national outbreak of *Salmonella typhimurium* caused by contaminated salami sticks. *Epidemiology and Infection* 1989; 103: 219–25.

52. Department of Health and Social Security. *Report of the committee of inquiry into an outbreak of food poisoning at Stanley Royd Hospital*. London: HMSO, 1986.

53. PHLS Malaria Reference Laboratory and CDSC. Malaria 1980. *BMJ* 1982; 284: 750.
PHLS Communicable Disease Surveillance Centre and PHLS Malaria Reference Laboratory. Malaria in Britain: 1981. *BMJ* 1983; 286: 1207–8.

54. Adler MW, Mindel A. Genital herpes: hype or hope. *BMJ* 1986; 286: 1767–8.

55. Berridge V. *AIDS in the UK*. Oxford: Oxford University Press, 1996.

56. Waterson AP. Acquired immune deficiency syndrome. *BMJ* 1983; 286: 743–6.

57. Adler MW. AIDS: the development of the epidemic. *BMJ* 1987; 294: 1083–5.

58. Adler MW, Weller IVD. AIDS: sense not fear. *BMJ* 1984; 288: 1177–8.
Pinching AL. Children with HIV: dealing with the problem. In: Morgan DR, editor. *Aids: a challenge in education*. London: Institute of Biology/RSM, 1990.

59. Dyer C. Doctors with AIDS and the *News of the World*. *BMJ* 1987; 295: 1339.

60. Aids advertising. *Daily Telegraph* 1986; Dec 19.
61. Crawfurd Md'A. Prenatal diagnosis of common genetic disorders. *BMJ* 1988; 297: 502–6.
62. Smith T. How will the new genetics work? *BMJ* 1983; 1: 1–2.
63. Langman MJS. What is happening to peptic ulcer? *BMJ* 1982; 284: 1063–4.
64. Warren JR, Marshall B. Unidentified curved bacillus on gastric epithelium in active chronic gastritis [letters]. *Lancet* 1983; 1: 1273–5.
    Marshall's hunch. *The New Yorker* 1993; Sep 20.
65. Woolfson AMJ. Artificial nutrition in hospital. *BMJ* 1983; 287: 1004–6.
66. Allen-Mersh TG, Earlam RJ. General surgical workload in England and Wales. *BMJ* 1983; 287: 115–18.
67. Second-best prostatectomy? [leading article] *BMJ* 1980; 280: 590.
68. Burn JMB. Responsible use of resources: day surgery. *BMJ* 1983; 286: 492–3.
69. Wickham JEA. Keyhole surgery. In: Walton J, Barondess JA, Lock S, editors. *The Oxford medical companion*. Oxford: Oxford University Press, 1994.
    Wickham JEA. Minimally invasive surgery – future developments. *BMJ* 1994, 308: 193–6.
70. Wickham JEA, Kellet MJ. Percutaneous nephrolithotomy. *BMJ* 1981; 283: 1571–2.
71. Wickham JEA, Webb DR, Payne SR et al. Extracorporeal shock wave lithotripsy. *BMJ* 1985; 290: 1188–9.
    Das G, Dick J, Bailey MJ et al. Extracorporeal shock wave lithotripsy: the first 1000 cases. *BMJ* 1987; 295: 891–3.
72. Hatfield ARW. The medical management of jaundice: endoscopic techniques. In: Dawson AM, Besser GM, editors. *Recent advances in medicine – 20*. London: Churchill Livingstone, 1987, 191–201.
73. Wickham JEA. The new surgery. *BMJ* 1987; 295: 1581–2.
    Wickham JEA. Recent advances in interventional management: renal stones. In: Dawson AM, Besser GM, editors. *Recent advances in medicine – 20*. London: Churchill Livingstone, 1987, 215–23.
74. Jones B, Smith P, Harrison D. Replantation. *BMJ* 1983; 287: 1–2.
75. O'Hickey SP, Pickering CAC, Jones PE, Evans JD. Manchester air disaster. *BMJ* 1987; 294: 1663–7.
76. Harrold AJ. Outlook for hip replacement. *BMJ* 1982; 284: 139.
    Ring PA. Outlook for hip replacement [letter]. *BMJ* 1982; 284: 509.
77. Bulstrode C. Keeping up with orthopaedic epidemics. *BMJ* 1987; 295: 514.
78. Freeman MAR. Reconstructive surgery in arthritis. In: Hadfield J, Hobsley M, editors. *Current surgical practice*, vol 3. London: Royal College of Surgeons, 1981.
79. Evans G, Jackson RK. Microdiscectomy for treating lumbar disc protrusion. *BMJ* 1988; 297: 5.
80. Chambers JB, Monaghan MJ, Jackson G. Echocardiography. *BMJ* 1988; 297: 1071–5.
    Simpson IA, Camm AJ. Colour Doppler flow mapping. *BMJ* 1990; 300: 1.
    Wren C. Paediatric cardiology. In: Eyre J, Boyd R, editors. *Paediatric specialty practice for the 1990s*. London: Royal College of Physicians, 1991.
81. Department of Health. *On the state of the public health*. Report of the CMO for 1988. London: HMSO, 1989, 39.
82. Calcium antagonists and the heart [leading article]. *BMJ* 1981; 282: 89–90.
    Maclean D, Feely J. Calcium antagonists, nitrates and new antianginal drugs. *BMJ* 1983; 286: 1127–30.
83. Davidson RG. Who needs paramedics? *Nursing Times* 1982; Feb 24: 336–7.
84. Mackintosh AF, Crabb ME, Grainger R et al. The Brighton resuscitation ambulances. *BMJ* 1978; 1: 1115–18.
85. Hampton JR. Coronary patient – early treatment. *British Heart Journal* 1981; 46: 117–20.
86. Simpson HK, Smith GB. Survey of paramedic skills in the UK and Channel Islands. *BMJ* 1996, 313: 1052–3.

87. Fibrinolytic therapy in myocardial infarction [leading article]. *BMJ* 1979; 2: 1017–18.

88. Poller L. Oral anticoagulants reassessed. *BMJ* 1982; 284: 1425.

89. Breckenridge A. Treating mild hypertension. *BMJ* 1985; 291: 89–90.
    MRC Working Party. MRC trial of treatment of mild hypertension. *BMJ* 1985; 291: 97–104.

90. Angina: the treatment revolution [leading article]. *BMJ* 1979; 2: 1167–8.

91. Surgery for coronary artery disease [leading article]. *BMJ* 1978; 1: 597–9.

92. English RAH, Bailey AR, Dark JF, Williams WG. The UK cardiac surgical register, 1977–82. *BMJ* 1984; 289: 1205–8.

93. Units for cardiac surgery [leading article]. *BMJ* 1979; 2: 2.

94. Williams A. Economics of coronary artery bypass grafting. *BMJ* 1985; 291: 326–9.

95. Petch MC. Unblocking coronary arteries. *BMJ* 1982; 284: 683–4.
    Petch MC. Coronary angioplasty: time for reappraisal. *BMJ* 1987; 295: 453–4.

96. Wood RFM. Organ transplantation. In: Dawson AM, Besser GM, editors. *Recent advances in medicine – 20*. London: Churchill Livingstone, 1987.

97. English TAH, Cooper DKC, Cory-Pearce R. Recent experience with heart transplantation. *BMJ* 1980; 2: 699–702.

98. Kay HEM. Bone marrow transplantation: 1982. *BMJ* 1982; 285: 1296–8.

99. Knapp MS. Renal failure – dilemmas and developments. *BMJ* 1982; 284: 847–50
    Wing AJ. A different view from different countries: United Kingdom. In: Kjellstrand CM, Dossetor JB, editors. *Ethical problems in dialysis and transplantation*. Dordrecht: Kluwer, 1992.

100. Department of Health and Social Security. *On the state of the public health*. Report of the CMO for 1981. London: HMSO, 1989.

101. Gonzalez-Carrillo M, Moloney A, Bewick M et al. Renal transplantation in diabetic nephropathy. *BMJ* 1982; 285: 1713–16.
     Wing AJ. Why don't the British treat more patients with kidney failure? *BMJ* 1983; 287: 1157–8.

102. Department of Health and Social Security. *On the state of the public health*. Report of the CMO for 1981. London: HMSO, 1982.

103. Klein R. Rationing health care. *BMJ* 1984; 289: 143–4.
     Hoffenberg R. *Clinical freedom*. Rock Carling Fellowship 1986. London: Nuffield Provincial Hospitals Trust, 1987.

104. Nicholls AJ, Waldeck S, Platts MM et al. The impact of continuous ambulatory peritoneal dialysis on the treatment of renal failure in patients over 60. *BMJ* 1984; 288: 18–19.

105. Ballantyne JC, Evans EF, Morrison AW. Electrical auditory stimulation in the management of profound hearing loss. *Journal of Laryngology and Otology* 1978; suppl 1: 1–117.

106. Kirk D. Prostatic carcinoma. *BMJ* 1985; 290: 875–6.

107. Oliver RTD. Rare cancers and specialist centres. *BMJ* 1986; 292: 641–2.

108. Davey P, Tudhope GR. Anticancer chemotherapy. *BMJ* 1983; 287: 110–13.

109. Baum M. Will breast self-examination save lives? *BMJ* 1982; 284: 142–3.

110. Warden J. Prevention is politically popular. *BMJ* 1987; 294: 657.

111. US Department of Health and Human Services. *The health consequences of involuntary smoking. A report of the surgeon general*. Rockville, MD: Public Health Service, Office on Smoking and Health, 1986.

112. Ryan R, Kidd GM. The Liverpool urban obstetric flying squad. *BMJ* 1987; 294: 97–9.

113. Lewis BV, Tipton RH, Sloper IMS. Changing pattern in a general practitioner obstetric unit. *BMJ* 1978; 1: 484–5.

114. Russell W. Dr Vaughan's enthusiasms *BMJ* 1981; 282: 1721.
     Chamberlain R, Macfarlane A. *Where to be born?* Oxford: National Perinatal Epidemiology Unit, 1994.

115. NIH Consensus statements. Caesarean childbirth. *BMJ* 1981; 282: 1600–3.

116. PC Steptoe [obituary]. *BMJ* 1988; 296: 1135.

117. Trounson A, Conti A. Research in human in-vitro fertilisation and embryo transfer. *BMJ* 1982; 285: 244–7.

118. Parliament. *The report of the committee of enquiry into human fertility and embryology.* (Chairman: Dame Mary Warnock.) Cmnd 9314. London: HMSO, 1984.
    A welcome report [leading article]. *BMJ* 1984; 289: 207–8.
    Warnock M. The Warnock report. *BMJ* 1985; 291: 187–9.

119. Dyer C. The Gillick judgement: contraceptives and the under 16s: House of Lords ruling. *BMJ* 1985; 291: 1208–9.

120. Colposcopy [leading article]. *BMJ* 1981; 282: 250–1.

121. Meadows R. Time past and time present for children and their doctors. In: Forfar JO, editor. *Child health in a changing society.* Oxford: British Paediatric Association/OUP, 1988.

122. Eyre J, Boyd R, editors. *Paediatric specialty practice for the 1990s.* London: RCP, 1991.

123. House of Commons. *Perinatal and neonatal mortality.* Second report from the Social Services Committee Session 1979/80. (Chairman: Mrs Renée Short) London: HMSO, 1980.

124. Gaston MH, Verter JI, Woods G et al. Prophylaxis with oral penicillin in children with sickle cell anemia. *New England Journal of Medicine* 1986; 314: 1593–9.

125. Experience with growth hormone treatment in Great Britain [leading article]. *BMJ* 1980; 1: 270.

126. Ban on growth hormone. *Lancet* 1985; 1: 1172.
    Buchanan CR, Preece MA, Milner RDG. Mortality, neoplasia and Creutzfeldt–Jakob disease in patients treated with human pituitary growth hormone in the UK. *BMJ* 1991; 302: 824–8.
    Trial begins into victims of CJD growth hormone. *BMJ* 1996, 312: 1057.

127. Health Advisory Service. *The rising tide: developing services for mental illness in old age.* Sutton: Health Advisory Service, 1982.

128. Special hospital transfers [leading article]. *BMJ* 1980; 281: 174.

129. Snowden PR. Regional secure units: arriving but under threat. *BMJ* 1987; 294: 1310–11.

130. Unsworth C. *The politics of mental health legislation.* Oxford: Clarendon Press, 1987.

131. Webster L, Dean C, Kessel N. Effect of the 1983 Mental Health Act on the management of psychiatric patients. *BMJ* 1987; 295: 1529–31.

132. King D. *Moving from mental hospitals to community care.* London: Nuffield Provincial Hospitals Trust, 1991.

133. House of Commons Social Services Select Committee. *Community Care (second report).* London: HMSO, 1985.

134. Bosanquet N, Leese B. Family doctors and innovation in general practice. *BMJ* 1988; 296: 1576–80.

135. Jenkins R. Developments in primary care of mental illness. A forward look. *International Review of Psychiatry* 1992; 4: 237–42.

136. Livingstone A, Widgery D. The new general practice: changing philosophies of primary care. *BMJ* 1990; 301: 708–10.

137. *Health and prevention in primary care.* Report from general practice no. 18. (Chairman: J Horder.) London: Royal College of General Practitioners, 1981.
    Prevention of arterial disease in general practice. Report from general practice no. 19. (Chairman: J Tudor Hart.) London: Royal College of General Practitioners, 1981.

138. Fowler G. What is preventable? *BMJ* 1982; 284: 1017–18.

139. Fullard E, Fowler G, Gray M. Facilitating prevention in primary care. *BMJ* 1984; 284: 1585–7.

140. Tudor Hart J. Community general practitioners. *BMJ* 1984; 288: 1670–3.

141. Noble J. An expanding remit for general practice. *BMJ* 1978; 1: 1566.

142. Parliament. *Royal Commission on the NHS* (Chairman: Sir Alec Merrison.) Cmnd 7615. London: HMSO, 1979, para 7.51.

143. Morrell D. London general practice – is there a solution? *BMJ* 1981; 282: 161–3.
144. Higgs R. Example of intermediate care: the new Lambeth community care centre. *BMJ* 1985; 291: 1395–6.
145. London Health Planning Consortium. *Primary health care in inner London.* (Chairman: Donald Acheson.) London: DHSS, 1981.
    London Advisory Group. *The development of health services in London.* London: DHSS, 1981.
146. Russell W. NHS a campaign issue for June election. *BMJ* 1983; 286: 1589.
147. Jarman B. Underprivileged areas: validation and distribution of scores. *BMJ* 1984; 289: 1587–92.
148. Pringle M, Dennis J, Hutton A. Computerisation, the choice. *BMJ* 1982; 284: 165–8.
149. Smith R. Computers in medicine: searching for the rainbow and the crock of gold. *BMJ* 1982; 284: 1859–6.
    Department of Health and Social Security. *On the state of the public health.* Reports of the CMO for 1982 and for 1985. London: HMSO, 1983 and 1986.
    Department of Health and Social Security. Joint Computer Policy Group. *Micros in practice: report of an appraisal of GP microcomputer systems.* (Chairman: J Chisholm.) London: HMSO, 1986.
150. Deputising circular strongly criticised [from the GMSC]. *BMJ* 1984; 288: 337–8.
151. Mr Fowler's statement on the limited list [from the GMSC]. *BMJ* 1985; 290: 724.
152. Doctors, drugs and DHSS [leading article]. *BMJ* 1984; 289: 1397–8.
153. Hoffenberg R. *Clinical freedom.* Rock Carling Fellowship 1986. London: Nuffield Provincial Hospitals Trust, 1987.
154. BMA: GMSC. *Report of the new charter working group.* London: BMA, 1979.
    GP Charter Working Group, *BMJ* 1979; 2: 1236–9.
155. Medical Practitioners' Union/ASTMS. *The future organisation of primary care.* London: MPU, 1986.
156. Marinker M. Developments in primary health care. In: Teeling Smith G, editor. *A new NHS Act for 1996?* London: Office of Health Economics, 1984.
157. Irvine D. The quality initiative. *Journal of the Royal College of General Practitioners* 1983; 33: 521–3.
158. Pendleton D, Schofield T, Marinker M, editors. *In pursuit of quality.* London: RCGP, 1986.
    Royal College of General Practitioners. *What sort of doctor? – assessing quality of care in general practice.* London: RCGP, 1985.
159. Towards quality in general practice: reform or be reformed [RCGP report]. *BMJ* 1985; 290: 1981.
    Royal College of General Practitioners. *Towards quality in general practice.* London: RCGP, 1985.
160. Incentives in the surgery [leader]. *The Times* 1985; Nov 9.
161. Maynard A. Performance incentives in general practice. In: Teeling Smith G, editor. *Health, education and general practice.* London: Office of Health Economics, 1985.
162. Department of Health and Social Security. *Primary health care – an agenda for discussion.* Cmnd 9771. London: HMSO, 1986.
163. BMA's statement. *BMJ* 1986; 292: 1152.
164. Marinker M, Gray DP, Maynard A. The doctor, the patient and their contract. I. The general practitioner's contract: why change it? *BMJ* 1986; 292: 1313–15; II. A good practice allowance; is it feasible? *BMJ* 1986; 292: 1374–6; III. Alternative contracts; are they viable? *BMJ* 1986; 292: 1438–40.
165. Hart TJ. Burnout or into battle [letter]. *British Journal of General Practice* 1994; 44(379): 96.
    Greenhalgh T. Money matters. *BMJ* 1995, 310: 132.
166. Minister opens debate on primary care review [from the GMSC]. *BMJ* 1986; 292: 1411.

167. Department of Health and Social Security Press Release. Primary health care. Norman Fowler's statement. 1986; Apr 21.

168. Final response submitted on primary health care [from the GMSC]. *BMJ* 1987; 294: 71.

169. Parliament. *Promoting better health. The government's programme for improving primary health care.* Cm 249. London: HMSO, 1987.

170. Hull R. Government proposals for primary care: white hope, elephant or sepulchre? *BMJ* 1987; 295: 1436.
    'Promoting better health.' *BMJ* 1987; 295: 1497–8.

171. Jarman B, Cumberlege J. Developing primary health care. *BMJ* 1987; 294: 1005–8.

172. Department of Health and Social Security. *Neighbourhood nursing: a focus for care.* (Chair: Julia Cumberlege.) London: HMSO, 1986.
    House of Commons. *Primary health care.* First report from the Social Services Committee Session 1986/7. London: HMSO, 1987.

173. Department of Health and Social Security and Welsh Office. Central Health Services Council (Chairman: Sir Desmond Bonham-Carter). *The functions of the district general hospital.* London: HMSO, 1969.

174. Avery Jones F. Getting the NHS back on course. *BMJ* 1978; 2: 5–9.

175. Department of Health and Social Security. *Hospital services: the future pattern of hospital provision in England.* London: DHSS, 1980.

176. Making a virtue of necessity [leading article]. *BMJ* 1980; 1: 1335.
    Smith J. Hospital building in the NHS. Policy I. *BMJ* 1984; 289: 1298–300.
    Smith J. Hospital building in the NHS. Policy II: reduced expectations. *BMJ* 1984; 289: 1368–70.

177. Wickings I, Coles JM, Flux R, Howard L. Review of clinical budgeting and costing experiments. *BMJ* 1983; 286: 575–8.
    Greenhalgh CA, Todd JN. Financial Information Project: message for the NHS. *BMJ* 1985; 290: 410–11.
    Management budgeting in the NHS [Annual Representatives meeting]. *BMJ* 1985; 290: 175.

178. Cross M. When the chips are down. *Health Service Journal* 1996; Nov 7: 14.

179. McPherson K. Length of stay and health outcome. *BMJ* 1984; 288: 1854–5.

180. Heyssell RM, Gaintner JR, Kues IW et al. Decentralised management in a teaching hospital. *New England Journal of Medicine* 1984; 310: 1477–80.

181. Johnson JN. Clinical directorates. *BMJ* 1990; 300: 488.

182. NHS/DHSS. Steering Group on Health Services Information. *First report.* (Chairman: Mrs Edith Körner.) London: HMSO, 1982.
    Körner E. Improved information for the NHS. *BMJ* 1984; 289: 1635–6.

183. *Accounting for health.* Report of a working group. (Chairman: Brian Abel-Smith.) London: King's Fund, 1973.
    Bodenham KE, Wellman F. *Foundations for health service management.* London: SCICON/Nuffield Provincial Hospitals Trust, 1972.

184. Knox EG, editor. *Health care information.* London: Nuffield Provincial Hospitals Trust, 1987.

185. Department of Health and Social Security. *Sharing resources for health in England.* Report of the Resource Allocation Working Party. London: HMSO, 1976.

186. Rivett GC.*The development of the London hospital system, 1823–1982.* London: King's Fund:1986, 335–6.
    Rivett GC.*The work of the London Health Planning Consortium.* King's Fund Project Paper no 25. London: King's Fund, 1980, part 3: 43–58.

187. London Health Planning Consortium. *Acute hospital services in London.* London: HMSO, 1979.
    London Health Planning Consortium [briefing]. *BMJ* 1980; 1: 734–5.

188. London Health Planning Consortium. *Towards a balance*. London: HMSO, 1980.

189. *London medical education. A new framework*. Report of a working party on medical and dental teaching resources. (Chairman: Lord Flowers.) London: University of London, 1980.

190. Department of Health and Social Security. *On the state of the public health*. Report of the CMO for 1979. London: DHSS, 1980.
London Health Planning Consortium. *Report by the study group on cardiology and cardiothoracic surgery*. London: DHSS, 1979.

191. Russell W. A new look at London's health service. BMJ 1980; 280: 805.

192. London Advisory Group. (Chair: Sir John Habakkuk.) *Acute hospital services in London*. London: DHSS, 1981.

193. Cuts and excellence [leading article]. BMJ 1982; 284: 294.

194. Jones W. Riverside district twice revisited. *Health and Social Service Journal* 1985: Feb 7: 162–3.
Davies P. North London marriage of convenience. *Health Service Journal* 1986: May 22: 686.

195. Department of Health and Social Security. *Future management of the London specialist postgraduate hospitals*. London: DHSS, 1978.

196. Department of Health and Social Security. *Management arrangements for the specialist postgraduate teaching hospitals*. Report by the London Advisory Group. London: DHSS, 1981.

197. Lambeth, Southwark & Lewisham AHA(T). NHS budgeting. BMJ 1979; 2: 398.
Cash limits squeeze in London AHA(T)s [briefing]. BMJ 1979; 2: 1600–2.

198. King's Fund. *Back to back planning*. Report on regional plans for inner London's health authorities. London: King's Fund, 1987.

199. Smith R. The starving of the medical schools. BMJ 1982; 284: 335–7.

200. Maynard A, Walker A. *Doctor manpower 1975–2000*. Research paper no. 4 for the Royal Commission on the NHS. London: HMSO, 1978.
Department of Health and Social Security. *Medical manpower – the next twenty years*. London: HMSO, 1978.

201. Further views on medical manpower [leading article]. BMJ 1979; 1: 573–4.
Parliament. *Royal Commission on the NHS*. (Chairman: Sir Alec Merrison.) Cmnd 7615. London: HMSO, 1979.

202. Social Services Committee. *Fourth report on medical education with reference to the number of doctors and the career structure in hospitals*. (Chair: Renée Short.) London: HMSO, 1981.
Consultants and their future [leading article]. BMJ 1981; 283: 1007–8.

203. Medical manpower in the year 2000 [from the HJSC]. BMJ 1983; 286: 1073.
Student intake should be cut [from the Senior Hospital Staffs conference]. BMJ 1983; 286: 2073.

204. Medical manpower planning: advisory committee's report. BMJ 1985; 290: 1088.

205. Reduction in medical school intake – a matter of urgency [from the Council]. BMJ 1985; 290: 1445.

206. Smith T. Thirty-four years at the Elephant: George Godber. BMJ 150th anniversary issue. 1982; Jul 5: A30–2.
Klein R. Policy options for medical manpower. BMJ 1977; 2: 136–7.
Parkhouse J. Simple model for medical manpower studies. BMJ 1977; 2: 530.

207. Government's plans to double consultant numbers. BMJ 1981; 283: 241.
Chief Medical Officer speaks on manpower [from the CCHMS]. BMJ 1982; 284: 525–6.

208. Appleyard WJ. Medical manpower mismanagement: mirage or miracle? BMJ 1982; 284: 1351–2.
Hospital staffing structure. BMJ 1982; 284: 1719.

209. Russell W. Resistance to changing the career structure. *BMJ* 1985; 290: 1444.
210. A promising package on hospital staffing [leading article]. *BMJ* 1986; 293: 87.
Hospital medical staffing. Achieving a balance. *BMJ* 1986; 293: 147–9.
211. *Hospital medical staffing. Achieving a balance: plan for action.* London: DHSS, 1987.
Hospital medical staffing: achieving a balance. *BMJ* 1987; 295: 1152–4.
Parkhouse J. Hospital medical staffing: our hope for years to come. *BMJ* 1987; 295: 1157–8.
212. Miller P. Junior doctors: the new deal. *BMJ* 1991; 303: 916–18.
213. Dopson L. A case for concern. *Nursing Times* 1982; Feb 24: 305.
214. Price Waterhouse. *Report on the costs, benefits and manpower implications of Project 2000.* London: UKCC, 1987.
215. Delamothe T. Voting with their feet. *BMJ* 1988; 296: 25–8.
216. Arnold N. A nursing view: where have all the nurses gone? *BMJ* 1980; 280: 199–201.
217. Delamothe T. Nursing grievances. III. Conditions. *BMJ* 1988; 296: 182–5
218. National Audit Office. *NHS: control of nursing manpower.* London: HMSO, 1985.
219. Davies C. Gender and the professional predicament in nursing. Buckingham: Open University Press, 1995.
220. Dopson L. Unfair to students? *Nursing Times* 1982; Feb 24: 306.
221. Chapman CM. Nurses' education. *BMJ* 1985; 291: 295–6.
Commission on Nursing Education. *The education of nurses: a new dimension.* (Chair: Dr Henry Judge.) London: RCN, 1985.
Davies C. Gender and the professional predicament in nursing. Buckingham: Open University Press, 1995.
222. Davies C. A new vision of professionalism. *Nursing Times* 1996: Nov 6: 44–6; Nov 13: 54–6.
223. Clark J. Why nursing education has to change. *BMJ* 1986; 293: 517.
224. Red alert warning on nursing, says RCN secretary. *BMJ* 1987; 294: 1044.
225. Bosanquet N. Nursing manpower. *BMJ* 1987; 294: 791–2.
226. Elkan R, Robinson J. *The implementation of project 2000.* Nottingham: Department of Nursing Studies, 1991.
227. Mitchell RG. Opening discussion. In: Duncan A, McLachlan G, editors. *Hospital medicine and nursing in the 1980s.* London: Nuffield Provincial Hospitals Trust, 1984.
228. Clark MO. Changing clinical practice. In: Duncan A, McLachlan G, editors. *Hospital medicine and nursing in the 1980s.* London: Nuffield Provincial Hospitals Trust, 1984.
229. Chapman A. A critical perspective; Wright S. Useless theory or aid to practice; Glasper A. A planned approach to nursing children. Chapters in: Salvage J, Kershaw B, editors. *Introduction to models for nursing 2.* London: Scutari Press/RCN, 1990.
230. Clark MO. Changing clinical practice in nursing. In: Duncan A, McLachlan G, editors. *Hospital medicine and nursing in the 1980s.* London: Nuffield Provincial Hospitals Trust, 1984.
231. Evers H. Key issues in nursing practice: ward management. *Nursing Times* 1982; Feb 24: 21–4.
232. Report of RCN conference. *BMJ* 1978; 1: 1632.
233. Payne LM. 'Guérir quelquefois, soulager souvent, consoler toujours'. *BMJ* 1967; 4: 47–8.
234. Mitchell JRA. Is nursing any business of doctors? A simple guide to the 'nursing process'. *BMJ* 1984; 288: 216–19.
235. Tierney AJ. A response to Professor Mitchell's 'simple guide to the nursing process'. *BMJ* 1984; 288: 835–8.
Roper N, Logan WW, Tierney AJ. *The elements of nursing.* London: Longman, 1980.
236. Salvage J. A root cause? *Nursing Times* 1982; Feb 17: 270.
237. Royal College of Nursing. *Towards standards: a discussion document.* London: RCN, 1981.
Doctors and nurses [leading article]. *BMJ* 1981; 283: 683–4.

238. Strong JA. Preface. In: Duncan A, McLachlan G, editors. *Hospital medicine and nursing in the 1980s*. London: Nuffield Provincial Hospitals Trust, 1984.

239. Salvage J, Wright SG. *Nursing development units*. London: Scutari Press, 1995.

240. Davies C. *Gender and the professional predicament in nursing*. Buckingham: Open University Press, 1955.

241. Kay R. *Historical review of the Southern California Permanente Medical Group*. Los Angeles CA: PMG, 1979.

242. Stilwell B. Nurse in a doctor's world. *Nursing Times* 1982; Apr 21: 651.
    Bowling A, Stilwell B, editors. *The nurse in family practice*. London: Scutari Press, 1989.

243. Hart TJ. Practice nurses: an underused resource. *BMJ* 1985; 290: 1162–3

244. Salvage J. Distorted images. *Nursing Times* 1983; Jan 5: 13–14.

245. Rowden R. Small is beautiful. *Nursing Times* 1982; Mar 10: 397.

246. Ellis N. A panic measure with hidden hazards. *BMJ* 1980; 280: 61–2.

247. A personal view of current medicopolitical events. *BMJ* 1979; 1: 207, 281.
    Industrial anarchy in the NHS [leading article]. *BMJ* 1979; 1: 364.
    NHS industrial disputes: effects on doctors and patients [leading article]. *BMJ* 1979; 1: 426.
    NHS industrial disputes: continuing effects. *BMJ* 1979; 1: 837.

248. Dyson R. Industrial action 1979: what can we learn? *BMJ* 1979; 278: 1435–7.

249. The week. A personal view. *BMJ* 1979; 1: 1293.

250. Russell W. Conservatives insurance scheme shelved. *BMJ* 1980; 280: 264.

251. Tory health [leading article]. *BMJ* 1979; 278: 1522.

252. Health services bill [parliamentary notes]. *BMJ* 1980; 280: 122–3.

253. Discussions to start on contract modifications [from the CCHMS]. *BMJ* 1979; 279: 684.

254. Parliament. *Report of the Royal Commission on the NHS*. Cmnd 7615. London: HMSO, 1979.
    Merrison A. The Royal Commission in retrospect. In: Teeling Smith G, editor. *A new NHS Act for 1996*. London: Office of Health Economics, 1984.
    'Much to praise, not a little to criticise...' [leading article]. *BMJ* 1979; 279: 227–8.

255. Department of Health and Social Security and Welsh Office. *Patients first*. London: HMSO, 1979.

256. New NHS structure needs new attitudes [leading article]. *BMJ* 1980; 281: 342.

257. Department of Health and Social Security. *Health service development: structure and management*. (HC(80)8) London: DHSS, 1980.

258. Reorganisation by stealth [leading article]. *BMJ* 1981; 282: 174.
    NHS reorganisation: a multidisciplinary discussion. *BMJ* 1981; 283: 1134–7.

259. Reorganisation a la carte [leading article]. *BMJ* 1982; 284: 769–70.

260. Medical advisory machinery. *BMJ* 1982; 284: 290.
    Department of Health and Social Security. *Health services development: structure and management*. HC(82)1. London: DHSS, 1982.

261. Department of Health and Social Security. *The NHS planning system*. (HC(82)6). London: DHSS, 1982.

262. Department of Health and Social Security. *Care in action*. London: HMSO, 1981.

263. Priorities again [leading article]. *BMJ* 1981; 282: 762.
    Klein R. The strategy behind the Jenkin non-strategy. *BMJ* 1981; 282: 1089–91.

264. Better accountability for the NHS. *BMJ* 1982; 284: 364.
    Russell W. Paper pushers and patients. *BMJ* 1982; 284: 1057.

265. Desperate nurses near the brink. *Nursing Times* 1982; Jan 27: 129.
    Edwards B. *A manager's tale*. London: Nuffield Provincial Hospitals Trust, 1993.
    Russell W. Fate of nurses may decide pay battle. *BMJ* 1982; 285: 70.
    Russell W. Standing firm on pay dispute. *BMJ* 1982; 285: 307.
    Health service strikes on pay. *BMJ* 1982; 284: 1573.

266. Morgan M. Hold the front page! *Nursing Times* 1983; Apr 6: 58–9.

267. Enough is enough [leading article]. *BMJ* 1982; 285: 669–70.

268. New pay review body for nurses. *BMJ* 1983; 287: 442.

269. Russell W. Health becomes a campaign issue. *BMJ* 1983; 286: 1909.

270. Day P, Klein R. Decoding the Griffiths report. *BMJ* 1983; 287: 1813–16.

271. NHS Management Inquiry. Letter dated 6 October 1983 to the Secretary of State, Norman Fowler, from Roy Griffiths, Michael Betts, Jim Blyth and Sir Brian Bailey.

272. Business management for the NHS? [leading article] *BMJ* 1983; 287: 1321–2.

273. Day P, Klein R. Decoding the Griffiths report. *BMJ* 1983; 287: 1813–16.

274. Dyson R. Griffiths inquiry: a personal perspective. *BMJ* 1984; 288: 255–6.

275. Owens P, Glennerster H. *Nursing in conflict.* London: Macmillan, 1990.

276. Russell W. BMA explains its reservations on Griffiths. *BMJ* 1984; 288: 336. Community medicine conference. *BMJ* 1984; 289: 262.

277. RCN. The nurse on the left established British nursing standards. The nurse on the right is being forced to compromise them [advertisement]. *BMJ* 1986; 292: Feb 1, i. Johnston P. Nurses' views on Griffiths made loud and clear. *BMJ* 1986; 292: 777. Johnston P. DHSS surprised by nurses' attack on management. *BMJ* 1986; 292: 282.

278. Association of Nurse Administrators. *Comments on the report of the NHS management inquiry.* London: ANA, 1984. Robinson J. Managed competition and the demise of nursing. In: Light D, May A, editors. *Britain's health system: from welfare state to managed markets.* New York: Faulkner and Gray, 1993.

279. Delamothe T. Nursing grievances. IV. Not a profession, not a career. *BMJ* 1988; 296: 271–4.

280. *Education for effectiveness.* A study commissioned from PA Management Consultants for NPHT. London: Nuffield Provincial Hospitals Trust. 1986.

281. Russell W. Letter from Westminster. *BMJ* 1982; 285: 985.

282. *Health services management: competitive tendering.* Prepared by Thornton Baker Associates for NPHT. London: Nuffield Provincial Hospitals Trust, 1984.

283. Butler J. Origins and development. In: Robinson R, Le Grand J, editors. *Evaluating the NHS reforms.* London, King's Fund Institute/Hermitage, 1994.

284. Smith J. RAWP revisited. *BMJ* 1987; 295: 1015.

285. Department of Health and Social Security. *Health care and its costs.* London: HMSO, 1983.

286. Hopes and realities in health care [leading article]. *BMJ* 1983; 286: 1079–81.

287. BMA and RCN act on NHS cuts. *BMJ* 1983; 287: 848.

288. Frustration over NHS resources [from the Council]. *BMJ* 1984; 288: 1468.

289. Bosanquet N. *Public expenditure and the NHS: recent trends and the outlook.* London: IHSM/BMA/RCN, 1985.

290. Minister responds to professions' attack on NHS financing. *BMJ* 1986; 292: 426. NHS financing: DHSS's response to Bosanquet report. *BMJ* 1986; 292: 503

291. Thompson RPH, Slack W and others. Hospital concern at London cuts. *The Times* 1986; May 13. Johnston P. London consultants light a political fuse. *BMJ* 1986; 292: 1504.

292. Department of Health and Social Security. *Resource distribution for 1987/8.* Health Circular HC(87) 1987; Jan 1.

293. Warden J. Financing the NHS Ltd. *BMJ* 1987; 294: 321.

294. Anderson F. Falling out over NHS beds. *Health Service Journal* 1987; Jan 15: 56.

295. Timmins N. Newsfocus. *Health Service Journal* 1995; Jun 29: 11–13.

296. The truth about the NHS? [leading article] *BMJ* 1986; 292: 1623–4.

297. Klein R. The state and the profession: the politics of the double bed. *BMJ* 1990; 301: 700–2

298. Warden J. Patients rule OK? *BMJ* 1987; 294: 1240.

299. Peet J. *Healthy competition – how to improve the NHS.* CPS Policy Study 86. London: Centre for Policy Studies, 1987.
300. Butler J. Origins and development. In: Robinson R, Le Grand J, editors. *Evaluating the NHS reforms.* London: King's Fund Institute/Hermitage, 1994.
301. Shock M. Medicine at the centre of the nation's affairs. *BMJ* 1994; 309: 1731.
302. Hart TJ. Clinical and economic consequences of patients as producers. *Journal of Public Health Medicine* 1995; 17(4): 383–6.
303. *Economist* 1982; Sep 18: 25.
304. Russell W. Think tank puts cat among the pigeons. *BMJ* 1982; 285: 985, 1058.
305. Enthoven AC. *Reflections on the management of the NHS: an American looks at incentives to efficiency in health services management in the UK.* London: Nuffield Provincial Hospitals Trust, 1985.
306. Butler E. *Good health. The role of health maintenance organisations.* London: Adam Smith Institute, 1986.
307. Gridlock and incentives in the NHS [leading article]. *BMJ* 1985; 291: 992–3.
308. Thwaites B. *The NHS: the end of the rainbow.* Southampton: University of Southampton Institute of Health Policy Studies, 1987.
309. Smith R. The wasted opportunity of the election. *BMJ* 1987; 294: 1438–9
    Economist 1987; May 23: 13–14.
310. Delamothe T. The way we live now. Casualties. *BMJ* 1987; 295: 1628–733.
311. Our fight to highlight health crisis. *London Standard* 1986; Jul 3.
312. Crisis in the National Health Service. Statement by the presidents of the RCP, RCS and RCOG. *BMJ* 1987; 295: 1505.

Chapter 5

1988–1997

New influences and new pathways

Chapter 5

1988–1997

New influences and new pathways

Chronology: the fifth decade

Background	Year	NHS events
Peak of housing boom Cows with BSE slaughtered PanAm Lockerbie bomb	1988	Measles/mumps/rubella (MMR) vaccine introduced Mrs Thatcher announces NHS review on *Panorama* *Community care, an agenda for action* 'Public Health in England' Nurse regrading Project 2000 agreed
Fall of Berlin Wall 'First Direct' phone banking Water privatisation Interest rates hit 15 per cent Tiananmen Square	1989	*Working for patients* (NHS reforms) Hepatitis C virus discovered General management in FPC *Caring for people*
Poll tax riots Electricity privatisation Hubble telescope in space John Major Prime Minister	1990	NHS and Community Care Act GPs' new contract
Gulf war	1991	Implementation of NHS reforms *The health of the nation* Patients' Charter Clinical Standards Advisory Group Beverley Allitt case
Conservative election victory (4th term) Charles and Diana separate Sterling leaves ERM; FTSE 100 reaches 3000 42 polytechnics become universities	1992	Inquiry into London's health services (Tomlinson Report) Select Committee report on maternity services
Rapid expansion of World Wide Web	1993	Review of regions Calman Report on hospital staffing Establishment of National Blood Authority

Background	Year	NHS events
Mandela is President of South Africa National Lottery Internet becomes popular Channel Tunnel opens	1994	14 Regions reduced to 8
	1995	Debate on rationing of health care GP 'out-of-hours' dispute Reorganisation of cancer services
Railtrack and British Energy privatisation EC bans British beef exports Dunblane massacre FTSE100 reaches 4000 Office for National Statistics replaces OPCS	1996	NHS electronic network Digital imaging at the Hammersmith Unification of districts and FHSAs Regions become outposts of NHS Executive Three White Papers: *Choice and opportunity*; *Primary care: delivering the future*; and *The NHS: a service with ambitions* Academy of Royal Colleges formed
General election: Labour landslide Hong Kong reverts to China Spice Girls Food Standards Agency Tobacco Industry financial settlement FTSE 100 reaches 5000 Death of Princess Diana Scots vote for devolution	1997	Centenary of King's Fund Dolly the sheep – first mammalian clone NHS (Primary Care) Act Further NHS legislation E. coli outbreaks

New influences

Each generation has expectations that cannot be fulfilled. Job security was no longer taken for granted, the concept of the family was less rigid, support in the form of Social Security was under threat, dreams of ever-increasing prosperity faded, and negative equity emerged with the decline of the housing market. Much to which people had believed themselves entitled was no longer guaranteed. Young adults born in 1961–1981, Generation X as some called it, had a different and sceptical view of society.[1] The NHS might not be there from cradle to grave. Their elders, in turn, discovered that young doctors and nurses sometimes lacked the vocational attitudes they expected. Although clinical medicine continued to advance inexorably, the health service was as ever in financial disarray. In its first issue of 1988 the *BMJ* called for a new health commission.

> *Let us be charitable. Let us assume that Mrs Thatcher and her health ministers really do believe that the NHS is bigger and better funded than ever before and that the concern voiced by the health professions is whingeing in response to tough, effective management. Then how do we convince the government that the NHS is moving towards terminal decline, and that innovatory thinking is needed to solve the crisis? . . . The message is that after years of squeezing the NHS has finally no more juice to give . . . Britain is not alone in facing a health crisis; in every Western country each year brings new and better treatments for populations that are living longer than ever. This is the insatiable demand that politicians have been citing to excuse their refusal to find more money. But in fact there are many ways of skinning the cat.[2]*

Bevan had said that the service must always be growing, changing and improving; Sir Patrick Nairne, a former Permanent Secretary at the Department of Health, doubted whether changes should include alteration in the basic organisation and financial structure.[3] He saw three developments as desirable. First, the NHS was a most important public service, but no public service thought less about the public. The NHS should treat people as responsible individuals and take them into its confidence. Second, better links with private medicine and local authorities were desirable. Third, the distrust between every level from central government to the hospital should end. Clinicians, administrators, district teams and regional teams criticised each other, and ministers. The NHS was the largest glasshouse in the world, and risked its own survival if it could not resist throwing stones. Not surprisingly, health was a media favourite. Major ethical issues were raised by the tabloids, to the surprise of doctors who were sometimes naive in their comments.[4] By 1996 the BBC was considering filming a natural death for a scientific programme. *Dr Kildare* and *Emergency – Ward 10* had glamorised medicine. Newer soaps, for example *Casualty* and *ER*, did not.

New forces were at work in health care internationally:[5]

- *The power of big buyers* – governments, private payers and patients were demanding cost-effectiveness.
- *The rise of sophisticated consumers* – patients were more knowledgeable, changing the doctor–patient relationship. In 1997 the US Health Department provided free access for everyone to MEDLINE, the world's most extensive collection of published medical information.
- *New technology* – including molecular biology, the internet and World Wide Web.

- *Shifts in the boundaries of health and medicine* – with the recognition of the complex relationship between the environment and medicine.
- *The ethics of controlling human biology* – death and dying, and the legitimacy of rationing. From transplant surgery to fertility drugs, technology strained the ability of traditional morality to provide authoritative guides to behaviour.[6]

In 1988 the Department of Trade and Industry published a Green Paper on anti-competitive practices. Subsequently the Monopolies and Mergers Commission investigated whether the professionally imposed restrictions had an adverse effect on the public interest. The ethical code of the medical profession precluded advertising to the public. The Conservatives encouraged the provision of information to the public so that it could decide in a medical marketplace. The Commission supported an embargo on advertising by consultants, but considered that the restrictions on GP advertising operated against the public interest.[7] There followed a series of organisational initiatives, which included a new GPs' contract, the NHS reforms, *The health of the nation*, *The patient's charter* and Community Care.[8] Previously, major organisational changes had taken place on a single appointed day. Now change became continuous, varying from place to place. Central was a move towards a market, made possible by a hierarchical system of accountability from local management through regions to the Secretary of State.

Medical progress

Health promotion and The health of the nation

Health promotion and illness prevention were increasingly seen as part of routine medical care and incorporated into the practice of many GPs. An emphasis on more targeted screening for problems and disease in its early stages replaced the earlier enthusiasm for a more general approach. Attention was paid to smoking, raised blood pressure, misuse of alcohol, diet, and cancer of the breast and cervix.[9] The effectiveness of screening procedures and the problems of ensuring they were actually carried out were examined. Much remained contentious in the young science of health promotion and it seemed that, no sooner were proposals implemented, than a study would appear casting doubt on their merit or cost-effectiveness. A population-based approach aimed to reduce risk factors by influencing the price of alcohol and tobacco, reducing salt in processed food or attempting to reduce social inequality. Disasters could also alter attitudes: the fire at King's Cross Underground in 1987 was followed by a ban on smoking in public places. Finally came a focus on 'green' issues, the belief that life style, environment and ecology should be linked. We should look after the things that look after us, and design agricultural, industrial and social systems to prevent environmental hazards. Population and resources needed to be in balance.[10] Public health physicians believed that health promotion spread wider than medicine into environmental issues and politics. The evidence that variations in health were correlated with income, both within nations and between them, was strong. Some people saw health promotion primarily in terms of social policies that redistributed income and believed that health care systems should be based on primary care, the participation of citizens and the principles of *Health for all*.[11] An increasing number of countries, including New Zealand and the USA, were publishing health strategies based on the World Health Organization's (WHO) *Health for all 2000* targets. The British government was seen as slow in following suit. In 1988 an independent expert committee, assembled by the King's Fund, produced *The nation's health, a strategy for the 1990s*.[12] In 1991 the Faculty of Public Health Medicine produced a report on *UK levels of health*,[13] centring its approach on risks, patterns of behaviour and how to alter them. In October 1990 Kenneth Clarke announced his intention to devise health targets and measure performance. The Chief Medical Officer (CMO), Donald Acheson, saw an opening for a project after his own heart. Clarke's successor, William Waldegrave, published *The health of the nation* in June 1991 as a consultative paper. It was timely because the WHO had provided a framework, the public were ready to hear the message not least because of the AIDS epidemic, the need for health care assessment was widely recognised with the publication of a report on the future of *Public health in England*,[14] there was a political consensus that more needed to be done, and it was a good diversionary tactic at a time when the government was under much pressure on the NHS.

Key areas: *Health of the nation*

- Coronary heart disease and stroke
- Cancers
- Mental illness
- HIV/AIDS and sexual health
- Accidents

After consultation a White Paper, *The health of the nation*, was issued in July 1992.[15] Unlike the report of the Faculty, the government rejected an approach based on risks and patterns of behaviour, opting for a disease-based structure. Five key areas were selected in which it was known that intervention could significantly reduce mortality or morbidity. National targets were set for the year 2000 and the contribution the NHS might make was examined.[16] *The health of the nation* received a cautious welcome, for the government had shown some commitment although critics believed that its approach was limited and that it overemphasised individuals' ability to control their own health. Some saw it as a rejection of the wider WHO *Health for all* strategy and the objective of redressing social inequalities and encouraging community participation.[17] Although originating in the Department of Health (DoH), the strategy involved many government departments because significant improvement involved society as a whole. As time passed there were doubts about the achievements. Many targets had been set in line with trends that were already apparent. Mortality rates for stroke and heart disease continued to fall, but sometimes changes were in the wrong direction; for example, obesity was rising, as were teenage smoking, drinking by women and suicide.[18] Although somewhat tardily, the Conservative government accepted that variations in health existed between different areas, ethnic and income groups, and that greater understanding was needed if effective action were to be taken. A working group looked at these variations, but did not stress the effect of poverty, which was, after all, not primarily the responsibility of the DoH. Labour, on election in 1997, announced a new health strategy to break the cycle of ill health due to poverty, inequality and deprivation. The *Health of the nation* initiative and 'health inequalities' would be reviewed, and there would be a White Paper to bring together the strands of public health strategy.[19]

Changing clinical practice

With advancing technology and shortening length of stay, patients in hospital now were likely to be very sick indeed or to be admitted briefly for investigation or minimally invasive surgery. New forms of treatment demanded mental and physical stamina from patients who were far better informed about what was happening. A 48-year-old man, after his third heart transplant, said 'I am just trying to enjoy life. It is not all a bed of roses.'[20] Patients with cancer were subjected to the most intensive protocols of chemotherapy, and emotional support might be lacking. Those with distressing or terminal illness were in need of comfort and continuity of care, difficult with continuously changing teams of doctors and nurses.[21] At a time when they were ill and vulnerable, people might not like to be in mixed sex wards. Hospital surveys of patient satisfaction invariably showed high ratings, but systematic interviews in a large random sample of hospitals showed major problems in communication. Patients often did not receive information about the hospital, their condition or its treatment. Many were in pain and often they were not offered pain relief. Discharge planning and follow-up was poor.[22] Since 1948 medical educators had urged the inclusion of social, ethical and non-technical issues into the student curriculum, hoping that this would produce more humane and self-motivated physicians. Although Sir Lancelot Spratts roamed the wards in fewer numbers, empathy was not always to be encountered.[23] The General Medical Council (GMC) issued new and clearer guidance to doctors, including advice on 'fly-on-the wall' TV programmes showing daily life in hospital or general practice. These were not always made with respect for the patients concerned. The GMC stressed the importance of informed consent by patients, and that doctors should be particularly vigilant where children, vulnerable people and the mentally ill or disabled were concerned.[24]

Interest in complementary medicine grew. Conditions such as bulimia and chronic fatigue syndrome attracted attention. More people went to non-orthodox practitioners, spending substantial sums, but they did not turn their backs on conventional health care.[25] In the hierarchy of evidence from the anecdotal to the randomised controlled trial and the meta-analysis, complementary medicine ranked low, but there was increasing pressure to give patients what they asked for. The medical profession relaxed its attitude and increasingly complementary medicine became part of the NHS. It was estimated that 60 per cent of health authorities and 45 per cent of GPs were either commissioning or providing it. Because it might be cheap to the NHS, there was a temptation to offer it in the absence of any evidence of effectiveness, especially in areas of care where conventional medicine was unsuccessful, for example in the management of chronic low back pain.[26] Acupuncture and aromatherapy might be provided as part of mainstream care as in cancer, where patients facing rigorous types of treatment might find at least psychological benefit. Political parties supported its development as an issue of choice for patients, and bodies were established in 1996 to regulate and register chiropractors and osteopaths.[27] Because of the lack of evidence of its clinical effectiveness, the Nuffield Institute for Health in Leeds set in hand a literature review while in the USA the Agency for Health Care Policy and Research awarded a contract to Beth Israel Hospital to measure its effectiveness.

The quality and effectiveness of health care

Interest increasingly centred on clinical guidelines. In 1990 an academic consortium of 12 US centres teamed up to develop guidelines on topics in which there was evidence of marked variability from place to place, and high costs. Cataract, aortic aneurysm resection and carotid resection were among those selected. John Wennberg, at Dartmouth, published an *Atlas of health care in the USA*, showing that operation rates and hospital beds were related more to the number of specialists than to any measure of clinical need. There was little evidence that populations receiving aggressive care lived longer. Supply appeared to drive demand, defying most people's basic economic beliefs.[28] Calls for a similar approach in Britain were often ignored. Health technology assessment threatened clinical freedom and although doctors did not want freedom to use ineffective forms of care, they wished to maintain the right to decide what was effective and not be delayed by procedures that slowed down innovation or might be overly concerned with cost containment.[29] The appointment of Michael Peckham as the first NHS Director of Research and Development in 1990 increased the momentum in the UK.[30] Peckham's position made it possible to establish a regional research strategy and network, and to obtain earmarked resources for research when new financial arrangements were under consideration.[31]

The influence of the enquiry into maternal deaths and the subsequent report by Lunn and Mushin on anaesthetic deaths was enhanced by the commitment of senior members of the specialties. A further report on 19,000 perioperative deaths in 1992/3 (National Confidential Enquiry into Perioperative Deaths, NCEPOD) showed a lack of high-dependency units in many of the hospitals in which deaths had occurred, and that patients were sometimes returned to ordinary ward areas too soon. Faults in care were revealed that could be remedied.[32] Patients who were 'outliers', on a ward not normally dealing with their problem, had poorer outcomes. During 1992 three further studies began, into stillbirths and deaths in infancy (Confidential Enquiry into Stillbirths and Deaths in Infancy, CESDI), counselling for genetic disorders, and homicides and suicides by the mentally ill. However, the Royal Colleges only haltingly went ahead with audit, and did not always work with the other professions whose contribution was essential to a good outcome. It also became apparent that studies needed to consider long-term effects as well as the immediate results.

Evidence-based medicine

Archibald Cochrane had argued for randomised controlled trials in the belief that it was not known whether most clinical interventions did any good. Increasingly clinicians and those purchasing health care became interested in 'evidence-based medicine', the conscientious, explicit and judicious use of current best evidence in making decisions about the care of individual patients.[33] Evidence-based medicine became a central health service policy, a new gospel for government ministers and clinicians. Previously it had been thought adequate to understand the process of a disease and use treatment known to interrupt or modify that process. However, if the outcome rather than the process was examined, some forms of care did not produce the expected improvement. Trials, now numbered in hundreds of thousands, revealed that some procedures, such as dilatation and curettage in women under 40 years of age, were either of doubtful value or harmful. How little of medical practice had a firm basis in evidence? How much of what was firmly based was applied in the front lines of patient care? New editions of textbooks were often out of date and doctors' knowledge even of the basics of disorders such as high blood pressure declined as they grew older. Evidence-based medicine was closely linked to continuing medical education.

There was little wrong with the proposition that the best available scientific evidence should be used in patient care, but there was an implication that the only medicine that should be practised was based on controlled clinical trials. Yet despite years of study and huge financial investment the research to answer many questions, for example the best way to treat neck pain, was not available.[34] New technology, for example minimal access surgery, became established without such an assessment. Even if most people clearly do better with one form of treatment, there is no guarantee that every individual will react in the same way; patients have the right to make a choice between different forms of treatment. In primary health care many conditions are simple and self-limiting, no clear diagnosis may ever be reached and controlled trials are not always practicable.

Guidance on effectiveness drawn up by groups rooted in economics or public health was greeted by managers with enthusiasm.[35] It was not always accepted by clinicians as representing ultimate wisdom, particularly if authorities refused to fund new forms of treatment not yet shown to be good value. It was one thing for managers to challenge clinical decision-making; now management sometimes dictated it. Although evidence from trials was increasingly incorporated into guidelines, clinicians did not automatically behave in accordance with them. Experience showed that where they were developed locally, for example practice prescribing policies, they were more likely to be followed than if they were developed centrally.[36] Robert Brook found that the great motivators in the USA were one-to-one contact with respected colleagues, or money. The effort required to develop guidelines based on research findings was considerable. Centralisation of effort was worth while to prevent the local application of dubious patterns of care. There was pressure to make guidelines available, and the US government decided that, as they were developed, they would be posted on its public web site.

The DoH and the NHS Executive made improving clinical effectiveness a key priority and invested heavily in fostering evidence-based health care.[37] In 1991 a research and development strategy was launched in the hope that clinical, managerial and policy decisions would be based on sound and pertinent information. The UK Cochrane Collaboration was established in 1992 as part of an international network to prepare, maintain and disseminate systematic reviews of research on the effects of health care.[38] Against some opposition from the Joint Consultants Committee (JCC), the DoH established a multiprofessional Clinical Outcomes Group and a subsidiary National Centre for Clinical Audit. Directorates of research and development were created in the regions. A standing committee on

Clinical Outcomes Group

Non-statutory and multi-professional, advising the NHS Executive on how to help the NHS in England to improve the outcome of clinical care through clinical audit, clinical guidelines and a clinical effectiveness programme. Members (appointed by the Chief Medical and Nursing Officers) include managers, patients' representatives and academics as well as the clinical professions. Subgroups prepare guidance to the NHS based on evidence of clinical effectiveness.

health technology was established to assess the methods.[39] Several forms of treatment, for example screening for colo-rectal cancer, were listed as priorities for assessment. Evidence-based medicine was turning into an industry with an NHS Centre for Reviews and Dissemination, the UK Clearing House on Health Outcomes, Effective Health Care Bulletins from the Universities of York and Leeds, and a CD-ROM providing a summary of systematic reviews. The impact at local level was patchy.

The NHS attempted to absorb and synthesise differing philosophies of quality improvement, effectiveness and audit. David Taylor, working at the Audit Commission, listed 25. Many followed quality philosophies from other sectors of public service and industry, particularly those pioneered by Deming and Juran, and used by Japanese industry in its search for reliability and market dominance.[40] These saw quality as organisation-wide and a responsibility of management, challenging traditional assumptions that it was largely a matter for the professionals. Quality was seen as a continuous process of evolution in which 'every defect was a treasure' enabling matters to be improved. Don Berwick, responsible for the quality programme at the Harvard Community Health Plan, contrasted traditional systems of inspection, discipline and penalties with the alternative, participation and incentives.[41] Another approach, business process re-engineering, redesigned the way care was provided to improve matters for both patients and staff.

Hospital accreditation was also introduced. Britain had the Health Advisory Service, and accreditation had long been required in North America where independent assessment was a pre-condition for payment. The DoH was wary of introducing accreditation into the UK. Would major hospitals always reach an appropriate standard? In 1989 the King's Fund launched its own pilot study that examined hospital organisation and assessed the extent to which standards were being met, and action was taken when they were not. The pilot evolved into a national accreditation scheme and by 1995 a third of the country's hospitals had submitted themselves voluntarily to the procedure.[42] To achieve accredited status a hospital had to demonstrate compliance with organisational standards that fulfilled legal obligations and respected the rights of patients. The standards were process-orientated, but covered every aspect of the hospital's systems and organisational procedures. An independent team of surveyors, for example a trust chief executive, a director of nursing, a consultant or clinical director and an operational manager then visited the hospital for two to five days, provided a verbal debriefing to its staff, and submitted their findings to the accreditation committee.[43] The standards were high and few hospital trusts met them in their entirety. The King's Fund extended the programme to general practice and primary health care, and to community and mental health services; other groups also entered the accreditation field.

In 1971 McKeown had suggested that health services had only a small effect on health or longevity.[44] While this might have been true in the nineteenth century, advances in treatment for some conditions had undoubtedly led to improvement in outcome. It was, however, difficult to disentangle the effects of health care and environmental improvement, for in most conditions improvements in diet and nutrition were also having an effect. Bunker challenged the McKeown hypothesis, attributing a gain of about 1.5 years to clinical preventive services, in particular diphtheria immunisation. The contribution of the curative services seemed twice as great. Cancer treatment had not had much effect but there had been major improvements in survival from heart disease and renal failure, a reduction in strokes probably from the treatment of high blood pressure, and far better results in diabetes, tuberculosis and maternity services. For the population as a whole Bunker considered that this meant that medical science could claim responsibility for an average gain of 3–4 years, out of about 7 years' total increase in life expectancy since 1950 in Britain and the USA. Bunker pointed out that the public demand was for improvement in the quality of life, not just survival. Well-being was a major goal of health care, for example the treatment of depression, osteoarthritis and cataract surgery.[45] There was pressure to develop measures reflecting the effect of medical intervention on morbidity.[46]

The GMC had been created in the nineteenth century to identify professionals and protect the public from quackery. In 1997 it obtained new powers to deal with serious deficiency in clinical competence.

The drug treatment of disease

Self-medication with medicines bought over the counter (OTC) had long been a feature of people's lives. A report from the Nuffield Foundation in 1986 argued that pharmacists were an under-used resource.[47] They could make a greater contribution to primary health care, especially as the public increasingly looked to them for advice on the widening range of OTC preparations. Sales were equivalent to a third of the NHS drugs bill, and governments world-wide saw self-medication as a way to shift some of the cost onto patients.[48] From the late 1980s it became easier to reclassify medicines from prescription-only status to allow counter sales when they were safe in use, had only minor side effects, and had well-defined indications. Among the medicines reclassified were ibuprofen for pain, acyclovir for cold sores, corticosteroid preparations for surface use, and H_2-antagonists such as cimetidine for indigestion. In 1992 the Medicines Control Agency, Britain's drug-licensing body, streamlined its procedures for deregulating drugs.

Major changes were under way in the pharmaceutical industry.[49] Two large mergers were those of SmithKline and Beecham in 1989 and Glaxo–Wellcome in 1995. Attempts to reduce expenditure on drugs in the USA and cuts in drug prices in Europe placed the industry under pressure. Drug prices could no longer rise at 10 per cent a year, as unbranded generic drugs increased their share of the market. The pharmaceutical industry commonly spent 10–15 per cent of turnover on research and development, a proportion far higher than most other industries. The cost of development, testing and gaining approval for new drugs, many of which would never be introduced to the market or be profitable if they were, raised the stakes.

Seldom was a drug now introduced for a previously fatal condition, as in the early days of the NHS. New ones were often potential replacements for previous ones of considerable potency. The comparative advantages of new forms of therapy were smaller, so larger trials were required, and new statistical techniques were needed. Since the introduction of streptomycin and drugs for major psychiatric disorders, improved medicines had meant that fewer patients needed to be in hospital.[50] This process was a continuing one; for example, cancer patients could often be treated as outpatients, and drugs that relieved nausea and vomiting associated with cancer chemotherapy meant that the length of hospital admission could be shorter. Patients undergoing surgery recovered more rapidly following an anaesthetic using new agents. The pharmaceutical industry was at pains to demonstrate that the savings achieved in hospital overheads were not outweighed by the cost of drugs. The industry tried to enter the wholesale distribution chain, to influence those providing health care or to become providers of health care themselves. 'Disease management' was pushed by the pharmaceutical industry, the proposal being that the care of patients with long-term conditions such as diabetes and asthma should be contracted out to the manufacturer supplying the product on which patients depended.[51] An idea from the USA, its limitations on the choice of treatment patients might receive caused concern on both sides of the Atlantic.

Shortlisted drugs for the Prix Galien (UK) 1995

- *Losartan potassium* – selective angiotensin II receptor antagonist for the management of hypertension; first major development since the angiotensin-converting enzyme (ACE) inhibitors
- *Lamotrigine* – anti-epileptic
- *Tacrolimus* – immunosuppressant for liver and kidney transplants
- *Dornase alpha* – recombinant DNA enzyme reducing the viscosity of mucus in cystic fibrosis
- *Resperidone* – anti-psychotic for schizophrenia (winner)
- *Interferon alpha-2b* – long-term treatment of hepatitis C

The need for blockbuster drugs to maintain profits was urgent. Firms overhauled their research programmes. It was predicted that by the turn of the century every new drug would be touched in its development by biotechnology and genetic manipulation.[52] Greater knowledge of the functions of individual genes and their amino-acid sequences opened new therapeutic possibilities, and the possibility of designing new drugs. SmithKline Beecham spent $125 million on a stake in the Human Genome Sciences company in return for rights to develop products from its huge gene database. 'Combinatorial chemistry' made it possible to produce new chemical entities at a remarkable speed, and high-speed screening systems were developed to assess them. Alliances with university departments and biotechnology companies gave the large companies an expanded horizon.[53] Genetic engineering was now being used to produce large amounts of well-known proteins, including insulin, growth hormone, hepatitis vaccine, interferons and monoclonal antibodies, and drugs reducing the frequency and severity of relapse in multiple sclerosis. The production of eythropoietin in substantial quantities by recombinant DNA technology made it possible to treat the anaemia that commonly accompanied renal failure. Clinical trials showed substantial improvement in well-being but it was also used illicitly by athletes to improve performance.[54] In 1991 a monoclonal antibody, centoxin, was launched for the treatment of Gram-negative septicaemia. It bound and neutralised bacterial endotoxins and though costly could possibly save the lives of patients who would otherwise die of this infection after burns, trauma or gastrointestinal surgery.[55] The pharmaceutical industry developed derivatives of erythromycin, one of the earliest antibiotics, that were more stable, more active and had a more prolonged action. Originally held in reserve for penicillin-resistant infections, they were found useful particularly in respiratory diseases.[56] A new type of antimicrobial treatment emerged, the antiviral drugs, hitting herpes, shingles and AIDS, although there was a risk that viral resistance might occur.[57]

One of the earliest of the synthetic drugs, aspirin, obtained a new lease of life. It was known to inhibit platelet function. Several reports suggested that it significantly reduced cardiovascular mortality and morbidity after heart attacks, and it also appeared to have a beneficial effect in cerebrovascular disease and strokes. Even a small daily dose seemed effective, and doctors regularly gave aspirin to any patient at risk of the two conditions.[58] Drugs that reduced serum lipid concentrations proved to be effective in reducing major coronary events in people with ischaemic heart disease.[59]

Effective treatment was now available for acid-related disorders such as duodenal ulcer and oesophageal acid reflux. The H_2-receptor antagonists such as cimetidine did not suppress acid secretion completely, and were challenged by omeprazole, a 'proton-pump inhibitor' that blocked the transport of hydrogen ions into the stomach, and healed most duodenal ulcers within two to four weeks.[60] This became the treatment of choice for resistant ulcers. The possibility that *Helicobacter pylori* might cause ulcers was open to a simple therapeutic test. Did eradication of the organism help? In 1988 Marshall and his co-workers announced that a combined antibiotic–bismuth regimen healed ulcers quicker and better than H_2-antagonists. Some improvement occurred when a single antibiotic was given, more when two were combined, and very substantial improvement with triple antibiotic therapy. Despite nearly universal initial scepticism, within a few years research workers had developed screening tests for the infection. There was progressive acceptance that there had been a major therapeutic advance that reduced the need for hospitalisation and for longer or more traumatic forms of treatment. When there was evidence of infection, eradication of *Helicobacter* became the accepted therapy in gastric and duodenal ulceration. The evidence of a link with stomach cancer also strengthened. The search was on for the simplest, shortest, most effective and best tolerated treatment.[61]

The first of a new generation of antidepressants, fluoxetine (Prozac), was introduced in 1987. These selective serotonin re-uptake inhibitors worked by increasing levels of serotonin, a neurotransmitter. Unlike previous antidepressants, they appeared to have fewer side effects, and by 1995 some 500,000 people in Britain were taking them, including children. Reserpine was found to be effective in schizophrenia. A new drug with some, albeit modest, effect on Alzheimer's disease (Aricept) was introduced.[62] Sumatriptan helped migraine. The management of night-time asthma was improved by the introduction of salmeterol, a long-acting inhaled beta-2 agonist that produced effective relief for 12 hours.[63] Since the introduction of oral contraception in 1961 attempts had been made to reduce the hazards from thrombo-embolic complications. The hormone content of modern pills was about a sixth of the early preparations, reduction having occurred in stages as new health risks emerged. Progestogen-only pills were also available for women in whom oestrogen was undesirable, as were injectable preparations. In 1995 evidence suggested that two of the newer 'third generation progestogens' were associated with an increased risk of venous thrombo-embolism and the Committee on Safety of Medicines issued a warning. The increased risk, though small, and less than the risk of thrombosis in pregnancy itself, received intense coverage in the media, alarming about half of the 3 million women using oral contraception.[64] Slimming drugs, given in combination, also produced adverse reactions – heart disease.

With a public increasingly well informed, the greater popularity of alternative medicine fuelled melatonin mania in 1995. A secretion of the pineal gland, melatonin seemed to reset the body clock, and help sleep and jet-lag. In spite of little scientific evidence it suddenly became wildly popular, particularly in the USA, where articles appeared suggesting that it also prevented ageing.[65]

The British National Formulary, which gave doctors and dentists updated information about medicines, went electronic in 1995. Tools for computer-based prescribing multiplied, and provided support for clinical decisions. They could check for potential interactions, calculate the appropriate dosage and suggest suitable preparations. Their use could also make for economy, increasing the number of prescriptions issued in generic form.[66]

Radiology and diagnostic imaging

Improvements in scanner technology meant that both magnetic resonance imaging (MRI) and computed tomography (CT) scanning could be carried out more rapidly. The introduction of ultra-fast CT, with imaging times of 0.1 second, made it possible to show calcification in the coronary artery walls, which seemed to occur much earlier in the development of coronary artery disease than had been thought, opening the possibility of an early diagnostic test. Special scanners were developed, for example for sick newborn babies. Spiral CT scans combined with dye injections could show the rate of blood flow in the spleen and kidney. All general hospitals in the 1980s had wanted CT scanning; in the 1990s all wanted MRI. However, doctors sometimes had to be content with a visiting mobile unit operated by the private sector, which made it difficult for those undertaking the imaging to discuss patients with the clinicians.

Improved isotope techniques made it possible to image body functions as well as structure. White blood cells could be labelled with an isotope, and gamma camera pictures could show the areas of inflammation where cells were concentrated, which lit up like a neon sign. Monoclonal antibodies, similarly labelled, would be concentrated in the tissues for which they had been prepared, and then imaged. Sugar compounds, which were concentrated in metabolically active areas such as tumours, could be demonstrated by PET, making it possible to identify secondary cancer rapidly without further distress to the patient. Bone mineral density measurement was improved by the introduction of dual-energy absorptionometry in 1987. This provided an accurate and repeatable way of assessing osteoporosis. The technique used two different X-ray sources that could separate bone and soft tissue because of differential absorption. Measurement of total body composition (lean and fat body mass) was also possible, and because the radiation dose was low, serial readings could be obtained to demonstrate the need for, or effectiveness of, treatment for bone loss.

New and complex imaging systems – CT, radionuclide scanning, digital subtraction angiography and MRI – now accounted for up to a third of the examinations in modern radiology departments. They all yielded digital data and it was possible to transform other examinations into digital form. In 1985 the Hammersmith Hospital expressed a wish to develop a filmless radiography department, and over the next ten years the first such system in the UK was created, partly from central funding but mainly from charitable donations. All forms of imaging equipment were interfaced to the computer system. Straight X-ray images were recorded on special screens and read digitally by laser. The data created were vast, as each chest X-ray required more storage space than the Bible. Images were fed to immense computing facilities, for distribution by fibreoptic cable to workstations throughout the hospital. The high definition of the images and the ability to magnify areas of interest and change their density and contrast were found by clinicians to be a substantial advance. More complex images, such as those produced by scanning, could be displayed, rotated and examined in three-dimensional form. Digital radiography opened immense possibilities for change and improvement in the NHS.[67]

Infectious disease and immunisation

Although immunisation had made a substantial impact on infectious disease, the ultimate goal of the programmes was disease eradication. The global eradication of smallpox had been achieved, and in 1988 the WHO announced the goal of the global eradication of poliomyelitis by the year 2000. Individuals could be protected by immunisation, but when most of a population was protected, transmission of a disease from one person to another became uncommon, reducing the risk even to those who were not immunised (herd immunity). This had been achieved for poliomyelitis in the UK. To ensure that more babies were immunised while attending baby clinics, and before their mothers returned to work, the basic immunisation schedule was rescheduled in 1990, starting earlier, at two months.

National introduction of vaccines

Diphtheria	1940
BCG (TB)	1953
Whooping cough	In the 1950s
Tetanus	Mid-1950s
Poliomyelitis	Salk 1956
	Sabin 1962
Measles	1968
Measles/mumps/rubella	1988
Influenza (Hib)	1992

Uptake of immunisation was used as an index of the performance of local health services. In 1988 the CMO's annual report published maps of the achievements of district health authorities (DHAs).[68] Districts with the lowest rates of immunisation tended to have a dense and mobile population but all were improving as targets were set and GPs were offered financial incentives. Each year GPs achieved higher rates of immunisation. More districts achieved first 90 per cent and then 95 per cent cover. The incidence of many childhood diseases was at the lowest ever level. There had been 46,000 cases of diphtheria and 2,480 deaths in 1940, but from 1986 to 1995 there were only 28 cases with one death. Cases of poliomyelitis fell from nearly 4,000 cases in 1955 to 28 between 1985 and 1995, 19 of which were vaccine related. With increased use of pertussis (whooping cough) vaccine and a coverage of 94 per cent, notifications of cases fell to 1,873 in 1995.[69]

Measles vaccine had been introduced in 1968 and had proved successful. Rubella vaccine had long been advised for schoolgirls aged 11–14 years to reduce the risk of multiple fetal defects from infection in early pregnancy. A combined vaccine for measles, mumps and rubella (MMR) had been used in the USA since 1975 and was introduced in Britain in 1988 with the aim of eliminating these illnesses. Coverage of more than 90 per cent was achieved, with a dramatic effect on all three; clusters of cases were often importations. Immunisation against a common cause of meningitis, *Haemophilus influenza* type b (Hib), was introduced into the routine programme in 1992 and by 1996 a national coverage of 95 per cent had been achieved. The decline in notifications was dramatic and there was only one death in 1995.

Infectious disease

World-wide, new agents responsible for infectious disease were continuously being identified; 22 between 1973 and 1994.[70] Some such as Lyme disease, originally identified in other countries, were subsequently found in the UK. The European Commission became increasingly involved in public health issues, and established surveillance and information networks for individual diseases. As a result the guidance on the reporting and management of outbreaks was more consistent. Tuberculosis had seemed on the path to elimination. Cases declined tenfold between 1948 and 1987 although high levels of immigration from the Indian sub-continent in the late 1960s slowed the fall. In the UK there were about 5,000 new cases a year but the numbers started to rise again. Internationally a major cause of the rise was HIV infection, which when combined with resistant strains of *Mycobacterium* led to rapid death. Migration of people, poverty, deprivation and homelessness were also responsible for the increased number of patients. Drug resistance and poor clinical results were often caused by patients failing to take drugs as prescribed. An approach called 'directly observed therapy', in which health care workers made sure that patients took the proper medicines for six to eight months, emerged as a major breakthrough. Cure rates as high as 95 per cent were possible even in poor countries.

Reported episodes of food poisoning were also on the increase, some international in origin as food increasingly crossed national borders.[71] *Salmonella enteritidis* infections had been rising for 25 years; by 1988 there were more than 20,000 cases annually. The problem appeared to be infected eggs.[72] In December 1988 Edwina Currie, a junior health minister, warned people that most of the egg production was infected with *Salmonella*. Almost all chickens and eggs in Europe derived from two genetic strains, bred for food conversion efficiency and egg production rather than disease resistance. Although not clear at the time, the problem was world-wide, not just British. Mrs Currie's comments led to a food scare of then unparalleled intensity: a crisis in the industry, the slaughter of flocks and her own resignation. She was, in fact, largely correct. Her vivid presentation of important health education issues had been useful and her departure was regrettable. Subsequently, under the aegis of the European Union, a European surveillance system was established, Salm-Net, based at the Communicable Disease Surveillance Centre, Colindale, part of the PHLS. Other processed foods were also implicated. Pâté was found to be a significant cause of food-borne listeriosis. The largest recorded outbreak of food-borne botulism in the UK occurred in 1989: 27 people were affected and one died. They had eaten one brand of hazelnut yoghurt that contained hazelnut conserve sweetened with aspartamine rather than sugar. A combination of inadequate sterilisation and a changed composition had allowed *Clostridium* spores to survive.[73] In 1996 an outbreak of *E. coli* 0157 infection from contaminated meat products killed 17 people and affected a further 400.[74] An independent Food Safety Agency was proposed, an idea accepted by the Labour Government in 1997.

In 1986 there had been an outbreak of a brain disease in cattle in southwest Britain.[75] The condition, bovine spongiform encephalopathy (BSE), was thought to be related to Creutzfeldt–Jakob disease (CJD), scrapie and kuru, all forms of degenerative brain disease transmissible by food; it appeared that the sick animals had been fed meat products. A working party recommended in 1988 that sick animals be destroyed and BSE was made a notifiable disease. The government banned feed products made from ground cattle and sheep remains and ordered the slaughter of infected livestock. How effectively these measures were carried out was open to question. The existence of the disease led many countries to restrict meat imports from Britain. A CJD Surveillance Unit was established in Edinburgh in 1990; the PHLS were not involved, there being no initial evidence of a human–animal relationship. A ten-year debate began, marked by contradiction, warning from meat producers against hysteria and unwavering reassurance from the government. Concern mounted in 1995 about transmission to humans when three farmers died of the disease; the media sounded alarm bells because it was a newsworthy story, government took a low key approach to prevent unwarranted panic, and medical scientists were divided in the evaluation of the possibility. In 1996 ten cases of a highly stereotyped variant of CJD in people below the age of 42 years pointed to a link between BSE and CJD, and strengthened the possibility of transmission from animals to humans. The credibility of government advice on public health issues had been undermined. The government, which for years had maintained that there was no evidence of transmission from animals or meat products to humans, had to revise its stance. There was public alarm, greater slaughter of cattle, government anxiety at the prospect of compensation for farmers and for victims' families who might argue that past reassurances were fallacious, and repercussions with the European Community after a worldwide ban on British beef was instituted.[76]

Overshadowing the antibiotic treatment of infection was the escalating problem of antibiotic (and antiviral drug) resistance, thought by some to herald the dawn of the 'post-antibiotic' era. About one patient in ten in acute hospitals had an infection acquired after admission. Elderly patients, neonates and those on immunosuppressive treatment were particularly vulnerable, and multi-drug-resistant organisms such as *Staphylococcus aureus*, Gram-negative bacilli and enterococci were present in many hospitals. The development of new antibiotics had largely ceased and only one, vancomycin, remained of real value in the management of resistant infections.

Blood transfusion had long been known to lead, on occasions, to illness, for example to liver disease. In 1989 the virus for hepatitis C was isolated. The first test available gave many false-positive results and the blood transfusion service delayed screening donors until 1991 when a better one was introduced. During the interval a substantial number of recipients contracted the disease and it was necessary to look back to identify patients who, unknowingly, might have been infected.[77]

Since surveillance of Legionnaires' disease had begun in 1979 there had been 100–200 cases every year, about half in travellers returning from overseas and the rest British in origin. Travel-related disease remained a problem. Malaria was a regular import with over 1,000 cases annually. In the former Soviet Union, where the immunisation rates were low, an epidemic of diphtheria accompanied the break-up. Ebola fever recurred in Zaire, and people were discouraged from going there.[78]

Sexually transmitted disease and AIDS

Sexually transmitted diseases were now second only to respiratory tract infections as a cause of reported morbidity from communicable disease in Europe.[79] Travel and migration raised concerns about the international emergence and spread of resistant strains, possibly as a result of non-specific use of broad-spectrum antibiotics. Trichomoniasis decreased; syphilis remained constant. Genital wart infections, chlamydia and herpes simplex virus infections were increasing. Gonorrhoea had increased steadily during the first three decades of the NHS, but the ten years from 1977 had seen a decline in the number of cases. Then the number of cases levelled out for a decade, but began to fall again from 1990. Radical innovations in treatment could not take credit, for effective drugs had long been available and drug resistance did not produce substantial difficulties. Early treatment and contact tracing were probably responsible. Surveys demonstrated that in most countries there were small, definable, sexually active groups that maintained the endemicity of disease through intragroup sexual contact. Young and poor people, non-white ethnicity, inner city residents, prostitutes and their male clients were, in different countries, the most visible members of these groups.[80]

AIDS diagnoses and AIDS deaths in England and Wales

Year	Diagnoses	Deaths
1983	46	20
1984	100	45
1985	225	112
1986	438	253
1987	614	325
1988	820	376
1989	947	615
1990	1,101	717
1991	1,220	870
1992	1,386	992
1993	1,397	1,135
1994	1,103	975

Source: CDR Review, January 1996.[81]

The 1988 prediction had been for a rapid growth of epidemic of AIDS; it was taking only 11 months for the number of cases reported in the UK to double. The projections were revised down over the next few years as evidence suggested that transmission among homosexual and bisexual men declined markedly between 1983 and 1987, with the adoption of safer sexual practices.[81] In England the annual number of reports of HIV infection levelled off in the 1990s, as did overt disease. However, the experience of poor countries was increasingly important because of international business and tourist travel. Edwina Currie said that the best protection for a businessman travelling overseas was to take his wife with him. In Thailand, with its lethal mix of cheap sex and heroin addiction, numbers rocketed in 1989 and cases were no longer largely among homosexuals. A 'second epidemic' began in heterosexual men and in prostitutes with the lowest costs and the greatest number of contacts, followed by further cases in children.[82] In the UK the great majority of heterosexual patients were infected abroad; most were refugees who had fled from conflict in Africa. The annual incidence of AIDS in injecting drug abusers rose steadily to about 100 per year; some came to London from Europe to benefit from more liberal social security and health care policies. By the end of 1994 there were 20,400 people in England who were HIV-positive, and the cumulative total of people with AIDS was 9,510, of whom 6,434 had died. Major health education programmes continued; a poster aimed at drug addicts read 'Shooting up once can screw you up. Forever.' Initially, AIDS policy was based less on a purely public health approach and more on the doctrine of individual rights. Debate on the ethics of unlinked anonymous testing ended in 1988/90 with the introduction of surveys on accessible populations. There had been objections on the grounds of confidentiality, the difficulty of treating people once identified and the personal consequences of infection. There was no way of telling individuals that they had tested positive and might spread the disease. Reports of HIV-infected surgeons working in hospital stirred up anxieties about the transmission of HIV from patients to doctors and from doctors to patients.[83] Surgeons, who might puncture their gloves during an operation, became concerned about the risk to themselves. British and American authorities published guidelines on clinical practice. Some surgeons argued for compulsory testing of patients. Testing for anti-HIV-1 and 2 improved screening of blood donations in 1990.

A residential and support centre for people with AIDS, Lighthouse, opened in London in November 1988.[84] It harnessed a vast amount of unusual and lucrative support, particularly from the performing arts, and provided for skilled counselling, long-term support in the community, and provision for terminal care and respite admissions.

In the early 1990s attitudes began to change. AIDS had remained, in general, a disease of large cities. When drugs that seemed to influence the disease began to appear, their development became potentially profitable. In the USA intense pressure on the Food and Drug Administration (FDA) turned it from a passive watchdog into an active participant in research and development. There were stronger scientific grounds for testing and contact tracing was given greater prominence.[85] Trials for the first major breakthrough in treatment, zidovudine (AZT), were hard to interpret. They suggested little benefit from use early in the disease, although there was some effect on fully established cases. It was hard to be optimistic in 1993, but by 1997 the 15-year search for treatment had become suddenly and amazingly successful. The virus seemed to require a protein, reverse-transcriptase, to reproduce; additional drugs, for example 3TC and protease inhibitors, were developed to block its production. The Delta controlled trial showed that drug combinations prolonged life and delayed disease progression.[86] Some patients, believing that they were slowly dying, had to readjust to the possibility of continued life. Almost overnight clinical practice changed, although multiple drug regimens cost 50–75 per cent more than single drug regimens and perhaps over £10,000 per year per patient. It was another pressure health authorities found difficult to resist. For the third world preventive measures remained the only viable approach. Slowly HIV infection came to be treated less as an exceptional condition to which different rules applied. Young people became used to intrusive questions from insurance companies. In 1996 the first over-the-counter HIV test was approved for sale in the USA, a doubtful advance as people might find themselves to be negative despite taking risks. Government-sponsored health promotion advertising had not specifically targeted the gay community – although the voluntary organisations did so. The gay community now argued that it had been neglected and for the first time government campaigns were directed in this direction.

Genetic medicine

Genetic medicine developed rapidly.[87] The most important, and the largest, research programme of the decade was the human genome project, aimed at creating sequence maps of all the nucleotides in humans, in the hope that basic knowledge of structure would cast new light on the cases of disease. Three agencies in the USA and workers in Japan and Russia were working on the project, and Europe with smaller resources was doing what it could. More than 2,000 disorders were said to be caused by inheriting a single faulty gene. In 1995 alone over 60 disease genes were isolated. By 1996 the genes responsible for most common single-gene disorders had been isolated and characterised. There was increasing interest in conditions caused by the interaction of multiple genes, for example insulin-dependent diabetes, high blood pressure and atherosclerosis, although in the short term few such patients were likely to benefit from basic research. Several cancer susceptibility genes were identified from studies of families showing 'autosomal dominant inheritance', in particular breast cancer in which 10 per cent of patients had a family history of the disease in a close relative. In the USA genetic tests went on open sale. DNA analysis became a standard investigation for ever more disorders. The genetic state of family members and pregnancies at risk could be determined for an increasing number of conditions, including haemoglobinopathies, Duchenne muscular dystrophy, cystic fibrosis, Huntington's chorea and phenylketonuria. The main clinical impact was on the detection of 'carriers', presymptomatic and prenatal diagnosis. Information and counselling for women at risk was provided, often in an ad hoc way, in cancer genetics clinics that were often funded from research moneys.[88] These provided access to preventive services, screening, diagnosis and treatment, so those at increased risk might be identified and encouraged to act accordingly. Few doctors were knowledgeable in this new field and primary care teams required education and specialist support. Patients and relatives needed help and counselling from doctors, social services and voluntary organisations.[89] Because there was a possibility that in future genetic techniques would enable the identification of people at risk of developing a wide range of diseases, such as asthma, cancer, diabetes and heart disease, both before and after birth, genetic experts believed that advances in technology would have a major impact on health care, its costs and its ethics. There was a risk that genetic screening, because it identified those at high risk, might lead to their exclusion from insurance schemes, health benefits and even employment. Geneticists asked for a strict regulatory framework; the government instead set up the Human Genetics Advisory Commission.[90]

In the previous 40 years there had been great improvement in the survival rate from cystic fibrosis, an inherited disease in which one person in 20 is a carrier, and which has an incidence of about 1 in 400. Cystic fibrosis produces progressive lung damage in childhood and adolescence, reduced by physiotherapy, antibiotics, better nutrition and the development of centres with a special interest in the disease.[91] It became one of the most intensively researched of the simple genetic diseases, and the discovery of the gene responsible gave an insight into what went wrong.[92] Several approaches to treatment were developed; none worked particularly well. Increased understanding of the basic science did not necessarily lead to cure, but it provided new starting points for the quest for practical treatment.

Surgery

The top ten procedures in 1992/3

- Endoscopy
- Termination of pregnancy
- Cystoscopy
- Dilatation and curettage
- Extraction of teeth
- Cataract surgery
- Tonsillectomy
- Correction of glue ear
- Hernia repair
- Hysterectomy

The excitement associated with surgical advance tends to distract attention from the more common procedures undertaken by the NHS. The number of operations performed was rising about 5 per cent per year. In 1992 the Royal College of Surgeons revised its guidance on day surgery, the conditions to which it might be applied and the information that should be given to patients.[93] Day surgery could be used more widely as a result of advances in anaesthetic techniques. Short-acting anaesthetics, such as propofol, and pain-relieving drugs provided good operating conditions and quick recovery, making it easier for patients to go home rapidly. The costs of day surgery were substantially less than admission, and purpose-built units increasingly provided an efficient environment for the staff and greater convenience for day patients. In 1994 the NHS Executive suggested that 60 per cent of all elective surgery could be conducted as day cases. Managers tried to persuade clinicians to deal with as many patients as they could in this way.

Minimal access surgery

Laparoscopy was initially used largely for diagnostic purposes but the development of high-quality imaging systems, ever-smaller electronic chip cameras, versatile instruments and linear stapling devices opened new fields in gynaecological, urological and general surgery. Rapid adoption of minimal access surgical techniques followed pioneering work on laparoscopic removal of the gall-bladder (1989). The laparoscope was fitted with a high-resolution colour television camera; the average length of stay seemed shorter, and two weeks later it was difficult to see that an operation had been done at all.[94] Soon most cholecystectomies were carried out in this way. Heralded as a major advance in surgical therapy that reduced hospitalisation and quickened post-operative recovery, the escalation in its use was accompanied by increasing concern that it caused more deaths and debilitating post-operative morbidity than conventional surgery. The speed of the introduction of the techniques meant that clinical reports inevitably related to small series with only a short period of follow-up, comparative studies available were often flawed and the evidence that it was better than standard operations was uncertain.[95] However, district general hospitals (DGHs) rapidly took up the new approach. Endoscopically assisted hysterectomy, appendicectomy and hernia repair were also introduced, joining day-case arthroscopy and transurethral prostatic resection to reduce inpatient stays. Minimally invasive surgery was used to treat prolapsed intervertebral disks ('slipped disks') causing back pain. In spite of the emphasis on evidence-based medicine, minimal access surgery was adopted largely without formal assessment of its efficacy. The new procedures often took longer to perform and few surgeons had experience of the special methods. Even in the best hands there might be clinical disasters, and not all surgeons prepared themselves adequately for the new techniques. An entire generation of surgeons required training in the new methods. A minimal access surgery training unit was established at the Royal College of Surgeons of England and other Royal Colleges established guidelines for training in the new methods.[96]

Orthopaedics and trauma

The pressure on orthopaedic units was increased by the steadily rising numbers of fractures of the femur; the main hope for reducing the load lay in prevention, perhaps by hormone replacement therapy. Greater numbers of total hip and knee replacements also increased the load on orthopaedic departments and the results of knee surgery were getting better all the time.[97] Although 60 different replacement hip joints were on the market, only for the Charnley pattern, widely regarded as the gold standard, had 20 years of follow-up results been published.[98] Hip replacement was increasing in younger patients and given enough time most would begin to wear. There was a case for some orthopaedic surgeons to specialise in revision operations, which were difficult and required familiarity with bone grafting techniques and the use of custom-made components.[99] Because of the risk of deep venous thrombosis complicating joint replacement, anticoagulant prophylaxis was increasingly used. Education in the management of fractures and the development of new techniques continued in Switzerland, and a new centre was established near Davos for experimental surgery and to provide training. Because of greater public participation in sport, sports injuries were becoming a large part of the work of orthopaedic departments, essentially self-inflicted injury proving expensive to the NHS. The management of backache, a major and long-standing problem, remained unsatisfactory. Neither orthodox nor alternative medicine offered any reliable form of treatment; normal activity might even be best.[100] Imaging procedures, in particular MRI, were increasingly adopted and began to replace arthroscopy in, for example, the diagnosis of sports injuries of the knee.[101]

Accident and emergency departments were under increasing pressure and the beds required to support them were in short supply. On occasion, they and intensive care services also had to cope with terrorist incidents, and disasters such as the air crash on the M1 motorway in January 1989, and the crush injuries and asphyxiation at Hillsborough football ground in April 1989 when 95 people died. The services were, however, increasingly well prepared. In 1988, when faulty signalling caused an express to plough into a packed commuter train in Clapham, 35 were killed and 500 injured but in general those alive when the rescue services arrived, survived. A policy of rapid transfer to hospital had been balanced by stabilisation before removal. Paramedics could maintain the airway and start intravenous fluids, and were helped by doctors trained in emergency medicine. In the belief that the management of patients with serious injuries would be improved if it were centralised on large trauma centres serving a population of 2 million, and seeing over 50,000 patients a year, the North Staffordshire Royal Infirmary, Stoke-on-Trent, was selected as a pilot centre in 1990. Six years later there was little evidence that it had improved survival. Doctors had argued for major trauma centres for 30 years,[102] but closure of local accident departments aroused vociferous protests. Now, however, the general standard of accident departments had improved substantially and the additional gain from larger units seemed not so great. Helicopter evacuation was also explored. They had been used to evacuate battlefield casualties since the Korean war and the first civilian service was started in Cornwall in 1987. After that ten further services began, including one based at the Royal London Hospital. From the outset there were doubts about an expensive method of transport that was cramped and noisy, and made treatment on board difficult; weather conditions could also prevent the operation of the service.[103] A review suggested that the London service did not improve survival over the short distances involved. What mattered was the speed of getting trained people to the incident to control haemorrhage and maintain the airway, rather than the method of transport used.[104]

Cardiology and cardiac surgery

Cardiology and cardiac surgery became ever more specialised; cardiologists might now specialise in cardiac imaging, interventional cardiology, or pacing and electrophysiology. Paediatric and fetal cardiology emerged as new specialties; children as well as adults could undergo cardiac catheterisation and operation through a catheter. Stenosis of the pulmonary valve could be treated in this way, and minimal access surgery also permitted the closure of heart septum defects in children. Cardiological services were increasingly decentralised, improving the access of the population. Much was being learned about the electrophysiology of the heart. Physiological pacing for disturbances of heart rhythm improved in sophistication. Dual chamber pacemakers, though more expensive, could sense heart activity, increase cardiac output and improve patient well-being.[105] The treatment of high blood pressure with diuretics and beta-blockers had been shown, beyond dispute, to reduce the risk of stroke. The impact on coronary heart disease seemed disappointingly small and there was inadequate evidence to say whether newer drugs, angiotensin-converting enzyme (ACE) inhibitors or calcium antagonists, had an effect on either condition.[106] After two studies of intravenous streptokinase, thrombolytic drugs (to break down clots) were widely adopted in 1988 for myocardial infarction, and aspirin was found to add to the benefit. The sooner blood flow could be restored, the more effective treatment was. Speed in diagnosis and transfer to hospital, and fast-tracking patients on arrival to minimise the delay in giving thrombolytics, was required. Disappointingly, there seemed little change in inpatient mortality.[107] Health promotion campaigns were given added impetus, such as 'Look after your heart!' launched by the Health Education Authority in 1989. Giving up smoking, lowering lipids, taking moderate exercise and controlling high blood pressure were their mainstays.

Whereas surgeons operated annually on about 1,000 patients with congenital heart disease and about 5,000 with heart valve problems, these numbers were now dwarfed by procedures for ischaemic heart disease. Angina pectoris and coronary thrombosis were amenable to the new surgical techniques, no longer the sole preserves of university hospitals. Simpler problems and younger cases tended to be managed by percutaneous transluminal angioplasty, which rose 15 per cent each year (13,000 in Britain in 1995), and was even more commonly used in continental Europe and the USA. New techniques included the use of intracoronary stents, metal mesh devices introduced with a balloon catheter to keep blood vessels open and reduce the chance of re-stenosis. Thrombosis around the stent was a common complication until the design was improved, and drugs were given to reduce the likelihood. Angioplasty during the early hours of a heart attack was an alternative to thrombolytic drugs. Where should it be undertaken – in sub-regional centres or in district hospitals where it would be more readily available? Coronary artery bypass grafting (CABG) was also increasing at 10 per cent a year, and showing no signs of reaching a plateau. The cardiovascular community had been studying the effectiveness of CABG for 25 years, and angioplasty for 15; large trials had been undertaken and it appeared that bypass surgery resulted in a reduction of mortality over four or five years compared with medical treatment, at least in those at moderate or high risk of death.[108] The pressure on cardiac surgical units was almost overwhelming, as patients on the waiting list were delayed because more urgent patients in hospital demanded attention. The stay in intensive care was shortened to the limit, and people were fast-tracked through progressive care and recovery facilities. Staff worked harder, longer and nearer the brink of safety.[109] New surgical techniques continued to be introduced, including minimal access coronary surgery, left ventricular reduction for heart failure and implantable mechanical pumps for heart failure.[110]

Organ transplantation

Several new immunosuppressive drugs were introduced that had different effects on the immune system, including tacrolimus and mycophenolate; combination therapy improved results. In January 1989 Papworth celebrated ten years of heart transplantation; surgeons there were now operating on 120 people a year and following up 260 survivors. The number of heart transplants carried out annually grew, as new centres were opened and the number of organs available for transplantation increased, assisted by publicity, including a special edition of BBC TV's *That's life*. However, a shortage of organs for transplantation meant that many who might benefit did not survive long enough to do so. Who should receive scarce organs? Should choice be local or should allocation be made on national criteria? Pigs were bred with genetic modifications to make them more suitable as a source of organs for transplantation, although some saw the risk that such organs might transmit retrovirus infection to humans.[111] Liver transplantation became more common, and techniques were developed that enabled the liver to be divided to transplant into two recipients. Small bowel transplantation had been attempted in the 1960s and 1970s without much success. The problems of long-term intravenous feeding, and better immunosuppressive drugs, led to further attempts. The success rate improved enough for it to become an option for the treatment of end-stage intestinal failure, mainly patients with anatomical abnormalities or intractable functional disorders. The survival rate was poorer than for many other transplant procedures, roughly two-thirds a year after operation, and a third after three years.[112]

Renal replacement therapy

The number of patients receiving renal replacement therapy rose steadily to about 65 per million, but a report prepared for the DoH in 1996 said that all patients with renal failure up to the age of 80 years should automatically be offered treatment, and those over 80 should be carefully considered for it. The target was now 75–80 new patients annually per million and Britain continued to lag behind the rest of Europe in the numbers under care.[113] Antony Wing argued for more units and better accessibility, for easy geographic access affected whether patients received the care that they needed. Nurse-practitioners played a key role in home supervision of the patients, who were increasingly elderly. The introduction of the Tenkhoff catheter made CAPD easier because, with careful technique, it allowed CAPD to be continued for several years. About a quarter of patients receiving renal dialysis continued to feel unwell because of anaemia caused by deficiency of erythropoietin, a hormone controlling red blood cell formation. A successful transplant solved the problem because the new kidney would produce this hormone, but not all patients could receive a transplant. Recombinant human erythropoietin became available but a year's treatment cost £5,000 – yet another call on health service funds that might be better spent on basic treatment, more transplants and patients undergoing dialysis.[114]

Neurology and neurosurgery

Neurology seemed to have more than its share of genetically determined disease, for example Friedreich's ataxia and Huntington's chorea. Advances in genetics stimulated a better understanding of the mechanisms of neurological disease. In the rare diseases in which there was weakness because of the failure of transmission of nerve impulses to muscles, many of which were related to the immune system, the exact site of the problem could often be determined and the biochemical mechanism understood. Gene mapping made it possible to identify missing genes in muscular dystrophy, opening up the possibility of antenatal diagnosis and selective abortion of those males affected, and the assessment of embryos before implantation. Such expertise was available in only a few places, large units with good laboratory facilities.

New imaging techniques improved the understanding of metabolic processes in health and sickness, in brain tumours, stroke and Alzheimer's disease. Positron emission tomography, in which glucose labelled with radioactive tracers was injected, made it possible to study biochemical activity in the brain. The introduction of virtual reality techniques improved the accuracy of brain surgery. New drugs such as GABA antagonists (e.g. lamotrigine) were a major advance in the management of epilepsy. Interferon-beta was used in an attempt to modify the immune process in multiple sclerosis, and to reduce the frequency of relapse. The management of chronic pain steadily improved, and the intensive care of patients with head injury was better. Imaging techniques and interventional radiology radically altered the treatment of cerebral aneurysms. New forms of drug therapy helped patients with incontinence and sexual dysfunction. Improved rehabilitation techniques underlined the fact that, although many neurological diseases were incurable, none was untreatable. Specialist teams of nurses, physiotherapists and social workers improved the care of people disabled by neurological disease, in hospital and in the community. Patient support groups and charities concerned with diseases such as motor neurone disease and multiple sclerosis provided physical and emotional support to patients, raised money for research and put pressure on government to improve public accessibility for people with physical disabilities.

ENT surgery

The treatment of sensory deafness continued to improve as better multi-channel cochlear implants, commercially produced on a worldwide basis, became available. The earliest implants in the UK were funded by charities but in March 1989 Graham Fraser, of University College Hospital, took one of his patients to meet MPs at the

House of Commons. So impressed were they that David Mellor, then Minister for Health, obtained £3 million to establish six cochlear implant centres. By 1996, 800 adults and 600 children had been implanted in a continuing programme.

Sophisticated imaging and fibreoptic instruments, initially introduced in Austria and Germany, transformed the diagnosis of nasal and sinus disease that could now be assessed, and sometimes treated, in the outpatient department. Like other forms of minimal access surgery, the technique suddenly became popular, but the potential for damage to surrounding structures, the optic nerve and the brain, was high.

Ophthalmology

The use of lasers of different types was increasing. Treatment with them was quick, relatively painless and some techniques could only be performed by laser. Photocoagulation was used for treating proliferative retinopathy (in which there was abnormal development of retinal blood vessels), diabetic retinal disease, macular degeneration (where there was damage to the area of the retina providing the most detailed images), retinal holes and chronic open-angle glaucoma.[115] A new method of treating short sight was introduced into the UK in 1989, modifying the refractive power of the cornea by reshaping the central area with excimer laser keratectomy.

Cataract surgery was ideally suited to day care, 90 per cent of patients being treated in this way. Improved techniques and equipment continued to reduce the period of visual rehabilitation after cataract surgery to about a week. The new methods involved the use of costly equipment, such as the phaecoemulsifier which is used to break up the now opaque lens before its removal and replacement. The use of self-sealing, sutureless wounds and foldable intraocular lens implants that could be introduced through a smaller incision made for an easier postoperative period.[116]

Cancer

The ageing population was inevitably leading to an increase in the number of people developing cancer. A major problem was undetected spread at the time of first treatment, so that the aim was often cancer control rather than cancer cure.[117] The hope was that molecular genetics would help to identify those at risk, assist early diagnosis and provide new forms of treatment. Cancer of the lung remained the commonest form, with 40,000 new cases in the UK each year. Whereas survival rates for several forms of cancer had improved over the previous 20 years, the advances had been modest because the great improvements had occurred in rarer cancers, accounting for less than 10 per cent of the total. In surgery the trend was towards operations that were less extensive and destructive. Radiotherapy remained a major form of treatment, used for about half the 200,000 people developing cancer each year.[118] It could be delivered ever more accurately using the new scanning techniques, having a potentially curative role for about two-thirds of patients and a palliative role in the remainder. Chemotherapy was increasingly used, opening the possibility that new drugs might in time become first-line treatment in common cancers. The appropriate balance of chemotherapy, surgery and radiotherapy was the centre of clinical trials. Newer drug regimens were expensive; intravenous immunoglobulin for chronic lymphatic leukaemia was perhaps most costly in terms of life saved. Several new anti-cancer agents were promising, including taxol (shown to extend life by an average of a year in patients with ovarian cancer), taxotere and gemcitabine. The problem of bone marrow toxicity from curative chemotherapy remained a problem but could be helped by using growth factors for mature blood cells, both red and white. Granulocyte, macrophage and red blood cell stimulating factors became available, as new technology based on genetic engineering moved from the laboratory to the bedside.[119]

Breast cancer had traditionally been regarded as a surgical disease, chemotherapy being reserved for treating locally advanced primary disease and secondary spread. Recognition that spread often occurred early led to more conservative surgery.[120] Radiotherapy followed by limited surgery gave survival comparable to that of radical mastectomy. Several years of tamoxifen significantly prolonged survival and combinations of chemotherapeutic agents gave good results, although it remained uncertain whether chemotherapy could completely replace surgery. In 1989 a study of chemotherapy as the initial treatment for smaller and operable tumours began, to reduce their size and make surgery easier.

The national breast cancer screening programme of women of 50–64 years, recommended in the Forrest Report,[121] started in 1988. It replaced the earlier recall system and aimed to screen that age group at least every five years. A major investment in equipment was required and the scheme used the lists of patients registered with GPs (the family health services register) to identify those to be called. Roughly a million women a year were screened. To begin with there were probably too many biopsies creating unnecessary anxiety in many women. The detection rate was about 6 per 1,000 and the apparent incidence of breast cancer rose 25 per cent in the age group being screened. There was, however, a reduction in the total mortality among women aged 55–69, but this might have been due either to screening or to the widespread use of tamoxifen for proven cases over the same period.[122] Some questioned the programme, as it appeared to bring about only a relatively small reduction in mortality, and at a substantial cost. Although the early trials had reported a 30 per cent relative reduction in mortality in women over 50 years of age, subsequent ones showed less benefit. Critics of the programme suggested that £27 million was being spent on a programme that might be saving few lives and engendering needless anxiety among many women.[123] Assessment of the programme for cancer of the cervix was affected by an apparent reduction in the incidence of the disease. The benefits of screening for cancer of the colon by a single fibreoptic examination at the age of 60 were examined.

In the late 1980s and early 1990s a number of hospitals discovered that there had been repetitive errors in planning radiotherapy. In Exeter (1989) it was found that over five years 260 patients had been given too high a radiation dose; in Stoke (1990) 1,000 patients had been given a 25 per cent under-dose; in Cambridge (1995) 25 patients had been treated incorrectly. There were also diagnostic errors; over several years the bone tumour service in Birmingham had treated some patients unnecessarily and wrongly reassured others that tumours were benign. At the Kent and Canterbury Hospital it was necessary to review over 90,000 cervical smears taken over six years; late diagnoses were followed by deaths and major surgery.

It was increasingly recognised that patients with cancer had better outcomes if cared for in hospitals treating many patients, or if they were part of a clinical trial. The establishment of the UK children's cancer study group in 1977 led to greater use of paediatric oncology centres, where those with leukaemia, retinoblastoma and Wilms' tumour of the kidney had better outcomes. In some of the rarer adult cancers there was also evidence of better survival rates where specialised care was available and the case-load of a unit was high.[124] In October 1993 Kenneth Calman, the CMO, appointed an Expert Advisory Group on Cancer. The Group recommended that everyone should have access to a uniformly high quality of care to ensure the maximum cure rates and the best quality of life. It proposed that the service should be structured at three levels. Primary care teams were the focus of care. Designated cancer *units* would be created in many – but not all – district hospitals. They would have the expertise to treat the more common cancers such as breast, bowel and lung. Designated cancer *centres* would treat the less common cancers that required particular skills and specialist equipment. They would be highly specialised and serve a population of at least a million. They would deal with children and adolescents, undertake complex procedures such as bone marrow transplantation and have sophisticated diagnostic facilities. With a death rate of 150,000 a year from cancer, improvement of survival by 5–10 per cent was considered realistic. The problem was to implement the system in a service that was increasingly fragmented, competitive and dispirited. Clinicians and managers mapped out the role of individual hospitals within region-wide schemes, designating cancer centres and units in 1997.[125] Smaller DGHs would be subordinate to the larger centres, where sub-specialisation was possible. So much of cancer therapy was now available on a day-basis that GPs had no problem working directly with cancer centres.

Obstetrics and gynaecology

The eleventh report of confidential enquiries into maternal deaths was published in 1988. It showed that, over the previous 40 years, the number of deaths had roughly halved every ten years, from 1,480 in 1955–1957 to 163 in 1982–1984. Pulmonary embolism, diseases of high blood pressure in pregnancy, anaesthetic deaths and amniotic fluid embolism were the four most frequent causes.[126] In 1992 the proportion of women in their early 30s bearing children exceeded that of women in their early 20s for the first time, as more women delayed childbearing. Emergency contraception, commonly by using oral contraceptive tablets within 72 hours of intercourse, became available. Deferring pregnancy was a gamble; women in their 30s and 40s took longer to become pregnant, and were at higher risk of fetal abnormality and permanent childlessness.[127] Screening for fetal abnormality by amniocentesis and karyotyping of fetal cells became common practice. The association of Down's syndrome with changes in placental hormone levels in maternal serum led to calls for screening for all who wanted it. Pre-test counselling was required, so that women understood better the options and the risks. Many abnormalities of the central nervous system, the heart, the kidneys and the gut could be picked up by ultrasound, some leading to termination of pregnancy and others to delivery in a special centre where immediate neonatal surgical care was available. Doppler studies to assess fetal blood flow were found useful in assessing fetuses that were small for the length of pregnancy and were therefore at risk.[128]

With roughly 99 per cent of deliveries in hospital, GPs were now seldom involved and most had lost their obstetric skills. Within the hospitals there was an ever-increasing tendency towards fetal monitoring and operative delivery. In Britain, as in the rest of the Western world, caesarean section rates were steadily increasing, reaching 15 per cent. There was little evidence to justify rates in double figures, the indications often being vague – 'failure to make progress' or 'fetal distress'. Many factors were influencing the rise. It might be convenient to repeat a caesarean section in a woman who had previously had one, and who therefore required careful watching in labour because, rarely, the uterus might rupture.[129]

Live births at home, England 1988–1995

Year	All live births	Live births at home	Percentage at home
1988	654,363	6,084	0.9
1989	649,357	6,560	1.0
1990	666,920	6,929	1.0
1991	660,806	7,398	1.1
1992	651,784	8,704	1.3
1993	636,473	9,900	1.6
1994	628,956	11,168	1.8
1995	613,257	11,732	1.9

Source: Office for National Statistics 1996

Childbirth had become increasingly professionalised, and women – at least of the *Guardian* reading classes – felt they had decreasing influence over the situation. To mitigate the problem some hospitals developed 'birth rooms' that were more domestic in nature. Midwives began to reassert their traditional role as an alternative to the high tech environment, which though lifesaving on occasion had less to offer the average woman. In 1991/2 the Health Select Committee produced a landmark report reversing 20 years of medical advice that all births should take place in hospital, concluding that this policy could not be justified on the grounds of safety. It was well crafted, comprehensive and controversial. It was 'pro-midwife', stating that women had a strong desire for continuity of care throughout pregnancy and midwives were seen as best placed for this.[130] The Royal College of Obstetricians and Gynaecologists opposed the report and there was no immediate change in government policy, but a small expert group was appointed. Its report appeared in 1993 as *Changing childbirth*.[131] Half of the expert group were consumers rather than professionals, and it was chaired by a Minister, Baroness Julia Cumberlege. This was unusual, for it was less easy for government to walk away from the findings if they proved inconvenient. It was concluded that women should be given greater choice of maternity care, for example about the place of birth and the type of carer. The aim should be to create 'women-centred' services, asking women what they wanted, testing satisfaction and monitoring clinical results. The midwifery profession welcomed the report and its principles were incorporated into later extensions to *The patient's charter*. The medical profession was less enthusiastic but government accepted that women should have a greater say in maternity care. Midwives took greater responsibility for the management of normal labour, and consultants, who needed to spend much time with high-risk cases and on patient counselling, might welcome less involvement when pregnancy was proceeding smoothly. There was a slight increase in home delivery, but even though observational studies supported the view that home could be safe if women were well selected, midwives found it costly to obtain cover against litigation.[132] There had never been good evidence of the effectiveness of frequent and regular antenatal visits. An assessment of a shorter six or seven visit schedule, in place of the traditional 13 check-ups, showed the outcome to be much the same. Those attending specialist clinics received more scans and day admissions, without demonstrable clinical benefit.[133]

Infertility treatment

In 1990 the Human Fertilisation and Embryology Act was passed, in line with recommendations of the Committee of Inquiry chaired by Dame Mary Warnock in 1984.[134] The Human Fertilisation and Embryology Authority (HFEA) was established to inspect and license the hundred or more centres carrying out any 'infertility treatment involving the use of donated eggs or sperm, treatment that involved the creation or use of embryos outside the body, and research on embryos'. The Authority maintained a register of all such treatments and the success rates of individual clinics. It established a code of practice and guidelines, for example on surrogacy, sex selection, research on fetal tissue and the age limits of those donating gametes.[135] The number of procedures undertaken and the success rate rose steadily from 1985 onwards; the success rate reached roughly 20 per cent per treatment cycle and increasingly the HFEA provided information to the public about donor insemination and in-vitro fertilisation. Another technique, the stimulation of ovulation by drugs such as clomiphene, became more common, for it was easier and cheaper. It was, however, more prone to result in multiple births. Taken together, by 1996 over 100,000 women a year were seeking help. Properly supervised, following protocols and carrying out the necessary range of tests before undertaking treatment, it took up an increasing amount of clinic time. Most multiple births became associated with fertility treatment, there being a trebling of the number of triplets. Inevitably many were premature, throwing strain and substantial costs on neonatal units.

Abortion

Of roughly 800,000 conceptions a year in English women, some 150,000 were terminated under the Abortion Act 1967, mostly at less than 13 weeks' gestation. One pregnancy in three ended in termination in some inner city districts. Abortion services were sometimes contracted out to the private sector, relieving the strain on NHS gynaecological units. In 1990 the limit for medical termination of pregnancy was reduced from 28 to 24 weeks in line with prevailing clinical opinion. A new ground for abortion, the risk of grave permanent injury, was established and for this there was no time limit. The law was clarified to permit selective reduction of multiple pregnancies on the same grounds as an abortion. Initially described in 1978, the procedure was mainly used to terminate an abnormal fetus. However, it was increasingly used when there were many babies following the use of fertility drugs, to reduce the risk of premature delivery and increase the chance of survival of the remaining fetuses.[136]
Drugs established a place in the management of induced abortion. Mifepristone, a steroid compound that blocked the action of progesterone required for the maintenance of pregnancy in its early stages, followed by vaginal administration of a prostaglandin, was shown to be effective in producing abortion in early pregnancy but did not achieve the acceptance initially predicted.

Hormone replacement therapy

Long-term hormone replacement therapy (HRT) was increasingly promoted as effective in reducing the risk of osteoporosis and cardiovascular disease in post-menopausal women, and was available in a variety of forms – patches, creams and implants.[137] The benefits were thought to be related to the duration of use and to outweigh risks such as an increased incidence of breast cancer and a higher risk of deep vein thrombosis or pulmonary embolism.[138] By the early 1990s about one in ten women in the appropriate age group was using HRT, and among women doctors the number was nearer a half.[139] The rate of use steadily increased, and roughly half of those starting HRT remained on the therapy for many years. Because of uncertainty about the benefits and disadvantages of long-term use, the MRC began an international controlled trial in 1996.[140]

Paediatrics

Neonatal paediatrics was ever more effective in keeping small premature infants alive, thereby creating ethical and financial problems. Respiratory difficulties were now treated more successfully using surfactant and, in cases of acute heart or respiratory failure, oxygen using a heart–lung machine (extracorporeal membrane oxygenation). The work of Ann Greenough in Cambridge led to the careful application of physiological principles to the ventilation of small babies, and reduced the risk of pneumothorax. It was known that the smaller the child, the higher the risk of long-term disabilities, although in the better units the quality of survival was often good. Just how small and premature should a baby be before it was deemed inappropriate to use high technology to preserve life? At 28 weeks the outcome was often excellent; at 23 weeks survival was rare and severe abnormalities common. While better neonatal care had increased the survival of extremely immature babies, a third of those weighing less than 1,700 g at birth had retinopathy of prematurity, the cause of which was not fully understood.[141] Current practice was to attempt to save premature infants of 25–26 weeks' maturity but not those of 22 weeks.[142]

Child health surveillance was increasingly undertaken by GPs, who received additional money if they were accredited in this field. Immunisation was one of the most cost-effective strategies for reducing mortality and morbidity in children. Minimally invasive investigation revolutionised paediatric diagnosis. Ultrasound – cheap, safe and widely available – had many applications from congenital dislocation of the hip to heart disease. Endoscopic techniques and MRI also helped. About 80 per cent of children in hospital had diseases with genetic or familial implications. 'Molecular' diagnosis was introduced, and gene therapy was increasingly used, as for example in immunodeficiency diseases. Transplants of heart, lung, liver and intestine were now options in specialised units.[143] Intrauterine surgery became technically possible in the late 1980s but remained semi-experimental because of the problems after opening the mother's uterus and operating on such fragile patients.

Bone marrow transplantation for thalassaemia could now be offered to many patients with severe disease. Oral chelating agents that assisted the excretion of iron, surplus as a result of repeated blood transfusion, were also under trial, in the hope that they would render subcutaneous injection obsolete. As in-vitro fertilisation improved, in 1995/6 it became possible to diagnose, pre-implantation, both thalassaemia and sickle-cell disease.

One of the most horrific episodes of the decade was the case of Beverley Allitt, a nurse at Grantham and Kesteven Hospital, who was sentenced for murdering four children, attempting to murder another three and causing grievous bodily harm to six others on a paediatric ward in 1991.

Geriatrics

In the early 1960s it had been shown that many elderly patients in the community were suffering from disorders not reported to or identified by their doctors.[144] Screening programmes found problems that might be remediable, for example with sight, hearing, mobility, social situation and mental state. Several later studies, not all of which concentrated on these simple but important faults, were unable to replicate these findings. The 1990 GP contract required practices to contact those more than 75 years of age to identify their health and social needs. Some GPs found that the health visitors and nurses in the practice could do this effectively, but others disputed whether problems were discovered that were not already recognised.

Seventy per cent of people admitted to an acute medical service were now likely to be over 65 years of age. The guiding principle of acute emergency medical care was now the absence of distinctions based on age, a principle followed to a greater extent in some units than others. Integration of geriatrics into general medical provision was economic and made it easier to develop rotas for junior doctors. Grimley Evans, Professor of Clinical Geratology at Oxford, pointed out that the result of modern aggressive medicine, for example thrombolytic therapy for heart attacks, might be at least as good in old people as in middle life. There was no rationale for separating old people from the rest of the human race. It was important that they should have equal access to specialist medical care, for example to cardiology and gastroenterology, as well as to the skills required in the management of disease in old age.[145]

At the outset the NHS had accepted responsibility for the long-term care of the chronic sick, although the standard of care was often unacceptably low. Over the years the NHS service improved, with an accent on rehabilitation. Categorisation of people into those needing health provision (that was free) and those requiring social support (that was chargeable) was difficult. Although frail elderly people often required both social support and health care, such responsibilities increasingly passed to the social services and the private sector. New nursing homes opened, sometimes managed by private companies, in which the quality of nursing care could be high. Specialised homes developed to care for people who were mentally infirm. Hospice care for terminal illness was more widely available.

Grimley Evans thought there were three issues to address.[146] First care must be as efficient as possible, for there were intriguing variations in policy and cost; the cost of support in the community might be far higher than residential care and little was known about the comparative merits. Second, efforts should be made to reduce the need for care in later life. Third, there needed to be agreement about how care was to be paid for. Was it to be by insurance, taxation or the liquidation of personal assets? The public money spent on residential accommodation was rising rapidly because of the ready availability of social security payments. After an Audit Commission report that criticised the spending of money on community care by the NHS, local authorities and the social security services, Norman Fowler commissioned Sir Roy Griffiths to review the way public funds were spent. Griffiths reported in March 1988 and argued that local authorities were well placed to manage care in the community, and should act as arrangers and purchasers but not monopoly suppliers of community care services. Purchasing and provision should be separated. Responsibility for care should be placed as near to the individual as possible, and people should have a greater say and a wider choice in what was being done to help them. They should be helped to stay in their homes as long as possible. He recommended a bigger role for GPs in assessment and the notification of needs to local authorities.[147] The Conservative government was not enthusiastic about local authorities and feared that spendthrift councils would invest millions in over-staffed unionised institutions. It was 17 months before a decision was reached, the government then accepting most of Griffiths, promising a White Paper and legislation.[148] The NHS and Community Care Act (1990) led to a fundamental change in the system of funding residential and nursing homes, transferring the responsibility from the Department of Social Security (DSS) to local authority social services departments. An open-ended and rapidly expanding budget was replaced by a limited one based on individual assessments of need. On the whole the transfer went smoothly, local authorities developing care managers who could organise support using either public funds or personal contributions. The funds for care were not earmarked and arguably they were less than was required. Long-stay care was increasingly phased out of the NHS. By the mid-1990s only 10 per cent of elderly people receiving long-term residential care did so in NHS facilities. The remaining 90 per cent had to pass a means test to qualify for funding from local authorities, now the principal budget holders for state-financed long-term care. The DoH issued guidance about the type of continuing care that the NHS should provide. Largely inpatient-orientated, it identified people whose clinical condition was unstable, who needed complex medical, nursing or other clinical care, frequent and not easily predictable intervention, or regular supervision by health service personnel.[149] The boundary was not easy to define and the Commons Select Committee criticised the government for failing to make clear the minimal level of provision people could expect, and from whom.[150]

Mental illness

In the 1960s the enthusiasm for early discharge and rehabilitation had come from psychiatrists. Then other forces became involved. Some sociologists saw the disabilities of people in hospital as partly a result of incarceration, and civil liberties lobbies sought to restrict or abolish compulsory detention. Health ministers, dismayed by embarrassing hospital scandals, saw abolition of the mental hospitals as a solution, but consistently reminded the NHS that community support must be available. This policy, however, required more money rather than less, because community care was staff-intensive and it was desirable to develop a local service *before* the asylums were closed. Government did not provide extra funds for double running-costs, and regions could seldom meet the bills. Nevertheless, in the 40 years from 1954 to 1993 the number of hospital beds fell by almost two-thirds to 50,278. Of 130 large mental hospitals open in 1960, 38 had closed by 1993, mostly in the late 1980s and early 1990s. A further 21 had agreed closure dates. Only 14 did not intend to close this century. In those remaining the number of beds had fallen continuously to an average of 223 per hospital in 1993, a fraction of their former size. The numbers of patients per nurse and per consultant had fallen, at least in part due to the reduction in patient numbers. The average length of stay had fallen from 162 days in 1986 to 76 days in 1993.[151]

Many features of the services for the mentally ill had improved. Shifting the emphasis from hospital had produced a more humane pattern of care, less disabling for patients and greatly preferred by them. Patients had a greater voice in their care and might be consulted about service plans. Voluntary organisations played a more substantial role, and multi-disciplinary teams were increasingly to be found. However, as money was needed for the new community health teams, beds were sometimes closed before alternative facilities were available. There could be delays for emergency admission and people with less urgent problems might not be admitted at all. Patients sometimes remained in hospital long after they were well enough for discharge, because there were insufficient residential places in the community. Particularly in the cities, the full range of community services was seldom available, certainly not 24 hours a day.

National policy for mental health was restated in the context of *The health of the nation*, and there were subtle changes.[152] Placing acute local units on DGH sites, which 'might have poor access and be over-large', was losing its lustre. The methods of care, were changing. Better drugs were available and new methods of psycho-social intervention were being used. Most people could be treated on an outpatient basis but those who were admitted now seemed to be more disturbed, aggressive and sometimes violent. Mental illness services were increasingly managed from a community base. Attempts were made to develop services locally, providing acute beds, beds for patients likely to need sanctuary or long-term rehabilitation, and specialised facilities for adolescents and for people needing to be housed under secure conditions. In the place of the old asylum or the more recent DGH wing, small residential units with 24-hour nursing, or intensive home care, were encouraged as effective and cost-effective. The aim was a care programme for each patient, with assessment, a care plan and a key worker. Social services departments co-operated in the provision of facilities and key workers, supported by a range of housing and hostel accommodation.

Theory and practice did not always coincide. More dispersed services carried the risk that some individuals with mental health problems could be lost to the system, become homeless or end up in prison. The disabilities of chronic schizophrenics did not melt away when the hospital gates closed behind them. Living a chaotic life and rejecting care, they required close supervision but did not always receive it. Sometimes because of shortage of accommodation they would be caught in a game of 'pass the parcel' from one agency to another.[153] Consultants who disagreed over the diagnosis and placement might dispute clinical responsibility. Many areas had no system of monitoring long-term care. Sometimes the private sector was used for secure accommodation, or for the management of addiction or behavioural problems.[154] Increasingly public attention was focused on the plight of former psychiatric inpatients adrift in an uncaring, uncomprehending society, and the burdens imposed on families.[155] In 1993, Ben Silcock, a diagnosed schizophrenic, climbed into the lion enclosure at London Zoo and was badly mauled. Georgina Robinson, an occupational therapist, was killed by a resident in a mental health centre. An inquiry led by Sir Louis Blom-Cooper demanded fundamental changes in the 1983 Mental Health Act to end 'the chaos of community care', so authorities would have to give a precise prescription of where patients would live and the treatment they would receive, by compulsion if necessary. 'Everyone knows what has happened' said the *Independent*. 'Hundreds of ex-patients have lost touch with the agencies involved in their care and now have miserable lives. At worst patients have become a danger to themselves and others.'[156] Professionals were expected to make a sophisticated judgement about the potential risk patients presented to themselves and others; how were the rights of patients to maximum liberty and greatest chance of improvement to be combined with the protection of the public from any possibility of harm?[157] The Mental Health (Patients in the Community) Act 1995 established the concept of supervised treatment in the community, and gave the supervisor authority to take and convey patients to hospital if it seemed desirable.

Some psychiatrists had always been convinced that patients with schizophrenia were often discharged prematurely and excessive throughput of cases was not conducive to good care.[158] The Clinical Standards Advisory Group (CSAG), a source of advice to ministers, reported that the quality of care for schizophrenics was unsatisfactory in over half the districts, because of low morale, poor communication between health and social services, and lack of strong local leadership particularly from psychiatrists. It warned that the movement of community psychiatric nurses away from consultant-led teams into primary care teams might divert nursing care away from the most ill and vulnerable.[159] The hospital scandals of the 1970s had been replaced by community scandals in the 1990s. The Royal College of Psychiatrists, asked to report on 39 killings and 240 suicides by mentally ill people over the previous three years, concluded that patients' refusal to comply with treatment was often responsible, but inadequate use of care plans by mental health staff was widespread. The recommendations of previous inquiries had seldom been acted on. Confusion over professional responsibilities, communication failures, lack of face-to-face contact between clinicians and patients, and insufficient use of legal powers were all to be found.[160] Following the NHS reforms a comparatively simple system in which central government and the NHS had been responsible for funding and operating local services, mainly hospital based, with a limited amount of community support from local authorities, was replaced by a system that might be more community orientated, but which carried a danger of fragmenting responsibility and funding.[161] Government, recognising the problems, published a Green Paper on mental health in 1997, with an emphasis on delivering a more reliable and focused spectrum of care at a local level, including emergency access facilities.

Counselling

The changing focal point of psychiatry from hospital to the community was accompanied by a growth in counselling. As organised religion declined, GPs had increasingly been the source of solace. Increasingly some displaced this function onto the community psychiatric nurses and employed counsellors who worked with their practices. Crisis services with out-of-hours helplines developed to provide immediate professional support. Adults who had been victims of sexual abuse asked for treatment. Debriefing after traumatic and stressful experiences became commonplace; a psychoanalyst and a biographer of Jung, whose car was robbed, was offered counselling by the police for his traumatic experience. Major incidents, deaths after road accidents or football stadium disasters, would lead to the influx of a team of counsellors to care for the near-victims, relief workers and even those who were mere spectators. The effectiveness of counselling was challenged, for though it met real and symbolic needs, it was costly and it was uncertain what was achieved.[162]

General practice and primary health care

A 'primary care led' NHS

Changes affecting primary care
• 1990 contract
• Financial incentives for health promotion
• Greater role for nurses
• Computerisation
• Stronger management
• Fundholding and commissioning
• Medical audit
• Patients' charter
• Shortage of doctors
• Two White Papers (1996)

Before 1948 GPs were central to health services, a position they lost with the growth of specialist medicine. The fifth decade saw a return of their power that few would have predicted. GPs were given financial incentives to improve standards. Primary health care teams grew larger and were increasingly well housed. The number of GPs in England rose by 10 per cent between 1985 and 1995, and 31 per cent were then female. Average list sizes fell. Nearly half GPs were in large partnerships, four to six in size. The distribution of general practitioners, evened out by the Medical Practices Committee, was remarkably uniform but doctors who had qualified outside the UK were to be found predominantly in the old industrial areas where single-handed practice remained more common. Management was given powerful levers to encourage better staffing, premises and cost-effective local services. Computerisation of many family health services authority (FHSA) administrative activities was complete, and the register of patients was used for clinical activities in health promotion and cervical cytology.

Primary care had four main tasks: the care of acute illness, the management of chronic disease, health promotion and, increasingly, organisational matters. Patients' problems changed only slowly. Every ten years the morbidity survey was repeated, to coincide with the census. For the first time, between September 1991 and August 1992, statistics were collected from spotter practices using practice computer systems.[163] Seventy-eight per cent of people were found to have consulted their GP at least once. As ever, the commonest reasons were respiratory diseases (31 per cent), nervous system disorders including ear problems (17 per cent) and musculo-skeletal problems such as arthritis (17 per cent). Patients expected longer consultations. More consulted for preventive health care, immunisation, contraception, screening and advice than for any other single disease grouping (33 per cent). Traditionally it was believed that GPs treated people without bothering too much about scientific medicine. One practice analysed its work and showed that the treatment of four patients out of five reflected the findings of good clinical trials.[164]

The negotiation of the 1990 GP contract

The GPs' contract was reviewed, negotiated, modified and reviewed repetitively throughout the decade. A White Paper in 1987 laid out ministers' goals.[165] Government was becoming convinced that firm negotiation would be necessary if they were to be achieved. Meetings with the profession began in 1988. Quality was to be raised through competition and financial incentives, for example target levels would be set for immunisation and cervical cytology. Patients should be given better information about services. GPs should receive more of their pay from capitation, health promotion would become an explicit part of the contract, and practice in deprived areas would be assisted by extra payments based on Brian Jarman's criteria. Whereas the changes of 1965 had altered the structure of practice, those of 1989/90 were more concerned with the process of care. Few were based on firm scientific evidence of benefit to patients but there was nothing new in this. The ideas came from many sources, including the Royal College of General Practitioners (RCGP), the work of Brian Jarman, and Julian Tudor Hart's views about the anticipation of the problems of patients and the long-term management of chronic disease.

It was legal for the Secretary of State to decide the terms on which family doctors worked, but in law there had to be a clear attempt to negotiate alteration. The profession liked the status quo while the government wished for change. There being little spare money, its distribution would alter. Some payments seemed outdated. Why should GPs be paid for group practice or vocational training when this was near-universal, or for seniority as opposed to quality? The GPs had rejected the good practice allowance. The DoH sought the same end in a different way, using incentives to encourage activities that were a proxy for quality. Because of the need to define the activities, the proposals seemed mechanistic. There was no new money to ease the introduction of performance-related pay. The package on offer meant more work for the same money; better organised practices would gain and others would lose. Deprived area payments would help those in the inner cities but there would be less for GPs elsewhere. Seniority awards, which went to the older and most powerful members of the profession, were at risk. The deal was hard for the profession's leaders to accept, and it was unusual for government to lay down so precisely what doctors should do in clinical terms, as in the assessment of those over 75 years of age.

After hours of negotiation the key differences were identified and the General Medical Services Committee negotiators met the departmental team for a weekend at Selsdon Park. In 1952 and 1965 ministers, not officials, had led the Department's team, and agreement was helped by substantial new money. Only at the end of the negotiations in May 1989 did the Secretary of State, Kenneth Clarke, meet the profession's representatives. During a ten-hour meeting both sides made concessions, seniority awards were reprieved, there was agreement and both sides celebrated. The secrecy that had made negotiation easy made acceptance by the rank-and-file difficult. GPs angrily rejected the package, one saying that the remaining problems could be solved by hanging the profession's negotiators. Kenneth Clarke implemented the package. GPs had not believed that their contract could be altered without agreement and had been proved wrong. In 1966 the profession's negotiators held a strong hand. General practice had been deteriorating and was widely regarded as second rate, and morale was low. GPs were leaving practice, Kenneth Robinson (the Minister) was the son of a GP, and Labour, just re-elected, saw the NHS as its political baby. In 1990 GPs were well motivated, worked in premises provided largely at public expense, had no difficulty in recruiting colleagues, and public attitudes to organised industrial action had changed. GPs faced a strong government determined on consumer-orientated reform and their negotiators held but modest hands.[166]

The aftermath

Those with a clearer view of the future felt that the concurrent NHS reforms would make more fundamental contractual alterations necessary. In spite of all the anger the 1990 contract did not represent a fundamental break with the past. Its outcome was not always as envisaged. Health promotion tended to be segregated in special clinics, rather than being incorporated into normal consultations. It was hard to convert the rhetoric of health promotion into contractual language or guidance to GPs about what they should do. Neither the GMSC nor the DoH had understood how effective financial incentives would prove. GPs appointed many more nurses, increased their minor surgery, organised their practices better, installed more computers, and achieved higher rates of immunisation and cervical cancer screening.[167] Julian Tudor Hart himself conceded that the new contract had reached parts of the profession other contracts had not reached. First the front runners and then other GPs improved their staffing, organisation, equipment, and clinical and educational activities.[168] The Medical Practitioners' Union continued to argue that the GP's future lay as a salaried public servant meeting the individual and collective needs of a geographically defined population.[169] Younger doctors often agreed. GPs became willing to talk about contractual modifications where improvement was possible, for example health promotion. Half new GPs were now women and many wished to alter their commitments from time to time. GP numbers, both in total numbers and in whole-time equivalents, increased between 1990 and 1994, but following the 1990 contract there was more part-time work and job-sharing. The previous system was better suited to a male profession working full-time and some doctors, nearing retirement, also wanted to reduce their work.[170]

Morale in general practice was poor, fewer doctors sought vocational training and GPs increasingly rebelled against their 24-hour responsibility and night calls. In 1983 45 per cent of doctors finishing their preregistration year listed general practice as their first career choice, but by 1993 this had fallen to 25 per cent. They felt that the public, increasingly accustomed to consumerism and 24-hour services from many organisations, wanted primary health care to be available on the same basis. Ian Bogle replaced Michael Wilson as Chairman of the GMSC and tried to establish better relationships between government and the profession. Contractual changes were made that gave GPs wider discretion on whether and where an out-of-hours consultation should occur. There was increasing emphasis on telephone advice and the development of out-of-hours 'co-operatives', often established in primary care centres to which patients could come. Some GPs were prepared to consider radical revision of their contract, a salaried service or the replacement of a national contract by a patchwork of national and local deals giving GPs more choice over their working arrangements and workload. Increasingly, GPs favoured a contract for 'core services' to define what should be done for the money they received. However, if the boundary was drawn too wide they might be asked to do too much, and if too narrow it opened the path to commercial contracting of some activities to other professional groups.

Following a further review a more flexible framework was proposed, with a shift towards primary care and a movement of resources to accompany this.[171] A White Paper, *Choice and opportunity*, was published in October 1996.[172] At its core was a proposal to deregulate general practice by allowing schemes that would pilot different forms of contract. If these were successful they could be made permanent. New options included salaried doctors within partnerships; practice-based contracts that could embrace non-medical professionals including nurses, therapists and managers; a single budget for general medical services, hospital and community health services and prescribing (that would open the path for cash-limiting primary health care); and NHS contracts for primary care with bodies such as NHS community trusts. This flexibility in the methods used to provide primary care made the GPs anxious about their independent status.[173] The NHS (Primary Care) Bill was introduced into Parliament. In December 1996 a further White Paper, *Primary care: delivering the future*, set out a raft of 70 initiatives of a practical nature to complement the legislation. The proposals were broadly welcomed by the GMSC, the Royal College of Nursing (RCN) and by the Labour Party, and covered education, research, clinical audit, resource distribution, the contractual options and problems of recruitment.[174] The 1997 pay review, however, gave GPs far less than they wished. Some of them argued that GPs should no longer negotiate for money alongside consultants, through the BMA, but should go it alone. They sought a review of their contracts and the system of setting their pay.[175]

Practice premises

Stretched to bursting point by new staff and services, and packed to the rafters with paperwork and computers, the GPs' premises had been operating at full capacity. Spending on premises had increased only modestly; the cost-rent scheme had done wonders after the 1965 GPs' charter but was not appropriate to the changes now in progress. GPs, who after the NHS reforms became fundholders, often applied savings to the improvement of their premises. The movement of services from secondary to primary care led to association of GPs, FHSAs and community health trusts. Schemes for new-style 'primary care resource centres', combining a range of services, were rapidly put together and new government proposals sought to encourage this. In a way, the 1948 vision of the health centres was being reinvented.[176]

Nurse-practitioners and practice nurses

Practice nurses, to their surprise, were beneficiaries. GPs found additional and congenial assistance with a rising workload and had no difficulty in recruiting nurses keen to develop their career and popular with patients.[177] They were recruited in their thousands at great cost to a rather surprised Treasury that had to pick up the bill. From fewer than 2,000 whole-time equivalents in 1984, the number of practice nurses rose to more than 9,000 in 1994. As their numbers grew, the range of their work increased. Nurses took over health promotion; although health visitors had always worked in this field, there were not enough of them, their employers restricted the work they did, and mothers and children came first. Practice nurses were subsequently involved in traditionally medical areas such as the care of chronic disease, the management of diabetes, asthma and high blood pressure.[178] Assessment of new patients, the follow-up of old ones, history taking and prescriptions were all were possible within protocols agreed by the team. Projects assessed the role of practice-based nurses in the treatment of depression and the management of epilepsy. Nurses undertook triage and, with misplaced enthusiasm, a former trust chairman suggested that as GP competence varied, one answer might be to scrap GPs and bring in nurse-practitioners as gatekeepers to hospital services, relocating the GPs to the hospital accident and emergency departments.[179]

The concept of the 'nurse-practitioner' became a semantic battleground.[180] There were two options for nurses. One was to continue to do what they were already doing, only more of it and at a higher level of skill and training. Alternatively they might become a first point of contact, assessing patients (making a diagnosis), determining treatment including the drugs to be prescribed, and becoming a member of a medical team with a defined role and accountability within that team.[181] Management saw that, as primary health care became central to the NHS and activities were transferred to the community, more staff would be needed. A study by the South Thames Region showed nurse-practitioners to be safe and effective, and in primary care they could work alongside GPs seeing medically unscreened patients. There was tension between the nursing profession's vision of nurse-practitioners and the natural role which they established within primary care moving out of a nurse-led hierarchy into a multi-disciplinary team.[182] British practice nurses and nurse-practitioners came from a variety of backgrounds. The RCN's definition of a nurse practitioner was oriented towards primary care, not hospitals. The College developed diploma and degree courses for nurse-practitioners but, unlike courses in the USA that concentrated primarily on clinical and medical issues, they were more concerned with the philosophy of nursing in the community than with crisp professional issues of diagnosis, examination and treatment.

The boundaries between the hospital and primary care

Problems in organisations often occur at structural boundaries, and boundaries existed between general practice and the hospital service, and between health and local authority services. There might be delays for outpatient appointments and admissions and a long wait for a hospital report to arrive in the surgery. When patients were discharged there might be difficulty in obtaining continuity of medical and nursing care, and delay before patients from hospital could be transferred to residential care. It became policy to shift the boundary, where possible, towards primary health care.[183] General practitioners and community nurses were encouraged to develop new skills and practice-based facilities. Shared care schemes were established for chronic disease management, paediatrics, mental health and maternity care. Some GPs and specialists experimented with direct booking to surgical waiting lists, avoiding the need for specialist outpatient consultations. Often, however, schemes such as the encouragement of minor surgery in general practice had little effect on the demand for hospital care, because they encouraged patients to come for treatment who otherwise might not have done so. Though never shown to be efficient, hospital-at-home schemes achieved prominence, and sought to avoid hospital admission and facilitate early discharge. Increasingly rapid discharge of patients from acute hospital care for reasons of efficiency meant that, although specialised medical treatment might no longer be needed, nursing care often was. The best way of providing this was a matter of dispute. There might be referral to domiciliary nurses attached to practices (favoured by GPs who knew and trusted their colleagues), or hospital 'outreach' nursing (favoured by many consultants who trusted the nurses with whom they regularly worked). Outreach nursing services might care for patients recently discharged from orthopaedic, gynaecological or cancer wards, and provide a 24-hour helpline and home visits. The administration of anti-cancer drugs in the home required a level of knowledge possessed by nurses who worked in an oncology unit but not by district nurses. Sometimes, however, outreach services were established by hospitals to guarantee care. If the hospital wished to discharge patients on a Friday, domiciliary services might not be able to handle a new case alongside their existing work.

The nature of general practice

The RCGP was concerned about the future direction of general practice but was not clear about what it should be.[184] GPs differed in their philosophies, some having a corporate and biomedical approach embracing other disciplines, for example health economics and management science, while others wished to concentrate on personal and continuing care of individuals and families.[185] Corporatists, such as Donald Irvine, saw organisation as inevitable and welcome. Doctors should define what they were trying to do with their resources, report their activity and evaluate what they had done. The practice might appoint directors, each with specific responsibilities, and this pattern of practice was early into fundholding. A second group, often with a left-wing outlook, had no objection to corporate organisation if it were community orientated. Practices should be accountable, reporting to their communities, give longer consultation times, look for cases of chronic disease and supervise those they found in special clinics.[186] The practice should be a democratic team in which the doctor was not always the key worker. Doctors should be salaried and practices zoned so that each team was responsible for a particular 'patch'. Epidemiology and the public health should play a greater part.[187] Then there were individualists, for example Iona Heath, a Camden GP, who followed a psycho-social model and thought the movement towards corporate general practice a threat to the nature of the discipline, traditionally committed to the needs of the individual. For them a dynamic role as an agent of distributive justice held little appeal. GPs who were involved in the wider arena of primary health care, public health and management faced the ethical conflicts and professional tensions of the real world. They did not see that a retreat into an isolated, mystical priestly role was practicable.[188]

The nature of the consultation had been a major preoccupation of GPs in the 1950s, the Balint years. Small studies subsequently showed that the formality of dress influenced the respect accorded to a doctor, and a directive approach to the consultation, in comparison with a 'sharing' style, led to greater patient satisfaction and feeling of having been helped.[189] Nicholas Bosanquet studied variations in general practice in urban and rural, affluent and deprived communities.[190] He identified 'innovative' and 'traditional' practices, using as markers features such as the employment of a practice nurse, the use of the cost-rent scheme to improve practice premises, and taking part in vocational training. Innovators took anything on offer. It was they who rebuilt their premises using practice loans, available on excellent terms. Because their premises were good, they developed primary health care teams. Innovators tended to cluster in particular parts of the country, the more rural areas and those undergoing rapid economic development such as the Thames Valley. The GPs in the older industrial areas, often traditionalists, did comparatively little to develop their practices. New methods of working often passed them by, though their work was tough and patients' needs were pressing.

Bosanquet repeated his study in 1992 and 1993, and found that practices in all areas had responded to the new contractual incentives, and invested heavily in equipment and services. This was particularly so in the more deprived practices, and was reducing inconsistency in standards. He found better equipment and premises, a wider range of services and substantial additions to nursing and other staff. The pace of improvement had increased more between 1985–1992 than in the previous 20 years. By 1993, 94 per cent of group practices had a computer. 'Traditional' practices had all but disappeared, though the urban and city practices still lagged behind those in rural and suburban areas. Although doctors still opposed the principles of the 1990 contract, many saw it as having improved the quality of the service. General practice was moving towards greater uniformity, a greater workload, less variation in incomes and increased stress.[191] Typical of the innovators was Marsh, a family doctor in Stockton on Tees. His practice area spanned both deprived and more salubrious areas. The group in which he worked expanded steadily over the years and his book, *Efficient care in general practice, or How to look after even more patients*,[192] was a 1990s version of Stephen Taylor's *Good general practice*. His group deployed the health visitors almost entirely in the depressed streets, for that was where the greatest health gain was to be had, and where immunisation and child health needed most attention. He explored the feasibility of an experienced practice nurse caring for patients with minor illnesses and found that trained nurses could diagnose and treat a large proportion of patients consulting GPs, provided there was immediate access to a doctor.[193]

There was increasing recognition, both in Britain and internationally, that part of the move towards accountability was acceptance of reaccreditation.[194] Many GPs supported the idea. There was consensus that the process should be professionally led rather than imposed by government, and the GMSC produced draft proposals. These involved peer review and participation in postgraduate education, and mirrored the well-established methods used to select trainers in the vocational training scheme.[195]

Computers in general practice

Enthusiastic GPs had used computers since the 1970s, but the costs were too high to be borne unaided. Remote batch systems made retrospective analysis of data possible but did not help in day-to-day care, and there were anxieties about confidentiality. The development of personal computers in the late 1980s was crucial, for they became affordable and could be based in the practice. Systems were installed in increasing numbers, and many software companies entered the market. Although often incompatible with each other, all supported a patient register, and most the printing of repeat prescriptions coupled with drug incompatibility tables, call and recall schemes, and clinical information including consultation summaries. As systems became more powerful, full clinical records were increasingly kept on computer. In the hope of gaining commercially useful information, drug companies subsidised the acquisition of practice computers. By 1990, 80 per cent of GPs had a system and the DoH began to offer financial support. The installation rate accelerated, stimulated by the new contract that increased the importance of information systems. By 1995, 90 per cent of practices were computerised and systems were regularly used for prescribing, call and recall, and medical audit. Newer systems now provided intercommunication with the health authorities and the local hospital. The national Healthlink scheme grew rapidly, involving the majority of practices that were computerised, enabling doctors to inform authorities of patient registration, to invoice them, and in many practices to receive pathology and radiology results, and waiting list, breast screening and cytology information, and patient discharge letters.

'Near-patient' tests

For many years some laboratory tests had been performed near the patient. Tests had become simpler, and boiling urine in test tubes had been replaced by more convenient paper dip-stick tests for sugar, protein, ketones and blood. Such tests potentially could improve the speed and accuracy of clinical decisions and the reliability of monitoring chronic diseases. Some tests could be used by patients, and tests for pregnancy, blood sugar and cholesterol levels were available over the counter. Technological advance made possible smaller and cheaper desk-top analysers, affordable in general practice, for a wider range of estimations. An alternative was an electronic link with a hospital laboratory to reduce the time before results were available The arguments for centralisation in a hospital laboratory included better quality control. The argument for peripheralisation was the speed with which information was available that might alter the initial diagnosis and avoid inappropriate prescribing. The costs and benefits were hard to establish.

Prescribing

The cost of prescribing continued to increase because of the interest in the care of long-term illness, for example high blood pressure and asthma, and the accent on 'case-finding'. The rising numbers of elderly people, many of whom were on several different forms of treatment, added to the increase. Because prescribing patterns and costs varied widely, GPs had long been sent information about their prescribing. In 1988 a better system was introduced, Prescribing Analyses and Cost (PACT). It compared each doctor's costs, broke down prescriptions into six major therapeutic groups, such as the cardiovascular drugs, and showed the percentage of items prescribed generically rather than by a brand name. Later, indicative drug budgets were produced, showing how much each practice would be likely to spend. Practices were encouraged to develop their own formularies of cost-effective drugs, and to prescribe generics. The Audit Commission calculated that about a fifth of the total GP prescribing budget was being wasted in over-prescribing, drugs of limited value or expensive ones where cheaper ones were equally effective.[196] With an increasing number of treatments available, which was the most cost-effective? Should pharmaceutical companies be required to submit economic analyses in support of requests for the listing of new products so that both comparative effectiveness and costs were considered?

The NHS review

Although NHS spending had increased in real terms by a third in the previous ten years, the fifth decade began in financial crisis. Technically the NHS was bankrupt. Regular reports of clinical disasters, bed closures and nursing crises were attributed to shortage of money. The existing system had several advantages, including easy movement of patients between hospitals and good cost control. However, there were few incentives for efficiency and some seemed perverse; extra work did not affect a hospital's allocation for three years.[197] There was widespread debate about the NHS and a Niagara of reports from think-tanks. Conservative ones generally suggested that the days of a fully funded health service were, or should be, numbered.[198] In November 1987 Mrs Thatcher asked David Willetts and the Centre for Policy Studies to review the NHS and produce proposals. In January 1988 Nigel Lawson, the Chancellor of the Exchequer, told the Prime Minister that, in spite of the pressures on the NHS, he would be reluctant to allow a further significant increase in NHS funding unless the service was reformed, and one could be sure that it would be well spent. Within a few days Mrs Thatcher, interviewed on *Panorama* by David Dimbleby, said that the government would examine the health service. When ready there would be proposals for consultation, and the review would be far quicker than any Royal Commission.[199] Both government supporters and critics were caught by surprise. Whether she was referring to a government review or one by the Centre for Policy Studies was not clear, but within days public reaction made it clear that it would have to be governmental. The Whitehall machine was set in motion and the new contract for GPs was promptly relegated to second place. A Cabinet team led by the Prime Minister herself, operating behind closed doors, considered many aspects of the service. The medical profession, for the first time in the history of the NHS, was excluded from the process. So was virtually everybody else. Public consultation would not have produced a consensus for radical change. An editorial in the *BMJ* offered advice: a radical solution was required and more money was crucial.[200] The best way to get that would be an insurance-based scheme. One civil servant, asked his private advice, said 'either leave the NHS alone, because it is too hot to handle, or put in train some small changes that would be progressive in effect. The result might not be visible at the outset, but they would free-up and destabilise the system and allow it to evolve, in time producing changes that would be hard to predict but probably in line with what was required.'

Mrs Thatcher accepted Powell's analysis that there was a potentially limitless demand for health care if it was provided free at the point of delivery, and that the NHS lacked the right economic signals to respond to the pressures. Had one been starting from scratch, she believed, one would have allowed for a bigger private sector in primary and secondary health care and given closer attention to additional sources of finance. But one was not, and the NHS inspired at least as much affection as exasperation.[201] For the first five months the review was all over the shop. No coherent plan emerged although there was pressure for greater reliance on private health insurance. The review originally excluded primary care because family practitioner committees (FPCs) had been given independence as recently as 1985. The House of Commons Social Services Committee, reporting on *The future of the NHS*, dismissed many options that were being canvassed – tax concessions for private care, HMOs and budgets for GPs. Ian McColl, Professor of Surgery at Guy's, showed David Willetts the commemorative plaque in the boardroom at Guy's, recording the last meeting of the board of governors in 1974. Willetts learned to his surprise that the teaching hospitals lost their boards of governors under the Conservatives in 1974, not Labour in 1948. McColl argued that hospitals should go back to the more self-managed style of years past.

In August 1989 Kenneth Clarke replaced John Moore as Secretary of State, a crucial change. He rapidly persuaded the Treasury to allocate an additional £1.8 billion to the NHS in England, as well as more money for nurses' training under *Project 2000*. He focused the review on the delivery of care, rather than the source of funding. From then on the key concepts were an internal market and self-governing hospitals, to free hospitals – like schools – from centralised control. Money would follow patients and incentives should encourage efficiency. By October *The Times* was reporting that the idea of allowing GPs to hold the purse strings for primary and secondary health care had been revived.[202] The family doctor would be an informed purchaser on behalf of the patients.

The White Paper

Key changes as a result of the 1989 reforms

- Regions and districts received funds according to the size of their resident populations, weighted for age and morbidity and for the differences in the cost of providing services. RAWP had almost established equity so it was easier to move from historic allocations to a weighted capitation system
- The hierarchy of the NHS management was replaced by a 'local dynamic', devolving decisions to those closest to the people and introducing greater local diversity, competition and choice
- Purchasing and provision were separated. Districts became purchasers, losing their hospital management responsibilities to concentrate on the assessment of needs and commissioning the necessary services
- Hospitals and community services could apply for self-governing status as NHS trusts (providers)
- GP practices with 11,000 or more patients could apply for their own NHS budgets to cover their staff costs, prescribing, outpatient care, and a defined range of hospital services, largely elective surgery
- Systems of medical audit were introduced to ensure quality of service
- Regional, district and family health services authorities were reduced in size and reformed on business lines, with executive and non-executive directors

Working for patients was published in January 1989.[203] It was a challenge to the status quo, the rigidity of organisation to which Enthoven had pointed and the assumption that the employment of highly trained health professionals would ensure that users got what they wanted.[204] Yet the Review accepted many basic principles of the NHS, to the surprise of the left that had predicted a move towards health insurance to provide additional money. The NHS would continue to be funded centrally from taxation, the simplest and cheapest way of raising money. It would remain largely free at the point of usage. There was no suggestion of major organisational change at the top of the management hierarchy. The idea that a major injection of funds was all that was needed was rejected. Instead productivity would be improved by reforming incentives and management and the introduction of a 'market'. The purchasing function would be separated from the provision of services. Health authorities would concentrate on the assessment of needs and contract for services; the services would be provided by hospitals and community units. Good performance would be rewarded, for money would follow the patients. It was clear, although not stated, that once contracts were in place any limitation of services for financial reasons would be laid at the door of the purchaser, and no longer at that of the hospital. It was a model well suited to elective surgery, but less appropriate for elderly people and for psychiatric services. Markets have winners and losers; would the poor, deprived and handicapped be at risk? Just as the USA was considering health care systems more like those in Europe, the UK was moving in the opposite direction.

No master plan was provided to guide implementation even when working papers were published.[205] There had not been time to work out the finer details. Many were alarmed by the concentration on 'how to get there' without a clear statement of 'where we want to be', and the lack of consultation and experiment. The medical profession attempted, in public and in private, to influence events. They failed, concluding that the ethos of the NHS would be changed irrevocably and the reforms would lead to privatisation and Americanisation of health care. The idea of an increased reliance on market forces, albeit forces that were managed and constrained, was so radical that few, even in the DoH, understood or agreed with what was happening.

Implementation and opposition

There was immediate concern in the medical profession and after four months the BMA rejected the proposals.[206] Its diagnosis was that the system was simply under-funded and the reforms were born amid anger and bitterness.[207] Sir Roy Griffiths believed that it would be impossible to implement change in the face of the united opposition of staff. There were calls for evaluation perhaps along the lines of the Rand studies of pre-paid health care. Ministers steadfastly refused to consider this. It was the opponents of the reforms who were most vociferously demanding evaluation or pilot trials, and pilots would delay the reforms beyond the next election that might well be won by Labour. The NHS itself was a matter of faith and political will, and the USA, where evaluation of change was best developed, did not have a health care system envied by Britain. The King's Fund planned an assessment but the fiercely partisan positions suggested that evidence would fuel argument rather than resolve it. In August 1989 the BMA began a forceful poster campaign to keep pressure on MPs during the summer recess. One read 'What do you call a man who does not take medical advice?'

The answer was apparently 'Kenneth Clarke'; Clarke said that the correct reply was 'healthy'. The profession failed to modify the plans either during the consultation period or during their passage through Parliament.[208] Some NHS staff sought a judicial review, which was rejected. Alain Enthoven found much to his liking in the separation of the demand and the supply side of the NHS, making money follow patients, and in greater local delegation. However, he commented on the lack of detail in the proposals and the absence of pilot projects. He was unclear how the proposals would work out in practice, and thought the timetable was amazingly fast, as did the Secretary of State himself.[209] Even within the government there was uncertainty about whether the new and untried system would work.[210] Much of the opposition to the NHS reforms was a matter of attitude. Those with a collectivist philosophy and a belief in altruistic co-operation could not accept a market-based approach with competitive elements.[211]

Kenneth Clarke made the running, changing little or nothing as a result of the doctors' opposition, and demanding a rapid timetable from his officials. Politically he was the right person to argue, explain and defend the policy day after day.[212] The electoral timetable meant that the reforms had to be implemented faster than NHS management believed possible. Implementation depended on regional and district managers; loyalty was demanded and dissent was discouraged.[213] Legislation passed in 1990. In November of that year William Waldegrave replaced Kenneth Clarke; less combative, he maintained the momentum in a quieter way. An East Anglia simulation of an internal market, the 'Rubber Windmill', ended in chaos and supported the belief that some management of the market was essential. The reforms were implemented in April 1991. Accounts had to balance because over-spending could not be carried forward, leading to a further financial crisis. The new system of contracts had to be in place and there was anxiety that purchasers would make radical changes. Ministers thought that the whole point of the reforms was to increase efficiency, but to minimise crises it was agreed to go slow in the first year, with a 'smooth takeoff' and the maintenance of existing patient flows. The Chancellor of the Exchequer allocated an additional 4.5 per cent in real terms to help. The election was fought in April 1992, health being a central issue. The Conservatives won, and the new Secretary of State was Virginia Bottomley.

NHS trusts

Acute hospital trusts, the 'self-governing hospitals', aimed to allow managerially élite hospitals substantial freedom. Only if they failed to meet financial targets or service standards, or if corporate governance broke down, would this be curtailed. Few were expected to take the trust route although there had to be enough to demonstrate the advantages; some were turned down because of an inadequate business plan.[214] It was hoped that hospital staff would support applications for trust status. In most places they rejected it, and local support ceased to be a precondition. At Guy's, which had a reputation for resource management that was not entirely justified, the staff were deeply divided. Seen by government as a potential flag-ship of the reforms, Guy's believed that trust status would ensure that a major building scheme would go ahead, guaranteeing hospital survival. Somewhat to people's surprise a number of community units saw the possibility of greater independence from hospitals, and applied for trust status. Fifty-seven trusts became operational in the first wave, a further 99 from April

1992 and after the surprise Conservative victory that month it became apparent that all units would do so. Between 1991 and 1995 NHS hospitals were progressively transformed into publicly owned self-governing bodies. Management was strengthened and some problems, for example the King's College Hospital Accident and Emergency Department, became easier to resolve.

In place of the traditional authorities an industrial model of governance was substituted. This was technocratic and, while it might promote efficiency and responsiveness, it also increased insecurity, the authority of the centre and short-term decision-making. Each trust had a board of directors including non-executive ones who brought skills from the business community. Interviews before appointment often had a political flavour. Key interest groups were excluded – the population, the local authorities and the clinicians. There had previously been members who represented the electorate on management bodies; they might have been viewed as a nuisance but they were in a minority and they added an authority to the decisions that were taken. New chief executives from outside the NHS did not always share the ethos of public service. They often improved the use of resources and challenged established practices, not always correctly. The turnover of chief executives was substantial and expensive; sometimes they and consultants battled for power. On fixed term contracts, sometimes as short as a year, they had their eyes on immediate problems, rather than the development of long-term collaborative arrangements with others whose assistance was essential to a good service.[215]

Trusts were able to employ staff, negotiate terms and conditions of service, own and dispose of their assets, retain surpluses, and borrow money from the government and the private sector. They generated their revenue by making contracts with districts, commissioning agencies and GP fundholders. In the early days trusts were highly visible and much public interest was concentrated on them. The need to balance the books was paramount. Some of the early 'flagship' trusts such as Guy's and Bradford faced multi-million pound deficits. To the embarrassment of the government they made headlines by ward closures and redundancy notices. Their managers, appearing before the Select Committee on Health, made an impressive case that the delivery of patient care was in no way proportional to the number of staff employed.[216] It was porters and domestics who had most to fear as jobs-for-life became subject to market testing and private contracting. Anti-waste campaigns had a new ferocity about them. As trusts were unable to guarantee the long-term future of their units, even professional staff, for example midwives, might be employed on a short-term basis. Were people afraid to speak out because of their jobs?[217]

Trusts needed good financial information for their business plans and they needed it rapidly, but much of the information required to compare relative costs did not exist; the necessary systems were not in place even at the resource management sites. Many hospitals had no price list. Block contracts, notional costs and wild price variations were commonplace. It took much work and a long time to sort things out.[218] Extra-contractual referrals maintained the GP's right to send the patient to the most appropriate unit, but generated substantial administrative costs.[219] Relationships between the 'purchaser' district health authorities and the 'provider' trusts were initially tense. The health authorities had to learn to work with the trusts as equals, not subordinates. Over the first few years there was little change in the pattern of patient flows, perhaps 5–10 per cent. Where changes were made, it was usually to create a local service for patients. District hospitals might provide services previously available only at a regional centre and purchasers wished to develop these if the price was right. In the case of city hospitals, particularly those in London, peripheral purchasers would do their utmost to restrict central flow in favour of their local hospitals, many of which were new, with young staff and spare capacity. Large hospitals in major centres of population, for example Stoke and South Tees, increasingly provided specialised services such as cardiac surgery, radiotherapy and urological surgery, stripping resources from more distant university hospitals. Teaching hospital trusts were at a disadvantage because of their high overheads and managerial complexity. Sometimes they treated purchasers with disdain and lost market share. Their countervailing advantage was that a high proportion of their medical and surgical consultants had sub-specialty expertise. This made them the natural place for junior medical training. They argued that only with a high volume of work could optimal care be provided; but that was not necessarily true of more common procedures. Some trusts progressively expanded their work and their catchment, others floundered. Acute trusts sometimes developed outreach services; community trusts looked at hospital-type day care. The borders could blur. Purchasers at first were poor at contracting and hospitals had the clinical expertise to run rings round them. Contracting slowly became more sophisticated and more firmly based in an assessment of local needs. In 1996 the first trust to be threatened with collapse was Anglian Harbours Trust, when two health authorities planned to withdraw contracts for spending too much on management rather than patient services.

Doctors were now employed by the trust, and not the RHA, so they began to think in a more corporate and local way. Each trust could define its organisational pattern. Clinical directorates were often established under medical control, on the 'Johns Hopkins' model. Decisions could be taken more rapidly, new patterns of staffing could be introduced and services could be improved without bureaucratic delays. Because their unit budgets were determined by contracts with purchasers, it was easier to persuade consultants to change their patterns of work. Nurses, when they were appointed as directors, were in a dilemma. While they wanted to see the 'big picture' and to contribute to strategic planning, the chief executives looked to them primarily to run an effective nursing service and ensure that quality assurance worked. Trusts frequently used their freedom to determine conditions of employment to set high salaries for the chief executives. The Institute of Health Service Management defended these saying 'they are certainly not outrageous in comparison with pay in other industries.'[220] Ministers set guidelines for management costs and asked managers to live with the same pressure for cost efficiency and good value that they quite properly imposed on the rest of the NHS.[221]

The need for hospital trusts to generate income led to visible changes. Lilac coloured carpeting and easy chairs, smiling receptionists, a florist's stall bursting with blooms, a bistro coffee bar and a newsagents would appear. Trusts spent money on glossy pamphlets on their services, and on logos. Leicester's mental health service trust drew the wrath of the anti-hunt brigade when it used the county symbol of a fox, particularly as the unfortunate animal appeared to have a leg missing. Caring hands, trees of life and groups of happy people were popular images.[222] Acute hospital trusts established private patient units to compete with private hospitals. Between 1988 and 1992 income from private units increased by 40 per cent to £157 million and the proportion of the UK private health care market (itself expanding) in NHS hands continued to rise.[223] Private hospitals in their turn treated NHS patients referred by fundholders. The boundary between the NHS and private medicine was becoming blurred and the phrase 'internal market' seemed increasingly inappropriate.

As community trusts developed, the nature of the services that they provided came to differ from the previous community units. Midwifery was usually hospital based, and community midwives might work for a hospital rather than a community trust. In contrast, services for elderly mentally frail people, and those with mental illness or learning difficulties, were increasingly based in the community and managed by a community trust. Some chief executives thought that community care meant 'no hospital beds' and closed these without providing an adequate spectrum of support in the community. Others were innovative, co-operating with voluntary bodies, setting up new projects, and extending their services by developing local teams to provide intensive nursing after hospital discharge or rehabilitation after a stroke. Because their services were delivered in the home or within a neighbourhood, community trusts attempted to develop good relationships with GPs and the local population.

Fundholding

The central idea of fundholding was that, although patients could not be given unlimited money to purchase their own health care, GPs could act as informed purchasers while keeping an eye on priorities. In this way they could be involved in shaping local services. In June 1984 the Office of Health Economics held a meeting to discuss the future of the NHS. One participant argued that salvation could be achieved only through private finance – insurance. Alan Maynard, the York economist, thought the problem was on the supply side and best approached by the introduction of practice budgets.[224] If GPs controlled the flow of money, good hospitals would flourish while bad ones would dwindle away. The meeting thought that over a decade the concept might be developed into something practical and it began to be discussed in academic circles.[225] When the Green Paper on primary health care was being drafted in 1985, Kenneth Clarke, then Minister, was intrigued by the idea. In the USA some HMOs controlled hospital costs by using primary care physicians; DoH officials, visiting the USA in 1985, saw the advantages of bringing the budget of the hospital and primary care under the same financial umbrella. Centres could compare costs with each other and see which specialist or hospitals appeared to be the best buys.[226] Kenneth Clarke's return to the DoH turned budgets into practical politics but the concept attracted little initial attention.[227] Most considered it a wild idea that would collapse and were surprised when the scheme, sometimes wrongly considered an afterthought, came to the forefront of the reforms. A GMSC negotiator said his first reaction was that GPs had three choices: they could join and control their own destiny; they could stay out and let others control them; or they could resign!

Fundholders were allocated money on the basis of their historic expenditure, although some regions ensured that the budgets were generous. They could then use it for practice staff, prescription medicines and hospital services such as laboratory tests, outpatient appointment care and around 110 elective operations covering the vast majority of elective surgery. Procedures could be purchased from the private sector as well as the NHS. Hospitals could increase their revenue at the margin by serving fundholders' patients and had an incentive to provide the care GPs wanted. Officials working on the details knew the risks of bankrupting the budget and introduced stop-loss systems. Some in Cabinet argued that efficient doctors should be able to make a personal profit from their management skill. Such incentives had created problems in the USA and Kenneth Clarke saw the political damage if this untested idea were to misfire. Because it is difficult to define the boundary between emergency and elective care, and between medical and surgical cases, it was argued that the range of services for which fundholders received money should be sufficiently wide to avoid boundary disputes. Ministers were unwilling to go 'one bridge too far' by including emergencies and general medicine at the outset. Indeed even the most enthusiastic fundholders initially believed they had quite enough to do to manage the modest range of services included.

Many in the hospital service believed that GPs were incapable of handling money, even were it desirable, and that fundholding clashed with the district as the purchaser, defining needs and contracting for services for the entire population. Those whose interests would be adversely affected did not mobilise opposition effectively. Some senior department officials were out of sympathy and work was carried out for ministers in the face of their opposition. A few regions lacked enthusiasm. That there would be GP volunteers was never in doubt. The professional press, predicting total failure, would provide free publicity to any success. First wave fundholders included some of the cream of the profession. Their prime motivation was the improvement of patient care, they were articulate and were not going to be pushed around by the Department or their professional colleagues. Were a new minister to be privately sceptical of the scheme, attending a fundholders' conference would be a conversion experience. Glennerster recorded the reactions of fundholders:

> As I sat down and I realised what we were about to do, I thought this is a revolution happening here. No consultant has ever talked to me about what I might think of his service, or any of the general problems we might have in twenty years of professional life.

GP fundholding: England

Year	Coverage
1991/2	7%
1992/3	13%
1993/4	25%
1994/5	35%
1995/6	41%
1996/7	53%
1997/8	59%

Source: DoH press releases

In April 1991, there were 720 GPs in 306 practices.[228] Budgets averaged £1.3 million. Initially practices could join if their lists were over 11,000, a level reduced first to 7,000 and then to 5,000. The expansion was driven by GP demand; it required courage, hard work and professional unpopularity. Few in prominent positions risked participation. It took consultants a year to recognise the extent to which fundholding moved power to family doctors; then they added their voice to the opposition. The services covered were expanded. In 1993 district nursing and health visiting, dietetics and chiropody were included. By 1994, 6 per cent of the total NHS budget, equivalent to £1.8 billion, was being spent by fundholders. Substantial variation existed; 80 per cent of the population was covered in places such as Derbyshire and Bury, but only 4 per cent in Camden and Islington. Inner cities, where the population was mobile and the workload high, were slow to adopt fundholding.[229]

Fundholders established counselling, physiotherapy and consultant outpatient clinics. They were energetic on behalf of their patients, and had more powerful levers when it came to negotiation. They did not have the ultimate responsibility of maintaining the viability of an essential district hospital although they shifted patients to other hospitals only as a last resort. Patients were seen sooner in practice-run consultant clinics, the costs were lower because hospital overheads were not incurred, and GP–specialist contact was possible. Hospital management was afraid to lose referrals that outreach clinics could generate and they rapidly increased in number.[230] However, consultants in particular argued that outreach clinics were a poor use of scarce resources, did not provide adequate facilities for investigation, and undermined teaching and the role of the DGH.

In 1994 ministers decided to encourage a variety of schemes.[231] Pilot trials were launched into total purchasing in which GPs purchased all hospital and community health services. There were other pilots incorporating maternity services (1995) and mental health (1996). From 1996 there was community fundholding including staff, drugs, diagnostic tests and community health services; standard fundholding, covering about 20–30 per cent of the NHS budget for each patient; and total purchasing. Total purchasing practices controlled large sums, £30 million or more. They employed high-quality managers who, like managers in trusts, tried to use money to the best effect and to influence practice thinking. Non-fundholders increasingly formed large consortia creating an alternative form of GP influence, locality commissioning, viewed with favour by the Labour Party. GPs in commissioning groups had less influence on the spending of money, but large numbers of doctors were involved in both systems and there was increased co-operation between GPs, health authorities and trusts. New kinds of primary care organisation were emerging, fundholding practices, multi-funds, total purchasing projects, GP-led commissioning groups and out-of-hours co-operatives. They broke down the traditional isolation of GPs and created opportunities for increased co-operation. The stimulation of alternative systems, designed for local circumstances and growing in number almost daily, was a major achievement. The proponents of the alternatives agreed that this was right and that GPs should be at the heart of decisions affecting patient care.[232]

Most assessments were written from an established political or philosophical position and the evidence on its success did not point in a consistent direction.[233] There were increased management costs, but studies by the National Audit Office and the OECD were generally positive. Entrepreneurial fundholders achieved much, and there was little doubt that they often obtained better services for their patients. An evaluation by Glennerster concluded that fundholding had a major influence on contracting, quality and value for money. The Audit Commission believed that some fundholders had difficulties in managing a budget, needing help to get the most out of their purchasing decisions. Universal fundholding was never the aim; there was no point in substituting one monopoly system for another. The rapid growth of fundholding left the GMSC in a quandary. An increasing number of GP fundholders believed that they could not trust the leadership to act on their behalf, and a national association of fundholders was established. As a result, the GMSC ultimately it found itself arguing with Labour in *favour* of fundholding, with *The Times* in support.[234] Many GPs were now fundholders, and were determined to keep their own budgets, irrespective of the politics. On election, Labour slowed entry to the scheme and introduced common hospital waiting lists. In the name of fairness, the Conservative reform that had done the most for efficiency was undermined.

Medical audit

While angry interchanges were taking place between government and the medical profession, medical audit was being developed in a calmer way. Doctors were anxious lest audit should become a management tool to coerce them into line. The almost complete absence of fuss was due to the establishment of mutual trust about audit between officials and leaders of the profession. Both believed that good clinical practice and audit could not be imposed, and chose their words carefully to ensure that coercion was never implied. Several features of the Department's scheme were derived from, but not attributed to, American experience in HMOs such as the Harvard Community Health Plan. The DoH knew that medical audit was a branch of quality assurance and should be multi-disciplinary. That was a bridge too far for the medical profession in 1989.[235] In general practice pilot groups were established to test ideas based on continuous quality improvement and to avoid national mistakes. Medical audit advisory groups (MAAGs) were formed, chaired by a doctor who was accountable to management for the proper conduct of audit. Their major task was to educate practices, usually through the appointment of medical or lay advisers and facilitators who visited practices.[236] Feedback from pilot studies was used to handle anxieties such as confidentiality. Local audit projects were funded and a textbook was written by the profession for the profession.[237] In parallel, medical audit systems were developed for hospital services, the Royal Colleges establishing audit units and supporting projects looking at clinical outcomes. There was a strong feeling that clinical audit should be undertaken, that it was an important part of practice and that it should become part of a wider range of educational, quality assurance and development systems.[238] However, as time passed there was disappointment that audit had not somehow delivered. There was not much evidence that audit was improving clinical care and some disillusionment was beginning to creep in. Part of the problem was that audit seemed to have at least two conflicting aims – the improvement of care by professionals as a result of an assessment of what they were doing, and the need for providers to demonstrate that they were meeting a purchaser's contractual requirements.

The patient's charter

In July 1991 government introduced the Citizens' Charter across public and private sectors. Organisations were to state the standards to which they aspired, and measure their performance. The NHS was included in the government-wide programme and the initiative was driven by Brian Edwards, Regional General Manager of the Trent RHA. Standards were set for matters such as the time it took to be seen in an accident or outpatient department and how long patients should wait for operations. These were measures of the process of health care, rather than its clinical quality, but in 1997 further standards were introduced that were related more closely to clinical performance. Hospital league tables were developed showing how far individual trusts met charter standards, and hospitals sometimes manipulated their figures. Subsequently the charter was extended into primary health care. The standards imposed became built into the NHS reforms, for they provided a benchmark of performance by which hospitals were judged. Computer systems that identified the length of time patients waited for admission produced information that affected the payments hospitals received under their contracts, and the way consultants ordered their work. The standards initially stated that patients should never wait for more than two years for surgery, a period reduced to 18 months. In July 1995 regions were asked to set a voluntary 12 month limit, difficult given the need to spend money on handling emergency admissions and deal with other priorities such as mental health initiatives. Some managers felt that their future careers depended on a politically motivated imperative.[239]

The roll-out of the reforms

Anxieties were fanned by the uncertainties of change. Managers needed to adapt. Consultants came to realise that their power base was smaller, there was a trend towards rolling contracts with less security of tenure and a prospect of performance-related pay. A move towards community-based health care reduced the claims of the acute hospital sector on the NHS budget. GP influence on purchasing replaced consultant influence on regional decisions, and consultants' 'clinical priorities' were increasingly distorted by the vagaries of different purchasing authorities and whether a particular patient came from a fundholding practice.[240] Posts in public health medicine were reduced as authorities merged, and, although cost-effective purchasing seemed to require their expertise, this was a new field and not one where public health was paramount. Nurses found that the reforms further strengthened the position of managers. GPs, angry at their new contract, assumed that the NHS reforms would be equally distasteful. Why should Kenneth Clarke impose a contract they disliked and simultaneously trust them as fundholders with NHS money?

Initially the Labour Party opposed the reforms in their entirety; however, after electoral defeat in 1992 it slowly accepted some of the concepts. Brian Abel-Smith and Howard Glennerster urged Labour to resist gut reaction, believing that many reforms moved in the right direction. FHSAs had ceased to be provider-dominated, long overdue. Fundholders were able to get a better deal for their patients, and making hospitals compete kept them on their toes. It made sense to build on what had been achieved.[241] A division between purchasers and providers was sensible, and the substantial autonomy of trusts made it easier for them to adjust to what was wanted. Trusts could easily have a change of membership to incorporate democratically elected representatives. Ecclesiastics, however, attacked the moral values of the new NHS; it needed a culture of generous service and unstinting care, in contrast to the business model which had replaced co-operation with competition. The BMA had not been won over. In 1995 its Chairman attacked the reforms as an infernal bazaar rather than an internal market.[242] While the medical profession believed that the reforms were detrimental to the principle of equity, private practice was expanding and doctors were clearly willing to treat an increasing number of patients who could pay, more rapidly and in hospitable surroundings.[243] Virginia Bottomley, Secretary of State, redefined the NHS as the provision of care on the basis of clinical need regardless of the ability to pay, not by who provided the service. She said that central strategic command could, with benefit, be replaced by a local dynamic. Clinically effective intervention, local innovation, use of new technology to reduce or eliminate the need for hospital admission and the move to community-based care would take root fastest if those taking the decisions were, like fundholders, close to the public and the patients concerned.[244] Nobody was willing, however, to define what 'clinical need' really meant. Did it encompass renal dialysis for the 90-year-old person, in-vitro fertilisation for the single would-be mother, breast enlargement and sex-change operations?

Whereas many policies were determined centrally, others were driven locally.[245] Entrepreneurial trusts might take decisions that alarmed the centre. In contrast to population-based health authority purchasing was the growing number of fundholders, purchasing a limited range of service for individual patients. How would these systems relate to each other? What balance would be struck between market competition and the management of a coherent service? What would be the number and configuration of NHS trusts? At first the talk was of contracting; everything would be resolved through provider competition. However, it was rapidly realised that a market red-in-tooth-and-claw would be unacceptable. The term 'contracting for health gain' was coined, easier to discuss than to define. Planning reasserted itself with alliances, partnerships and the importance of multi-agency relationships.[246] The strategic plans of yesteryear were replaced by 'purchasing guidelines', often with a clinical flavour. Operational plans reappeared under the guise of purchasing (commissioning) intentions. Evidence-based contracts became the new nostrum, to provide care known to be effective. 'Accountability' became the watchword, but accountability to whom – should purchasing be population focused or responsive to the demand of consumers, or both? Less priority was placed on competition and more on improving health; greater priority was given to primary health care, and improved standards were sought through *The patient's charter* and the adoption of evidence-based medicine. Planning and competition began to exist side by side; groups of fundholders began to align their purchasing intentions with those of health authorities. The way money was being spent was clearer as a result of the separation of purchasing and provision. Common ground between the Conservatives and Labour was being established and the outcome of the reforms was neither as appalling as its opponents had predicted nor the major leap forward for which its protagonists had hoped.[247] Labour's commitment to financial probity would not allow a promise of more generous funding; money would have to come from a reduction in management costs that had risen substantially as a result of the accounting procedures generated by the internal market.[248] Labour came to accept that many changes of the Thatcher era had changed Britain's institutional landscape, and the pattern of the NHS. It dropped root-and-branch opposition to the entire package, and focused its attack on the internal market, trusts run as independent competing units and fundholding. It mellowed even on these; a quiet agreement on some issues was beginning to emerge. Trusts, in some form, were likely to persist. The distinction between fundholding and approaches that had been developed in reaction to it (such as locality commissioning in which practices covering a geographical population collaborated) were crumbling. GP participation in commissioning seemed here to stay, although it was impossible to predict what form it would take. The return of Labour, however, foreshadowed further organisational change and an end to the internal market.

Clinical Standards Advisory Group

Statutory and multi-professional, advising UK health ministers on standards of clinical care, and access to/availability of services to NHS patients. Has a lay chairman and members appointed by Royal Colleges. It assesses clinical services against standards previously set by professional bodies and monitors the use (but does not set) clinical guidelines. Normally starts two studies a year, published by HMSO/Stationery Office

---

During the implementation of the NHS reforms the medical profession had been concerned that they would have an adverse effect on clinical standards. After discussion, ministers established a Clinical Standards Advisory Group (CSAG) in 1991.[249] Its function was defined as monitoring standards within the NHS. Its first remits were neonatal intensive care, childhood leukaemia, cystic fibrosis, coronary artery bypass grafts, emergency and urgent admissions to hospital, the management of normal labour and services for people with diabetes. Each study was undertaken by an ad hoc committee with co-opted experts and research support. The initial reports, for example that on coronary artery disease, demonstrated marked variations in patterns of care and a clear gap between demand and the resources provided. What the reports were unable to do was to demonstrate whether the reforms were 'good' or 'bad'. There were no measurements made before the reforms with which the new results could be compared.

Mergers, amalgamations and structural changes

NHS regions in England

- Northern and Yorkshire
- Trent
- Anglia and Oxford
- North Thames
- South Thames
- South and West
- West Midlands
- North West

As trusts were established, districts ceased to have responsibility for hospital management. Combining a residual management function with purchasing was, in any case, difficult. It was argued that districts should amalgamate with matching FHSAs. At first ministers were reluctant to authorise this lest it prove the wrong path. However, the pressure for amalgamation was unstoppable. By 1995 the number of health authorities had halved. Vertical integration of primary and secondary care was prevented by the separation of purchasers and providers. In the USA patients had a choice of competing systems, each complete in itself, as hospital services extended into the community.

Control of the market became an issue. To take away regional command merely to substitute regional market management was not attractive to the trusts, with their new-found freedoms. Regions might reduce the impact of the internal market. Devolution had often been preached but few believed it would happen. Industrial concerns had been removing middle management, 'downsizing' and producing 'flatter' organisations.

NHS structure from April 1996

Secretary of State
Accountable to Parliament for NHS

NHS Executive and 8 regional offices
Co-ordinates local services within a single NHS

100 health authorities (integrated DHAs/FHAs)
Cover both primary and secondary care
Primary expertise planning, administration and contracting for services
Accountable for the NHS within their districts
Responsible for efficient use of resources examining the detail of care available
Challenge variations in treatment rates

Adapted from S Dorrell's Millennium lecture 1996

Only a few foresaw that regions might be treated in this way.[250] Their last major task was to oversee the implementation of the NHS reforms, managing the fundholding scheme and supporting districts in their purchasing functions. Many politicians and managers, and some consultants, wanted to abolish regions because they were *controlling*. Others saw professional advantages in their co-ordination of services, and political ones as they acted as a buffer between local problems and the Secretary of State. Desperate attempts were made to retain their function. However, a review of the relationship of the 14 RHAs with the centre in 1993 recommended that regions should be slimmed, and then amalgamated into eight in April 1994. Finally they should be abolished in favour of eight regional offices of the DoH. To the government this proposal was 'simpler and sharper'; to Labour it was 'highly centralist and undemocratic'. The Conservatives had done what Kenneth Robinson had proposed in the 1968 Green Paper. After 48 years the regions that had been central to the development and evolution of the NHS were disbanded, the Health Authorities Act 1995 providing the statutory authority. Regional outposts had less power, they had few staff and money no longer flowed through them. The Act also enabled the formation of 100 single health authorities by merging the residual 105 DHAs and 90 FHSAs, saving £150 million a year. These, established five years after the start of the reforms, inherited the statutory functions of DHAs and FHSAs. They would commission a range of services within their allocated funding, provide and secure the provision of services, work with GP purchasers, and make arrangements with GPs and other contractors. They would agree strategies, monitor purchasing and support primary health care. Being under financial pressure, they looked for economies, pressed trusts to merge to reduce their overheads, and for the concentration of care in fewer hospitals.[251] The publication of a further White Paper in 1996, *Choice and opportunity*, created yet a further dynamic for change.[252] Subsequent legislation, the NHS (Primary Care) Act 1997, had substantial bipartisan support and provided new opportunities for the transfer of resources between primary and secondary health care, and the development of comprehensive packages of primary care by new 'provider' organisations such as community trusts. The principles of piloting and 'opting-in', initially seen with fundholding, could now be applied more generally. With the approach of the election in May 1997, Labour was poised to win. It pledged itself to appoint a Minister for Public Health, to ban tobacco advertising, to replace fundholding with locality purchasing and to end the internal market. Change would, however, be evolutionary and more money was not to be expected.

Hospital and specialist services

Never had the acute hospitals been so efficient, and never had they been under such strain.[253] The NHS reforms generated competitive pressures, particularly in the conurbations. Clinicians knew that if their hospital service and waiting times fell below the standards available elsewhere, the budget of their hospital might suffer. Other hospitals would be keen to offer an alternative. The drive to cut costs and treat the maximum number of patients with limited resources could have a devastating effect on clinicians and might make a lean and efficient department with good morale unsafe, hyperefficient, exhausted and demoralised.[254] To improve efficiency, patients were discharged more and more rapidly. Readmission rates rose. As discharge was often delayed because special investigations had not been carried out, it became important to streamline such procedures. The number attending A and E departments rose steadily. Between 70 and 95 per cent of medical admissions were emergencies and from 1990/1 to 1994/5 there was a 10 per cent rise in their number. It was the result of increased capacity to help people with life-threatening conditions, an ageing population, greater patients' expectations, changes in primary health care, social factors and defensive medicine. As well as shortages of staff in key departments, there was a lack of beds and patients had to wait while beds were found. Lack of operating theatres for emergency cases by day meant that emergencies might be operated on at night by relatively junior staff. In the search for efficiency, performance indicators were developed further, league tables were introduced and the variations between hospitals were examined. The Audit Commission looked at the use of medical beds in acute hospitals, finding inappropriate admissions, poor admission procedures, patients on inappropriate wards, inexplicable variation in lengths of stay, lack of consensus on clinical practice, poor discharge procedures and outdated bed allocation systems.[255]

Reshaping the acute hospital system

The hospital system was being reshaped by the changes in clinical methods and management. Competitive ambitions became apparent. To remain a 'major player' trusts, sometimes encouraged by purchasers, attempted to develop new services or to maintain existing ones even if the workload did not justify it. Because of duplication, units might see fewer patients than was desirable to maintain a high level of skill (as in the case of cancer treatment), equipment might be under-utilised, staff levels might be too meagre for safety and costs higher than necessary. Synergies were postulated between the subspecialties. Too much was happening too fast; trusts did not want heavy-handed control, but rational co-ordination of services was at risk. Hospital practice had experienced a radical change with the progressive separation of sub-specialties from the mainstream of general medicine and surgery. Purchasers looked at the number of trusts and the extent of their duplication. Providers looked at costs, inefficiencies and the case for mergers.[256] In the 1960s there was a clear concept of the nature of a DGH; nobody now had a master plan. The Royal College of Physicians (RCP), under the presidency of Sir Leslie Turnberg, became more deeply involved in the pattern of hospital services. There was debate about the distribution of hospitals providing secondary care for patients with the more common disorders. One model involved a marked reduction in the number of hospitals, leaving a smaller number that were strategically placed and offered a full range of secondary and tertiary services, coupled with more local supporting facilities. Developments in policy on specialty provision and medical staffing transformed the criteria for judging the size a hospital had to be to carry out clinical services safely.[257] The RCP, echoing the thinking of the Bonham-Carter Report (1969), believed that a single general hospital now should serve populations of 200,000–300,000. Such hospitals should have access to a tertiary service provided on a population base of around a million. Geographically isolated towns with populations of fewer than 150,000 might be unable to sustain a viable DGH. The RCS also thought that bigger hospitals serving populations of 450,000–500,000 would be better able to cope with rising patient expectations, the need for increased specialisation, new working and training arrangements and the demands for expensive new technology.[258] Already a new tier of large hospitals was emerging, alongside the university teaching hospitals, with advanced skills and substantially better equipment than smaller DGHs. Sub-regional centres, serving a population of a million or more became apparent, as in Stoke and South Cleveland, often having a substantial academic base. Such hospitals could become cancer centres, dealing with the more complex tumours. They could accommodate the emerging specialties, such as diseases of the lower bowel and rectum (coloproctology), and vascular surgery, which was becoming distinct, dealing with the repair of aortic aneurysms, lower limb ischaemia and carotid artery stenosis.

The provision of emergency care was a key problem for smaller DGHs but attempts to close facilities on the grounds of safety or to enable money to be spent more sensibly could lead to public and political opposition.[259] The growth of specialisation could be accommodated in a large hospital alongside a rota for emergency admissions, but not so easily in smaller DGHs. If patients were admitted to any of a number of wards their care might be fragmented and poorer. Whereas many younger doctors continued to see the need for a generalist approach, in practice consultants might be so specialised that they lacked the broader skills necessary to provide emergency care and resuscitation. A surgeon spending the majority of the week on cancer of the breast was unlikely to be able to operate successfully on an emergency aortic aneurysm. Many specialist physicians and surgeons no longer participated in on-call rotas, which depended increasingly on those retaining a generalist approach, for example the geriatricians. The RCP examined different models of care. Half of the hospitals surveyed had adopted an emergency admission ward, perhaps of 20 beds, with a system of assigning patients to specialist units. Alternatively, all consultants might combine interest in a particular field with more general clinical work, although this would dilute specialist skills. Or there might be a hybrid approach in which there was a combination of specialists and generalists.

Under pressure to improve the volume and quality of services without higher costs, some trusts, for example the Central Middlesex, introduced business process re-engineering. If the stages in the delivery of care were examined, was there a better way of designing the system? Given better drugs and anaesthetics allowing more speedy recovery, state-of-the-art diagnostics and imaging, minimum intervention techniques and better information systems, could any stages be omitted, or be arranged more economically to save the time and money of both patients and staff? Could protocols and clinical guidelines be written? Would the quality of care be at least as good? In accident and emergency work, could minor injuries be separated from major trauma? Should elective care be separated from emergency work? If so, could nurse-practitioners undertake work traditionally regarded as medical, and did staff have the right mix of skills? The Central Middlesex began to develop a Mayo Clinic style ambulatory care and diagnostic centre, designed to provide 80 per cent of basic elective treatment. Outpatients usually had to attend different departments for blood tests, ECGs and X-rays. Leicester Royal Infirmary 're-engineered' the process, and provided a suite in the middle of the clinic that could provide 80 per cent of the tests outpatients required. This meant retraining staff to carry out several tasks, taking blood samples, ECGs and the preparation of patients for X-rays.[260] Increasingly, efficiency was sought not through further organisational changes but in the improvement of clinical practice. Three things mattered: first a knowledge of the pattern of disease, the alternative methods of treatment, their economic costs and benefits, and clinical guidelines founded on evidence-based medicine; second, a delivery system that co-ordinated all carers, primary, secondary and social; and, third, a quality improvement system to audit performance against evolving standards.[261]

Rationing

Far from being at odds with the ethos of the NHS, rationing had always been the essence of the system.[262] In the 1960s Enoch Powell drew attention to the limited resources, rising expectations and improving technology. The requirements of an ageing population added to the difficulty. Rationing took many forms, for example the reluctance of a patient to visit a busy doctor, the family doctor's hesitation to refer when there were lengthy waiting lists or services were not available in the locality, and the decision of consultants to select for treatment those expected to do best. Politicians might allocate priority; the *Priorities* document (1976) had aimed to move resources to the care of elderly people and those who were mentally ill at the cost of the acute services.[263]

Cost in £ per year of quality-adjusted life	
GP advice to stop smoking	270
Hip replacement	1,180
Heart transplant	7,840
Coronary artery surgery	18,830

Source: Maynard 1991[264]

The use of QALYs to grade alternative treatments was examined.[264] Although the promotion of a comprehensive health service was the statutory function of the Secretary of State, that had never meant the provision of everything, or indeed everything that might possibly help a particular individual. This had been tested in the courts on several occasions, as it was in 1995 when, after providing several years' care, the Cambridge and Huntingdon Health Commission refused to fund further treatment with only a small chance of success for 'Child B', an 11-year-old girl with leukaemia.[265] *Panorama* ran a programme on the issues. Child B, Jaymee Bowen, emerged as one of the brightest, shrewdest and feistiest kids on the block. She told viewers 'you can't really refuse a child who needs help . . . if you refuse one child then other parents are going to be worried you'd refuse their child.'[266] *The Times* said that the most pressing point to emerge was the uncertain future of experimental medicine in a system that separated purchaser from provider. A health authority with finite resources would be reluctant to spend money on unproven procedures, yet the case illustrated how quickly an unproven procedure could become accepted medical practice. The danger of orderly rationing was that no gambles would be taken, no hunches pursued. Nobody expected health managers to waste money on moonshine; but there must be space for uncertainty and risk taking.[267] Sadly, although treatment was continued, Jaymee Bowen died in 1996.

Doctors, with a strong belief in their duty to do everything possible for their patients or to allow them a dignified and peaceful end, chafed under restrictions. Fifty years previously they made life-or-death decisions quietly and privately. Now they were in the open and it was often a young nurse who, believing herself to be the patient's advocate, would demand the continuation of life-maintaining procedures in the face of the evidence. Adult intensive care units featured in tragic confrontations, for beds could be hard to find and expensive treatment often deferred rather than prevented death.[268] The measurement of physiological variables provided a sounder basis for prediction than a professional's gut feeling, and computer programs could detect hopeless cases with 95 per cent accuracy. Most people had, however, an emotional revulsion from 'death by computer' yet there were advantages in the early detection of futile intensive care.[269] There were discussions about surgeons refusing coronary artery bypass operations to smokers, people denied treatment on the grounds of age, older women or those who were HIV positive being treated for infertility, the use of interferon-beta in multiple sclerosis, and cosmetic procedures such as breast enlargement. There were no experts – everyone's opinion was as good as everybody else's.[270] A substantial number of purchasers decided, individually, not to fund particular types of treatment. The government, however, did not accept that there should be firm rules governing eligibility.

There was little conceptual or philosophical basis for discussion on how priorities might be set, save an agreement that ineffective care had few claims on resources. In no country was there a publicly accepted set of principles that could determine who got what health care and when; drawing up the principles of selection proved extremely difficult. All countries had to grapple with the problem. The British tradition was to leave it to individual clinicians to take the decision as to who should be referred and who should be placed on a waiting list, guaranteeing that care was rationed by rules that differed, were inconsistent and implicit.[271] In the USA, Oregon became well known for its explicit acceptance of the conditions for which the public health system would pay, and their priority order. Treatments were ranked according to the ratio of cost to the improvement in quality of life produced. Categories of care were listed in rank order based on cost and health gain criteria.[272] Faced with a previous system that rationed by excluding some from care, Oregon made an attempt to limit services to those that were most effective rather than rationing the *people* to whom services were provided. Sweden explicitly rejected the idea that choices must be made to confer the greatest benefit on the greatest number. In the Netherlands and New Zealand an attempt was made to list core services that were effective, efficient and allowed individuals to function in society. Rabbi Julia Neuberger maintained that three things were necessary to assist the debate about priorities: admission of the extent of the uncertainty that existed about what was known about effectiveness; language easily accessible to the public to describe outcomes and effectiveness; and the engagement of a better educated public in the complex issues, something easier said than done.[273]

Some argued, like Wennberg, that the elimination of ineffective procedures would go far to solve the problem; others, that the drive of technology and the introduction of costly new drugs meant that, sooner or later, the problem of rationing had to be squarely faced. In 1994 Duncan Nichol, erstwhile NHS Chief Executive, established a group to stimulate debate and clarify policy. It believed that a universal tax-funded NHS was becoming unsustainable. The gap in resources would have to be met by a mixture of rationing and private provision. Stephen Dorrell, the Secretary of State, quoting HL Mencken, said Nichol's analysis was simple, obvious and wrong. He questioned the prophesies of doom and thought that the NHS could continue to sustain the twin cost pressures of ageing and medical advance. The number of elderly people, though rising, had been rising for a long time, and some technological advances made treatment quicker and simpler. The time had not come when the principles of a health service based on clinical need, and without payment in time of sickness, should be abandoned and he opposed blanket bans on particular procedures.[274] Leslie Turnberg, President of the Royal College of Physicians, chaired a group that proposed a national body to advise on the principles of priority setting, and the way those principles should be applied. It appealed for greater state funding and the elimination of treatment that was not cost-effective.[275] Not everyone believed that evidence-based medicine would save substantial sums but in the government view no clinically effective treatment should be excluded from the NHS as a matter of principle.

Hospital development and design

The 1960s and 1970s were the hey-day of innovation in hospital design; the 1980s and 1990s were a period of consolidation. 'Best Buy' hospitals were not replicated; although basically a good design it was difficult to modify them, although with ingenuity it was possible. For example, at Bury St Edmunds a day hospital, a day surgery centre and an assessment centre were added at the periphery of the hospital. Internal modifications were more difficult and space had to be found for intensive care by moving the kitchen and dining rooms. 'Nucleus' maintained its popularity and British architects tended to use the standards that had been set, rather than maintaining the impetus of innovation. Some trusts therefore turned to North American firms who seemed to have a greater understanding of building for modern patterns of health care. The first low-energy Nucleus, at St Mary's, Isle of Wight, was designed to save half the energy of the conventional type. It was completed in 1990. Delays in construction increased costs, and changes in fuel costs and in environmental legislation added to the difficulties, but by its second year of operation St Mary's was approaching its energy-saving target. A second low-energy Nucleus designed to save 60 per cent was opened in 1992 at Ashington on the Northumberland coast. More innovative technology was incorporated, including a wind turbine generator to provide 10 per cent of the electricity. It was uncertain whether the hospitals were a step too far into a new world of design or a valuable trail-blazing exercise.[276] Hospital building remained prone to delays and escalating costs. Occasionally, projects became the subject of enquiries by the National Audit Office and the Public Accounts Committee. Guy's new phase III, promised as the largest and most sophisticated ambulatory care centre, was approved in 1985, to cost of £29 million. Delays and rising costs brought the sum to over £152 million. A superb piece of NHS real estate had turned into one of the most disastrous building projects the NHS had seen.[277]

Traditionally all new hospital building was financed from the Treasury, because it could raise money at the best rates and control over public sector expenditure was thought necessary. However, following the NHS reforms, private finance became first acceptable and then important. The *Capital investment manual*, in June 1994, set out the terms of the Private Finance Initiative (PFI), making it clear that future capital schemes had to explore private finance and be tested to see whether this was preferable to the use of public money.[278] Although many projects were small, by the end of 1995 plans existed nation-wide for 60 schemes costing £2 billion to be funded by the private sector and leased to the NHS, although contracts took a long time to sign. Large construction companies, with experience of putting together large projects, took the lead.[279] The new system froze major capital expenditure for two to three years while projects explored the option. PFI was a way of maintaining a capital programme at a time of restriction on government spending. The NHS capital budget was cut in the expectation that the private sector would fill most of the gap, yet by the election in May 1997 not one major privately financed hospital project had started.[280] The PFI sometimes led to a radical reshaping of local proposals that had previously been agreed in consultation, and schemes generated by individual trusts did not necessarily take account of interaction between trusts and other parts of the health service. A major problem was how to transfer risks to the private sector at a cost that gave sufficient return but was affordable to the purchasers. There was also a risk that a policy of buy now, pay later, would store up problems for the future, and pose a threat to the integrity of the district hospital and the ésprit of the staff.[281] On return to power in 1997 Labour, needing to restrict public spending, backed the PFI. They chose the schemes to go ahead and tried to speed their implementation.[282]

Health service information and computing

After the RHAs took over the experimental computer programme in the 1970s, most pursued hospital computerisation in a less radical way. Nevertheless, there were steady advances in the computerisation of FPC services and the installation of hospital information systems. The key was to link systems across organisational boundaries, for example general practice and the hospitals. However, the NHS reforms completely overturned the assumptions on which development had been based, requiring a massive expansion of information-flow to underpin the internal market, and the Hospital Information Support System (HISS) initiative was launched in 1989. From then until 1996 much effort was required to provide information systems that would support contracting. The market could work only if people knew what they were paying for, difficult because of the lack of a national patient-identifier. When the NHS began, it took over the wartime national identity numbers. It was apparent by the 1960s that these were inappropriate in an IT environment because of their complexity and varying formats. In 1992 a project to replace the NHS number was announced, to generate and issue more than 50 million new numbers. The NHS central register had recently been computerised, and in December 1995 new blocks of numbers were issued to registrars of births to allocate to new babies. In March 1996 GPs were given new numbers for their existing patients. Because of anxieties that the NHS number might be seen as an infringement of civil liberties, FHSAs were discouraged from telling patients their new number.[283] A second requirement was an NHS Internet-type system, allowing the sort of information exchange that had been routine in banks and airlines for 30 years. It would carry contract data between purchasers and providers, information about GP registration and payments, laboratory results, and letters between hospitals and GPs. After a number of setbacks, a national system was put in place in 1996, although alternative commercial systems were already in widespread use.[284]

The problem of London's health services

Piecemeal change in London's hospital services continued. In 1988 Parkside district was created, uniting St Mary's and the Central Middlesex, and progressively leaving St Charles' as a non-acute community hospital. The plan involved the part-rebuilding of St Mary's and rebuilding the Central Middlesex. The new Chelsea and Westminster Hospital, which enabled the closure of five separate hospitals, opened in 1993. The MRC, under financial pressure, decided to pull out of its Northwick Park Clinical Research Centre and concentrate at the Hammersmith Hospital. This freed modern accommodation and research space. A small specialist hospital concerned with coloproctology, St Marks, needed to move from its poor accommodation in City Road, but the space offered by St Bartholomew's was little better. St Marks had the foresight to realise that it had more to gain than lose from a merger and grasped the alternative, Northwick Park, with enthusiasm. Relocation in 1995 provided the hospital with immediate access to intensive care, theatres and state-of-the art imaging and service departments. St Marks had its own front door, clinical directorate and all the advantages of association with a busy district general hospital.[285]

The internal market had a major effect on central London and the existing pattern of services was not sustainable. The internal market could have been allowed to refashion London's hospital service but this would have been unpredictable in its effects. There were two major planning exercises, one by the King's Fund and one initiated by government.

The King's Fund Commission

London's health services were reviewed by a commission appointed by the King's Fund to develop a broad vision of services that would make sense in the early years of the next century. The Fund spent £500,000 commissioning 12 research reports on which the conclusions, published in June 1992, were based.[286] However, the Commission spent less time on data analysis and its examination of educational issues than had the London Health Planning Consortium (LHPC). Substantial attacks were mounted on its findings because of a belief that it was working towards a pre-determined conclusion and that some of its members had little sympathy for London or for specialists. The report accepted the case for substantial change and reduction in acute services with a complementary build-up of primary health care. It did not consider the paucity of back-up beds in nursing and residential homes, which barely existed in the metropolis. It reported that at least 5,000 beds must be closed if the capital were to be guaranteed a good standard of health into the next century. 'Costs in London are not just expensive, they are extremely expensive . . . change is inevitable . . . Inner London hospitals are top-heavy with doctors and the rate of patients going through is slower.'[287]

Tomlinson

The government, though committed to market solutions, embarked in London on strategic planning and consultation. William Waldegrave, the Secretary of State, announced his review at the 1991 Conservative Party conference. Sir Bernard Tomlinson, Chairman of the Northern RHA, would form a strategic view of the future needs for service, education and research in London. *The Times* said that Mr Waldegrave was 'wringing his hands' over what should be done in London. However, he needed to be convinced that major decisions were intellectually based. Already expansion had been approved at Guy's, the Chelsea and Westminster was established and St Mary's was being developed. UCH/Middlesex, strongly supported by the scientific community because of the quality of its work, also wanted a new building.

Bernard Tomlinson reported in October 1992, and was influenced by the King's Fund Commission.[288] He emphasised the need to improve primary and community care, bringing primary care up to national standards and providing services for people with special needs such as the homeless. This prescription was widely accepted, for there was a general belief (without much supporting evidence) that improved primary health care was fundamental for the degree of rationalisation envisaged for London's acute services. An idea that had emerged at a Nuffield-sponsored meeting of professional leaders and health service managers was a 'free-fire' zone where normal health service rules could be modified to facilitate the development of primary health care. Tomlinson adopted this and the government provided £170 million over six years in a 'London Initiatives Zone' covering about 4 million people, where heath care needs were great and an innovative approach was required. Money would be concentrated on this territory and educational and management effort would be strengthened.[289] Most people under-estimated the complexities of building new and better facilities for GPs and primary health care teams. Neither was it easy to turn a theoretically attractive plan for the teaching hospitals and medical schools into schemes on the ground. The money helped new projects and encouraged the study of long-standing problems of inner London practice. The pace of change was, however, slow and the effect on acute hospital services minimal. Neither the changes to the hospitals nor those to primary health care were universally popular and it was politically hard to fight on both fronts simultaneously.[290] A primary care support force worked to improve matters, and was disbanded in 1997; it was hardly possible to maintain that the issues the group was set up to address had been resolved.

The Tomlinson Report foresaw a surplus of 2,000–7,000 beds because of the withdrawal of inpatient flows from outside central London and the increasing efficiency with which beds were used. Tomlinson revived earlier proposals for rationalisation. They involved change at UCH/Middlesex that had become a single, powerful and scientifically important organisation. There would be a single management unit for St Bartholomew's and The Royal London; the loss of one hospital from among the south London hospitals of Guys', King's, St Thomas' and Lewisham; rationalisation at Charing Cross/Chelsea and Westminster with relocation of specialist postgraduate hospitals to the Charing Cross site; and changes to specialist postgraduate teaching hospitals to bring them into closer relationship with general hospitals. Tomlinson supported the removal of St Marks to Northwick Park.

In February 1993 the DoH's response accepted the general thrust of the recommendations, and the need to develop primary health care.[291] A London Implementation Group was formed, chaired by Tim Chessells, Chairman of South East Thames RHA. Six specialty reviews were established to examine clinical requirements; the clinicians in the specialty under consideration came from outside London and could be brutal when faced with the pretensions they sometimes encountered. The reviews proposed that the best centres should be developed, the smaller ones should be closed or merged, and new ones established where they were needed as at St George's where there was a long-standing requirement for renal replacement therapy.[292] Several initiatives now came together, making change possible. There was a research review of the London postgraduate hospitals, which pointed to the need for a wide range of skills including biophysics and molecular biology, and association with general hospitals and university facilities. The specialty reviews were published in the middle of 1993.[293] Medical school deans had to play a difficult hand; most were privately supportive of the need for change and prepared to work for it, but in public they had to take their colleagues with them as far as possible. Trust chairmen had been appointed knowing there was a job to be done. They and their chief executives were heavyweights who did not fool around, although transitional funds were available to sugar the pills of change and mergers. Ministers were far more involved than they had been in the work of the LHPC; Virginia Bottomley, always in the public eye, was continuously involved in the decisions being taken.

University proposals for London medical schools

Multi-faculty college	Constituent medical schools
Imperial College	St Mary's
	Westminster/Charing Cross
King's College	King's United Medical and Dental Schools
Queen Mary and	The Royal London
Westfield College	St Bartholomew's
University College	University College/Middlesex
	Royal Free

(St George's maintained an independent position within the University of London)

There were four broad responses to Tomlinson: the optimistic that primary and community care could be brought up to the standards elsewhere; the realistic accepting the recipe but gloomy about the money and the difficulties; the despairing who doubted whether anything would be accomplished; and the reaction at St Bartholomew's that was to indulge in old-style emotional campaigning against the proposals. St Bartholomew's had come to believe its own rhetoric and dismissed any proposal not to its liking, however well founded. Its campaign was given a voice by the *Evening Standard* in probably the most ferocious media war ever waged against health service managers and NHS policy, unparalleled in its unstinting aggression and partiality.[294] 'During the past twenty years,' wrote Lord Flowers in *The Times*, 'with a few honourable exceptions every attempt to reform London medicine has been defeated by vigorous rearguard action on behalf of any hospital or medical school adversely affected. The result has been that the standing of teaching and research in London's famed medical schools has been steadily slipping. The time has come for the government to stand firm.'[295] Virginia Bottomley took decisions that her predecessors had been canny enough to defer and for which her successors would be forever in her debt. She narrowly escaped defeat in Parliament and a rebellion of some senior London Tory MPs. Her reward was the Department of National Heritage. Robert Maxwell, Secretary of the King's Fund, said that the creation of big medical centres across London, the main tertiary centres of service, research and education for the future, had been talked about for 50 years. Now it looked set to happen and would be Mrs Bottomley's best legacy.[296] Changes in London's hospital service once more had ripple effects on medical education. The university re-introduced proposals for merger. There would be four centres, each related to a multi-faculty college, St George's maintaining an independent position.

Increasingly a five radial sector framework became the basis for discussion, although inevitably decisions in one sector affected others. In east London the Royal Hospitals Trust provided services on three sites, St Bartholomew's, the London Chest Hospital and, increasingly, at The Royal London where a major capital project was planned. In north central London services were focused on the University College London hospitals – UCH, the Middlesex, the Hospital for Tropical Diseases and the Elizabeth Garrett Anderson. In northwest London there was less clarity, with the Hammersmith, Queen Charlotte's/Chelsea Hospital for Women, Charing Cross and, in close proximity St Mary's, the Chelsea and Westminster and two specialist hospitals, the Royal Marsden and the Royal Brompton. In south London the position of St George's was secure. In southeast London there was protracted discussion about the future of Guy's and St Thomas', the latter becoming the main site for acute inpatient and emergency care. With the demise of the London Implementation Group in April 1995, the two Thames RHAs north and south of the river became responsible for co-ordinating change, and that at a time when they were themselves facing demise.[297] With the election of the Labour government in May 1997 yet a further review of the future of London's hospitals was set in train, chaired by Sir Leslie Turnberg. The King's Fund, in a further report, called for changes in the structure, organisation and finance of London's health services.

Probity in public life

The entrepreneurial ethos of the 1980s, and the move towards a market in which care was costed and contracts were placed, may have been associated with a decline in the old-time values of the public service. Performance-related pay encouraged subordinates to tell their seniors what they wished to hear, at every level from the hospital to the

DoH. Performance targets on which bonuses depended might be set to fit with levels already achieved. There had been fraud in hospitals back into the nineteenth century. The Audit Commission found plenty of examples in the fifth decade of the NHS, and there were a crop of questionable activities ranging from the unwise to the out-and-out fraudulent, for example bogus prescriptions. Wessex Region planned a massive computer system that proved difficult to commission and costly; a series of regional decisions wasted millions of pounds and a prosecution was attempted. West Midlands region was similarly criticised for its financial dealings during the privatisation of some support services.

In 1996 the National Audit Office reported a series of irregularities and breaches of rules in the former Yorkshire RHA, subsequently confirmed by the Public Accounts Committee, which bore comparison with earlier ones. The disposal of surplus land to a developer had resulted in a substantial loss to the NHS, large sums had been spent on lavish hospitality and senior staff had received irregular relocation payments. The most senior levels of management had been involved and the NHS Executive had difficulty in disciplining managers for wrong-doing in one post once they had moved to another.[298] Neither was professional life free of misdemeanour. The publication of accounts of treatment that had never taken place and a false claim to success in the re-implantation of a tubal pregnancy led the General Medical Council to strike a consultant gynaecologist off the medical register. The editor, a senior obstetrician who was listed as a co-author, resigned.[299]

An Audit Commission report showed that some consultants did fewer than their contracted hours and probably did more private practice than they should, a finding supported by John Yates, who had lengthy experience in the field of health service efficiency. Others were stopped from working as hard as they wished by restrictions placed upon their outpatient clinics and theatre time.[300]

Medical education and staffing

Hospital medical staff

	Total	Consultants
England and Wales (whole-time equivalents)		
1949	11,735	3,488
1959	16,033	5,322
1963	17,971	6,049
1968	21,232	7,544
England*		
1973	24,829	8,988
1978	31,013	10,382
1983	33,155	11,849
1988	37,600	13,204
1993	43,801	15,210

*The removal of Wales from the figures reduced the total numbers by about 1,250.
Source: NHS Executive data 1996

In the mid-1980s the BMA had been concerned that there would be too many doctors. Luckily, because demand rose substantially, government had not reduced the number of student places. Progress in medicine, rising expenditure on the NHS, continued demographic change, public expectations, the 1990 GP contract and the NHS reforms all increased the requirements for doctors. However, low morale, more doctors retiring early and concerns about doctors' health boded ill for the NHS. Shortages arose both in hospital and in general practice, and Britain was no longer self-sufficient. Trusts had to have the staff to provide the services that purchasers required. It became increasingly difficult to fill some consultant vacancies, particularly in anaesthesia, ophthalmology and psychiatry, in unattractive areas, places where housing was expensive or where there was little prospect of private practice. Young psychiatrists were recruited by the private sector, which was rapidly developing profitable services providing care to NHS patients. Recruitment agencies began to be employed, and trusts, using the greater flexibility they had been given, might pay over the odds to get people to move.[301] Junior doctors were in short supply and an increasing number were recruited from the EC, especially the Netherlands and Germany. In 1992 a new Medical Manpower Standing Advisory Committee predicted a continuing shortfall and recommended an increase in the annual medical school intake of 240 to 4,470 UK places, a target met almost immediately. The target for the year 2000 was 4,970.

Medical staffing

The profession had never come to terms with the inherent conflicts between academic medicine, private practice and the requirements of the NHS. Rigid central control of staffing had not solved the problem of a career structure in the hospital service. The simpler system for general practice, where there were fewer factors involved, had been more successful in balancing supply and demand. Attempts were made to adjust the number of career registrars to the expected number of consultant opportunities. However, the rate of growth of junior staff was often larger than that of consultants; it varied between the specialties, being lowest in anaesthesia (1 : 1) and highest in obstetrics and gynaecology (2.5 : 1).[302] In 1990/1 efforts were made to reduce the strain and the working hours of hard-pressed junior doctors and offer them a 'new deal'; substantial progress was made in reducing the number on call for over 72 hours per week.[303] Any changes to the patterns of rotas had, however, substantial effects on consultants and some saw the shorter hours as a threat to the adequacy of training.

The Calman Report

The Calman Report (1993)

- Reduce the minimum length of specialist training to 7 years
- Introduce more explicit training curricula and a certificate of completion of specialist training
- Merge registrar and senior registrar grades into a single specialist registrar training grade

Under European legislation specialists registered in one country had a right to practice elsewhere in the community. British training was longer than in the other countries and, following a court case, had to be brought into line. It was also necessary to have a defined endpoint marked by the award of a certificate by a body responsible for regulating training. To deal with the European dimension, the CMO, Kenneth Calman, and the profession had to look at training and its timescale and modify the traditional system. *Achieving a balance* was put on ice. There was an opportunity to look at other workforce issues; for example, improvements in the quality of training, the reduction of juniors' hours (often more than 72 per week), protected time for study and continuing medical education. A working group produced recommendations more rapidly than had the previous exercises, and agreement was achieved on some matters to which there had previously been opposition.[304] The proposals went some way to completing the work that the Royal Commission on Medical Education (1968) had begun. There were, however, widespread anxieties for they would have an impact on the organisation and provision of hospital services, the structure and management of specialist training, the balance between career grade doctors and trainees in hospitals, and the career pattern of hospital doctors. A single specialist registrar training grade was created, into which existing registrars and senior registrars were slotted. In 1996 a guide to training set out the experience required, and the number of slots providing structured training was determined for each region and specialty.[305] Junior doctors were appointed to fill these slots, created to provide educational opportunities and not for service reasons. After five or six years the doctor might be awarded a certificate of completion of specialist training, without which appointment as a consultant would be impossible. Juniors were concerned about the difficulty of changing their chosen specialty and finding a permanent post, particularly if career posts were in short supply. Being supernumerary, departments should in theory be able to run in their absence. Trusts were asked to make forward estimates of the senior staff likely to be needed over the next three to five years, and agree these with purchasers. The cost of consultant expansion remained a problem, but the need for more consultants to provide the services purchasers were demanding fuelled consultant expansion, which rose to 4–6 per cent per year.

The changing requirements of the health service in the fields of audit, contracting and management, and the clinical demands of scientific advance and the pace of care, exacerbated the problems of maintaining cover and staffing hospitals around the clock, altering the traditional pattern of specialist work. Calman aimed to alter the delivery of acute hospital services from being consultant *led* to consultant *based*. In the minds of the seniors this seemed to mean consultant *provided*, not what the leaders of the hospital doctors had intended. The demands, on the one hand to change the pattern of staffing and on the other to work more cheaply and effectively, faced trusts with a dilemma. Increasing numbers of sub-specialties, stiffer College criteria for the approval of training posts and junior doctor cover with a sensible rota system placed smaller DGHs at a disadvantage. It was even more important to bring hospitals together onto a single site where this had not as yet been done. Hospitals unable to create attractive training opportunities faced problems. For example, the West Suffolk Hospital, with 70 consultants, calculated that to provide 24-hour on-site consultant cover would require an additional 21 consultants, and if the service were to be consultant-provided the need would rise to a further 56. Nor was it clear how some departments would continue to run if there were local reductions in junior staff; or whether consultants would welcome direct participation in emergency care, day and night, any more than they had in the 1960s.[306]

The traditional concept of 'firm'-based care had been eroded. Consultants found themselves responsible for 'outlier patients' who, because of bed allocation problems, were housed in wards not designed for their specialty. Time and energy were wasted as doctors moved from ward to ward. Laboratory reports and important papers might be in the wrong place. One doctor had to work with many different nurses, and vice versa, a problem aggravated by the introduction of team nursing, for no longer could calls be channelled through a single ward sister.[307] Juniors worked shifts, looking after upwards of 200 patients. Professional morale, disillusion and disenchantment with medicine grew. The RCP produced proposals to try to mitigate the problems resulting from alterations in the organisation of the NHS, in training, in junior doctors' hours, increased emergency work and the loss of a geographic focus to clinical work. It saw the need for teams operating within defined conditions of time and space. Some young doctors said that they regretted their career choice. Women were especially affected by a pervasive competitive atmosphere, a process of 'teaching by humiliation' and the pressure to get good jobs. There was resentment at inadequate career counselling, on-call responsibilities and being used as workhorses. Isobel Allen, who had studied the careers of doctors, and especially women doctors, pointed to the problems facing women who entered medical school in the same numbers as men, but needed flexible training and work, with part-time possibilities. There was no evidence that medical schools were recruiting students less able to stand the pace of medicine, but the present generation of doctors was less inclined to accept things than their predecessors. They wanted to be treated as professionals but felt like ants at the bottom of the heap.[308]

Nursing

Nursing education and staffing

In 1948 nurses were badly paid and worked long hours, but they knew they were respected and valued, they were well looked after in the nursing homes and they wore smart uniforms. Now they were better paid (starting salary over £12,000/year) but had less job security, they were worried about litigation and they had little reason to believe that anyone cared about them. They looked to their professional organisations, the RCN, RCM and HVA, for union support. Nursing was in crisis; there was industrial strife, supported by NUPE and COHSE but not the RCN. Government took action not just because of the strikes but because recruitment was poor, wastage was high, nurses were voting with their feet, and demographically the number of school leavers was falling fast. Three factors turned recruitment around. First, the government had been discussing a new grading structure and this was agreed in May 1988. As part of the 1988 pay review a nationwide regrading of posts took place, coupled with a rise of 4–30 per cent. The government hoped that this would lead to greater flexibility of pay, and in time to geographical variation. The new scales were meant to keep nurses at the bedside by providing a sensible career progression for clinical staff, and recognition of qualifications, skills and wider responsibilities.[309] The grading system stressed the importance of a single ward sister (grade G), with total responsibility for the ward at all times. The Review Body wanted the grading of all staff to be complete within six months. Sometimes flexibility was used by management to mitigate recruitment problems, generating ill-will and many appeals. The second factor was that the country moved into recession and people neither wanted nor were able to change jobs so easily. Third, in May 1988 the Secretary of State accepted *Project 2000*, on which nurses had pinned their hopes, with the proviso that its timing and detail did not jeopardise a proper nursing service. Nursing leaders hailed the announcement as a significant milestone and a historic victory.[310] John Moore recorded a joint understanding with the nursing professional bodies that education would retain a clinical focus and the time students spent in clinical areas would not be reduced. On that basis government accepted that nurses in training should have student status, non-means-tested bursaries, and move towards a supernumerary position. However, demographic factors made it unlikely that a professionally qualified workforce of the size needed could be attained so the gate of entry should be widened, and more work was needed on developing vocational training for support workers. Forty years earlier the matrons and hospital administrators had refused to allow education to be uncoupled from service, removing students from the labour force. After Griffiths, chief nursing officers and matrons were no longer there. To replace the service contribution made by the students, extra money was allocated to recruit additional trained and untrained staff. When this was clear, hospital managers had little to gain from managing a nurse training school. *Project 2000* had an easy ride.

Project 2000

Project 2000 brought to an end the system of nurse education developed by Florence Nightingale and by Mrs Bedford Fenwick of St Bartholomew's. In moving to an American academic and theory based model, nurses distanced themselves from domestic or medical roots. University affiliation and academic status were seen as strengthening the claim to be 'a profession'. Academic nurses disparaged the earlier pattern of apprenticeship in hospital-based nursing schools, where the accent had been on clinical knowledge of disease and basic skills, hygiene and sterile technique, and in which the safety and comfort of the patient were paramount.[311] Students had once been selected by a matron who would try to assess whether the candidate really wanted to nurse; now this was an academic responsibility. People who might be natural nurses might be put off or considered ineligible, for example the caring and capable young person who wanted to do something active but did not wish to be judged by exam results, to go back to school or to become a health care assistant.[312] The government wanted to increase the number of people in higher education without too large an increase in costs. The new universities, polytechnics that had obtained university status around 1992, were geared to student numbers in tens of thousands, high volume teaching and slim academic staffs. They had the capacity, the flexibility and lower overheads than older universities. They had teachers in psychology, biochemistry and social sciences, and the large budgets of the new nursing colleges were attractive. In their financial bids they were often successful in obtaining a linked nursing college. However, nursing academics were seldom considered part of the university mainstream. Existing nurse tutors might be poorly prepared in academic terms and were often replaced. Course objectives might be expressed in psycho-social jargon. One handbook said 'During the course students will undertake modules that are both theme based and praxis based. Don't worry if it seems confusing at first, that's all part of the learning process!'[313]

There was now a single point of entry for students with a wide range of abilities. Of the 15,000 entering registered nurse training in 1987/8, 30 per cent had fewer than five 'O' levels. The new three-year course had a common 18-month foundation programme, after which students could choose general nursing, children's nursing, nursing of the mentally ill or of people with learning difficulties. Theoretical work was supplemented by clinical experience under supervision one to three days a week at district hospitals, and the loyalty of the student was now to a college, not a hospital. Those successfully completing their course were awarded a diploma in higher education and a professional nursing qualification. Midwifery courses also became university based. Health visiting remained a post-diploma qualification and, because basic nurse education was the main priority of the UKCC, midwives and health visitors were worried that the loss of their training bodies would affect clinical practice in their spheres.

Demonstration schemes were established in 1989 and *Project 2000* was rapidly implemented. The gap between nursing theory and practice was not overcome. As students were seldom part of a ward team, they felt unskilled in comparison with their predecessors. Because students could not be relied on to provide a predictable contribution to ward work, busy ward staff could not be counted on to provide educational support. Occasionally there were placements in private hospitals, where the students were well supervised by experienced nurses. Many, entering nursing to nurse, found courses concentrated so much on health, psychology and research studies that they barely admitted the existence of disease. They compensated for the lack of a practical focus in their courses by taking agency work as care assistants.[314] There was much still to learn on qualification. The course had swung too far towards theory at the expense of practice and did not prepare students for their future responsibilities.[315] Private hospitals preferred to recruit those with a year's clinical knowledge and experience. It had been argued that *Project 2000* would reduce levels of wastage because of its association with higher education. However, because of economic recession wastage fell to around 5 per cent well before *Project 2000* was implemented.

Nurse education placed an accent on the processes of daily living, the role of the nurse, the psychology of the patient and the interrelationships. Firmly based in the social sciences and educational theory, nurse education was distancing itself from experienced clinical nurses as well as medicine. In the 1950s the Nuffield work study had identified clearly who did what; such studies were no longer carried out. Nursing research was less interested in what nurses did, more in philosophies of nursing, sometimes from a feminist perspective. Doctors were perpetrators of past nursing oppression, nurses were a victimised group, and nursing 'a woman's occupation in a man's world, marginalised by medicine and government'.[316] 'Reflective nursing' became the profession's new enthusiasm.[317] Reflection was derived from educational theory, not clinical care. It involved examining life's experience to obtain new understandings and perspectives. Florence Nightingale had encouraged nurses to think about what they were doing. They were now asked to prepare psychological profiles of themselves, to examine uncomfortable feelings and thoughts and to learn to know themselves.

In the past British nurses, unlike their North American counterparts, had little opportunity to enter nursing through university education. The first degree course was established in Edinburgh in 1960. Thirty years later, 14 universities, including former polytechnics, were offering a degree course leading to a BSc in nursing studies, although the total number of places was only 400, one hundredth of the number following the diploma course. To maintain their registration all had to conform with Post Registration Education and Practice (PREP), a new system of continuing education. PREP placed the accent on health promotion, counselling, educational development and research.[318]

Personnel planning

Hospital nursing staff	
England and Wales (numbers) including registered nurses, students, enrolled and pupil nurses	
1949	137,636
1959	190,946
1963	215,219
1968	255,641
England (whole-time equivalents)*	
1973	251,778
1978	292,640
1983	329,965
1988	330,669
England (excludes 28,000 Project 2000 students)	
1993	296,414
1994	286,093

*The removal of Wales from the figures, and the use of whole-time equivalents, reduced the figures by about 26,000

Source: NHS Executive data 1996

Statistics were difficult to come by and the information about motivation to enter or continue in nursing was often lacking. Because of the recession, people in the late 1980s did not change jobs and vacancies were few. Nurses were appointed to particular wards and, as their grade and salary were determined by their experience within a particular specialty, they tended to remain in that field. After four decades of growth the number of nurses reached a plateau, in spite of increasing NHS activity from shorter lengths of hospital stay, the intensity of patient care and the feelings of stress among nurses. In 1993 responsibility for funding nurse education was transferred from national professional boards to regional consortia of health authorities and trusts. Nursing lost its ability to protect its numbers. Each region had a target based on organisational requirements. This 'employer-led system' resulted in a reduction in the entry to Project 2000 courses. The English entry in 1994 and 1995 was roughly 11,000 per year, comparable to 1948. As Britain came out of recession in the mid-1990s, wastage began to rise again to about 20 per cent.[319] Nursing shortages reappeared in the headlines in 1996, and the Nursing Times carried many advertisements for vacancies. Nursing agencies flourished, especially in London, where many hospitals were heavily dependent on temporary staff. Some trusts began to examine how they could become more attractive employers, looking to Scandinavia and Australasia for staff and offering recruitment incentives. Bogus sickness and absenteeism soared.[320] Two in three nurses over 25 were married, and many others reported a partner. Almost half reported the existence of dependent children. Many had a second job – 30 per cent in the south-east.[321] The 1991 census found that 140,000 nurses, midwives and health visitors in England, trained at NHS expense, had left the profession. Half were working in other jobs and 40 per cent of these did not intend to return to nursing. NHS training equipped nurses with good, transferable, skills.[322] A large and varied workforce, nurses could not be expected to have unswerving vocational commitment, and the disappearance of the hospital as the traditional centre of loyalty fuelled instability. They moved rapidly, selecting posts providing the experience they wanted, seldom staying for more than a year. Feminists blamed the NHS, rather than the inherent characteristics of people in modern society.

Nurses in senior positions, though wanting highly skilled nurses to provide the direct nursing care of patients, faced a situation in which managers needed to reduce costs.[323] The large proportion of hospitals' budgets that was spent on nursing, coupled with the disappearance of students as part of the labour force, led the NHS to attempt to control costs by substituting less skilled staff for registered nurses where possible. Enrolled nurses were offered conversion courses so that they could be registered and simultaneously the door was opened to the replacement of nurses by health care assistants, now with National Vocational Qualifications. A second-level nurse had provided basic nursing care for many years, and it was suggested that generic carers with comparatively brief training could provide most care in the future. A new, broader-based role encompassing nursing but not conforming to traditional job descriptions was proposed.[324] Such workers were introduced to acute wards to undertake a variety of tasks for which a skilled nurse, though desirable, might not be strictly necessary.

Since the end of the 1980s government had favoured some local discretion in pay scales, to which health service unions were opposed. In 1995 nurses were enraged by a Review Body offer of 1 per cent across the board plus an extra rise of between 0.5 and 2 per cent to be determined locally.[325] Leaders of the RCN urged conference representatives to bring down the government, and nurses voted to end the no-strike policy. They had chosen an odd pretext, said *The Times*. The principle for which they were prepared to sacrifice their long-held rule was that a nurse in Aberdeen should be paid the same as one in Aberystwyth. Why should not variations in cost be reflected in different salaries across the country as they were in the private sector?[326]

Nursing practice

In 1948 medicine had few answers to serious illness, many hospital patients were gravely ill and good nursing was a major factor in recovery. Young doctors learned much from the ward sisters. They relied on the nurses' careful observation of patients and the nurses would make the work of the junior doctor easier, particularly at night. Student nurses, generally responsible and intelligent people, provided much care that now falls to health care assistants.

Work at Brunel University had suggested that the only person in a hospital apparently responsible for individual patients was the consultant whose name usually appeared above the bed. However, the delivery of personalised nursing care had long been one of nursing's aims. Could nurses who worked only 37 hours out of 168, have personal accountability comparable to that of the consultant? In 1991 *The patient's charter* gave patients the right to a named, qualified nurse, midwife or health visitor responsible for nursing or midwifery care. The widespread popularity of the new policy in the upper échelon of the profession owed much to an apparent conversion of government to primary nursing. It was received as an important symbol to be grasped with enthusiasm.

> *Named nursing is part of the unfolding story of nursing coming into its own. It will not produce instant perfection, it is not a panacea, it will not solve nursing's problems overnight. It is a tool which can be used to further the quality of patient care. Whether it succeeds or not will be largely in the hands of nurses themselves.*[327]

Primary nursing was a complex system that worked best when patient turnover was low, the staff were stable and their numbers adequate. This seldom being the case, it was not generally applied in a pure form. Patients were divided among teams, often identified by a colour, each consisting of one or two staff nurses and several health care assistants.

Task allocation
Each nurse does a particular set of tasks for all patients on the ward

Patient allocation
Each nurse looks after the needs of an allocated group of patients for the duration of that shift

Team nursing
Led by a staff nurse, a team of nurses is responsible for care planned and delivered to individual patients throughout their stay

Primary nursing
Each patient keeps the same nurse who evaluates their care and has responsibility for ensuring that care is delivered by her/himself or by one of a small number of associate nurses

Source: Audit Commission 1991 (cf Catherine Hall, *Nursing Times* 1958; May 2)

A two-team system was commonest; a greater number of teams led to problems with the organisation of shifts. A staff nurse, perhaps the one admitting the patient, would be identified as the 'named nurse' and that nurse's name might now be over the bed rather than the consultant's. When care was long term, the nurse and patient had time to get to know each other. However, when patients were acutely ill, and their condition was changing rapidly, they might be moved between hospital wards. High-technology medicine was businesslike, patients were very sick and there was less to be gained by emphasising primary nursing.

There was more diversity of role among ward sisters, who might have to choose whether to devolve care, and to act as detached ward managers concerned with budgets and general issues, or to maintain a clinical leadership role. When there was an accent on primary nursing, the ward sister might have less clinical involvement and ability to maintain common standards and to teach a tradition. The Audit Commission thought that, with the increased speed and complexity of medicine, it was no longer possible for ward sisters to know everything that was happening in their ward; delegation of responsibility to staff nurses was inevitable.[328] The Commission considered different patterns of ward nursing, but was handicapped by the lack of evidence as to which was best, or most cost-effective. Advised by people with progressive views, it came down firmly in favour of primary nursing. Primary nursing was less practised than was claimed, particularly at night when the small numbers on duty meant that nurses had to work as a single group. Although task allocation was anathema to nursing academics, the criticism was overdone. It worked, it did not mean the abandonment of a holistic approach and it capitalised on the expertise of all staff from the most junior to the most experienced. It ensured that the least skilled carried out the simplest tasks. All patients received some attention from the most experienced, nurses were more accessible to patients and relatives, and juniors were not expected to assume responsibilities for which they were ill-prepared, having an opportunity to consolidate their skills.[329]

In most NHS hospitals nurses no longer looked like those of old. American style trouser suits were increasingly in evidence. Sometimes nurses' casual approach to uniform verged on the scruffy; catering assistants might be better turned out. At times patient handling was empathetic and young nurses might be deeply affected by the fate of the patients into whose world they had entered. Not always; one elderly woman who objected to a nurse using her Christian name was told she should be in a private hospital. Wards might be dirtier and noisier, with TV on late into the night. In some wards bed sores reappeared. Feeding and washing patients was downgraded in importance.[330] Was anyone now in charge? Nurses might dissociate themselves from apparently mundane parts of patient care – making people comfortable, keeping them clean and seeing that they ate their meals and took their tablets; if performed, these duties fell to health care assistants. As nurses became more psychology minded, their writings conveyed the message that mere care was second best. They were at risk of selling their caring birthright for a mess of psychological pottage.[331] Staff with special skills, for example physiotherapists, might provide services that in times past had fallen to the nurses. Because discharge could be rapid, care in acute illness was often provided by relatives at home. The nurse allegedly advocate, supporter and counsellor was replacing the nurse who comforted and made comfortable. Time spent on the nursing process, nursing models and personal stress counselling reduced the time spent with patients, although the evidence that models improved clinical decision-making was largely anecdotal.

In 1992 the UKCC issued guidance on the scope of professional practice and the codes of professional conduct.[332] It maintained that nurses were responsible for developing their own competence and practice, and were not dependent on doctors. The UKCC provided ethical statements of how nurses should safeguard the interests of patients, serve the interests of society, justify public trust and uphold the reputation of the nursing professions. With the exception of the prescription of drugs and the signing of death certificates, nurses were able, in law, to do almost anything but should consider whether they had the authority to act and the necessary skills, ability and competence. Nurses should seek training when they thought they were inadequately prepared for their duties, rather than seeking many certificates. Studying allegations of misconduct, the UKCC thought they sometimes demonstrated poor management and lack of effective supervision for staff.[333] In some hospitals there was little oversight of ward nursing standards. With a huge workforce of varying quality, reliance on professional autonomy in place of a nursing hierarchy was risky. It was often in the private sector that traditional approaches were maintained. A uniform code would be in force and the nurses knew that high standards were expected of them. Advertisements for private medicine frequently showed a nurse in cap and apron. Lacking junior medical staff, consultants and ward sisters were mutually dependent. The chief nursing officer was responsible for nursing standards and these were subject to external inspection. Line management of nurses by nurses remained.

Matters were better in specialised units, where doctors and nurses worked together in a collegiate fashion, across the traditional boundary separating medicine and nursing, sharing the same objectives. There senior clinical nurses would undertake a variety of skilled tasks. They provided leadership and clinical supervision, and sometimes moved into a largely medical role. Medical budgets were tight, and when it was difficult to fill a junior post doctors would examine the possibility of a nurse with additional training taking on the role. Nurses might take a lead in asthma, diabetes, cancer care, neonatal units and intensive care. In theatre, they might act as a surgeon's assistant.[334] The boundary between the work of doctors and nurses was changing; generally patients did not mind and there was no evidence that the quality of care was poorer.[335] In South Cleveland a nurse trained in protocols, working under supervision, replaced a house officer, admitting and diagnosing patients with medical emergencies such as stroke and intracranial haemorrhage. In Bristol three nurse-practitioners replaced house officers in newly established units dealing with gastroenterology, urology and general surgery, and neonatal care.[336] Within nursing there was tension between nurses, nurse specialists and nurse-practitioners about the theory and practice of advanced nursing. There might be confusion about training, status, working relationships, career structure and the pay of those undertaking responsibilities well beyond their traditional roles.[337] Many courses in 'advanced nursing' appeared, to provide the background nurses needed for the new functions.

District nurses were increasingly incorporated into general practice, some feeling that there had been a loss of autonomy. Health visitors, lacking the ability to quantify what they did, were under pressure from management. Psychiatric nursing was quite altered. Many more patients went to day hospitals and returned home at night. The increasing number of community psychiatric nurses had to establish their role – the care outside hospital of major psychoses or the counselling and management of depression and minor problems. Sometimes they preferred the latter, and to divorce themselves from consultant community psychiatrists.

Nursing development units

Nursing development units (NDUs) had been established in the mid-1980s; in 1988 the King's Fund financed additional ones and established a programme to evaluate their work. NDUs were found mainly in clinical areas where caring and rehabilitation dominated, rather than in acute care, a decreasing part of the NHS. The central philosophy was nursing autonomy; nurses determined how work should be carried out and the methods to be adopted. Units aimed to monitor and evaluate the care given and develop nurses personally and professionally, while offering the best standards of (nursing) care. NDU mission statements savoured of motherhood and apple pie; a statement that everyone is a worthwhile individual whose beliefs need to be respected, and who is naturally creative and effective, is laudable but is not a definition of specific aims. The literature contained much material on the interrelationship and personal development of nurses, less about the details of the nursing therapy patients received, and virtually nothing about the role of doctors.[338] Some units combined staff development with 'reflective nursing'.[339]

Nursing administration

In 1948 sisters led the ward teams, closely aware of patients' progress and the detailed care they received. Matrons, and superintendents in the community, considered the effects on nursing of changes in medicine and management. It was now difficult to see where professional leadership lay; the very concept was open to question. If it existed, it centred on philosophers and educationalists, not experienced and active clinical nurses. Organisational changes had eliminated many middle management posts in nursing, making it harder for nurses to move into it from clinical work. Nursing management was now often in the hands of managers who might come from any of a number of disciplines. Management wanted a flexible workforce, able to accept new roles, explore the interface between medicine and nursing, and to monitor the health care assistants who often provided basic care. Many senior nurses went into posts concerned with quality; some obtained business qualifications and returned to the NHS as unit business managers. Changes in the composition of trust boards reduced the nursing voice at a senior level although sometimes academic nurses might fill the gap. Nursing tried to adapt to the NHS reforms, *Caring for people*, *The health of the nation*, the Children Act (1989) and *The patient's charter*. Application of the jargon of management – targets, visions, missions and performance indicators – did not work well. Rather than concentrating on the bedside, senior nurses tried to reflect government priorities. Some trust reports lacked data, and made up in length what they lacked in meaning.[340] Centrally, attempts were made to develop a strategy of nursing for nurses.[341] The starting point was a rephrasing of the first section of Virginia Henderson's definition of nursing.[342]

> The philosophical basis of nursing, midwifery and health visiting is concerned with enabling the individual, whether adult or child, and his/her family to achieve and maintain their optimal physical, psychological and social well being when that individual or his/her carers cannot achieve this unaided.

An attempt was made to identify the challenges facing nursing and midwifery. Nurses 'must look for where they can properly take a lead, not settle into a secondary role . . . to advance confidently nurses need to consider who they are and what they want to be.' There was, however, no clear path ahead. Nursing was slanted towards health promotion and needs assessment rather than curative medicine.[343] The nursing profession seemed to want to take the lead in the improvement of public health, rather than to work in partnership with doctors in medical care. The professions of medicine and nursing remained curiously apart; if nurses were becoming less enthusiastic about curative medicine, who would take their place? If the electronics technician and the engineer took over high-tech tasks, perhaps the nurse would once again be increasingly concerned with personal care, like her medieval predecessor.[344] In the past, nursing's acceptance of medical leadership in the NHS had the advantage that with it came medicine's protection. Having opted for professional autonomy, nursing now had to fight its battles alone. The concentration on higher education and the distraction of high-status professionalism left nursing dangerously exposed.[345]

The condition of the NHS

In the fifth decade the health service was redefined in terms of what would be provided and how the provision was to be organised. Primary care was stronger than it ever had been, ensuring ease of access. Technological progress and an international research base had transformed the hospitals. Managed care was introduced. But basic problems of rationing care persisted. Cash limits on purchasing authorities and the continual pressure of efficiency savings limited the work that providers could do. By 1997,

---

Some tools of 'managed care'

Managing demand
Capitation
Gatekeepers
Advice lines to patients
User fees
Consumer education.

Medical management
Review of use
Disease management
Greater use of guidelines

Care delivery
Telemedicine
Greater use of non-doctors

Source: Smith R: *BMJ* 1997; 314: 1495

---

although special programmes had greatly reduced the number of patients who waited more than a year for admission, waiting lists in general were lengthening, services were being cut and operations were being postponed nation-wide because purchasers had run out of money. Consultants warned that during the winter months the NHS might be reduced to treating emergencies only, if under-funding was not remedied. The NHS was facing its worst financial crisis for a decade and was heading for financial meltdown.[346] The reforms of the 1990s had not solved the basic NHS dilemma outlined by Powell in the 1960s, to which neither political party, nor indeed any other country, had an answer.

The NHS: a service with ambitions[347]

The principles on which the NHS is built
Universal population coverage
High-quality care
Available on the basis of clinical need
Responsive to the needs and wishes of patients and carers

Strategic objectives
A well-informed public
A seamless service
Knowledge-based decision-making
A highly trained and skilled workforce
A responsive service

As the decade drew to its end, and the majority of the Conservative government dwindled, the commitment to the NHS was reaffirmed in a White Paper, *A service with ambitions*.[347] The NHS must continue to be there when we needed it. Doubts about the viability of the NHS were nothing new, but the government believed that throughout its history the NHS had found ways of accommodating to the pressures upon it. Others were less certain. The new Labour government, elected in May 1997 with a landslide majority, sought to move the NHS in new directions. It placed greater emphasis on public health, appointing the first ever Minister for Public Health (Tessa Jowell) and undertaking a review of inequalities in health with the assistance of the former CMO, Sir Donald Acheson. It also announced a commitment to end all forms of tobacco advertising. As regards NHS organisation, the new government said it would end the internal market which its predecessors had created. The distribution between purchasing (or commissioning) health care and providing it would be retained; but GP fundholding would be phased out and simplified arrangements developed to replace the internal market's contracting system. An emphasis would be placed on co-operation and public service rather than competition. The new government also placed great emphasis on improving the effectiveness of the relationships between the NHS and the local authority social services, perhaps by setting up a Royal Commission on Long Term Care to promote this, and embarked on a further programme of legislation and organisational change, the outcome of which was far from clear. There would be fewer authorities and trusts, more local involvement in services, and action zones to improve their integration. Facing the financial problems of its predecessors, a further review of health service financing was begun.

References

1. Ritchie K. *Marketing to generation X*. New York: Simon and Schuster, 1995.
2. Smith T. New Year's message. *BMJ* 1988; 296: 1–2.
3. Nairne P. The NHS: reflections on a changing service. *BMJ* 1988; 296: 1518–20.
4. Duncan N. Light the blue touchpaper and stand well clear. *BMJ* 1996; 313: 432.
5. Morrison I, Smith R. The future of medicine. *BMJ* 1994; 309: 1099–100.
6. New life, new questions. *The Times* 1996; Aug 13.
7. Monopolies and Mergers Commission. *Services of medical practitioners – a report on the supply of services of registered medical practitioners in relation to restrictions on advertising*. Cm 582. London: HMSO, 1989.
   Havard J. Competition among doctors. *BMJ* 1989; 299: 406–7.
8. Griffiths Sir Roy. *Community care: an agenda for action*. Report. London: HMSO, 1988.
9. Mant D, Fowler F. Mass screening: theory and ethics. *BMJ* 1990; 300: 916–18.
10. Leder S, Gliksman M. Prospects for preventing heart disease. *BMJ* 1990; 301: 1004–5.
    Ashton J. Sanitarian becomes ecologist: the new environmental health. *BMJ* 1991; 302: 189–90.
11. Smith GD. Income inequality and mortality: why are they related? *BMJ* 1996; 312: 987–8.
    Watt GCM. All together now: why social deprivation matters to everyone. *BMJ* 1996; 312: 1026–9.
    The Ljubljana Charter on reforming health care. *BMJ* 1996; 312: 1664–5.
    Richards T. European health policy: must redefine its *raison d'être*. *BMJ* 1996; 312: 1622–3.
12. Smith A, Jacobson B, editors. *The nation's health: a strategy for the 1990s*. London: King's Fund, 1988.
13. *UK levels of health*. First Working Party Report. (Chair: WW Holland.) London: Faculty of Public Health Medicine of the Royal Colleges of Physicians, 1991.
14. Department of Health. *Public health in England*. Cm 289. London: HMSO, 1988.
15. Department of Health. *The health of the nation*. Cm 1986. London: HMSO, 1992.
16. Department of Health. *The health of the nation: one year on*. London: HMSO, 1993.
17. Radical Statistics Health Group. Missing: a strategy for health. *BMJ* 1991; 303: 299–302.
18. Health of the nation could be better. *BMJ* 1996; 313: 382.
19. Department of Health. *Variations in health*. London: DoH, 1996.
20. Brave new world. [leading article] *Health Service Journal* 1997; July 10: 15.
    Warden J. Public health strategy will tackle inequality in England. *BMJ* 1997; 315: 75.
    The Times 1995; Apr 25.
21. Weatherall DJ. The inhumanity of medicine. *BMJ* 1994; 309: 1671–2.
22. Bruster S, Jarman B, Bosanquet N et al. National survey of hospital patients. *BMJ* 1994; 309: 1542–9.
23. Dubovsky SL. Coping with entitlement in medical education. *New England Journal of Medicine* 1986; 315: 1672–4.
24. General Medical Council. *Duties of a doctor: filming patients for television programmes*. London: GMC, 1995.
25. Thomas KJ, Carr J, Westlake L, Williams BT. Use of non-orthodox and conventional health care in Great Britain. *BMJ* 1991; 302: 207–10.
26. Smith I. Complementary medicine. *Health Service Journal* 1996; Jan 25: 24–5.
27. British Medical Association. *Complementary medicine: new approaches to good practice*. London: BMA, 1993.
    Smith I. Commissioning complementary medicine. *BMJ* 1995; 310: 115–16.
28. Wennberg JE, editor. *Dartmouth atlas of health care in the United States*. Chicago: American Hospital Publishing, 1996.
29. Jennett B. Health technology assessment. *BMJ* 1992; 305: 67–8.
30. Smith R. The scientific basis of health services. *BMJ* 1995; 311: 961–2.

31. Godlee F. Research and development in the NHS. *BMJ* 1991; 303: 738–9.
32. Campling EA, Devlin HB, Hoile RW, Lunn JN, editors. *Report of the national confidential enquiry into perioperative deaths, 1992–3.* London: NCEPOD, 1995.
33. Evidence based medicine [editorial]. *BMJ* 1995; 310: 1085–6.
    Sackett DL, Rosenberg WMC. The need for evidence based medicine. *Journal of the Royal Society of Medicine* 1995; 88: 620–4.
    Thompson R, Lavender M, Madhok R. How to ensure that guidelines are effective. *BMJ* 1995; 311: 257–42.
    Sackett DL, Rosenberg WMC, Muir Gray JA et al. Evidence based medicine: what it is and what it isn't. *BMJ* 1996; 312: 71–2.
34. On not knowing about the everyday [editor's choice]. *BMJ* 1996; 313: before 1271.
35. NHS Management Executive. *Improving clinical effectiveness.* EL(93)(115). Leeds: NHSME, 1993.
36. Hayward J. Purchasing clinically effective care. *BMJ* 1994; 309: 823–4.
    NHS Management Executive. *Improving clinical effectiveness.* EL(93)(115). Leeds: NHSME, 1993.
37. Walshe K, Ham C. Who's acting on the evidence? *Health Service Journal* 1997; Apr 3: 22–5.
    West E, Newton J. Clinical guidelines. *BMJ* 1997; 315: 324.
38. Godlee F. The Cochrane Collaboration. *BMJ* 1994; 309: 969–70.
39. Department of Health. *Standing group on health technology: 1994 report.* London: DoH, 1994.
40. Taylor D. Quality and professionalism in health care: a review of current initiatives in the NHS. *BMJ* 1996; 312: 626–9.
    Irvine D, Donaldson L. Quality and standards in health care. *Proceedings of the Royal Society of Edinburgh* 1993; 101B: 1–30.
41. Berwick DM. Sounding board: continuous improvement as an ideal in health care. *New England Journal of Medicine* 1989; 320: 53–6.
    Berwick DM, Enthoven A, Bunker JP. Quality management in the NHS: the doctor's role. *BMJ* 1992; 304: 235–9.
42. Accrediting hospitals [editorial]. *BMJ* 1995; 310: 755–6.
43. Brooks T, editor. *The King's Fund organisational audit information pack.* London: King's Fund, 1995.
44. McKeown T. *The role of medicine: dream, mirage or nemesis.* London: Nuffield Provincial Hospitals Trust, 1976.
45. Bunker JF, Frazier HS, Mosteller F. Improving health: measuring effects of medical care. *Milbank Quarterly* 1994; 72: 225–58.
    Bunker JF. Medical care does add to life expectancy. *BMJ* 1994; 309: 1657.
    Appleby J. What's the NHS ever done for us? *Health Service Journal* 1995; May 11: 28–9.
46. Holland WW, Fitzgerald AP, Hildrey SJ, Phillips SJ. Heaven can wait. *Journal of Public Health Medicine* 1994; 16: 321–330.
47. Committee of Inquiry: Pharmacy. *A report to the Nuffield Foundation.* London: Nuffield Foundation, 1986.
48. Blenkinsopp A, Bradley C. Patients, society and the increase in self medication. *BMJ* 1996; 312: 629–32.
49. Mergers in the drug industry. *BMJ* 1989; 299: 813–14.
50. Bryan J. Can more be less? *Health Service Journal* 1997; May 1: 26–7.
51. Lilley R. Scrap GPs, bring on Florence Nightingale. *Sunday Times* 1996; Jan 7.
52. Weatherall D. Tomorrow's biotechnology. *BMJ* 1991; 303: 1282–3.
53. Ahmad S. Goodbye serendipity, hello big bytes. *Investors Chronicle* 1995; Dec 15.
54. Cotes PM. Erythropoietin: the developing story. *BMJ* 1988; 296: 805.

55. Taylor D. Centoxin – birth of a budget buster. *BMJ* 1991; 302: 1229.

56. Wood MJ. More macrolides. *BMJ* 1991; 303: 594–5.

57. Pillay D, Geddes AM. Antiviral drug resistance. *BMJ* 1996; 313: 503–4.

58. Orme M. Aspirin all round? *BMJ* 1988; 296: 307–8.

59. Byrne CD, Wild SH. Lipids and secondary prevention of ischaemic heart disease. *BMJ* 1996; 313: 1273–4.

60. Colin-Jones DG. Acid suppression: how much is needed? *BMJ* 1990; 301: 564–5.

61. Axon AR. Duodenal ulcer: the villain unmasked? *BMJ* 1991; 302: 919–20.
    Marshall's hunch. *The New Yorker* 1993; Sep 20.
    Savarino V, Vigneri S. How should we decide on the best regimen for eradicating *Helicobacter pylori*? *BMJ* 1995; 311: 581–2.

62 Kelly CA, Harvey RJ, Cayton H. Drug treatment for Alzheimer's disease. *BMJ* 1997; 314: 693–4.

63. Fitzpatrick MF, Mackay T, Driver H, Douglas NJ. Salmeterol in nocturnal asthma. *BMJ* 1990; 301: 1365–8.

64. Guillebaud J. Advising women on which pill to take. *BMJ* 1995; 311: 1111–12.

65. Melatonin mania. *Newsweek* 1995; Nov 6: 60–3.
    Arendt J. Melatonin. *BMJ* 1996; 312: 1242–3.

66. Wyatt J, Walton R. Computer based prescribing. *BMJ* 1995; 311: 1181–2.

67. Dawood RM. Radiology about to go digital. *BMJ* 1989; 299: 340–1.

68. Department of Health. *On the state of the public health*. Report of the CMO 1988. London: HMSO, 1989.

69. Health Departments. Salisbury DM, Begg NT, editors. *Immunisation against infectious disease*. London: HMSO, 1996.

70. Centre for Disease Control. Emerging Infectious Diseases. 1995; 1, 3.

71. Tauxe RV, Hughes JM. International investigation of outbreaks of foodborne disease. *BMJ* 1996; 313: 1093–4.

72. Sharp JCM. Salmonellosis and eggs. *BMJ* 1988; 297: 1557–8.

73. O'Mahony M, Mitchell E, Gilbert RJ. An outbreak of foodborne botulism associated with contaminated hazelnut yoghurt. *Epidemiol and Infect* 1990; 104: 389–95.

74. Christie B. *E. coli* infection calls for stricter laws on selling meat. *BMJ* 1997; 314: 249.

75. Holt TA, Phillips J. Bovine spongiform encephalopathy. *BMJ* 1988; 296: 1581–2.

76. Almond JW, Brown P, Gure SM et al. Creutzfeldt–Jakob disease and bovine spongiform encephalopathy. A series of reviews. *BMJ* 1995; 311: 1415–22.
    The Times 1996; Mar 21.
    Brown P. Bovine spongiform encephalopathy and Creutzfeldt–Jakob disease. *BMJ* 1996; 312: 790–1 and 795.
    Brown C. Meat is murder for DoH. *Doctor* 1996; Apr 4

77. BBC TV. *Panorama* 1995; Jan 16.
    Department of Health. CMO Letter: CMO (95)1. 1995; Apr 3.

78. Ebola virus outbreak kills 170 in Zaire. *The Times* 1995; May 12.
    Bennett D, Brown D. Ebola virus. *BMJ* 1995; 310: 1344–5.

79. Catchpole MA. Sexually transmitted diseases in England: 1981–90. *CDR Review* 1992; 2: R1–7.

80. Catchpole MA. The role of epidemiology and surveillance systems in the control of sexually transmitted disease. *Genitourinary Medicine* 1996; 72: 321–9

81. The incidence and prevalence of AIDS. *CDR Review* 1996; 6: January

82. Anderson J. AIDS in Thailand. *BMJ* 1990; 300: 415–16.

83. Jeffries DJ. Doctors, patients, and HIV. *BMJ* 1992; 304: 1258–9.

84. Spence C. To the Lighthouse. *Health Service Journal* 1996; Aug 8: 24–5.

85. Berridge V. Crisis what crisis? *Health Service Journal* 1996; Aug 8: 20–3.

86. Johnson AM, DeCock KM. What's happening to AIDS? *BMJ* 1994; 309: 1523–4.
Breckenridge A. Clinical pharmacology and therapeutics. *BMJ* 1995; 310: 377–80.
Pinching AF. Managing HIV disease after Delta. *BMJ* 1996; 312: 521–2.
Delta Co-ordinating Committee. Delta: a double-blind controlled trial. *Lancet* 1996; 348, 283–91.

87. Yates JRW. Medical genetics. *BMJ* 1996; 312: 1021–5.

88. Campbell H, MacKay J, Porteous M. The future of breast and ovarian cancer clinics: no longer just research, now a clinical need. *BMJ* 1995; 311: 1584–5.

89. Clarke A. Population screening for genetic susceptibility to disease. *BMJ* 1995; 311: 35–8.
Harris R, Harris HJ. Primary care for patients at genetic risk. *BMJ* 1995; 311: 579–80.

90. Chadda D. Experts seething over government rejection of genetics commission. *Health Service Journal* 1996; Jan 18: 5.

91. Hodson ME. Managing adults with cystic fibrosis. *BMJ* 1989; 298: 471–2.

92. Savill J. Molecular genetic approaches to understanding disease. *BMJ* 1997; 314: 126–9

93. Royal College of Surgeons. *Guidelines for day case surgery.* London: RCS, 1992.

94. Wastell C. Laparoscopic cholecystectomy. *BMJ* 1991; 302: 303–4.

95. Downs SH, Black NA et al. A systematic review of the effectiveness and safety of laparoscopic cholecystectomy. *Annals of the Royal College of Surgeons of England* 1996; 78, no. 3 part 2: 241–323.
Baxter JN, O'Dwyer PJ. Laparoscopic or minilaparotomy cholecystectomy. *BMJ* 1992; 304: 559–60.

96. Royal College of Obstetricians and Gynaecologists. *Report of the working party on training in gynaecological endoscopic surgery.* London: RCOG, 1994.

97. Noble J, Chilton R. Total knee replacement. *BMJ* 1991; 303: 262.

98. Sochart DH, Long AJ, Porter ML. Joint responsibility: the need for a national arthroplasty register. *BMJ* 1996; 313: 66–7.

99. Villar RN. Failed hip replacement. *BMJ* 1992; 304: 3–4.

100. Deyom RA. Acute back pain: a new paradigm for management. *BMJ* 1996; 313: 1343–4.

101. Bulstrode CJK. Recent advances in orthopaedic and trauma surgery. *BMJ* 1995; 310: 917–19.

102. Royal College of Surgeons. *Report of the working party on the management of patients with major injuries.* (Chairman: M Irving.) London: RCS, 1988.

103. Delamothe T. Here come the helicopters. *BMJ* 1989; 299: 639.

104. Nicholl JP, Brazier JE, Snooks HA. Effects of London helicopter emergency medical service on survival after trauma. *BMJ* 1995; 311: 217–22.

105. Petch MC. Who needs dual chamber pacing? *BMJ* 1993; 307: 215–16.

106. Swales JD. First line treatment in hypertension. *BMJ* 1990; 301: 1172–3.

107. Julian DG, Pentecost BL, Chamberlain DA. A milestone for myocardial infarction. *BMJ* 1988; 297: 407–8.
Mayor S. Angioplasty shows no benefit over thrombolysis. *BMJ* 1996; 313: 1102.
Brown N, Young T, Gray D et al. Inpatient deaths from myocardial infarction 1982–92. *BMJ* 1997; 315: 159–164.

108. Rihal CS, Yusuf S. Chronic coronary artery disease: drugs, angioplasty, or surgery? *BMJ* 1996; 312: 265–6.

109. Treasure T. Cardiac surgery in the Dunkirk spirit. *BMJ* 1995; 311: 1648.

110. Treasure T. Recent advances: cardiac surgery. *BMJ* 1997; 315: 104–7

111. Millis JM, Thislethwaite JR. Transplantation. *JAMA* 1997; 277: 1902–3.

112. Brouse N, Goulet O. Small bowel transplantation. *BMJ* 1996; 312: 261–2.

113. Wing AJ. Can we meet the real need for dialysis and transplantation? *BMJ* 1990; 301: 885–6
Renal services in UK are underfunded, says report. *BMJ* 1996; 312: 267.

114. Appleby J. Erythropoietin: justifying its cost? *BMJ* 1991; 302: 434–5.
     Gabriel R. Picking up the tab for erythropoietin. *BMJ* 1991; 302: 248–9.
115. O'Neill D, Gregson R, McHugh D. Current uses of ophthalmic lasers. *BMJ* 1992; 304: 1161–5.
116. Towler MA, Lightman S. Recent advances in ophthalmology. *BMJ* 1996; 312: 889–92.
117. *Our vision for cancer*. London: Imperial Cancer Research Fund, 1995.
118. Horwich A. Radiotherapy update. *BMJ* 1992; 304: 1554–7.
119. Khwaja A, Goldstone AH. Haemopoietic growth factors. *BMJ* 1991; 302: 1164–5.
120. Rayter Z, Phipps RF. Primary medical treatment in breast cancer. *BMJ* 1991; 302: 2–3.
121 DHSS. *Breast cancer screening*. (Chairman: Sir P Forrest.) London: HMSO, 1986.
122. UK Association of Cancer Registries. Changes in the incidence of and mortality from breast cancer in England and Wales since the introduction of screening. *BMJ* 1995; 311: 1391–5.
123. Wright J, Barber Mueller C. Screening mammography and public health policy: the need for perspective. *Lancet* 1995; 346: 29–32.
124. Survival of patients with cancer [leading article]. *BMJ* 1989; 299: 1058–9.
125. Department of Health and Welsh Office. *A policy framework for commissioning cancer services. Guidance for purchasers and providers of cancer services*. London: HMSO, 1995.
     Department of Health. *A policy framework for commissioning cancer services*. (EL(96)15) London: Department of Health, 1996.
126. Department of Health. *On the state of the public health*. Report of the CMO for 1988. London: HMSO, 1989.
127. Gosden R, Rutherford A. Delayed childbearing. *BMJ* 1995; 311: 1585.
128. Steer P. Obstetrics. *BMJ* 1995; 311: 1209–12.
129. Lomas J. Holding back the tide of caesareans. *BMJ* 1988; 297: 569–70.
130. House of Commons. Health Committee. *Maternity services. Session 1991/2*. (Chairman: N Winterton.) London: HMSO, 1992.
     Warden J. Maternity landmark. *BMJ* 1992; 304: 662.
     Home truths about maternity services. *BMJ* 1992; 304: 657.
131. Department of Health. *Changing childbirth. Part 1*. Report of the Expert Maternity Group. (Chairman: Baroness Cumberlege.) London: HMSO, 1993.
132. Springer NP, van Weel C. Home birth. *BMJ* 1996; 313: 1276–7.
133. Sikorski J, Wilson J, Clements S et al. A randomised controlled trial comparing two schedules of antenatal visits. *BMJ* 1996; 312: 546–53.
134. Committee of Enquiry into Human Fertilisation and Embryology. *Report*. (Chairman: Dame Mary Warnock.) Cm 9314. London: HMSO, 1984.
135. Human Fertilisation and Embryology Authority. *Annual Reports*. 1992/3/4/5. London: HFEA, 1992–5.
136. Berkowitz RL. From twin to singleton. *BMJ* 1996; 313: 373–4.
137. Toozs-Hobson P, Cardozo L. Hormone replacement for all? Universal prescription is desirable. *BMJ* 1996; 313: 350–1.
138. Daly E, Vessey MP, Hawkins MM et al. Risk of venous thromboembolism in users of hormone replacment therapy. *Lancet* 1996; 348, 977–80.
     Jick H, Derby LE, Myers MW et al. Risk of hospital admission for idiopathic venous thromboembolism among users of postmenopausal oestrogens. *Lancet* 1996; 348: 981–3.
     Grodstein F, Stampfer MJ, Goldhaber SZ et al. Prospective study of exogenous hormones and risk of pulmonary embolism in women. *Lancet* 1996; 348: 983–7.
139. Issacs AJ, Britton AR, McPherson K. Utilisation of hormone replacement therapy by women doctors. *BMJ* 1995; 311: 1399–401
140. HRT study will follow fortunes of 30,000 women. *The Times* 1996; Nov 4.
141. Holmström G. Retinopathy of prematurity. *BMJ* 1993; 307: 694–5.

142. Tin W, Wariyar V, Hey E. Changing prognosis for babies less than 28 weeks' gestation, in the north of England between 1983 and 1994. *BMJ* 1997; 314: 107–11.

143. Pearn J. Recent advances in paediatrics. *BMJ* 1997; 314: 801–5

144. Williamson J, Stokoe IH, Gray S. Old people at home; their unreported needs. *Lancet* 1964; 1: 117–20.

145. Royal College of Physicians. *Ensuring equity and quality of care for elderly people.* London: RCP, 1994.

146. Grimley Evans J. Long-term care in later life. *BMJ* 1995; 311: 644.

147. Griffiths R. *Community care: agenda for action.* London: HMSO, 1988.
Local authorities should co-ordinate community care, says Griffiths [from the GMSC]. *BMJ* 1988; 296: 945.

148. Warden J. Griffiths lock, stock and barrel. *BMJ* 1989; 299: 146.

149. Department of Health. *NHS responsibilities for meeting continuing care needs.* HSG(95)8. London: DoH, 1995.
Saper R, Laing W. Age of uncertainty. *Health Service Journal* 1995; Oct 26: 22–3.

150. Eaton L. Long division. *Health Services Journal* 1995; Nov 30: 11.

151. Davidge M, Elias S et al. *Survey of English mental illness hospitals March 1993. Interauthority consultancy and comparisons.* Birmingham: University of Birmingham, 1993.
Thornicroft G, Strathdee G. How many psychiatric beds? *BMJ* 1994; 309: 970–1.

152. Department of Health. *Mental health: health of the nation key area handbook,* 2nd edn. London: HMSO, 1994.
Department of Health. *The spectrum of care: local services for people with mental health problems.* Mental Illness Key Area. London: DoH, 1996.

153. Coid JW. 'Difficult to place' psychiatric patients. *BMJ* 1991; 302: 603–4.

154. Mental Health Act Commission. *Sixth biennial report 1993–5.* London: HMSO, 1995.

155. Kendell RE. The future of Britain's mental hospitals. *BMJ* 1989; 299: 1237–8.

156. Care endangering the community. *Independent* 1995; Jan 17.

157. McCrystal C. Balancing act. *NHS Magazine* 1996; Winter: 10–11.

158. Harding Price J, Thompson IG. Letters to *The Times* 1995; Oct 2.

159. Improvements in mental health care called for. *BMJ* 1995; 311: 586.

160. Royal College of Psychiatrists. *Report of the confidential inquiry into homicides and suicides by mentally ill people.* London: RCPsych, 1996.
Inadequate care linked to homicides and suicides. *BMJ* 1996; 312: 140–1.

161. Ham C. Where now for the NHS reforms? *BMJ* 1994; 309: 351–2
The future of purchasing – tolerance of diversity will be necessary. *BMJ* 1994; 309: 1032–3.
Hadley TR, Goldman H. Effect of recent health and social service policy reforms on Britain's mental health system. *BMJ* 1995; 311: 1556–8.

162. Raphael B, Meldrum L, McFarlane A C. Does debriefing after psychological trauma work? *BMJ* 1995; 310: 1479–80.

163. Ehbrahim S. Changing patterns of consultation in general practice: fourth national morbidity study, 1991–1992. *British Journal of General Practice* 1995; 45: 283–4.

164. Gill P, Dowell AC, Neal RD et al. Evidence based general practice: a retrospective study of interventions in one training practice. *BMJ* 1996; 312: 819–21.

165. Parliament. *Promoting better health: the government's programme for improving primary health care.* Cm 249. London: HMSO, 1987.

166. Government's formidable firepower on GPs' contract. *BMJ* 1989; 299: 1068.

167. Department of Health. *On the state of the public health.* Report of the CMO for 1991. London: HMSO, 1992.

168. Baker R, Thompson J. Innovation in general practice: is the gap between training and non-training practices getting wider? *British Journal of General Practice* 1995; 45: 297–300.

169. Medical Practitioners' Union. *The future of primary care.* London: MPU, 1992.

170. Taylor DH, Leese B. Recruitment, retention and time commitment of general practitioners in England and Wales, 1990–1994. *BMJ* 1997; 314: 1806–10.
171. NHS Executive. *Primary care: the future.* London: NHS Executive, 1996.
172. Parliament. *Choice and opportunity. Primary care: the future.* Cm 3390. London: Stationery Office, 1996.
    Warden J. Government proposes new deal for family doctors. *BMJ* 1996; 313: 959.
    Crail M. Pilot light. *Health Service Journal* 1996; Oct 24: 10–11.
173. Pringle M, Heath I. Distributing primary care fairly. *BMJ* 1997; 314: 95–9.
    Kendrick T, Hilton S. Broadening team work in primary care. *BMJ* 1997; 314: 672–5.
174. Parliament. *Primary care: delivering the future.* Cm 3512. London: Stationery Office, 1996.
    Warden J. White Paper boost for primary care. *BMJ* 1997; 314: 7.
175. Beecham L. GPs demand a major review of their contracts and pay. *BMJ* 1997; 314: 625.
176. Warburton A. Back to the centre. *Health Service Journal* 1995; Sep 21, Special report: 1–4.
177. Nursing the hope of lighter GP workload. *Doctor* 1994; Dec 15.
178. Hasler J. The primary health care team. *BMJ* 1992; 305: 232–4.
179. Lilley R. Scrap GPs, bring on Florence Nightingale. *Sunday Times* 1996; Jan 7.
180. Lenehan C, Watts A. Are nurse-practitioners here to stay? *British Journal of General Practice* 1994; 44: 291–2.
181. Stilwell B, Greenfield S, Drury M, Hull FM. A nurse practitioner in general practice. *Journal of the Royal College of General Practitioners* 1987; 37: 154–7.
    Rivett GC. In: Salvage J, editor. *Nurse practitioners: working for change in primary health care.* London: King's Fund Centre, 1991
182. Touche Ross. Evaluation of nurse practitioner pilot projects. London: NHS Executive South Thames, 1994.
183. Coulter A. Shifting the balance from secondary to primary care. *BMJ* 1995; 311: 1447–8.
    NHS Management Executive. *Integrating primary and secondary care.* London: Department of Health, 1991.
    Hughes J, Gordon P. *An optimal balance?* London: King's Fund, 1992.
184. Royal College of General Practitioners. *The nature of general medical practice.* London: RCGP, 1996.
185. Keeley D. The future of general practice: personal care or the polyclinic. *BMJ* 1991; 302: 1514–16.
186. Tudor Hart J, Thomas C, Gibbons B et al. Twenty five years of case finding and audit in a socially deprived community. *BMJ* 199; 302: 1509–13.
187. Livingstone A, Widgery D. The new general practice: changing philosophies of primary care. *BMJ* 1990; 301: 708–10.
    Gibbons B, Groom H, Singer R. *What we do and the way we should do it.* London: MPU, 1996.
188. Fugelli P, Heath I. The nature of general practice. *BMJ* 1996; 312: 456–7.
    Moore A. The nature of general practice [letter]. *BMJ* 1996; 312: 1421–2.
189. Savage R, Armstrong D. Effect of a general practitioner's consulting style on patients' satisfaction. *BMJ* 1990; 301: 968–9.
190. Bosanquet N, Leese B. Family doctors and innovation in general practice. *BMJ* 1988; 296: 1576–80.
191. Leese B, Bosanquet N. Family doctors and change in practice strategy since 1986. *BMJ* 1995; 310: 705–8.
    Leese B, Bosanquet N. Changes in general practice and its effects on service provision in areas with different socioeconomic characteristics. *BMJ* 1995; 311: 546–55.
192. Marsh GN. *Efficient care in general practice.* Oxford: Oxford University Press, 1991.
193. Marsh GN, Daces ML. Establishing a minor illness nurse in a busy general practice. *BMJ* 1995; 310: 778–80.

194. Nicol F. Making reaccreditation meaningful. *British Journal of General Practice* 1995; 45: 321–4.
195. Richards T. Recertifying general practitioners. *BMJ* 1995; 310: 1348–9.
196. Audit Commission. *A prescription for improvement*. London: HMSO, 1994.
197. Maynard A, Bloor K. Introducing a market to the UK's national health service. *New England Journal of Medicine* 1996; 334: 604–7.
198. Warden J. Make or break year for NHS? *BMJ* 1988; 296: 302.
199. Warden J. The price of success. *BMJ* 1988; 296: 440.
     BBC2. *The New Jerusalem*. Nigel Lawson and Margaret Thatcher. July 1995.
     BBC2. *Safe with us*. 1996; Sep 8.
200. Smith T. A time to choose: either health insurance or higher taxes. *BMJ* 1989; 298: 1–2.
201. Thatcher M. *The Downing Street years*. London: HarperCollins, 1993, 606–16.
202. Warden J. Clarke's ringing testimony to the health service. *BMJ* 1989; 297: 1006.
203. Parliament. *Working for patients*. Cm 555. London: HMSO, 1989.
204. Plamping D. The new NHS. *BMJ* 1991; 302: 737–8.
205. Ham C. Where now for the NHS reforms. *BMJ* 1994; 309: 351–2.
206. Smith T. BMA rejects the Review but . . . *BMJ* 1989; 298: 1405–6.
207. Beecham L. No more trusts and fundholders please. *BMJ* 1991; 303: 152–3.
     Klein R. The NHS reforms revisited. *BMJ* 1996; 313: 504–5.
208. Grabham T. Divided we fall (yet again). *BMJ* 1994; 309: 1100–1.
209. Smith R. Words from the source: an interview with Alain Enthoven. *BMJ* 1989; 298: 1166–8
210. Timmins N. *The five giants: a biography of the welfare state*. London: HarperCollins, 1995.
     BBC2. *Safe with us*. 1996; Sep 8.
211. Black D. A view on NHS reforms. *Journal of the Royal College of Physicians* 1995; 29: 442–5.
     Keen H. The new apostasy. *BMJ* 1996; 313: 566.
212. Roberts J. Kenneth Clarke: hatchet man or remoulder? *BMJ* 1990; 301: 1383–6.
213. BBC2. *Safe with us*. 1996; Sep 8.
214. First NHS trusts announced. *BMJ* 1990; 301: 1347–8.
215. Rosen R, McKee M. Short termism in the NHS. *BMJ* 1995; 311: 703–4.
216. Warden J. The manager is king. *BMJ* 1991; 302: 1298.
217. Pain in the health factory. *Financial Times* 1995; Aug 12.
218. No case yet for extending RMI [from the CCSC]. *BMJ* 1989; 299: 984.
     Freeman Hospital: countdown to self government. *BMJ* 1991; 302: 580–2.
219. Ghodse B. Extracontractual referrals: safety valve or administrative paper chase? *BMJ* 1995; 310: 1573–6.
220. NHS chiefs' performance pay soars. *Sunday Times* 1995; Aug 20.
221. Dorrell S. Letter to *HSJ*. *Health Service Journal* 1996; Jan 18: 20.
222. Dix A. Do the logomotion. *Health Service Journal* 1995; Aug 17: 20–2.
223. Cohen P. Robbing Peter to pay Paul. *Health Service Journal* 1994; Sep 15: 16.
224. Maynard A. Performance incentives in general practice. In: Teeling Smith G, editor. *Health, education and general practice*. London: Office of Health Economics, 1985.
     Teeling Smith G, editor. *A new NHS Act for 1996? Some issues for discussion: the GP as a 'budget holder'*. London: Office of Health Economics, 1986.
225. Maynard A, Marinker M, Gray DP. The doctor, the patient, and their contract. III. Alternative contracts; are they viable? *BMJ* 1986; 292, 1438–40.
226. Rayner B, Rivett GC. Report on a visit to HMOs in the USA. Internal Department of Health paper. 1985.
227. Ford JC. General practice fundholders. *BMJ* 1990; 300: 1027–8.
228. Appleby J. Fundholding. *Health Service Journal* 1994; Aug 11: 32–3.
229. Fundholding GPs winning the battle for London? *Pulse* 1994; Sep 17: 34.

230. Bailey J. The Special Branch. *Health Service Journal* 1994; Jul 28: 30–1.

231. NHS Executive. *Developing NHS purchasing and GP fundholding. Towards a primary care-led NHS.* EL(94)79. Leeds. NHSE, 1994.

232. Shapiro H. GP commissioning. *Health Service Journal* 1996; Jun 27: 28–31.
Ham C. A primary care market. *BMJ* 1996; 313: 127–8.
GP lobbies unite to fight their corner. *Health Service Journal* 1996; Oct 3: 6.

233. Glennerster H, Matsaganis M, Owens R, Hancock S. GP fundholding: wild card or winning hand? In: Robinson R, Le Grand J, editors. *Evaluating the NHS reforms.* King's Fund Institute/Hermitage, 1994, 74–107.
Ham C, Shapiro J. The future of fundholding. *BMJ* 1995; 310: 1150–1.
Dixon J, Glennerster H. What do we know about fundholding in general practice? *BMJ* 1995; 311: 727–30.
Stewart-Brown S, Gillam S, Jewell T. The problems of fundholding. *BMJ* 1996; 312: 1311–12.
Audit Commission. *Fundholding: what the doctor ordered.* London: Audit Commission, 1996.

234. New Year, New Labours. *The Times* 1996; Dec 31.
Timmins N. Labour's unhealthy prescription. *Financial Times* 1997; July 19, 9.

235. Berwick DM. Sounding board. Continuous improvement as an ideal in health care. *New England Journal of Medicine* 1989; 320(1): 53–6.

236. Houghton G, Sproston B. MAAGic powers. *Health Service Journal* 1995; Jul 27: 28–9.

237. Marinker M, editor. *Medical audit and general practice.* London: MSD Foundation/BMJ, 1990.

238. Teasdale S. The future of clinical audit: learning to work together. *BMJ* 1996; 313: 574.

239. Moore W. Time waits for no manager. *Health Service Journal* 1996; Feb 8: 15.

240. Warden J. Reform begets reform. *BMJ* 1992; 304: 466.
English Sir Terence. Letter to *The Times* 1994; Aug 4.

241. Abel-Smith B, Glennerster H. Labour and the Tory health reforms. *Fabian Review* 1995; 107, June.

242. Smith J. The bottom line is a moral one. *BMJ* 1995; 309: 789.
The Times 1995; Jul 4.

243. Yates J. BMA should look at inequalities in the NHS. *BMJ* 1996; 312: 913.

244. Bottomley V. National health, local dynamic. *Independent* 1994; Aug 22.

245. Ham C, Shapiro J. The future of fundholding. *BMJ* 1995; 310: 1150–1.

246. Thornton S. After the storm. *Health Service Journal* 1994; Oct 6: 24–6.

247. Ham C. Contestability: a middle path for health care. *BMJ* 1996; 312: 70–1.

248. Klein R. Labour's health policy marks a retreat from ideology. *BMJ* 1995; 311: 75–6.

249. Warden J. Peace formula on clinical standards. *BMJ* 1990; 300: 1610.

250. Ham C. What future for regions? *BMJ* 1992; 305: 130–1.

251. Dawe V. More trust mergers on the cards. *BMJ* 1996; 313: 773.
Merton, Sutton and Wandsworth Health Authority. *Commissioning intentions 1997/8.*

252. Parliament. *Choice and opportunity. Primary care: the future.* Cm 3390. London: Stationery Office, 1996.
Meads G, Wilkin D. Legislation of primary importance. *Health Service Journal* 1996; Oct 24: 19.

253. BBC2. *Safe with us.* 1996; Sep 15.

254. Adams CBT. OxDONS syndrome: the inevitable disease of the NHS reforms. *BMJ* 1995; 311: 1559–61.

255. Audit Commission. *Lying in wait: the use of medical beds in acute hospitals.* London: HMSO, 1993.

256. Millar B. Warwickshire trust mergers. *Health Service Journal* 1997; Mar 6: 11

257. Royal College of Physicians. *The future patterns of care by general and specialist physicians.* London: RCP, 1996.

258. Royal College of Surgeons. The provision of emergency surgical services: an organisational framework. London: RCS, 1997.

259. BBC1. Medicine's missing millions. *Panorama.* 1997; Jan 6.

260. Morris-Thompson T. Once and for all. *Health Service Journal* 1996; Aug 15: 28–9.

261. Lawrence M, Williams T. Managed care and disease management in the NHS. *BMJ* 1996; 313: 125–6.

262. Rational rationing. *The Times* 1994; Jul 29.
    Smith R. Rationing health care: moving the debate forward. *BMJ* 1996; 312: 1553–4.
    New B. The rationing agenda in the NHS. *BMJ* 1996; 312: 1593–601.

263. Department of Health and Social Security. *Priorities for health and personal social services in England.* London: HMSO, 1976.

264. Maynard A. Developing the health care market. *Economic Journal* 1991; 101: 1277–86.

265. Rationing needs a rational policy [opinion]. *Health Service Journal* 1995; Mar 16: 17.

266. The kid who conquered cancer – and the NHS: child B. *Sunday Times* 1995; Oct 29.

267. Rational rationing. *The Times* 1995; Oct 27.

268. Bion J. Rationing intensive care. *BMJ* 1995; 310: 682–3.

269. Bihari DJ. Care and computers [letter]. *The Times* 1994; Sep 5.

270. Smith R. Rationing: the debate we have to have. *BMJ* 1995; 310: 686.

271. Klein R. Priorities and rationing: pragmatism or principles. *BMJ* 1995; 311: 761–2.
    Maynard A. Rationing health care. *BMJ* 1996; 313: 1499.

272. Honigsbaum F. *Who shall live? Who shall die?* London: King's Fund College, 1991.
    Oregon Health Service Commission. *The 1991 prioritisation of health services.* Oregon: OHSC, 1991, 40.
    Bride GM. Oregon revises health care priorities. *BMJ* 1991; 302: 549.
    Dixon J, Welch HG. Priority setting: lessons from Oregon. *Lancet* 1991; 337, 891–4.

273. Neuberger J. Last but not least. *Health Service Journal* 1995; Nov 16: 23.

274. Dorrell S. Speech to the Conservative Medical Society. 1995; Sep 28.
    Dorrell S. The Millennium lecture. Manchester Business School, 1996.
    Warden J. Healthcare analysis cuts no ice in Whitehall. *BMJ* 1995; 311: 898.

275. Leader and letters.*The Times* 1995; Sep 19.
    Royal College of Physicians. *Setting priorities in the NHS: a framework for decision making.* London: RCP, 1995.
    'Dear Mr Dobson.' [Open letter] *BMJ* 1997; 317: 147.

276. Dix A. Blowing in the wind. *Health Service Journal* 1995; Sep 7: 10.

277. Dix A. Planning blight. *Health Service Journal* 1995; Nov 2: 10.

278. NHS Executive. *Capital investment manual.* London: HMSO, 1994.

279. Millar B. The big push. *Health Service Journal* 1995; Feb 2: 14.

280. Boyle S. The private finance initiative. *BMJ* 1997; 314: 1214–15.

281. Ham C. Private finance, public risk. *BMJ* 1995; 311: 1450.
    Ham C. Profiting from the NHS. *BMJ* 1995; 310: 415–16.
    Private finance initiative [special report]. *Health Service Journal* 1996; Feb 15.

282. Cervi B.Flexible friends [special report]. *Health Service Journal* 1997; Feb 27: 5.

283. Cross M. Numerical control. *Health Service Journal* 1996; Jan 25: suppl 5–8.

284. Cross M. Will the NHS get wired? *Health Service Journal* 1995; Sep 14: 24–5.

285. One London success story. *BMJ* 1993; 306: 882.
    Smith J. Merging hospitals can benefit everybody. *BMJ* 1996; 312: 144.

286. King Edward's Hospital Fund for London. *London Health 2010 – the report of the King's Fund London Initiative.* London: King's Fund, 1992.
    Beardshaw V. London's health services. *BMJ* 1991; 303: 939–40.

287. *The Times* 1992; Jun 24.

Top hospitals face axe. *Daily Telegraph* 1992; Jun 22.

288. Department of Health. *Report of the inquiry into London's health service, medical education and research.* (Chairman: Sir Bernard Tomlinson.) London: HMSO, 1992.
    Thoughts crystallise on Tomlinson. *BMJ* 1992; 305: 1456.

289. Beardshaw V, Gordon P, Plamping D. Primary care development zones. *BMJ* 1993; 306: 323–5.

290. Crail M. The view from the bridge [news focus]. *Health Service Journal* 1994; Sep 8: 13.
    Snell J. Three years after Tomlinson. *Health Service Journal* 1995; Oct 12: 22–4.
    Boyle S, editor. *The guide to health services in the capital.* London Monitor no. 3. London: King's Fund, 1996.

291. Department of Health. *Making London better.* London: DoH, 1993.

292. London Implementation Group. *Report of the cardiac specialty review group.* London: HMSO, 1993.

293. Review Advisory Committee. *Review of the research and development taking place in the London postgraduate special health authorities.* Report by the Review Advisory Committee. London: HMSO, 1993.
    London Implementation Group. *Cardiac services; Cancer services.* Reports of independent reviews of specialist services in London. London: HMSO, 1993.

294. Crail M. The standard bearer. *Health Service Journal* 1995; Mar 9: 12–13.

295. Lord Flowers. London's hospitals. *The Times* 1995; Apr 15.
    Tories survive revolt over hospital plans. *The Times* 1995; May 11.

296. What you really think of Golden Virginia. *Health Service Journal* 1995; Jul 13: 11.

297. Boyle S, editor. *The guide to health services in the capital.* London Monitor no. 3. London: King's Fund, 1996.

298. Our friends in the North *Health Service Journal,* 1996; Mar 21: 2.
    Scandals heaped high [opinion]. *Health Service Journal* 1997; Apr 3: 10–11, 15.

299. Lock S. Lessons from the Pearce affair: handling scientific fraud. *BMJ* 1995; 310: 1547–8.

300. Audit Commission. *The doctors' tale: the work of hospital doctors in England and Wales.* London: HMSO, 1995.
    Butler P. A sting in the tale [news focus]. *Health Service Journal* 1995; Mar 16: 11.

301. Need a doctor? Ring the agency. *The Times* 1996; Jun 9.

302. Audit Commission. *The doctors' tale: the work of hospital doctors in England and Wales.* London: HMSO, 1995.

303. NHS Management Executive. *Hours of work of doctors in training: the new deal.* (EL(91)82). London: NHSME, 1991.
    Department of Health. *On the state of the public health.* Annual report of the CMO for 1995. London: HMSO, 1996.

304. Department of Health. *Hospital doctors: training for the future: the report of the working group on specialist medical training.* (Chairman: Kenneth Calman.) London: DoH, 1993.

305. NHS Executive. *A guide to specialist registrar training.* Leeds. Department of Health, 1996.

306. Mather HM, Elkeles RC. Attitudes of consultant physicians to the Calman proposals. *BMJ* 1995; 311: 1060–2.

307. Royal College of Physicians. *The consultant physician: responding to change.* A report of the RCP. London: RCP, 1996.

308. Allen I. *Doctors and their careers.* London: PSI, 1994.
    Doctors are more miserable than ever. *BMJ* 1994; 309: 1529.
    Richards P, McManus C, Allen I. British doctors are not disappearing. *BMJ* 1997; 314: 1567.

309. Delamothe T. Nurses make the grade. *BMJ* 1988; 296: 1344.

310. Moore J. Letter to UKCC. London: Department of Health, 1988; May 20.
    Salvage J. Thumbs up from government for reform of nurse training. *BMJ* 1988; 296: 1553.

311. Clarke J. Nursing: an intellectual activity. *BMJ* 1991; 303: 376–7.

312. Lawson Nigella. Is it the end for nurses? *The Times* 1996; Dec 26.

313. North London College of Health Studies. *Student handbook*. London: NLCHS, 1994.

314. Elkan R, Robinson J. Project 2000: a review of published research. *Journal of Advanced Nursing* 1995; 22(2): 386–92.
    Mangan P. Wise up to the real world. *Nursing Times* 1996; Apr 17: 53.

315. English Nursing Board. *Project 2000: perceptions of the philosophy and practice of nursing*. London: ENB, 1996.

316. Salvage J. What's happening to nursing? *BMJ* 1995; 311: 274–5.

317. Atkins S, Murphy K. Reflection: a review of the literature. *Journal of Advanced Nursing* 1993; 18: 1188–92.

318. Wallace M. Preparing for the future. *Nursing Times* 1993; Aug 4: 42–4.

319. Review body for nursing staff, midwives, health visitors and professions allied to medicine. Evidence from the health departments, 1988 and 1990.
    Mark A. Ill-staffed by moonlight. *Health Service Journal* 1996; May 23: 17.

320. Buchan J. Nursing shortages. *BMJ* 1996; 312: 134–5.
    Bolton A. Nursing shortfall hits Britain. *BMJ* 1996; 312: 139.
    Nurses get airmiles for turning up. *Sunday Times* 1997; Aug 10.

321. Institute of Manpower Studies. *Nurses' work and worth*. Brighton. IMS, 1991.

322. One third of trained nurses quit NHS. *The Times* 1995; Aug 25.

323. Robinson J. Managed competition and the demise of nursing. In: *Britain's health system: from welfare state to managed markets*. New York. Faulkner and Gray, 1993.

324. *The future healthcare workforce*. (Chair: M Schofield.) Manchester: Manchester University Health Services Management Unit, 1996.

325. Nurses seek to lift ban on striking. *The Times* 1995; Apr 28.

326. The local nurse. *The Times* 1995; May 16.

327. Wright S. The named nurse, midwife and health visitor – principles and practice, 7–21. In: Wright S, editor. *The named nurse, midwife and health visitor*. London: Department of Health, 1993.

328. Audit Commission. *The virtue of patients: making the best use of ward nursing resources*. London: HMSO, 1991.

329. Hilton P, Goddard M. Taken to task. *Nursing Times* 1996; Apr 17: 44–5.

330. Price M. Looking for an answer. *BMJ* 1996; 312: 1165.
    Hancock C. Sisters doing it for themselves. *Health Service Journal* 1997; Oct 30: 2.

331. Kitson A. Does nursing have a future? *BMJ* 1996; 313: 1647–51.

332. UKCC. *Guidelines for professional practice*. London: UKCC, 1996.

333. Carlisle D. Mismanaged misdemeanours. *Health Service Journal* 1996; Oct 17: 13–14.

334. Peysner J. The nurse as a surgeon's first assistant. *Journal of the Medical and Dental Defence Unions* 1996; 11: 62–3.

335. Hopkins A, Solomon J, Abelson J. Shifting boundaries in professional care. *Journal of the Royal Society of Medicine* 1996; 89: 364–71.

336. Dowling S, Barrett S, West R. With nurse practitioners, who needs house officers? *BMJ* 1995; 311: 309–13.

337. English T. Medicine in the 1990s needs a team approach. *BMJ* 1997; 314: 661–3.

338. Salvage J, Wright S. *Nursing development units*. London: Scutari Press, 1995.

339. Palmer A, Burns S, Bulman C, editors. *Reflective practice in nursing*. Oxford: Blackwell Science, 1994.

340. Bromley Hospitals NHS Trust. *Nursing and Midwifery Annual Report 1994/5*.

341. NHS Management Executive. *A vision for the future*. Leeds. NHSME, 1993.
    UK Chief Nursing Officers. *The challenges for nursing and midwifery in the 21st century*. London: Department of Health, 1993.
    Department of Health. *Report of the consultation exercise*. London: DoH, 1995.

342. Smith JP. *Virginia Henderson: the first ninety years.* Harrow: Scutari Press. 1989.
Henderson V, Nite G. *Principles and practice of nursing.* New York: Macmillan, 1978.
343. Robinson J, Elkan R. *Health needs assessment.* London: Churchill Livingstone. 1996.
344. Hector W. Nursing in the UK. In: Walton J, Barondess JA, Lock S, editors. *The Oxford medical companion.* Oxford: Oxford University Press, 1994.
345. Casey N, Smith R. Bringing nurses and doctors closer together. *BMJ* 1997; 314: 617–18.
Salter B, Snee N. Power dressing. *Health Service Journal* 1997; Feb 13: 30–1.
346. Dixon J, Boyle S, Harrison A. Financial meltdown for the NHS? *BMJ* 1996; 312: 1432–3.
NHS consultants warn of dire cash crisis. *BMJ* 1996; 313: 964.
Cash crisis cripples the NHS. *Sunday Times* 1996; Nov 3.
Warden J. Review of NHS spending begins. *BMJ* 1997; 314: 1781.
347. Parliament. *The NHS: a service with ambitions.* Cm 3425. London: Stationery Office, 1996.
The vision thing [newsfocus]. *Health Service Journal* 1996; Nov 7: 12–13.
Ham C. The future of the NHS. *BMJ* 1996; 313: 1277–8.

Envoi

A perspective of 50 years

In 1948 Everest had not been climbed, food was rationed, people rode the city streets in trams and crossed the Atlantic in Cunarders. Since then there have been major changes in society – increased affluence, far wider car ownership, a desire for greater individuality and self-development, a loosening of discipline, authority and hierarchy, loss of both certainties and stability, and developments in the media and communications beyond imagination in 1948.

The pattern of health service in the minds of its founders owed much to Lord Dawson's report of 1920 and was already conceptually 25 years old when the NHS Act (1946) was passed. The NHS was the political creation of a particular epoch when, because of the experience of war, 'we were all neighbours' and used to a life organised with great purposes in mind. The underlying principle was that members of society were entitled to what they needed in health care and social support. Few other countries, outside the Eastern bloc, followed the same route. The Act created a hierarchical structure that could adapt to the growth of specialisation and clinical science. This structure avoided much of the duplication and the unnecessary expenditure characteristic of the competing hospitals, and the gaps that existed before 1948. Unusually, for such a vast organisation, most of the highest talent worked on the 'shop floor'. The NHS was created to solve problems of inequity, many of which could be remedied by better organisation without great expenditure. It dealt with a largely indigenous population that could still consider itself an island nation. As with many great ventures, things did not turn out as had been predicted.

What was not, and could not have been, foreseen was the impending rate of change in medical and allied sciences. In medicine more has happened since 1948 than in all the centuries back to Hippocrates. Countries do not stand in isolation; many developments are world-wide in their impact, for example the new drugs and the new technologies that have been introduced. Until they are listed, as many are in this book, it is hard to comprehend how great the advances have been. People rapidly come to accept advances as the normal order of affairs, and yesterday's revolution becomes today's routine.

Summarising the decades, from 1948 to 1957 the NHS had to develop its basic pattern of organisation, establish systems of governance and finance, and begin to move towards a rational and even spread of specialist services. Building materials were in short supply, the new service made do with outdated and inadequate buildings, and much attention was paid to hospital consultant staffing. Steadily rising costs created anxiety, and the Guillebaud Committee was established to examine the NHS and its expenditure. The Committee showed that in real terms expenditure was barely rising at all, but pointed out deficiencies requiring attention, among them services for the elderly and midwifery services.

By the second decade the NHS was taking shape and Britain was entering a period of economic growth. Attention turned to general practice, where morale was low and standards variable. The GPs' Charter of 1965 introduced a structural framework that made future development easier. Enoch Powell's Hospital Plan (1962) provided the basis for the creation of a national scheme of district general hospitals (DGHs).

Governments of both persuasions came to believe that more priority should be given to those who required protection, the chronic sick and the mentally ill. However, in the real world these 'Cinderella' specialties commonly took second place to the demands of acute medicine and surgery. It became policy to begin to transfer the care of the mentally ill from the asylum to the community, and a similar approach was adopted in respect of the mentally handicapped who had often been accommodated in large hospitals in the country, away from relatives and friends. This movement was accelerated by a series of scandals involving the care of these groups, as well as the 'frail chronic sick' many of whom were not, as yet, receiving active geriatric care.

The decade 1968–1977 was a time of transition. Economic growth was reduced in 1973 when the OPEC countries raised the price of oil. The ripple effects of the international recession gradually overtook the NHS and the medical schools. The Hospital Plan had to be cut back, although many new hospitals were now being built. In the UK, as in many countries, low-paid manual workers were increasingly dissatisfied, union power grew and industrial action became prevalent. General practice was, however, flourishing, partly as a result of the GPs' Charter, and medical technology was increasing. Nevertheless, money had to be found to deal with problems in the long-stay sector revealed by reports on the hospitals for the mentally ill and mentally handicapped. The combination of economic recession, labour disputes and rapidly rising health care costs stimulated organisational change. The managerial revolution began with NHS reorganisation (1974), which established coterminosity of local authority and health service boundaries, and a planning and prioritisation system. The Labour government also established a resource allocation system to even disparities between the regions. As a result, the most serious financial problems since the NHS began appeared in London's acute hospitals.

By the fourth decade it was clear that similar problems were emerging in many countries as health care costs rose faster than the funds available. Pessimism replaced optimism. There was increasing disenchantment with the idea of a welfare state, and professionals were challenged as to whether they always knew best. The principles underlying health care and the NHS were questioned at the Alma-Ata conference of the World Health Organization. The Black Report on inequalities, far from popular with the Conservative government of the day, demonstrated that not all was well. More emphasis was placed both on advantages of diversity in treatment and on the organisation of the NHS. Managerial solutions proved, each in turn, a chimaera. NHS reorganisation was followed by restructuring (1982) that reduced co-terminosity and increased the importance of health districts. The Griffiths Report (1983) established general management, and moves to contracting support services to the private sector began. Enthoven reviewed the NHS (1985). Medical progress, the technological imperative and the importance of caring well for the growing numbers of elderly people drove demands ever higher while resources grew more slowly, so that, by the end of the ten years, the Presidents of the Colleges were announcing that something had to be done. The political consensus on the NHS was breaking down.

The fifth decade saw continuing clinical developments, for example genetic medicine and minimally invasive surgery. Primary care was accorded increasing importance, and care was transferred from institutions into the community where possible – and sometimes where it was not particularly desirable. GPs had a new contract imposed on them. The hospital service was being reshaped, driven by increasing medical specialisation. Nurses reorganised their education with *Project 2000*. The NHS reforms radically altered the system of health service finance as the purchaser/provider system was implemented. More decisions could be taken at local level. Many fundholders energetically set about changing their services. Hospital trusts enjoyed new freedoms to alter the way they worked. Hospitals came under two conflicting pressures: to decentralise and improve access to services; and to concentrate other activities on fewer sites, where this improved the outcome and the quality of care. Belatedly the medical profession was beginning systematic review of the results of its work. The ordered structure of Ministry, Region and District was removed. No longer was the pattern of provision necessarily similar from place to place. However, the fundamental pressures remained the same – changes in population structure with an increasing number of old people, changes in the level of morbidity particularly in the chronic diseases, new technologies, and increasing public and professional expectations. While the service did not collapse, it showed signs of continuing strain, defying either political party to solve problems within the restrictive financial framework that had been in place since 1948. Nurses and doctors continued to regard the root of the problems of the NHS as a shortage of resources, inadequate staffing, poor facilities, all of which limited performance.

The achievements

The overall verdict on the NHS must be positive. It has achieved Bevan's main aims, largely removing the fear that care during illness would be unavailable or unaffordable (and at the same time redistributing income from the rich to the poor). However, some things were done better than others. While many achievements and some problems are world-wide, others, particularly those that are organisational or financial, are particular to the NHS or are predominantly found in countries that have provided health services from taxation and not by insurance-based schemes.

Benefits of organisational unity

The NHS made it possible to systematise care. The health service formalised a rational system of provision based on the GP as gatekeeper, supported by district hospitals and tertiary centres of referral. Unlike the situation in many other countries, because the NHS was a single organisation it had the potential to deal with significant problems on a national basis. Professional advice, once obtained, could be implemented throughout the country. This applied both to clinical problems and to structural issues, for example the development of group practice and district hospitals. Shortly before the NHS began, the surveillance of communicable disease came under the aegis of the Public Health Laboratory Service and the benefits of a single national organisation, capable like micro-organisms of transcending geographical boundaries, were repeatedly demonstrated. The PHLS became a flagship of excellence, part of a national security system against the dangers of the development of drug resistance and the emergence of new infections. In the second decade the Committee on Safety of Drugs became responsible, after the thalidomide debacle, for licensing new drugs. Although the UK was tardy in the adoption of some vaccines, a national immunisation programme was introduced and progressively refined. By any standard this was a success. Central organisations have also recently become important in assessing the effectiveness of medical procedures.

Some opportunities of national organisation were missed. Although the GPs, the district hospitals and the regional centres provided an effective structure for care, there were repeated failures to develop methods to assess health care needs and, until recently, the effectiveness of treatment. Innovative schemes such as the national morbidity studies were seldom developed, as they might have been, into useful tools that could satisfy scientific or health care policy requirements. Such studies as the review of maternal deaths or deaths under anaesthesia were the exceptions.

Clinical progress

Clinical improvements fall into two groups. Some are based on definable scientific advance, for example the prevention of haemolytic disease of the newborn or phenylketonuria. If such developments provide obvious advantages to patients, are comparatively simple and there is no substantial cost, they are often introduced rapidly once the science is firm. The application of scientific knowledge is slower, however, if the benefits are less clear cut, or if a professional group believes it will be adversely affected by the change.

Secondly, there are changes in working practice, for example the acceptance of group general practice, improvement in geriatric care or immunisation coverage. These may take far longer to implement. It was 30 years before day surgery became commonplace. In the case of immunisation, it was a management decision to pay GPs if they reached WHO target levels that spurred improvement. Incentives may be required to reap potential advantages.

The control of the infectious diseases was the advance that, above all others, probably influenced the shape and work of the health care system. Within the first 20 years the incidence of tuberculosis and its death rate were greatly diminished. Sanatoria and fever hospitals closed, and are forgotten. Immunisation controlled other infections, such as diphtheria, poliomyelitis and measles. Antibiotics altered the pattern of chest infections out of all recognition, affecting the acute episodes and the long-term pattern of disease. The almost complete disappearance of rheumatic fever brought to an end one of the commonest causes of chronic heart failure. The control of syphilis largely eliminated diseases such as tabes dorsalis and general paralysis of the insane, conditions unknown to the medical students of today but featured regularly in examinations in 1948. As a result, the case-mix of wards has changed. Persistence of smoking maintains diseases that otherwise would have fallen in incidence.

The hospital phase of serious illness was shortened by more effective drugs, less traumatic operations and, on the social side, improvements in housing that allowed discharge to a reasonable environment. Orthopaedic patients, who had often stayed in hospital a long time, could be discharged earlier once the principles of internal fixation and joint replacement were understood. Cataract extraction used to involve a week or more of total immobility, with the head supported by sandbags; now patients are discharged the same day. The existence of midwifery services in the community and a change in obstetric practice allowed early discharge of maternity patients. Pharmaceutical research gave doctors an immensely improved armamentarium, making care in the community possible for many who had previously required hospital admission. It all added up to a wider range of preventable and treatable disease, therapy that was less traumatic to young and old alike, more rapid hospital throughput and different demands on primary care.

Doctors with a bent for research or an idea about how a service can be provided better, and industries with the necessary money and skills, have provided the impetus for clinical progress. Many new regimens have come from the pharmaceutical industry, technology and engineering, or clinical centres often in North America. Diagnostic accuracy has increased, and there is more specific treatment and more rapid recovery. New tests, automation in haematology and biochemistry and improvements in diagnostic imaging have made it possible to rewrite much of clinical medicine. Sophisticated systems of measurement allowed the application of scientific and physiological principles to medicine and surgery. Surgical instruments have been refined beyond the dreams of 1948. Only when an attempt is made to itemise the developments to which the NHS has had to adapt and for which funds have been necessary, is it clear how vast these have been. The public has quite correctly come to value advances in health care so there is a continuing tension between the expectations of the public and the capacity to cure, on the one hand, and the ability of the health service to deliver, on the other. Sadly, Britain has been slow to integrate much of the new technology into the NHS, and even now lags behind Europe and the USA in fields such as renal replacement therapy and cardiac surgery. There are several reasons for this. People, particularly the elderly, may be accepting of their fate. The insistent public demand for new technology is less apparent in the UK than, for example, in the USA. Sometimes the NHS has lacked managerial incentives to improve performance. The money necessary may not be available as was the case when ministers, although providing substantial extra funds for renal replacement therapy, did not obtain enough for an appropriate level of service.

Improving performance and increasing clinical activity

Qualitative change in clinical care was paralleled by a quantitative increase in activity, a fourfold increase in the number of hospital doctors and doubling of hospital nursing staff. A consistent time series showing the growth in primary health care is not available. It is easier for the hospitals, in which activity was measured in 'discharges and deaths', although during the first decade an estimate for England has to be derived from totals for England and Wales (see Table). There are also discontinuities with the introduction of the Körner systems, and the move to 'finished consultant episodes'. Industrial action interrupts the rise, but there is a rebound in the following years. Over the 50 years of the health service the age structure of the population has become more elderly, increasing demand. The population has become healthier, which in theory should reduce clinical activity, but patients and their doctors have increasingly high expectations and a well-founded belief that medical care is often beneficial. People have become increasingly aware of what is possible and clinicians define clinical need more broadly. Clinical progress, as in joint replacement for arthritis, generates new and justifiable demands for care. Changes in people's tolerance of distress lead to demands not previously experienced, as in psychological counselling. Sometimes demand may fall, with the reduction in incidence or the disappearance of conditions such as the

Hospital activity: all specialties 1949–1995/6 – England

Year	Ordinary admissions (000s)	Day cases (000s)	Increase (%)
Discharges and deaths			
1949	2,778		
1959	3,783		
1960	3,912		3.4
1961	4,035		3.1
1962	4,150		2.9
1963	4.318		4.0
1964	4,455		3.2
1965	4,540		1.9
1966	4,617		1.7
1967	4,742		2.7
1968	4,848		2.2
1969	4,968		2.5
1970	5,012		0.9
1971	5,171		3.2
1972	5,223	398	8.7
1973	5,132	409	–1.4
1974	5,172	452	1.5
1975	4,976	422	–4.0
1976	5,255	480	6.2
1977	5,345	536	2.5
1978	5,370	562	0.9
1979	5,400	592	1.0
1980	5,670	671	5.8
1981	5,760	714	2.1
1982	5,720	706	–0.7
1983	6,019	813	6.3
1984	6,178	903	3.6
1985	6,354	963	3.3
1986	6,414	1,050	2.0
1987/8	6,619	881	0.5
1988/9	6,586	1,016	1.4
Finished consultant episodes			
1988/9	7,335	1,016	
1989/90	7,477	1,163	3.5
1990/1	7,524	1,261	1.7
1991/2	7,755	1,547	5.9
1992/3	7,828	1,808	3.6
1993/4	7,988	2,106	4.8
1994/5	8,065	2,474	4.4
1995/6	8,379	2,845	6.5

Source: Department of Health statistics

infectious diseases, or with the recognition that some procedures are obsolescent. However, treatment that is largely outdated can continue to generate activity, as in tonsillectomy and dilatation and curettage (D and C), although the recognition of the importance of 'evidence-based medicine' is a pressure in the right direction.

GPs and primary health care

In 1948 Britain had GPs throughout the country, yet their distribution was uneven and their standards were variable. The service was barely adequate for the needs of the time, let alone those to come. It was known from the beginning that primary health care was essential if the function of the hospital service, woefully deficient in many places, was to be maintained. The characteristic ease of access to and continuity of care by GPs, often over many years, was almost unique to the UK and underpinned the NHS. Community care, family practice and referral by the GP to hospital for specialist care form an ordered sequence from self-assessed minor illness to disease benefiting from the most complex forms of treatment. The emphasis on the GP and the existence of a strong community nursing service have proved to be economical and make for equity. Progressively, GPs became less involved in acute and potentially fatal illness, childhood infections, tuberculosis and home delivery, and had greater responsibilities for health promotion, chronic conditions and the care of elderly people. General practice underwent revolutionary change in its organisation, adapting to the new requirements. A cottage industry of single-handed doctors, working from their own homes and with little support, evolved into a network of organised and sizeable groups, in good accommodation, with a substantial infrastructure and more influence on other parts of the NHS. Vocational training and continuous medical education were developed, based on district postgraduate centres. Improvements were not however uniform. Inner city primary health care lagged, and it may be that the system of partnership, organisation and finance found elsewhere is not ideal for conurbations. Such have been the changes in the work of the family doctor that there must be doubts about the appropriateness of undergraduate and postgraduate education. Although there have been complaints about the failure of some GPs to grasp the opportunities that modern primary health care can provide, few groups of professionals have changed their pattern of work more. The cultural change from single-handed doctors and community-based nurses to team workers is even more significant. From working within the context of a local authority service on a geographical basis, nurses moved to practice-based populations and increasingly into clinical activities sometimes previously undertaken by GPs.

Hospital services and secondary health care

Hospital services can also, on balance, be regarded as a success story. Increasingly, hospital consultants were appointed and distributed more evenly throughout the country. New forms of treatment were steadily introduced. A national and regional system made it possible to improve clinical services, as in obstetrics, by applying improved policies for health care in all localities. In 1948, because patients were in hospital for longer, wards were more leisurely than today although there were always gravely ill people to be nursed. The development of medical technology and the shortening length of stay led to increased activity and later to a reduction in the physical size of the hospital service.

Progress had been made before 1948 towards the better organisation of hospitals. Some local authorities, for example Birmingham, London and Middlesex, had rationalised services. King Edward's Hospital Fund (King's Fund) had long used its influence to improve the pattern of London's voluntary hospitals. The Nuffield Provincial Hospitals Trust, already active in arguing for regionalisation, worked with the Ministry on the Hospital Surveys, which backed a region/district pattern. Increasingly, hospital specialties were dependent on each other. Once an adequate range of consultant services was available in each locality, it became important to bring them into closer relationship. The DGH policy was implemented. First hospitals were grouped under a single hospital management committee to form a functional entity. Later came merger, closure and rebuilding, spurred by the 1962 Hospital Plan. Because the NHS was a monopoly service operating within a fixed budget, the pressure was always to move towards a unified hospital service for any given area. The idea of a single hospital for a specific population, rather than competitive services, was in tune with the professional wishes of the doctors who generally did not object to closing old hospitals. Sometimes hospitals lost their *raison d'être*, for example the fever hospitals. Solidly built and on large sites they provided assets of incalculable value to the NHS. Their revenue could be reallocated to other and more modern uses. The closure of the hospitals for tuberculosis also provided a financial boost for newly developing services. Later, the back wards of district hospitals, where elderly people had been placed, were upgraded and bed numbers reduced, as modern geriatric care replaced a largely custodial service. The management of an acute hospital became ever more complex. In ways quite undreamt of in 1948 management has to respond to national priorities and political imperatives, and to pay more attention to health and social care in the community.

Specialisation, responsible for great improvements in patient care, is now reshaping the pattern of hospital services. Some activities, such as cardiology and vascular surgery, are becoming decentralised to improve patient access in emergencies. Clinical factors may force the concentration of services onto fewer sites to ensure the quality of a service, or lead to the development of hub and spoke arrangements in which a centre of high expertise is brought into a relationship with peripheral supporting centres. Cancer care is an example. Sometimes hospitals that have had a long tradition as a DGH lose specialties such as paediatrics that cannot be provided effectively in a small unit. A new type of hospital is emerging, the sub-regional centre. Such hospitals, serving a population of a million or more, are not teaching hospitals in the traditional sense, although they generally have important roles in teaching and often in research. They provide a range of sub-specialty services beyond the range of smaller district hospitals. Purchasers may now press for concentration on the single-site DGH, or for care to be moved into a community setting, within general practice or in 'stand-alone' facilities. Purchasers may wish to reduce the organisational overheads of hospitals and trusts by encouraging mergers. The medical profession needs to provide highly specialised services and good professional training, which can involve a change in the pattern of hospitals. In the 1960s there was a clear vision of the pattern of a hospital service. This clarity is now lacking.

Residual problems

The continual development of the NHS has created new problems, while not always solving old ones. One difficulty concerns the organisation of clinical staff in a way that is efficient and conducive to the provision of good treatment. In primary health care the developments have been largely beneficial and coherent, with the development of well-housed group practices. The same has not been the case in the acute hospitals. The NHS inherited a 'firm' system, in which each patient was the responsibility of a single consultant, who usually held beds on two wards, male and female. Consultant-led teams were the rule, and each covered its own emergencies. The consultant had a small and well-defined team of juniors and close relationships with the nursing staff. Now, the firm system has largely gone and no effective alternative has as yet emerged. More patients are admitted and they spend less time in hospital. Patients, nurses and doctors have less time to get to know each other. Beds are seldom allocated to specific specialties and each ward may contain a continually changing mixture of cases. Junior doctors find that their patients are distributed widely around the hospital, and receive less support than they did in the past from experienced ward sisters. More junior doctors, ward sisters and staff nurses need to relate to each other. Juniors who, in 1948, had almost no time off for the six months of their job, now cover for each other and see patients previously unknown to each other. Lacking the support of resident seniors, they may be under great stress. Team nursing on the wards has removed some of the responsibility of the ward sisters for patients, and with it the crucial role they played in maintaining contact with doctors, relatives and the widening range of special departments within the hospital. The result may be inefficiency, and sometimes inhumanity.

Waiting for care

From a financial point of view the NHS is highly cost-effective in comparison with health care in other developed countries. The fact that Britain spends substantially less might be regarded as a success. There are two views on this: although the UK achieves good value for money, it can be argued that the UK does not spend enough. Queues for care tend to be found in centrally funded systems with public provision of care, paid out of taxation and with a limit on total expenditure, as opposed to insurance-based systems in which rising demand tends to lead to rising provision and expenditure. For example, while not all Americans have health insurance, and those who do may be worried by the cost, for most people when care is required it is usually available rapidly and often from a doctor of the patient's choice. From the perspective of the population and the clinician no pride can be taken in the length of time patients wait for elective procedures in hospital, for the difficulty experienced in the admission of emergencies or for failures in some sectors of community care.

Bevan chose central taxation to fund the NHS and that meant parliamentary control. The measure of freedom that could be allowed to nationalised industries with a product to sell was not possible for the health service. Bevan had a second objective for the NHS, the redistribution of income. All would receive the same service, those who were better off being taxed to meet most of the bill. There are, however, limits to taxation. From its earliest years there were arguments about whether the country could afford the

NHS, the extent to which it was under-funded and the pay and conditions of its staff. Lord Knutsford, in 1924, said that the record of the state in health care was that, whilst it might do its bare duty, it would be done without grace. Enoch Powell expressed similar sentiments. The expansion of the number of consultants and hospital development increased clinical activity and the range of services, but service development has always been considered with an eye on the costs. Government stimulated the more even spread of specialist services, and the improvement in primary health care, but these developments have been kept within the politically and financially affordable.

The result has been a queue, a waiting list to control demand. A shortage of consultants constrains the apparent level of service required. When there are long delays for treatment, GPs refer fewer people; when there is only a minimal service, as in the early days of renal dialysis, activity is constrained. While of symbolic and political importance, waiting lists need to be taken with a grain of salt; attempts to reduce them are laudable but resemble Lewis Carroll's seven maids with seven mops trying to sweep the beach clear of sand. As services are expanded, hidden demands are revealed. Enoch Powell was among many ministers to make abortive efforts to eliminate waiting lists by special initiatives.

As the decades passed, new technology and pharmaceutical developments produced an inexorable rise in costs. Advances in operative surgery, by making more diseases amenable to cure, also increased expenditure. New treatments such as bone marrow transplantation were sprung on management that learned late in the day of their adoption. Specialists were slow to appreciate the potential for economy, for example by shorter stay in hospital. The obsolescent forms of treatment were comparatively cheap; the newer ones were vastly more expensive, placing the service under continuing and increasing financial pressure.

Yet doctors cannot, or are loath to, ration care, to deny it to people who may not be entitled to it, to those seeking to enrich their lives rather than to maintain their health or earning power, to those who pay substantial sums to engage in activities that endanger health, for example smoking and skiing, and are costly to the NHS, and to those who wish to push the boundaries of life beyond reasonable limits. Enoch Powell said that even the wealthiest country could not afford to finance in its entirety a health service free to the consumer, open to all and offering every procedure from which anyone might benefit. Something has to give. It cannot be the exclusion of particular individuals or groups. It must be a priority system based on the nature of the clinical problem – including an assessment of problems that are marginal and can be a matter for decision and payment by patients – and the efficacy of available treatment. The notion of an equitable health service implies that somebody makes a judgement, or somehow a judgement is made. Although we distrust experts and challenge professional judgements, as patients we lack the information of cost and benefit that would enable a rational choice. Because professionals treat, and people are treated, at somebody else's expense, the patient cannot take all decisions in the way that is possible with one's own disposable income. Some new forms of treatment such as anti-cancer drugs produce only minimal advantages in survival for a substantial additional cost. It may be that the elimination of less effective forms of treatment would free resources for more effective ones, but the decision is seldom a black and white one. There is always the possibility that the patient under consideration will be one of the few who will gain from a procedure; and who is to make the judgement when there is a finite chance of improvement? Two extreme positions only need to be stated to be rejected. First, rationing could be handled purely by the individual's ability to pay, either personally or through an insurance scheme. Alternatively, eligibility might be determined solely by the professional expertise of an organisation that allocated treatment on the basis of the maximum benefit for the maximum number. To make matters more difficult, there is likely to be a conflict of interest between the specialist's desire to pursue exotic developments and the care of simpler and commoner problems.

The NHS, needing to respond to ever-increasing financial pressures that are almost uncontainable, has tried a number of strategies. Attempts to improve the efficiency of hospitals go back to the early years of the King's Fund. Since the NHS began there have been attempts to constrain expenditure by seeking clinical and organisational efficiency, better information and costing systems, improved methods of management, the introduction of the management systems said to operate in the private sector, and by systems re-engineering. Among the methods used to restrict demand have been payment by patients, much used in the USA, and seen in the UK as prescription charges. Although it was never stated as public policy, the scope of the NHS has also been restricted. Patient charges for optical and dental services increased the number of people seeking private care, and reduced the strain on the NHS. The growth of the private sector has had a similar effect. Payment by patients when they need care, widely used in countries with insurance-based schemes, was anathema to Bevan, although it is not necessarily inappropriate when a population is comparatively wealthy.

Another approach has been the transfer of care from hospital to the community, unimagined at the outset of the NHS. The place for serious illness in 1948 was in hospital, until medical science could clearly do no more. Clinical progress has made it possible to handle many conditions safely in the community, and the maintenance of the general practitioner/primary health care system has made this practical and largely acceptable to the community. The hospice movement provides substantial services for the terminally ill. Successive governments of both political persuasions advocated shifting the care of those with chronic conditions and the mentally ill from institutions into the community, a policy judged to be socially compassionate that happened to free expensive hospital beds while imposing a financial and social burden on the community and the primary care services. Long-term care, commonly provided by the NHS in 1948, was increasingly moved to local authority social service departments, for the social security regulations provided money and permitted charges for residential accommodation. The Griffiths' recommendations on community care followed, transferring the lead role to local authorities. Off-loading commitments where possible was inevitable if money was to be found for developments.

Nursing

One of the saddest features is a common belief that nursing is not as good as it ought to be. Changes in the nature of society, which have provided increasing employment opportunities, and the pressures of family and social activities have played their part. Within the profession there has been a view that nursing, an honourable and worthy job, needed academic status to give it respectability. This was partly the result of an uncritical acceptance of ideas developed within the different cultural context of North America, for which they might have been appropriate. A fight for higher status and university affiliation was accompanied by disparagement of traditional values and systems of management, such as the hospital matron. Instead there are a myriad of new initiatives, patient-focused care, nursing audit, shared care, named nurses and nursing development units. Nurses persuaded government to put in place *Project 2000*, and adopted new but untested philosophies, at a time when the demands on their profession were altering radically.

The increased tempo of hospital life alters many assumptions traditional to a hospital nursing service, just as the development of primary health care has affected community nursing services. In 1948 trained nurses could expect to care for very sick patients for many days or weeks. Student nurses gained much practical experience and were supervised by competent ward sisters. Explicit standards of care were stressed in the school of nursing. There was time to get to know patients as individuals, and the nurses' role was careful observation, the maintenance of the physical and if possible the mental comfort of their patients, and to work co-operatively with others. Many patients came from poor social circumstances, some were malnourished and few knew much about their ailments. Now people are fitter, more knowledgeable and can face major illness or surgery with more resilience. Patients are discharged so fast that there is often little chance for nurses to establish a relationship. Medicine has a confidence that makes the provision of skilled nursing over days or weeks less important to physical recovery. Clinical observation is replaced by tests and monitoring equipment. Specialisation in medicine demands increased specialisation in nursing if the two professions are to work side by side. Many basic and technical nursing duties are now performed by others – health care assistants, relatives or technicians. But this was the moment at which nursing moved away from the practical and basic into psychological and sociological paths which do not fit easily with the work of the hospitals, although better adapted to community care, health promotion and the management of chronic disease. Some of the territory vacated by nurses was occupied by others.

Long-term care

Better management of acute illness and of diseases in the neonatal period, childhood and the young adult exposed more clearly the problems of chronic illness, mental and physical. Here the inheritance of the NHS was not a good one, either in terms of staff or of building stock. From the early 1960s the priorities have always been to improve the care of those who need protection.

The results have been mixed. In the field of mental disability, now termed the care of those with learning difficulties, few people would wish to see the return of the large institutions that have now all but disappeared. Local units have enormously increased the quality of life. For the mentally ill the picture is not so good. The NHS inherited a service based on the asylums. Stimulated by media interest and public pressure, a move towards community care was partly a response to the scandalous conditions behind the walls of the institutions. In the 1950s and 1960s policy changed and psychiatric units within the curtilage of the DGH, supported by services in the community, were seen as the way forward. In the event, though it was a good policy, better community support should have matched the impetus as Enoch Powell would have wished. It did not. The mechanics went wrong, and health and welfare services that should have been bonded together remained in opposing camps.

Even now substantial numbers of inpatients receive care in the old mental hospitals, and the DGH policy has also proved to have drawbacks. Although few people with mental illness are now admitted, many of those who are have special needs or are disruptive. Such patients are not appropriately housed in the middle of a busy acute hospital. Small local acute units, dispersed throughout the community, are being tried but whether this is a better solution is as yet unknown. Consulting the community is difficult, but there is little evidence of public agreement with this new approach. Indeed there is increasing anxiety about community care and the regular reports, almost monthly, of assaults or murders committed by the mentally ill following what is, in retrospect, premature discharge.

Organisational upheavals

A health service reflects many of the changes taking place in the society it serves. One type of change has been in management philosophy. Whereas the fundamental task of the doctor and nurse remains much as ever, management repeatedly redefines its goals and techniques. Strategic planning, centralised decisions, devolution, large organisations, small and closely focused ones, democratic representation of the community or management by technocrats have followed in swift succession. In my time I have preached many of these, yet I would not claim that there has been a major improvement in the value added by management over the 50 years of the service. For the staff delivering care at the 'grass roots', where the majority of the expertise lies, the cumulative effect on morale has been detrimental. Sadly there is little sign that the naive hope of salvation through reorganisation has disappeared.

The introduction of a managerial culture sought to improve efficiency. Griffiths and the Thatcher reforms emphasised management of the money and sight was lost of the original ethos of a community-based and regional collaborative service. Member-based management authorities, at region and district, disappeared and with them the work of many people from local government and the local community. The last vestiges of local democratic participation were removed, creating a single managerial hierarchy from hospital to central government. Central government's most recent anxieties became local imperatives. Managers on short-term contracts ignored central guidance at peril to their jobs, and long-standing institutional loyalties became a relic. Direction from the centre produced resistance, sometimes rational but sometimes perverse. By introducing the idea of markets and competition, the NHS reforms (1989) risked the development of fragmented pieces of care, sometimes organised on the basis of least cost and with little local involvement of the population. The purchaser/provider division owes as much to dogma as to logic in a service in which key decisions are usually taken near to the patient. Some of the most effective services in the world (for example, Kaiser-Permanente HMO in the USA) do not follow this pattern. The split is part of the process of deconstructing the NHS, reversing the pattern of 1948. The NHS was designed to bring together disparate units, to reduce inappropriate competition and to eliminate gaps in the system. A system was developed that concentrated complex care in a few places, while providing a general level of competence more widely in the district hospitals. Currently such a systematic approach is being lost, and whether a new and better service will emerge is far from certain.

Attempts to solve one problem may create another. Health systems are sometimes discussed in terms of whether their underlying principle is that of business or service. However, while too great an emphasis on management can divert attention from sound clinical decision making, the most businesslike health system cannot survive unless it produces a service acceptable to its clientele. Similarly, the most charitably inclined service has to pay bills, and bills the size of those generated by health care demand a businesslike approach to their settlement. There is no ideal and trouble-free pattern of provision that can simultaneously provide comprehensive care to all, free of charge to the individual, at a cost society can afford, satisfy patients, avoid queues, meet professional aspirations and provide a basis for teaching and research. Discontents are built into the design of the NHS, arising from the tension outlined by Enoch Powell of a service aiming to be comprehensive, universally accessible, free and paid for out of limited funds.

The lack of long-range strategies

Many of the questions for which answers are needed have been around a long time. It is strange that over 50 years the NHS has not developed more effective mechanisms for long-range reviews. Neither does the NHS have a staff college, as does the military. The approach developed by the Nuffield Provincial Hospitals Trust of focusing sharply on major issues, evaluating current initiatives and then taking action has seldom been used at national level. For example, what is the appropriate pattern for a modern hospital service, if one discounts the idea that it should be determined entirely by market forces? Are there major problems in the relationship between management and the consultant body? What is the proper function of a nurse and how should nurses be recruited and educated if *Project 2000* proves to have shortcomings? How can community care be made more coherent, both for the frail elderly and for the mentally ill? Long-range policy studies have been out of fashion for some years, neither has health care research been regarded with enthusiasm. *The health of the nation* is one of the few strategies extant. Important questions remain to be answered. In 1959 the Acton Society, in its sixth report, said that there was a central responsibility, which could not be abdicated. It was the responsibility to inspire, lead and guide; to interpret the lessons of decentralised experience; and to invoke national resources for dealing with problems that could only be dealt with effectively on a national basis. General staff and operational thinking, using the full range of expertise available in the service to develop and review policies of a comprehensive character, are lacking.

Envoi

As one looks back once more under a Labour administration, some things are not going to change. Medical innovation – for example, genetic medicine, diagnostic imaging and ever-increasing expertise – will result in continually growing expectations, both public and professional. The last 50 years have also seen changes in societal values, and the NHS operates against the background of these. Not all have been predictable; few would have imagined the widespread doubts in many quarters about the welfare state. We are in an era of uncertainty and a clash between social obligations and personal autonomy. Even within the limited confines of the health service there is conflict between, on the one hand, the older public service ethos and a belief in the need for solidarity in society, and, on the other, a belief in the primacy of the individual and an acceptance that not everyone will receive an excellent service. Valid questions are raised about the proper role of a health service. Some patients with minimal claims on a welfare state appear to receive costly care, while others – for example the elderly – do without. The gaps are too obvious: waiting lists for routine procedures of proven efficacy, intolerable conditions in some emergency rooms, rapid transit through wards with little rest or nursing care, and a hospital environment that may be unsatisfactory. In spite of everything, we support the NHS and look for a solution that is equitable, provides the best care to all, allows us to take charge of our own bodies and does so at a cost to ourselves personally that we believe we can afford.

Striking a balance between cost, quality, equity and the timeliness of care is an international problem. It is arguable whether the present system in this country can contain the pressures for increased expenditure much longer. On the other hand, it is not obvious that any other country has a better answer. Clinical advance will continue to create costly opportunities to extend life or improve health. It is possible that we will be able to maintain our traditional vision of the NHS, trimming here and advancing there. The NHS might continue to muddle along, as Lord Horder said in 1939, making an apparently unworkable system work. The honourable partnership between the professions and the state, for which Lauriston Shaw argued in 1918, might ultimately be established. The alternatives are few and not politically easy to accept. Yet we may have to face the unpleasant possibility that, in the second 50 years of the NHS, the ever-growing opportunities and costs will make it impossible for health services to maintain themselves outside the laws of cost, supply and demand that influence distribution of services and products elsewhere in our society. One would wish to maintain a system of which its founders would approve. However, the costs and opportunities are continually growing. We have to face the unpleasant possibility that it might be impossible to maintain a comprehensive NHS. There lies our dilemma.

Appendix A

NHS Expenditure 1949 to 1996/7 – UK

Year	Adjusted GDP (£ million)	Gross UK NHS (£ million)	Proportion of GDP (%)	Real terms (1993/4 prices)
1949	12,405	433	3.5	7,876
1950	13,193	478	3.6	8,444
1951	14,614	499	3.4	8,113
1952	15,832	497	3.1	7,604
1953	16,968	521	3.1	7,759
1954	17,992	537	3.0	7,831
1955	19,325	579	3.0	8,077
1956	20,871	633	3.0	8,362
1957	22,015	685	3.1	8,679
1958	22,736	728	3.2	8,958
1959	24,298	788	3.2	9,589
1960	25,704	861	3.3	10,268
1961	22,171	928	4.2	10,711
1962	28,575	971	3.4	10,865
1963	30,799	1,035	3.4	11,304
1964	33,590	1,130	3.4	11,812
1965	35,960	1,275	3.5	12,719
1966	38,162	1,401	3.7	13,414
1967	40,461	1,558	3.9	14,498
1968	43,849	1,693	3.9	14,993
1969	47,106	1,773	3.8	14,922
1970	52,238	2,024	3.9	15,738
1971	58,227	2,299	3.9	16,379
1972	66,406	2,650	4.0	17,457
1973	73,674	3,013	4.1	18,572
1974/75	87,791	4,229	4.8	21,823
1975/76	109,215	5,583	5.1	22,968
1976/77	127,702	6,373	5.0	23,095
1977/78	148,624	7,068	4.8	22,549
1978/79	170,644	8,103	4.7	23,251
1979/80	204,863	9,633	4.7	23,684
1980/81	233,460	12,486	5.3	25,942
1981/82	256,293	14,041	5.5	26,601
1982/83	280,698	15,304	5.5	27,067
1983/84	304,434	16,265	5.3	27,492
1984/85	326,177	17,479	5.4	28,132
1985/86	358,362	18,496	5.2	28,222
1986/87	385,732	19,863	5.1	29,419
1987/88	427,013	21,829	5.1	30,698
1988/89	475,491	24,283	5.1	32,007
1989/90	516,994	26,208	5.1	32,291
1990/91	556,626	29,178	5.2	33,291
1991/92	581,219	33,048	5.7	35,435
1992/93	606,844	36,242	6.0	37,289
1993/94	639,718	37,511	5.9	37,522
1994/95	676,831	39,398	5.8	38,713
1995/96	708,492	41,209	5.8	39,493
1996/97[1]	746,000	42,989	5.8	40,194
1997/98[2]	787,000	44,203	5.6	

[1] provisional outturn
[2] forecast outturn

Source: Department of Health statistics

Appendix B

Government officers from 1948

Ministers of Health

Bevan	Labour	August 1945 to January 1951
Marquand	Labour	January 1951 to November 1951
Crookshank	Conservative	November 1951 to May 1952
Macleod	Conservative	May 1952 to December 1955
Turton	Conservative	December 1955 to January 1957
Vosper	Conservative	January 1957 to September 1957
Walker-Smith	Conservative	September 1957 to July 1960
Powell	Conservative	July 1960 to October 1963
Barber	Conservative	October 1963 to October 1964
Robinson	Labour	October 1964 to October 1968

Secretaries of State for Social Services

Crossman	Labour	November 1968 to June 1970
Joseph	Conservative	June 1970 to March 1974
Castle	Labour	March 1974 to April 1976
Ennals	Labour	April 1976 to May 1979
Jenkin	Conservative	May 1979 to September 1981
Fowler	Conservative	September 1981 to June 1987
Moore	Conservative	June 1987 to July 1988

Secretaries of State for Health

Clarke	Conservative	July 1988 to November 1990
Waldegrave	Conservative	November 1990 to April 1992
Bottomley	Conservative	April 1992 to July 1995
Dorrell	Conservative	July 1995 to May 1997
Dobson	Labour	May 1997 –

Ministers of State

Ennals	Labour	1968–1970
Aberdare	Conservative	1970–1974
Owen	Labour	1974–1976
Vaughan	Conservative	1976–1982
Clarke	Conservative	1982–1985
Hayhoe	Conservative	1985–1986
Newton	Conservative	1986–1988
Mellor	Conservative	1988–1989
Lord Trafford	Conservative	1989

Bottomley	Conservative	1989–1992
Mawhinney	Conservative	1992–1994
Malone	Conservative	1994–1997
Jowell	Labour	1997–
Milburn	Labour	1997–

Chief Medical Officers of Health

Wilson Jameson	1940–1950
John Charles	1950–1960
George Godber	1960–1973
Henry Yellowlees	1973–1983
Donald Acheson	1984–1991
Kenneth Calman	1991–

Permanent Secretaries

William Douglas	1945–1951
John Hawton	1951–1960
Bruce Fraser	1960–1964
Arnold France	1964–1968
Clifford Jarrett	1968–1970
Philip Rogers	1970–1975
Patrick Nairne	1975–1981
Kenneth Stowe	1981–1987
Christopher France	1987–1992
Graham Hart	1992–

Chief Executives

Victor Paige	1985–1986
Leonard Peach	1986–1989
Duncan Nichol	1989–1994
Alan Langlands	1994–

Recommended reading

Abel-Smith B. *The hospitals, 1800–1948*. London: Heinemann, 1964.

Edwards B. *The National Health Service. A manager's tale 1946–1992*. London: Nuffield Provincial Hospitals Trust, 1993.

Klein R. *The new politics of the NHS*. 3rd edn. London and New York: Longman, 1995.

Pater JE. *The making of the National Health Service*. London: King's Fund, 1981.

Rivett GC. *The development of the London hospital system 1823–1982*. London: King's Fund, 1986.

Timmins N. *The five giants: a biography of the welfare state*. London: HarperCollins, 1995.

Walton J, Barondess JA, Lock S, editors. *The Oxford medical companion*. Oxford: Oxford University Press, 1994.

Watkins B. *Documents on health and social service, 1834 to the present day*. London: Methuen, 1975.

Webster C. *The health services since the war*. vol 1. *To 1957*. London: HMSO, 1988.

Webster C. *The health services since the war*. vol 2. London: The Stationery Office, 1996.

Index